Depreciation Amount, Straight Line:

$$D_{sl\ of}(n) = \frac{P - S}{N}$$

Depreciation Amount, Declining Balance:

$$D_{db}(n) = BV_{db}(n - 1) \times d$$

Depreciation Rate:

$$d = 1 - \sqrt[n]{\frac{S}{P}}$$

Effective Interest Rate:

$$i_e = \left(1 + \frac{r}{m}\right)^m - 1 \text{ or}$$

$$i_e = (1 + i_s)^m - 1$$

Effective Interest Rate for Continuous Compounding:

$$i_e = e^r - 1$$

Financial Ratios:

- **Acid Test Ratio** $= \dfrac{\text{quick assets}}{\text{current liabilities}}$

- **Current Ratio** $= \dfrac{\text{current assets}}{\text{current liabilities}}$

- **Equity Ratio** $= \dfrac{\text{total equity}}{\text{total assets}}$

- **Inventory Turn Over** $= \dfrac{\text{sales}}{\text{inventories}}$

- **Return on Total Assets** $= \dfrac{\text{profits after taxes}}{\text{total assets}}$

Growth Adjusted Interest Ratios:

$$i^o = \frac{1 + i}{1 + g} - 1$$

Internal Rate of Return:

$$\sum_{t=0}^{T} \left(R_t - D_t\right)(1 + i^*)^{-t} = 0 \text{ or}$$

$$\sum_{t=0}^{T} R_t(1 + i^*)^{-t} = \sum_{t=0}^{T} D_t(1 + i^*)^{-t}$$

Linear Interpolation:

$$x^* = x_1 + (x_2 - x_1)\left[\frac{y^* - y_1}{y_2 - y_1}\right]$$

Modified Benefit-Cost Ratio:

$$\text{BCRM} = \frac{\text{PW(benefits)} - \text{PW(operating costs)}}{\text{PW(capital costs)}}$$

Payback Period:

$$\text{payback period} = \frac{\text{first cost}}{\text{annual savings}}$$

Present Worth:

$$\text{PW}(i) = \sum_{t=0}^{T} A_t(1 + i)^{-t}$$

Real Dollars:

$$R_{0,tN} = \frac{A_N}{I_{0,N}/100}$$

$$R_N = \frac{A_N}{(1 + f)^N}$$

$$R_N = A_N(P/F, f, N)$$

Real MARR:

$$\text{MARR}_R = \frac{1 + \text{MARR}_A}{1 - f} - 1$$

Real Interest Rate:

$$i' = \frac{1 + i}{1 + f} - 1$$

Real IRR:

$$\text{IRR}_R = \frac{1 + \text{IRR}_A}{1 + f} - 1$$

Simple Interest of Amount:

$$I_s = PiN$$

ENGINEERING ECONOMICS
IN CANADA

Niall M. Fraser

UNIVERSITY OF WATERLOO

Irwin Bernhardt

UNIVERSITY OF WATERLOO

Elizabeth M. Jewkes

UNIVERSITY OF WATERLOO

Prentice Hall Canada Inc.
Scarborough, Ontario

Canadian Cataloguing in Publication Data

Fraser, Niall M. (Niall Morris), 1952– .
    Engineering Economics in Canada

ISBN 0-13-303694-4

1. Engineering economy – Canada.   I. Bernhardt, Irwin.
II. Jewkes, Elizabeth M. (Elizabeth Marie), 1958–   .
III. Title.

TA177.4.F73 1997 658.15 C96-930860-4

© 1997 Prentice-Hall Canada Inc., Scarborough, Ontario
A Division of Simon & Schuster/A Viacom Company

Prentice-Hall, Inc., Upper Saddle River, New Jersey
Prentice-Hall International (UK) Limited, London
Prentice-Hall of Australia, Pty. Limited, Sydney
Prentice-Hall Hispanoamericana, S.A., Mexico City
Prentice-Hall of India Private Limited, New Delhi
Prentice-Hall of Japan, Inc., Tokyo
Simon & Schuster Asia Private Limited, Singapore
Editora Prentice-Hall do Brasil, Ltda., Rio de Janeiro

ISBN 0-13-303694-4

ACQUISITIONS EDITOR: Sarah Kimball
DEVELOPMENTAL EDITOR: Maurice Esses
PRODUCTION EDITOR: Kelly Dickson
COPY EDITOR: Carol Fordyce
PRODUCTION COORDINATOR: Julie Preston
COVER AND INTERIOR DESIGN: David Murphy/ArtPlus Limited
PAGE LAYOUT: ArtPlus Limited

1 2 3 4 5   RRD   01 00 99 98 97

Printed and bound in the USA.

Visit the Prentice Hall Canada Web site! Send us your comments, browse our catalogues, and
more. **www.phcanada.com** Or reach us through e-mail at **phcinfo_phcanada@prenhall.com**

Table of Contents

Preface   *x*

List of Symbols   *xvi*

CHAPTER 1: Engineering Decision Making   *1*

Engineering Economics in Action, Part 1A: Naomi Arrives   2
1.1   Engineering Decision Making   *2*
1.2   What is Engineering Economics?   *3*
1.3   Making Decisions   *4*
Engineering Economics in Action, Part 1B: Naomi Settles In   6
1.4   Dealing with Abstractions   *7*
1.5   The Moral Question: Three True Stories   *10*
1.6   Uncertainty and Sensitivity Analysis   *13*
1.7   How This Book Is Organized   *14*
Canadian Corporate Case 1.1: Bata Industries Ltd. and Trioxide Inc.   *14*
Engineering Economics in Action, Part 1C: A Taste of What Is to Come   *15*
Problems   *16*

CHAPTER 2: Time Value of Money   *19*

Engineering Economics in Action, Part 2A: A Steal For Steel   *20*
2.1   Introduction   *20*
2.2   Interest and Interest Rates   *21*
2.3   Compound and Simple Interest   *23*
2.4   Effective and Nominal Interest Rates   *26*
2.5   Continuous Compounding   *29*
2.6   Cash Flow Diagrams   *30*
2.7   Equivalence   *33*
    2.7.1   Mathematical Equivalence   *33*
    2.7.2   Decisional Equivalence   *34*
    2.7.3   Market Equivalence   *35*
Canadian Corporate Case 2.1: Canada Trust's Powerline Account   *36*
Review Problems   *37*
Summary   *41*
Engineering Economics in Action, Part 2B: You Just Have to Know When   *41*
Problems   *42*

CHAPTER 3: Engineering Decision Making   47

Engineering Economics in Action, Part 3A: Apples and Oranges   48
3.1 Introduction   *49*
3.2 Timing of Cash Flows and Modeling   *49*
3.3 Compound Interest Factors for Discrete Compounding   *50*
3.4 Compound Interest Factors for Single Disbursements
or Receipts   *51*
3.5 Compound Interest Factors for Annuities   *54*
3.6 Conversion Factor for Arithmetic Gradient Series   *63*
3.7 Conversion Factor for Geometric Gradient Series   *66*
3.8 Non-Standard Annuities and Gradients   *69*
3.9 Present Worth Computations When $N \to \infty$ *71*
Canadian Corporate Case 3.1: A New Distribution Station for
Kitchener-Wilmont Hydro   72
Review Problems   72
Summary   76
Engineering Economics in Action, Part 3B: No Free Lunch   77
Problems   78
Appendix 3A: Continuous Compounding and Continuous Cash Flows   85
Appendix 3B: Derivation of Discrete Compound Interest Factors   89
      3B.1 Compound Amount Factor   *89*
      3B.2 Present Worth Factor   *90*
      3B.3 Sinking Fund Factor   *90*
      3B.4 Uniform Series Compound Amount Factor   *91*
      3B.5 Capital Recovery Factor   *91*
      3B.6 Series Present Worth Factor   *92*
      3B.7 Arithmetic and Geometric Gradients   *92*

CHAPTER 4: Comparisons Methods Part 1   *93*

Engineering Economics in Action, Part 4A: What's Best?   94
4.1 Introduction   *95*
4.2 Relations Among Projects   *96*
4.3 Minimum Acceptable Rate of Return (MARR)   *100*
4.4 Present Worth (PW) and Annual Worth (AW)
Comparisons   *101*

4.4.1 Present Worth for Independent Projects   *101*

4.4.2 Present Worth for Mutually Exclusive Projects   *104*

4.4.3 Annual Worth Comparisons   *104*

4.4.4 Comparison of Alternatives with Unequal Lives   *107*

4.5 Payback Period   *112*

Canadian Corporate Case 4.1: Rockwell International of Canada   *116*

Review Problems   *117*

Summary   *121*

Engineering Economics in Action, Part 4B: Doing it Right   *121*

Problems   *123*

Appendix 4A: The MARR and the Cost of Capital   *132*

4A.1 Risk and the Cost of Capital   *132*

4A.2 Company Size and Sources of Capital   *133*

CHAPTER 5: Comparisons Methods Part 2   *135*

Engineering Economics in Action, Part 5A: What's Best? Revisited   *136*

5.1 Introduction   *136*

5.2 The Internal Rate of Return   *137*

5.3 Internal Rate of Return Comparisons   *140*

5.3.1 IRR for Independent Projects   *140*

5.3.2 IRR for Mutually Exclusive Projects   *142*

5.3.3 Multiple IRRs   *148*

5.3.4 External Rate of Return Methods   *150*

5.3.5 When to Use the ERR   *153*

5.4 Rate of Return and Present/Annual Worth Methods of Compared   *154*

5.4.1 Equivalence of Rate of Return and Present/Annual Worth Methods   *154*

5.4.2 Why Choose One Method over the Other?   *159*

Canadian Corporate Case 5.1: Air Canada Supply and Stores   *160*

Review Problems   *161*

Summary   *165*

Engineering Economics in Action, Part 5B: The Invisible Hand   *166*

Problems   *167*

Appendix 5A: Tests for Multiple IRRs   *173*

CHAPTER 6: Depreciation and Financial Accounting   185

Engineering Economics in Action, Part 6A: The Pit Bull   186
6.1   Introduction   186
6.2   Depreciation and Depreciation Accounting   187
    6.2.1   Reasons for Depreciation   187
    6.2.2   Value of an Asset   187
    6.2.3   Straight-Line Depreciation   189
    6.2.4   Declining-Balance Depreciation   191
6.3   Elements of Financial Accounting   194
    6.3.1   Measuring the Performance of a Firm   196
    6.3.2   The Balance Sheet   198
    6.3.3   The Income Statement   200
    6.3.4   The Statement of Changes in Financial Position   202
    6.3.5   Estimated Values in Financial Statements   203
    6.3.6   Financial Ratio Analysis   204
    6.3.7   Financial Ratios   206
Canadian Corporate Case 6.1 Capital Expenditure or Business Expense?   212
Review Problems   213
Summary   218
Engineering Economics in Action, Part 6B: Usually the Truth   218
Problems   219
An Extended Case: Welcome to the Real World   232

CHAPTER 7: Replacement Decisions   237

Engineering Economics in Action, Part 7A: You Need the Facts   238
7.1   Introduction   238
7.2   Reasons for Replacement or Retirement   239
7.3   The Relevance of Capacity Costs   241
7.4   The Irrelevance of Sunk Costs   243
7.5   Economic Life and Cyclic Replacement   245
7.6   Challenger is Different from Defender   250
    7.6.1   Sequence of Identical Challengers   250
    7.6.2   Challenger is Not Repeated   253
Canadian Corporate Case 7.1 Canadians Holding on to Vehicles Longer   255
Review Problems   255
Summary   261
Engineering Economics in Action, Part 7B: Decision Time   262
Problems   263

CHAPTER 8: Taxes   *283*

Engineering Economics in Action, Part 8A: It's in the Details   *284*
8.1   Introduction   *284*
8.2   The Capital Cost Allowance (CCA) System   *285*
8.3   Undepreciated Capital Cost   *290*
8.4   The Capital Cost Tax Factor   *293*
8.5   Components of a Complete Tax Calculation   *296*
8.6   Approximate After-Tax Rate of Return Calculations   *300*
Canadian Corporate Case 8.1 MT&T Tries to Reduce Its Taxes   *302*
Review Problems   *302*
Summary   *308*
Engineering Economics in Action, Part 8B: The Work Report   *308*
Problems   *309*
Appendix 8A: Deriving the Capital Cost Tax Factors   *315*

CHAPTER 9: Inflation   *317*

Engineering Economics in Action, Part 9A: The Inflated Expert   *318*
9.1   Introduction   *318*
9.2   Measuring the Inflation Rate   *319*
9.3   Real and Actual Dollars   *321*
    9.3.1   Converting between Real and Actual Dollars   *322*
9.4   The Effect of Correctly Anticipated Inflation   *325*
    9.4.1   The Effect of Inflation on the MARR   *325*
    9.4.2   The Effect of Inflation on the IRR   *328*
9.5   Economic Evaluation with Inflation   *329*
Canadian Corporate Case 9.1: Economic Comparison of High Pressure
    and Conventional Pipelines: Associated Engineering   *336*
Review Problems   *337*
Summary   *341*
Engineering Economics in Action, Part 9B: Exploiting Volatility   *341*
Problems   *342*
Appendix 9A: Computing a Price Index   *353*

CHAPTER 10: Sensitivity Analysis *357*

Engineering Economics in Action, Part 10A: Filling a Vacuum *358*
10.1 Introduction *358*
10.2 Sensitivity Graphs *360*
10.3 Break-Even Analysis *363*
  10.3.1 Break-Even Analysis for a Single Project *364*
  10.3.2 Break-Even Analysis for Multiple Projects *366*
10.4 Scenario Analysis *371*
Canadian Corporate Case 10.1: Metro Toronto's Main Treatment Plant *373*
Review Problems *374*
Summary *378*
Engineering Economics in Action, Part 10B: Where the Risks Lie *378*
Problems *378*
Appendix 10A: Other Methods of Dealing with Uncertain Outcomes *388*

CHAPTER 11: Public Sector Decision Making *395*

Engineering Economics in Action, Part 11A: Trouble in Lotus Land *396*
11.1 Introduction *396*
11.2 Market Failure *397*
  11.2.1 Market Failure Defined *398*
  11.2.2 Remedies for Market Failure *399*
11.3 Decision Making in the Public Sector *401*
  11.3.1 Measuring the Costs and Benefits of Government
      Services *402*
  11.3.2 Benefit-Cost Ratios *406*
  11.3.3 The MARR in the Public Sector *413*
*Canadian Corporate Case 11.1: Wood Pulp Mill Effluent Treatment
    in Alberta* *414*
Review Problems *414*
Summary *420*
Engineering Economics in Action, Part 11B: Look at It from Their Side *421*
Problems *422*

CHAPTER 12: Qualitative Considerations and Multiple Criteria *431*

Engineering Economics in Action, Part 12A: Don't Box Them In *432*
12.1 Introduction *432*
12.2 Efficiency *434*
12.3 Decision Matrices *438*
12.4 The Analytic Hierarchy Process *441*
12.5 The Consistency Ratio for AHP *447*
Canadian Corporate Case 12.1: Northwind Stoneware *447*
Review Problems *448*
Summary *451*
Engineering Economics in Action, Part 12B: Moving On *451*
Problems *452*
Appendix 12A: Calculating the Consistency Ratio for AHP *460*

APPENDIX A: **Compound Interest Factors for Discrete Compounding, Discrete Compounding Periods** *467*

APPENDIX B: **Compound Interest Factors for Continuous Compounding, Discrete Compounding Periods** *491*

APPENDIX C: **Compound Interest Factors for Continuous Compounding, Continuous Compounding Periods** *509*

APPENDIX D: **Answers to Selected Problems** *527*

Glossary *531*

Index *539*

Preface

A course in Engineering Economics is traditionally found in engineering curricula, in Canada and throughout the world. The course deals with deciding among alternatives with respect to expected costs and benefits. In Canada, the Canadian Engineering Accreditation Board requires that all accredited professional engineering prorgams provide at least one course in engineering economics. Many engineers have found that a course in engineering economics can be as useful in their practice as engineers as any of the more technical courses they took.

There are several stages in making a good decision. One of them is being able to determine whether a solution to a problem is technically feasible. This is one of the roles of the engineer, who has specialized training to make such technical judgments. Another stage is deciding which of several technically feasible alternatives is best. Deciding among alternatives does not require the technical competence needed to determine which alternatives are feasible, but is equally important in making the final choice of the course of action. Some engineers have found that choosing among alternatives can be a more difficult problem than deciding what alternatives there are.

The role of engineers in Canadian society is changing. In the past, engineers tended to have a fairly narrow focus, concentrating on the technical aspects of a problem, and on strictly computational aspects of engineering economics. Consequently, engineering economics texts generally focussed on the mathematics of the subject. Increasingly, engineers are more likely to be the decision makers, and need to be able to take into account strategic and policy issues.

This book is designed for teaching a course in engineering economics to match engineering practice in Canada today. It recognizes the role of the engineer as a decision maker who has to make and defend sensible decisions. Such decisions must take into account a correct assessment of costs and benefits, but also must reflect an understanding of the environment in which the decision is made. It also recognizes that Canadian engineers have a unique set of circumstances that warrant a text with a specific Canadian focus.

BOOK STRUCTURE

Much of this book is similar in content and structure to traditional texts on the same topic. The mathematics of finance has not changed, and there is a natural order to the course material that can be seen in many books. However, a modern view of the role of the engineer flavours the entire text, and provides a balanced exposure to the subject that has not been seen in other texts.

In particular, Chapter 1 frames the problem of engineering decision making as one involving many issues. Manipulating the cash flows associated with an engineering project is an important process for which useful mathematical tools exist. These tools form the bulk of the remaining chapters. However, throughout the text the student is kept aware of the fact that the eventual decision depends not only on the cash flows, but also on less easily quantifiable considerations of business policy, social responsibility, and ethics.

The remaining chapters are organized in a style that is appealing and useful to the student. The content is logically ordered from the fundamental to the supplementary. Chapters 2 and 3 present tools for manipulating monetary values in time. Chapters 4 and 5 show how the student can use his or her knowledge of manipulating cash flows to make comparisons between alternative engineering projects. Chapter 6 provides an understanding of the environment in which the decisions are made by examining depreciation and the role it plays in the financial functioning of a company and in financial accounting. Chapter 7 deals with the analysis of replacement decisions. Chapters 8 and 9 are concerned with considerations, such as taxes and inflation, which can affect decisions based on cash flows.

Most engineering projects involve estimates of future cash flows. Since the future is uncertain, decisions based on these estimates involve risk. Sensitivity analysis is an integral part of understanding the effect of this risk on the decision process. Chapter 10 deals with this subject in a way that does not require knowledge of probability theory by the student.

Chapter 11 provides an introduction to public sector decision making. Finally, ways of accounting formally for the non-quantifiable aspects of a decision are covered in Chapter 12.

Appendices provide tables of important values and answers to selected chapter-end problems. A glossary of terms used in the text is also included. Symbols used in the text are listed on the front endpapers, and formulas are listed on the back endpapers.

FEATURES OF THIS TEXT

There are several special features of this text that distinguish it from others. For one thing, it is wholly Canadian. Canada is a unique country with its own culture and laws. Although the mathematics governing the time value of money are the same everywhere, there are things that make Canada different. First, Canadian firms make decisions according to norms and standards that reflect Canadian views on social responsibility, environmental concerns, and cultural diversity. This perspective is reflected in the content and tone of much of the material in this book. Second, Canadian tax regulations are complicated and directly affect engineering economic analysis. These regulations and their effect on decision making are covered in detail in Chapter 8.

In each chapter of the text, there is a two- or three-part story that reflects and supports the chapter material. These vignettes link to form a narrative that runs throughout the entire book. For example, one character is Naomi, a recently graduated engineer. In the first chapter, she starts her job in the engineering department at Canadian Widget Industries, and is given a decision problem by her supervisor. Over the course of the book, Naomi learns about engineering economics on the job as the student learns from the book. There are several characters who relate to one another in various ways, exposing the student to practical, ethical, and social issues as well as mathematical problems.

The majority of the examples and exercises have been placed in realistic engineering contexts. Although the decisions have been simplified for clarity, most of the engineering examples are based on real situations encountered in the authors' consulting experiences. This provides an educational and appealing realism to the text.

The course material is grounded to the student's everyday life in a variety of ways. For one thing, in addition to examples and exercises with an engineering focus, there are a number that involve decisions that an ordinary student might make, such as buying a car, renting an apartment, or getting a job. Other examples in the text are taken from Canadian newspapers and other sources that are within a student's common experience. Finally, each chapter has a Canadian Corporate Case; these cases tell interesting stories about how familiar Canadian companies have used engineering economics principles in practice.

Between Chapter 6 and Chapter 7, an extended case study is presented. This case study concerns a complex problem situation which incorporates much of the material in the preceding chapters. Unlike chapter examples, which are usually directed at a particular concept being taught, the extended case requires the student to integrate what he or she has learned. The case can be used for assignments, class discussions, or independent study by the student.

Chapter 12 concerns formal ways of taking into account the fact that a good engineering decision cannot be based only on selecting the least-cost alternative. The increasing influence on decision making of health and safety issues, environmental responsibility, and human relations, among other concerns, makes it necessary for the engineer to understand some of the basic principles of multi-criteria decision making. This is the first text to recognise the desirability of including these important tools as an integral part of an engineering economics course.

The use of computers by engineers is now as commonplace as the use of slide rules was thirty years ago. In particular, students using this book will likely be very familiar with spreadsheet software. Consequently, such knowledge is assumed in the text rather than taught. Example problems or end-of-chapter problems involving spreadsheets are noted in the book margin by a special spreadsheet icon, as illustrated in the margin here. The icon indicates that the spreadsheet is available on the supplemental *Spreadsheet Disks* (see below under *Supplements*). The spreadsheet examples are presented in such a manner that they could be done by any popular spreadsheet program.

Only a background in high-school mathematics is required as prerequisite material for a course based on this text. In particular, the student is not required to have knowledge of probability theory, calculus, or linear algebra, except for the appendices to Chapters 10 and 12. This means that the course can be taught in the first or second year of an engineering program. This is often desirable, in order to provide the student with some practical subject material in addition to the basic mathematics and physics courses that form the bulk of the student's subjects at that level.

ORGANIZATION OF CHAPTERS

Each chapter is organized in a way that is useful for both the instructor and the student. At the beginning of the chapter is an outline of the major sections to provide an overview of the material. Next is the first part of a short story concerning Naomi's experiences at Canadian Widget Industries. This half of the story usually has one of the characters trying to deal with a problem for which only reading the chapter can reveal the solution.

The introductory section of the chapter frames the material covered, and describes the approach to be taken in the chapter. Each section explains an idea in detail; the explanation is followed by one or more descriptive examples. The section material is sometimes supported by a Close-Up, which explains a related concern that is important but would otherwise complicate the flow of the chapter.

Near the end of the chapter is a Canadian Corporate Case, showing how the chapter material is reflected in real life. Then there are several review exercises, which provide more complex problems that integrate the chapter material. A summary restates the important information learned in the chapter.

The chapter closes with the second half of the story episode, resolving the dilemma presented in the first half, using the knowledge learned in the chapter. Finally, each chapter has about 30 problems of various levels of difficulty covering all of the material presented in the chapter.

APPLICABLE COURSES OF STUDY

The book is ideal for a one-term course but, with supplemental material, could also be used for a two-term course. It is intended to meet the needs of students in all engineering programs, including, but not limited to, aeronautical, chemical, computer, electrical, industrial, mechanical, mining, and systems engineering. Certain programs emphasizing public projects as may wish to supplement Chapter 11 on public projects with additional material.

The text is also particularly appropriate for students in college technology programs. It does not require a high level of mathematical background, so that the principles of engineering economics are accessible to a wider range of students than are served by other texts.

This book is also suitable for self-study by a practitioner or anybody interested in the economic aspects of decision making. It is easy to read and self contained, with many clear examples. It can serve as a permanent resource for practicing engineers or anyone involved in decision making.

SUPPLEMENTS

An *Instructor's Solution Manual with Transparency Masters and Spreadsheet Disks* is available to facilitate instruction. The *Instructor's Solution Manual* provides complete solutions to all the text problems found at the end of the chapters as well as the extended case following Chapter 6. Spreadsheets involved in the solutions are also printed here.

The *Transparency Masters* consist of all the figures and many of the tables and spreadsheets that occur in the text. The masters can readily be converted to transparencies through the use of most photocopiers or thermal imagers.

The two *Spreadsheet Disks* have been prepared in EXCEL format, but they can be read and used by most popular spreadsheet programs (such as Lotus 1-2-3 and Quattro Pro). One disk contains spreadsheets that are found in the body of the text. The other disk contains spreadsheets that can be used to solve some of the problems. Each spreadsheet on these disks is identified in the textbook by a special spreadsheet icon.

ACKNOWLEDGEMENTS

The authors wish to acknowledge the contributions of a number of individuals who assisted in the development of this text. First and foremost are the hundreds of engineering students at the University of Waterloo who suffered through early drafts, mostly without complaint. They brought to our attention innumerable errors of writing, of mathematics, and of theory, and immeasurably improved the book through their joint efforts. There are too many individuals to name in person, but we are very thankful for their patience and diligence.

While teaching from draft versions, we had several graduate student teaching assistants who went beyond the expectations of their jobs to help improve the text. Noteworthy among these is Tim Nye, whose background in mechanical engineering helped us to avoid more than one embarrassing error. Others who made significant contributions include

Fazle Baki, Metin Cakanyildirim, Hugo Caviedes, William Chung, Salim Dastagir, Bob Dawson, Ron Fraboni, Peter Hall, Qi-Ming He, David Leadbeater, Paul Miller, Omar Rana, Weiya Ren, Alfred Sham, May Tajima, William Woo, Asad Zia, and Mingshan Zhou.

Thanks are also due to another graduate student, Peter Chapman. Peter accepted the job of reviewing and correcting the set of chapter end problems. His thoroughness and perceptiveness have helped to ensure a comprehensive and, hopefully, relatively error-free set of problems.

During the development process, our developmental editor at Prentice Hall, Maurice Esses, arranged for the anonymous review of the manuscript by instructors of engineering economics courses at other Canadian universities. These reviews were extremely beneficial to us, and many of the best ideas incorporated in the final text originated with these reviewers. We can now thank them by name: Michel L. Bilodeau, McGill University, S.P. Dutta, University of Windsor; Isobel W. Heathcote, University of Guelph; Donald J. Mallory, British Columbia Institute of Technology; John F. Morrall, The University of Calgary; Ronald Pelot, Technical University of Nova Scotia; K. Rose, Queen's University; S. M. Taboun, University of Windsor; Claude Théoret, University of Ottawa.

Shelley Donald of the Ernst & Young accounting firm kindly reviewed Chapter 8 for us. She saved us from making several mistakes, and we thank her for her efforts.

Other individuals who deserve our thanks for their contributions and assistance include: Lisa Arnold, David Fuller, Adam Grosser, Stan Laiken, Jerry Van Ooteghem, Ron Pelot, and Marion Reid.

Finally, we want to express our appreciation to the various editors at Prentice Hall Canada for their professionalism and support during the writing of this book. Maurice Esses had a particularly strong role in bringing the project to completion. Others to mention include Jackie Wood, Allan Gray (who are no longer at Prentice Hall), Kelly Dickson, and Valerie Adams. Paul McInnis, the sales representative from Prentice Hall for the University of Waterloo, provided us with support and enthusiasm at the outset of the project; Carol Fordyce, engaged by Prentice Hall to copy edit the book, also deserves credit for her professionalism and diligence.

To all the above, thank you again for your help. To those of you we forgot to thank: our appreciation is just as great even if our memories fail us. And to the reader, any errors that remain cannot be blamed on those who helped us. The remaining errors are perhaps the only thing for which we can claim sole credit.

Niall M. Fraser
Irwin Bernhardt
Elizabeth M. Jewkes

List of Symbols

$(A/F, i, N)$	sinking fund factor	**AHP**	anaytic heirarchy process
$(A/G, i, N)$	arithmetic gradient to annuity conversion factor	A_N	actual dollars in year N
$(A/P, i, N)$	capital recovery factor	A_{tot}	total annuity for arithmetic gradient to annuity conversion factor
$(F/A, i, N)$	uniform series compound amount factor		
$(F/P, i, N)$	compound amount factor	**AW**	annual worth
$(\overline{A}/P, r, T)$	continuous capital recovery factor	**B**	present worth of benefits
		BCR	benefit-cost ratio
$(\overline{A}/F, r, T)$	continuous sinking fund factor	**BCRM**	modified benefit-cost ratio
$(F/\overline{A}, r, T)$	continuous uniform series compound amount factor	$BV_{db}(n)$	book value at end of period n using declining balance method
$(P/\overline{A}, r, T)$	continuous uniform series present worth factor	$BV_{si}(n)$	book value at end of period n using straight line method
$(P/A, g, i, N)$	geometric gradient to present worth conversion factor		
		C	present worth of costs
		CI	consistency index
$(P/A, i, N)$	series present worth factor	**CCA**	capital cost allowance
$(P/F, i, N)$	present worth factor	**CCTF**	capital cost tax factor
λ_{max}	the maximun eigenvalue	CCTF_{new}	CCTF currently valid
λ	an eigenvalue	CCTF_{old}	CCTF valid on salvage values or assets purchased before Nov, 13 1981
μ_{01}	Laspeyres price index		
$\overline{A}$	continuous cash flow over a period	d	depreciation rate for declining balance method
A	annuity amount, equivalent annual cost	$D_{db}(n)$	depreciation amount for period n using declining balance method
A	a PCM		
A'	base annuity for arithmetic gradient to annuity conversion factor	$D_{si}(n)$	depreciation amount for period n using straight line method

e	a column vector $[111...111]^T$	**m**	number of sub-periods in a period
EAC	equivalent annual cost	**MARR**	minimum acceptable rate of return
ERR	external rate of return		
F	future value, future worth	$MARR_A$	actual dollar MARR
f	inflation rate per year	$MARR_R$	real dollar MARR
FW	future worth	**MAUT**	multi-attribute utility theory
g	growth rate for geometric gradient	**MCDM**	multi-criterion decision making
i	actual interest rate	N	number of periods, useful life of an asset
I	interest amount	P	present value, present worth, purchase price, principal amount
i'	real interest rate		
I_c	compound interest amount		
i_e	effective interest rate	**PCM**	pariwise comparison matrix
$I_{0,N}$	the value of a global price index at year N, relative to year 0	**PW**	present worth
		r	nominal interest rate, rating for a decision matrix
IRR	internal rate of return	**RI**	random index
IRR_A	actual dollar IRR	$R_{0,N}$	real dollar equivalent to A N relative to year), the base year
IRR_R	real dollar IRR		
i_s	interest rate per sub-period	S	salvage value
I_s	simple interest amount	t	tax rate
i^*	internal rate of return	**UCC**	undepreciated capital cost
i_e^*	external rate of return	**w**	an eigenvector
i_{ea}^*	approximate external rate of return		
i°	growth adjusted interest rate		

Engineering Decision Making

Engineering Economics in Action, Part 1A: Naomi Arrives

1.1 Engineering Decision Making

1.2 What Is Engineering Economics?

1.3 Making Decisions

Engineering Economics in Action, Part 1B: Naomi Settles In

1.4 Dealing with Abstractions

1.5 The Moral Question: Three True Stories

1.6 Uncertainty and Sensitivity Analysis

1.7 How This Book Is Organized

Canadian Corporate Case 1.1: Bata Industries Ltd. and Trioxide Inc.

Engineering Economics in Action, Part 1C: A Taste of What Is to Come

Problems

Engineering Economics in Action, Part 1A: Naomi Arrives

Naomi's first day on the job wasn't really her first day on the job. Ever since she had received the acceptance letter three weeks earlier, she had been reading and rereading all her notes about the company. Somehow she had arranged to walk past the plant entrance going on errands that never would have taken her that exact route in the past. So today wasn't the first time she walked through that tidy brick entrance to the main offices of Canadian Widget Industries—she had done it the same way in her imagination a hundred times before.

Clement Shih, the Engineering Manager who had interviewed Naomi for the job, was waiting for her at the reception desk. His warm smile and easy manner did a lot to break the ice. He suggested that they could go through the plant on the way to her desk. She agreed enthusiastically. "I hope you remember the engineering economics you learned in school," he said. Naomi did, but rather than sound like a know-it-all, she replied, "I think so, and I know I still have my old textbook. I suppose you're telling me I'm going to use it."

"Yes. That's where we'll start you out, anyhow. It's a good way for you to learn how things work around here. We've got some projects lined up for you already, and they involve some pretty big decisions for Canadian Widgets. We'll keep you busy."

1.1 Engineering Decision Making

Engineering is a noble profession with a long history. The first engineers supported the military, using practical know-how to build bridges, fortifications, and assault equipment. In fact, the term "civil" engineer was coined to make the distinction between engineers who worked on civilian projects and engineers who worked on military problems.

In the beginning, all that engineers had to know was the technical aspects of their jobs. Military commanders, for example, would have wanted a bridge built fast and strong. The engineer would be challenged to find a solution to the technical problem, and would not have been particularly concerned about the costs, safety, or environmental impacts of the project. As years went by, however, the engineer's job became far more complicated.

All engineering projects use resources, such as raw materials, money, labour, and time. Any particular project can be undertaken in a variety of ways, each one calling for a different mix of resources. For example, a standard light bulb requires inexpensive raw materials and little labour, but is inefficient in its use of electricity and does not last very long. On the other hand, a high-efficiency light bulb uses more expensive raw materials and is more expensive to manufacture, but consumes less electricity and lasts longer. Both products provide light, but choosing which is better in a particular situation depends on how the costs and benefits are compared.

Historically, as the kinds of projects engineers worked on evolved and technology provided more than one way of solving technical problems, engineers were faced more often with having to choose among alternative solutions to a problem. If two solutions both deal with a problem effectively, clearly the cheaper of the two is preferred. The practical science of engineering economics was originally developed specifically to deal with determining which of several alternatives was, in fact, the cheapest.

Choosing the cheapest alternative, though, is not the entire story. Though a project might be technically feasible and the cheapest solution to a problem, if the money isn't available to do it, it can't be done. The engineer had to become aware of the *financial* constraints on the problem, particularly if resources were very limited. In addition, an engineering project can meet all other criteria, but may cause detrimental *environmental* effects. Finally, any project can be affected by *social* and *political* constraints. For example, a large irrigation project called the Garrison Diversion Unit in North Dakota was effectively cancelled because of political action by Canadians and environmental groups, even though over $2 000 000 000 had been spent.

Engineers today must make decisions in an extremely complex environment. The heart of an engineer's skill set is still technical competence in a particular field. This permits the determination of possible solutions to a problem. However, necessary to all engineering is the ability to choose among several technically feasible solutions, and to defend that choice credibly. The skills permitting the selection of a good choice are common to all engineers and, for the most part, are independent of which engineering field is involved. These skills form the discipline of engineering economics.

1.2 What Is Engineering Economics?

Just as the role of the engineer in society has changed over the years, so has the nature of engineering economics. Originally, engineering economics was that body of knowledge that allowed the engineer to determine which of several alternatives was economically best—the cheapest, or perhaps the most profitable. In order to make this determination properly, the engineer needed to understand the mathematics governing the relationship between time and money. Most of this book deals with teaching and using this knowledge. Also, for many kinds of decisions the costs and benefits are the most important factors affecting the decision, so concentrating on determining the economically "best" alternative is appropriate.

In earlier times, an engineer would be responsible for making a recommendation based on technical and analytic knowledge, including the knowledge of engineering economics, and then a manager would decide what should be done. A manager's decision would often be different from the engineer's recommendation because the manager would take into account issues outside the engineer's range of expertise. Recently, however, the trend has been for managers to become more reliant on the technical skills of the engineers, or the engineers are themselves the managers. Products are often very complex; manufacturing processes are fine-tuned to optimize productivity; and even understanding the market sometimes requires the analytic skills of an engineer. As a result, it is often only the engineer who has sufficient depth of knowledge to make a competent decision.

Consequently, understanding how to compare costs, although still of vital importance, is not the only skill needed to make suitable engineering decisions. One must also be able to take into account all the other considerations that affect a decision, and to do so in a reasonable and defensible manner.

Engineering economics then can be defined as that science which deals with techniques of quantitative analysis useful for selecting a preferable alternative from several technically viable ones.

The evaluation of costs and benefits is very important and has formed the primary content of engineering economics in the past. The mathematics for doing this evaluation is well developed, and it still forms the bulk of studies of engineering economics. However, the modern engineer must be able to recognize the limits and applicability of these economic calculations, and must be able to take into account the inherent complexity of the real world.

1.3 Making Decisions

All decisions, except perhaps the most routine and automatic ones, or those that are institutionalized in large organizations, are made, in the end, on the basis of belief as opposed to logic. People, even highly trained engineers, do what *feels* like the right thing to do. This is not to suggest that one should trust only one's intuition and not one's intellect, but rather to point out something true about human nature and the function of engineering economics studies.

Figure 1.1 is a useful illustration of how decisions are made. At the top of the pyramid are preferences, which directly control the choices made. Preferences are the beliefs about what is best, and are often hard to explain coherently. They sometimes have an emotional basis and include criteria and issues that are difficult to verbalize.

The next tier is composed of people and politics. Politics in this context means the use of power (intentional or not) in organizations. For

FIGURE 1.1   Decision Pyramid

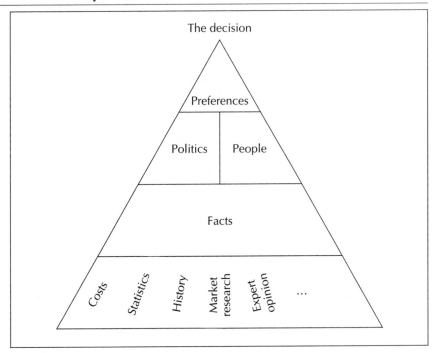

example, if the owner of a factory has a strong opinion that automation is important, this has a great effect on engineering decisions on the plant floor. Similarly, an influential personality can affect decision making. It's difficult to make a decision without the support, either real or imagined, of other people. This support can be manipulated, for example, by a persuasive salesperson or a persistent lobbyist. Support might just be a general understanding communicated through subtle messages.

The next tier is a collection of "facts." The facts, which may or may not be valid or verifiable, contribute to the politics and the people, and indirectly to the preferences. At the bottom of the pyramid are the activities that contribute to the facts. These include the history of previous similar decisions, statistics of various sorts, and, among other things, a determination of costs.

In this view of decisions, engineering economics is not very important. It deals essentially with facts and, in particular, with determining costs. There are many other facts that affect the final decision, and even then the decision may be made on the basis of politics, personality, or unstated preferences. However, this is an extreme view.

Although preferences, politics, and people can outweigh facts, usually the relationship is the other way around. The facts tend to control the politics, the people, and the preferences. It is facts that allow an individual to develop a strong opinion, which then may be used to influence others. Facts accumulated over time create intuition and experience that control our "gut feeling" about a decision. Facts, and particularly the activities that develop the facts, form the foundation for the pyramid in Figure 1.1. Without the foundation, the pyramid would collapse.

Engineering economics is important because it facilitates the establishment of verifiable facts about a decision. The facts are important and necessary for the decision to be made. However, the decision eventually made may be contrary to that suggested by analysis. For example, a study of several methods of treating effluent might determine that Method A is most efficient and cheapest, but Method B might in fact be chosen because it requires a visible change to the plant which, it is felt, will contribute to the company's image in environmental issues. Such a final decision is appropriate because it takes into account facts beyond those dealt with in the economic analysis.

Engineering Economics in Action, Part 1B: Naomi Settles In

As Naomi and Clement were walking, they passed the loading docks. A honk from behind told them to move over so that a forklift could get through. The operator waved in passing and continued on with the task of moving coils of sheet metal into the warehouse. Naomi noticed shelves and shelves of packaging material, dies, spare parts, and other items that she didn't recognize. She would find out more soon enough. They continued to walk. As they passed a welding area, Clem pointed out the newest recycling project in Canadian Widgets: the water used to degrease the metal was now being cleaned and recycled rather than being used only once.

Naomi became aware of a pervasive, pulsating noise emanating from the distance. Suddenly the corridor opened up to the main part of the plant, and the noise became a bedlam of clanging metal and thumping machinery. Her senses were assaulted. The ceiling was very high, and there were rows of humpbacked metal monsters unlike any presses she had seen before. The tang of mill oil overwhelmed her sense of smell, and she felt the throbbing from the floor knocking her bones together. Clem handed her hearing and eye protectors.

"These are our main press lines." Clem was yelling right into Naomi's ear, but she had to strain to hear. "We go right from sheet metal to finished widgets in 12 operations." A passing forklift blew propane exhaust at her, momentarily replacing the mill-oil odour with hot-engine odour. "Engineering is off to the left there."

As they went through the double doors into the Engineering Department, the din subsided and the ceiling came down to normal height. Removing the safety equipment, they stopped for a moment to get some juice at the vending machines. As Naomi looked around, she saw computers on desks more or less sectioned off by acoustic room dividers. As Clem led them farther, they stopped long enough for him to introduce Naomi to Carole Brown, the receptionist and secretary. Just past Carole's desk and around the corner was Naomi's desk. It was a nondescript metal desk with a long row of empty shelving above. Clem said that her computer would arrive within the week. Naomi noticed that the desk next to hers was empty, too.

"Am I sharing with someone?" she asked.

"Well, you will be. That's for your co-op student."

"My co-op student?"

"Yep. Don't worry, we have enough to do to keep you both busy. Why don't you take a few minutes to settle in, while I take care of a couple of things. I'll be back in, say, fifteen minutes. I'll take you over to Personnel. You'll need a security pass, and I'm sure they have lots of paperwork for you to fill out."

Clem left. Naomi sat down and opened the briefcase she had carefully packed that morning. Alongside the brown-bag lunch was an engineering economics textbook. She took it out and placed it on the empty shelf above the desk. "I thought I might need you," she said to herself. "Now, let's get this place organized!"

1.4 Dealing with Abstractions

The world is far more complicated than what can ever be described in words, or even thought about. Whenever one deals with reality, it is done through models or abstractions.

For example, consider the following description:

Naomi watched the roll of sheet metal pass through the first press. The die descended and punched six oval shapes from the sheet. These "blanks" dropped through a chute into a large metal bin. The strip of sheet metal jerked forward into the die and the press came down again. Pounding like a massive heart 30 times a minute, it kept the operator busy full-time just providing the giant coils of metal, removing the waste skeleton scrap, and stacking blanks in racks for transport to the next operation.

This gives a description of a manufacturing process that is reasonably complete, in that it permits one to visualize the process. But it is not absolutely complete. For example, how thick were the blanks? How big was the metal bin? How heavy was the press? How long did it take to change a die? These questions could be answered, but no matter how many questions are asked, it is impossible to express all of the complexity of the real world. It is also undesirable to do so.

When one describes something, one does so for a purpose. In the description, one selects those aspects of the real world that are relevant to that purpose. This is appropriate since it would be very confusing if a great deal of unnecessary information were given every time something was talked or written about. For example, if the purpose of the above description were to explain the exact nature of the blanks, there would be considerably less emphasis on the process, and many more details about the blanks themselves.

This process of simplifying the complexities of the real world is necessary for any engineering analysis. For example, in designing a truss for a building, it is usually assumed that the members exhibit uniform characteristics. However, in the real world these members would be lumber with individual variations; some would be stronger than average, and some would be weaker. Since it is impractical to measure the characteristics of each piece of wood, a simplification is made. As another example, the various components of an electric circuit, such as resistors and capacitors, have values that differ from their nominal specifications because of manufacturing tolerances, but such differences are often ignored and the nominal values are the ones that are used in calculations.

Figure 1.2 illustrates the basic process of modelling that applies in so much of what humans do, and applies especially to engineering. The world is too complicated to express completely, as represented by the amorphous shape at the top of the figure. People extract from the real world a simplification (in other words, a model) which captures information that is useful and appropriate for a given purpose. Once the model is developed, it is used to analyze a situation, and perhaps make some predictions about the real world. The analysis and the predictions are then related back to the real world to make sure that the model is valid. As a result, the model might need some modification, so that it more accurately reflects the relevant features of the real world.

The process illustrated in Figure 1.2 is exactly what is done in engineering economics. The model is often a mathematical one that simplifies a more complicated situation, but does so in a reasonable way. The analysis of the model provides some information, such as which solution to a problem is cheapest. This information must always be related back to the real problem, however, to take into account the aspects of the real world that may have been ignored in the original modelling effort. For example, the economic model might not have included taxes or inflation,

FIGURE 1.2   The Modelling Process

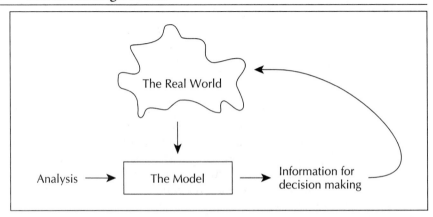

and an examination of the result might suggest that taxes and inflation should not be ignored. Or, as already pointed out, environmental, political, or other considerations might modify any conclusions drawn from the mathematical model.

EXAMPLE 1.1

Naomi's brother Ben has been given a one-year assignment in Alaska, and he wants to buy a car just for the time he is there. He has three choices, as illustrated in Table 1.1. For each alternative, there is a purchase price, an operating cost (including gas, insurance, and repairs), and an estimated resale value at the end of the year. Which should Ben buy?

TABLE 1.1 Buying a Car

	57 Chevy	93 Geo	83 Mercedes
Purchase	$12 000	$7 000	$20 000
Operation	200/month	50/month	150/month
Resale	13 000	5 000	20 000

The next few chapters of this book will show how to take the information from Table 1.1 and determine which alternative is *economically* best. As it turns out, under most circumstances, the Chevy is best. However, in constructing a model of the decision, we must make a number of important assumptions.

For example, how can one be sure of what the resale value of something is until one actually tries to sell it? Along the same lines, who can tell what the actual maintenance costs will be? There is a lot of uncertainty about future events that is generally ignored in these kinds of calculations. Despite this uncertainty, estimates can provide insights into the appropriate decision.

Another problem for Ben is getting the money to buy a car. Ben is fairly young, and would find it very difficult to raise even $7000, perhaps impossible to raise $20 000. The Chevy might be the best value, but, if the money isn't available to take advantage of the opportunity, it doesn't matter. In order to do an economic analysis, we may assume that he has the money available.

If an economic model is judged to be appropriate, does that mean that Ben should buy the Chevy? Maybe not.

A person who has to drive to work every morning would probably not want to drive an antique car. It is too important that the car be reliable (especially in Alaska in the winter). The operating costs for the Chevy are high, reflecting the need for more maintenance than with the other cars, and there are indirect effects of low reliability that are hard to capture in dollars.

If Ben were very tall, he would be extremely uncomfortable in the compact Geo car, so that, even if it were economically best, he would hesitate to resign himself to driving with his knees on either side of the steering wheel. Ben might have strong feelings about the environmental carelessness of one of the car manufacturers, and might want to avoid driving that car as a way of making a statement.

Clearly, there are so many *intangibles* involved in a decision like this that it is impossible for anyone but Ben himself to make such a personal choice. An outsider can point out to Ben the results of a quantitative analysis, given certain assumptions, but cannot authoritatively determine the best choice for Ben.

1.5 The Moral Question: Three True Stories

Complex decisions often have an ethical component to them. Recognizing this ethical component is important for engineers, since society relies on them for so many things. The following three anecdotes concern real Canadian companies—although names and details have been altered for anonymity—and illustrate some extreme examples of the forces acting on engineering decision making.

EXAMPLE 1.2

The process of making sandpaper is similar to that of making a photo-copy. A two-metre-wide roll of paper is coated with glue and given a negative electric charge. It is then passed over sand (of a particular type) which has a positive charge. The sand is attracted to the paper and sticks on the glue. The fact that all of the bits of sand have the same type of charge makes sure that the grains are evenly spaced. The paper then passes through a long heated chamber to cure the glue. Although the process sounds fairly simple, the machine that does this, called a *maker*, is very complicated and expensive. One such machine, costing several mil-lion dollars, can support a factory employing hundreds of workers.

Preston Sandpapers was the Canadian subsidiary of a large United States firm, and was located in a small town. Its maker was almost 30 years old, and desperately needed replacement. However, rather than replace it, the parent company could choose to close down the Canadian plant and transfer production to one of the American sister plants.

The chief engineer had a problem. The costs for installing a new maker were extremely high, and it was difficult to justify a new maker economically. However, if he could not do so, the plant would close and hundreds of workers would be out of a job, including perhaps himself. What he chose to do was lie. He fabricated figures, ignored important costs, and exaggerated benefits to justify the expenditures. The invest-ment was made, and the Canadian plant is still operating.

EXAMPLE 1.3

Hespeler Meats is a medium-sized meat processor specializing in deli-style cold cuts and European process meats. Hoping to expand their product offerings, they decided to add a line of canned patés. They were eligible for a government grant to cover some of the purchase price of the necessary production equipment.

Government support for manufacturing is generally fairly sensible. Support is usually not given for projects that are clearly very profitable, since the company should be able to justify such an expense itself. On the other hand, support is usually not given for projects that are clearly not very profitable, because taxpayers' money should not be wasted. Support is directed at projects that the company would not otherwise undertake, but which have good potential to create jobs and expand the economy.

Hespeler Meats had to provide a detailed justification for their canned paté project in order to qualify for the government grant. Their problem was that it was necessary to predict both the expenditures and the receipts for the following five years. This was a product line with which they had no experience, and which, in fact, had not been offered in North America by any meat processor. They had absolutely no idea what their sales would be. Any numbers they picked would be guesses, but to get the grant they had to give numbers.

What they did was select an estimate of sales that, given the equipment expenditures expected, fell exactly within that range of profitability that made the project suitable for government support. They got the money. As it turned out, the product line was a flop, and the canning equipment was sold as scrap five years later.

EXAMPLE 1.4

When a large metal casting is made, as for the engine block of a car, it has only a rough exterior, and often has *flash*, which is ragged edges of metal formed where molten metal seeped between the two halves of the mould. The first step in finishing the casting is to grind off the flash, and to grind flat surfaces so that the casting can be held properly for subsequent machining.

Galt Casting Grinders (GCG) made the complex specialized equipment for this operation. It had once commanded the world market for this product, but lost market share to Japanese competitors. The competitors did not have a better product than GCG. They were able to increase market share by adding fancy display panels with coloured lights, dials, and switches that looked very sophisticated.

GCG's problem was that, when designing their equipment, their idea of sensible design was to omit the features the competitors included (or the customers wanted). GCG reasoned that these features added nothing to the capability of the equipment, but did add a lot to the manufacturing cost and to the maintenance costs that would be borne by the purchaser. They had no doubt that it was unwise, and poor engineering design, to make such unnecessarily complicated displays, so they made no changes.

GCG went bankrupt several years later.

In each of these three examples, the technical issues are overwhelmed by the non-technical ones. For Preston Sandpapers, the chief engineer was pressured by his social responsibility and self-interest to lie and recommend a decision that was not justified by the facts. In the Hespeler Meats case, the engineer had to choose between stating the truth—that future sales were unknown—which would deny the company a very useful grant, and selecting a convenient number that would encourage government support. For Galt Casting Grinders, the issue was marketing. They found it difficult to recognize that a product must be more than technically good; it must also be salable.

Beyond these principles, however, there is a moral component to each of these anecdotes. As guardians of knowledge, engineers have a vital responsibility to society to behave ethically and responsibly in all ways. When there are so many different issues that must be taken into account in engineering decision making, it is often difficult to determine what course of action is ethical.

For Preston Sandpapers, most people would probably say that what the chief engineer did was unethical. However, he did not exploit his position simply for personal gain. He was, in his mind, saving a town. Is the principle of honesty more important than several hundred jobs? Perhaps it is, but when the job holders are friends and family it is understandable that unethical choices can be made.

For Hespeler Meats, the issue is more subtle. Is it ethical to choose figures that match the ideal ones to gain a government grant? It is, strictly speaking, a lie, or at least misleading, since there is no estimate of sales. On the other hand, the bureaucracy demands that some numbers be given, so why not pick ones that suit your case?

In the Galt Casting Grinders case, the engineers apparently did no wrong. The ethical question concerns the competitors' actions. Is it ethical to put features on equipment that do no good, add cost, and decrease reliability? In this case, and for many products, this is often done, whether ethical or not. As seen in the GCG case, if it is unethical, then the ethical suppliers will, at least sometimes, go out of business.

There are no general answers to difficult moral questions. The practising engineer often has to make choices with an ethical component, and can sometimes rely on no stronger foundation than his or her own sense of right and wrong. More information about ethical issues for engineers can be obtained from provincial professional engineering associations.

1.6   Uncertainty and Sensitivity Analysis

Whenever people predict the future, errors occur. Sometimes predictions are correct, whether the predictions are about the weather, a ball game, or company cash flow. On the other hand, it would be unrealistic to expect anyone always to be right about something that hasn't happened yet.

Although exact predictions are unreliable, approximate ones may not be. A weather forecaster can dependably say that it will not snow in July, for example, even though it is more difficult to be sure of the exact temperature.

Engineering economics studies are quantitative in nature, and most of the time the quantities involved are estimates of future, and thus uncertain, amounts. Consequently, errors will occur. These errors can be very important, since often decisions with expensive consequences and significant health and environmental effects will be made from the economic calculations. How can these errors be minimized?

One way to control the errors is to make sure that the information being used is valid and as accurate as possible. The GIGO rule—Garbage In, Garbage Out—applies here. There is little else as useless or potentially dangerous as a precise calculation made from inaccurate data. However, even accurate data from the past is only of limited value when predicting the future. Even with sure knowledge of past events, the future is still uncertain.

Sensitivity analysis is a process of assessing the effect of possible errors in data and is very useful in engineering economics. The idea is that, although a particular value for a parameter can be known with only a limited degree of certainty, a range of values can be assessed with reasonable certainty. In sensitivity analysis, the calculations are done several times, varying each important parameter over its range of possible values. Usually only one parameter at a time is changed, so that the effect of each change on the conclusion can be assessed independently of the effect of other changes.

In Example 1.1, Naomi's brother Ben had to choose a car. He made an estimate of the resale value of each of the alternative cars, but the *actual* resale amount is unknown until the car is sold. Similarly, the operating costs are not known with certainty until the cars are driven for a while. Before concluding that the Chevy is the right car to buy (on economic grounds at least), Ben should assess the sensitivity of this decision by varying the resale values and operating costs within a range from the minimum likely amount to the maximum likely amount. Since these calculations are often done on spreadsheets, this assessment is not hard to do, even with many different parameters to vary.

Sensitivity analysis is an integral part of all engineering economics decisions because data regarding future activities are always uncertain. In this text, emphasis is usually given to the structure and formulation of problems rather than to verifying whether the result is robust. In this context, robust means that the same decision will be made over a wide range of parameter values. It should be remembered that no decision is properly made unless the sensitivity of that decision to errors in the underlying data is assessed.

A related issue is the number of significant digits in a calculation. Modern calculators and computers can carry out calculations to a large number of decimal places of precision. For most purposes, such precision is meaningless. For example, a cost calculated as \$1.0014613076 is not of any more use than \$1.00 in most applications. It is useful, though, to carry as many decimal places as convenient to reduce the magnitude of accumulated round-off errors.

In this book, all calculations have been done with as many significant digits as could conveniently be carried, even though the intermediate values are shown with three to six digits. As a rule, only three significant digits are assumed in the final value. For decision-making purposes, this is plenty.

1.7 How This Book Is Organized

There are eleven chapters remaining in this book. The first block of chapters, Chapters 2 to 5, forms the core material of the book. Chapters 2 and 3 provide the mathematics needed to manipulate

CANADIAN CORPORATE CASE 1.1

Bata Industries Ltd. and Trioxide Inc.

Bata Industries Ltd. of Toronto is one of the largest manufacturers of footwear in the world. Although one might think shoe production would be a relatively benign business, on February 2, 1992, the Ontario Court of Justice found the firm liable for significant environmental damage. Metal drums filled with toxic waste were improperly managed, and the contents leaked. Bata had to pay \$500 000 in clean-up costs, the corporation was fined \$90 000, and both the company president and vice-president were fined \$6000.

This was the first time in Canada that directors of a large company were convicted of an environmental offence. The court held that both the president and vice-president had sufficient knowledge and control over the company's daily activities that they should be held responsible for the damage.

The largest penalty to date for environmental damage in Canada was to Trioxide Inc. The corporation and five of its directors pleaded guilty to charges of permitting the discharge of waste water into the St. Lawrence River. The company was fined \$1 000 000 and was ordered to donate \$3 000 000 to environmental protection programs.

Source: Canadian Consulting Engineer, July/August 1994.

monetary values over time. Chapters 4 and 5 deal with comparing alternative projects. Chapter 4 illustrates present worth, annual worth, and payback period comparisons, and Chapter 5 covers the internal rate of return (IRR) method of comparison.

The second block of chapters, Chapters 6 to 8, broadens the core material. It covers depreciation and analysis of a company's financial statements, when to replace equipment (replacement analysis), and taxation. An extended case is provided between Chapter 6 and Chapter 7 to bring together some of the ideas presented in the first half of the book.

The third block includes Chapters 9 to 12. These chapters provide supporting material for the previous chapters. Chapter 9 concerns inflation, and Chapter 10 concerns sensitivity analysis. Chapter 11 explores what to do for projects owned by or affecting the public, rather than an individual or firm. Finally, Chapter 12 provides some formal methods for taking into account the intangible components of an engineering decision.

Each chapter begins with a story about Naomi and her experiences at Canadian Widgets. There are several purposes to these stories. They provide an understanding of engineering practice that is impossible to convey with short examples. In each chapter, the story has been chosen to make clear why the ideas being discussed are important. It is also hoped that the stories make the material taught a little more interesting.

The extended case between Chapter 6 and Chapter 7 is a problem that is too complicated to include in a particular chapter, but it reflects a realistic situation that would likely be encountered in engineering practice.

Throughout the text there are boxes which contain information that is associated with, and supplements, the text material. One set of boxes contains *Canadian Corporate Cases*, which report on how engineering economics is used in familiar Canadian companies. Another set of boxes contains *Close-Ups* which focus on topics of relevance to the chapter material.

Engineering Economics in Action, Part 1C: A Taste of What Is to Come

aomi was just putting on her newly laminated security pass when Clem came rushing in. "Sorry to be late," he puffed. "I got caught up in a discussion with someone in Marketing. Are you ready for lunch?" She certainly was. She had spent the better part of the morning going through the benefits package offered by Canadian Widgets and was a bit overwhelmed by the paperwork. Dental plan options, pension plan beneficiaries, and tax forms swam in front of her eyes. The thought of food sounded awfully good.

As they walked to the lunchroom, Clem continued to talk. "Maybe you will be able to help out once you get settled in, Naomi."

"What's the problem?" asked Naomi. Obviously Clem was still thinking about his discussion with this person from Marketing.

"Well," said Clem, "currently we buy small aluminum parts from a sub-contractor. The cost is quite reasonable, but we should consider making the parts ourselves, as our volumes are increasing and the fabrication process would not be difficult for us to bring in-house. We might be able to make the parts at a lower cost. Of course, we'd have to buy some new equipment. That's why I was up in the Marketing Department talking to Prabha."

"What do you mean?" asked Naomi, still a little unsure. "What does this have to do with Marketing?"

Clem realized that he was making a lot of assumptions about Naomi's knowledge of Canadian Widgets. "Sorry," he said, "I need to explain. I was up in Marketing to ask for some demand forecasts so that we would have a better handle on the volumes of these aluminum parts that we might need in the next few years. That, combined with some digging on possible equipment costs, would allow us to do an analysis of whether we should make the parts in-house or continue to buy them."

Things made much more sense to Naomi now. Her engineering economics text was certainly going to come in handy.

PROBLEMS

1.1 For each of the following items, describe how the design might differ if the costs of manufacturing, use, and maintenance were not important. On the basis of these descriptions, is it important to consider costs in engineering design?

(a) a car

(b) a television set

(c) a light bulb

(d) a book

1.2 Leslie and Sandy, recently married students, are going to rent their first apartment. Leslie has carefully researched the market, and has decided that, all things considered, there is only one reasonable choice. The two-bedroom apartment in the building at the corner of University and Erb Streets is the best value for the money, and is also close to school. Sandy, on the other hand, has just fallen in love with the top half of a duplexed house on Dunbar Road. Which apartment should they move into? Why? Which do you think they will move into? Why?

1.3 Describe the process of using the telephone, as you might describe it to a six-year-old child using it for the first time to call a friend from school. Describe using the telephone to an electrical engineer who just happens never to have seen one before. Which is the correct way to describe a telephone?

1.4 (a) Karen has to decide which of several computers to buy for school use. Should she buy the cheapest one? Can she decide on the best choice on price alone?

(b) Several computers offer essentially the same features, reliability, service, etc. Among these, can she decide the best choice on price alone?

1.5 For each of the following situations, describe what you think you *should* do. In each case *would* you do this?

(a) A fellow student, who is a friend, is copying assignments and submitting them as his own work.

(b) A fellow student, who is *not* a friend, is copying assignments and submitting them as her own work.

(c) A fellow student, who is your only competitor for an important academic award, is copying assignments and submitting them as his own work.

(d) A friend wants to hire you to write an essay for school for her. You are dead broke and the pay is excellent.

(e) A friend wants to hire you to write an essay for school for him. You have lots of money, but the pay is excellent.

(f) A friend wants to hire you to write an essay for school for her. You have lots of money, and the pay is poor.

(g) Your car was in an accident. The insurance adjuster says that the car was totalled, and they will give you only the "blue book" value for it as scrap. They will pick up the car in a week. A friend points out that in the meantime you could sell the almost-new tires and replace them with bald ones from the scrap yard, and perhaps sell some other parts, too.

(h) The CD player from your car has been stolen. The insurance adjuster asks you how much it was worth. It was actually a very cheap one, of poor quality.

(i) The engineer you work for has told you that the meter measuring discharge effluent from a production process exaggerates, and the measured value must be halved for record keeping.

(j) The engineer you work for has told you that your job is to make up realistic-looking figures reporting effluent discharge from a production process.

(k) You observe unmetered and apparently unreported discharge effluent from a production process.

(l) An engineer where you work is copying directly from a manufacturer's brochure machine tool specifications to be included in a purchase request. These specifications limit the possible purchase to the particular one specified.

(m) An engineer where you work is copying directly from a manufacturer's brochure machine tool specifications to be included in a purchase request. These specifications limit the possible purchase to the particular one specified. You know that the engineer's best friend is the salesman for that manufacturer.

1.6 Ciel is trying to decide whether now is a good time to expand her manufacturing plant. The viability of expansion depends on the Canadian economy (an expanding economy means more sales), the relative value of the Canadian dollar (a lower dollar means more exports), and changes in international trade agreements (lower tariffs also mean more exports). What two things can she do to help make sure she makes a good decision?

1.7 Trevor started a high-tech business two years ago, and now wants to sell out to one of his larger competitors. Two different buyers have made firm offers. They are similar in all but two respects. They differ in price: the Investco offer would result in Trevor's walking away with $2 000 000, while the Venture Corporation offer would give him $3 000 000. The other way they differ is that Investco say they will recapitalize Trevor's company to increase growth, while Trevor thinks that Venture Corporation will close down the business so that it doesn't compete with several of Venture Corporation's other divisions. What should Trevor do?

2

Time Value of Money

Engineering Economics in Action, Part 2A: A Steal for Steel

2.1   Introduction

2.2   Interest and Interest Rates

2.3   Compound and Simple Interest

2.4   Effective and Nominal Interest Rates

2.5   Continuous Compounding

2.6   Cash Flow Diagrams

2.7   Equivalence

    2.7.1   Mathematical Equivalence

    2.7.2   Decisional Equivalence

    2.7.3   Market Equivalence

Canadian Corporate Case 2.1: Canada Trust's Powerline Account

Review Problems

Summary

Engineering Economics in Action, Part 2B: You Just Have to Know When

Problems

Engineering Economics in Action, Part 2A: A Steal For Steel

"*Naomi, can you check this for me?*" *Terry's request broke the relative silence as Naomi and Terry worked together one Tuesday afternoon. "I was just reviewing our J-class line for Clem, and it seems to me that we could save a lot of money there."*

"O.K., tell me about it." Since Naomi and Terry had met two weeks earlier, just after Naomi started her job, things had being going very well. Terry was a second-year engineering student at the local university, and was on a four-month co-op work term at Canadian Widgets.

"Well, mostly we use the heavy rolled stock on that line. According to the pricing memo we have for that kind of steel, there is a big price break at a volume that could supply our needs for six months. We've been buying this stuff on a week-by-week basis. It just makes sense to me to take advantage of that price break."

"Interesting idea, Terry. Have you got data about how we have ordered before?"

"Yep, right here."

"Let's take a closer look."

"Well," Terry said, as he and Naomi looked over his figures, "the way we have been paying doesn't make too much sense. We order about a week's supply. The cost of this is added to our account. Every six months we pay off our account. Meanwhile, the supplier is charging us 2% of our outstanding amount at the end of each month!"

"Well, at least it looks as if it might make more sense for us to pay off our bills more often," Naomi replied.

"Now look at this. In the six months ending last December, we ordered steel for a total cost of $1 600 000. If we had bought this steel at the beginning of July, it would have only cost $1 400 000. That's a saving of $200 000!"

"Good observation, Terry, but I don't think buying in advance is the right thing to do. If you think about it . . ."

2.1 Introduction

Engineering decisions frequently concern benefits and costs that occur at different times. A typical situation involves giving up something now to get something in the future. This chapter is concerned with methods of comparing the values of benefits and costs that occur at different times. The key to making comparisons of values across time is the interest rate. In sections 2.2 to 2.5 we introduce and illustrate through examples some interest and interest rate terminology. Section 2.6 deals with how to display money graphically at different points in time using a cash flow diagram. Following this, section 2.7 contains a discussion of what it means to say that benefits or costs that occur at different times are equivalent.

2.2 Interest and Interest Rates

Everyone is familiar with the idea of interest from their everyday activities:

From the furniture store ad: *Pay no interest until next year!*
From the bank: *Now 5.6% daily interest on passbook accounts!*

Why are there interest rates? If people are given the choice between dollars now and the same number of dollars next year, most would choose the dollars now. If they have the dollars now, they can do something with them. For instance, they could buy a productive asset like a machine or a delivery truck which they would use to help make or do something that was worth more than the initial amount of money. Or they may want to buy some consumer good and don't want to wait to enjoy the good. What this says is that one dollar now is worth more than one dollar next year. This means that people will give up one dollar now in exchange for some number, greater than one, of dollars to be received next year.

That people would rather have money now than later means that they must be compensated for lending money. The compensation is in the form of a payment of interest, *I*. More formally, **interest** is the difference between the amount of money lent and the amount repaid. It is the compensation for giving up the use of money for the period of the loan.

An amount of money today, *P* (also called the *principal amount*), can be related to a *future amount F* by the interest amount *I* or interest rate *i* . This relationship is illustrated graphically in Figure 2.1, and can be expressed as $F = P + I$. The interest *I* can also be expressed as an *interest rate i* with respect to the principal amount so that $I = Pi$. Thus

$$F = P + Pi$$
$$F = P(1 + i)$$

EXAMPLE 2.1

Samuel bought a one-year guaranteed investment certificate for $5000 from a bank on May 15, 1994. The bank was paying 10% on one-year

FIGURE 2.1   Present and Future Worth

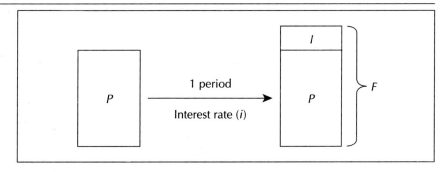

guaranteed investment certificates at the time. One year later, on May 15, 1995, Samuel cashed in his certificate for $5500.

We may think of the interest payment that Samuel got from the bank as compensation for giving up the use of money. When Samuel bought the guaranteed investment certificate for $5000, he gave up the opportunity to use the money during the following year in some other way. On the other hand, the bank got use of the money for the year. In effect, Samuel lent $5000 to the bank for a year. The $500 interest was payment by the bank to Samuel for the loan. The bank wanted the loan so that they could use the money for the year. (They may have lent the money to someone else at a higher interest rate.)

This leads to a slightly different formal definition of interest rates. Divide time into periods like days, months, or years. If the right to P at the beginning of a time period exchanges for the right to F at the end of the period, where $F = P(1 + i)$, i is the **interest rate** per time period. In this definition, P is called the **present worth** of F, and F is called the **future worth** of P.

EXAMPLE 2.1   Restated

Samuel bought a one-year guaranteed investment certificate for $5000 from a bank on May 15, 1994. The bank was paying 10% on one-year guaranteed investment certificates at the time. The certificate gave Samuel the right to claim $5500 from the bank on May 15, 1995.

Notice in this example that there was a transaction between Samuel and the bank on May 15, 1994. There was an exchange of $5000 on May 15, 1994, for the right to collect $5500 on May 15, 1995. On May 15, 1994, the bank got the $5000 and Samuel got the right to collect $5500 one year later. Evidently, having a dollar on May 15, 1994, was worth more than the right to collect a dollar a year later. Each dollar on May 15, 1994, was worth the right to collect $\frac{5500}{5000} = 1.1$ dollars a year later. This 1.1 may be written as $1 + 0.1$ where 0.1 is the interest rate. The interest rate, then, gives the rate of exchange between money at the beginning of a period (one year in this example) and the right to money at the end of the period.

The dimensions of interest rates are $\frac{\text{dollars/dollars}}{\text{time period}}$. For example, a 9% interest rate means that for every dollar (or other unit of money) lent, 0.09 dollars is returned for each time period. The value of the interest rate depends on the length of the time period. Usually, interest rates are expressed on a yearly basis, although they may be given for periods other than a year, such as a month or a quarter. This base unit of time over which an interest rate is calculated is called the **interest period**. Interest periods are described in more detail in Close-Up 2.1. The longer the interest period, the higher the interest rate must be to provide the same return.

CLOSE-UP 2.1   INTEREST PERIODS

The most commonly used interest period is one year. If we say, for example, "6% interest" without specifying an interest period, the assumption is that 6% interest is paid for a one-year period. However, interest periods can be of any duration. Here are some other common interest periods:

Interest period	Interest is calculated
Semi-annual	twice per year, or once each six months
Quarterly	four times a year, or once each three months
Monthly	12 times per year
Weekly	52 times per year
Daily	365 times per year
Continuous	for infinitesimally small periods

Interest concerns the lending and borrowing of money. It is a parameter that allows an exchange of a larger amount of money in the future for a smaller amount of money in the present, and vice versa. As we will see in Chapter 3, it also allows very complicated exchanges of money over time.

Interest also has a physical basis. Money can be invested in financial instruments, like a bond or a savings account, that pay interest, and money can also be invested directly in industrial processes or services that generate wealth. In fact, the money invested in financial instruments is also, indirectly, invested in productive activities by the organization providing the instrument. Consequently, the root source of interest is the productive use of money, as this is what makes the money actually increase in value. The actual return generated by a specific productive investment varies enormously, as will be seen in Chapter 4.

2.3   Compound and Simple Interest

We have seen that, if an amount, P, is lent for one interest period at the interest rate, i, the amount that must be repaid at the end of the period is $F = P(1 + i)$. But loans may be for several periods. How is the quantity of money that must be repaid computed when the loan is for N interest periods? The usual way is "one period at a time." Suppose that the amount P is borrowed for N periods at the interest rate i. The amount that must be repaid at the end of the N periods is $P(1 + i)^N$, that is

$$F = P(1 + i)^N \qquad (2.1)$$

This is derived as shown in Table 2.1.

TABLE 2.1: Compound Interest Computations for Example 2.2

Beginning of Period	Amount Lent	Interest Amount	Amount Owed at Period End
1	P	$+ \, Pi$	$= P + Pi = P(1 + i)$
2	$P(1 + i)$	$+ \, P(1 + i)i$	$= P(1 + i) + P(1 + i)i$
3	$P(1+i)^2$	$+ \, P(1+i)^2 i$	$= P(1+i)^2 + P(1 + i)^2 i$
...	...		
N	$P(1 + i)^{N-1}$	$+ \, [P(1 + i)^{N-1}]i$	$= P(1 + i)^N$

This method of computing interest is called *compounding*. Compounding assumes that there are N sequential one-period loans. At the end of the first interest period, the borrower owes $P(1 + i)$. This is the amount borrowed for the second period. Interest is required on this larger amount. At the end of the second period $[P(1 + i)](1 + i)$ is owed. This is the amount borrowed for the third period. This continues so that at the end of the $(N-1)^{th}$ period $P(1 + i)^{N-1}$ is owed. The interest on this is $[P(1 + i)^{N-1}]i$. The total interest on the loan over the N periods is

$$I_c = P(1 + i)^N - P \tag{2.2}$$

I_c is called **compound interest**. The interest period when compounding is used to compute interest is called the **compounding period**.

EXAMPLE 2.2

If you were to lend $100 for three years at 10% per year compound interest, how much interest would you get at the end of the three years?

If you lend $100 for three years at 10% compound interest per year, you will earn $10 in interest in the first year. That $10 will be lent, along with the original $100, for the second year. Thus, in the second year, the interest earned will be $11 = $110(0.10). The $11 is lent for the third year. This makes the loan for the third year $121; $12.10 = $121(0.10) in interest will be earned in the third year. At the end of the three years, the amount you are owed will be $133.10. The interest received is then $33.10. This can also be calculated from equation (2.2):

$$I_c = \$100(1 + 0.1)^3 - \$100 = \$33.10$$

Table 2.2 summarizes the compounding process.

TABLE 2.2

Beginning of Year	Amount Lent	Interest Amount	Amount Owed at Year End
1	100	+ $100 × 0.1	= $110
2	110	+ $110 × 0.1	= $121
3	121	+ $121 × 0.1	= $133.10

If the interest payment for an N-period loan, at the interest rate i per period, is computed without compounding, the interest amount, I_s, is called **simple interest**. It is computed as

$$I_s = PiN$$

EXAMPLE 2.3

If you were to lend $100 for three years at 10% per year simple interest, how much interest would you get at the end of the three years?

The total amount of interest earned on the $100 over the three years would be $30. This can be calculated by using $I_s = PiN$:

$$I_s = PiN = \$100(0.10)(3) = \$30$$

Interest amounts computed with simple interest and compound interest will yield the same results only when the number of interest periods is one. As the number of periods increases, the difference between the accumulated interest amounts for the two methods increases exponentially.

When the number of interest periods is significantly greater than one, the difference between simple interest and compound interest can be very great. Recently, a couple in Nevada presented the state government with a $1000 bond issued by the state in 1865. The bond carried an annual interest rate of 24%. The couple claimed the bond was now worth several trillion dollars (*Source: Newsweek*, August 9, 1993, p. 8). If one takes the length of time from 1865 to the time the couple presented the bond to the state as 127 years, the value of the bond could have been $732 trillion = $1000(1 + 0.24)^{127}$. This would be what the state owed at the end of 127 years if it were required to pay compound interest for 127 years.

If, instead of compound interest, a simple interest rate given by $iN = (24\%)127 = 3048\%$ were used, the bond would be worth only $31 480 = $1000(1 + 30.48)$. Thus, the difference between simple and compound interest can be dramatic, especially as in this example when the interest rate is high and the number of periods is large. The graph in Figure 2.2 shows the difference between compound interest and simple interest for the first twenty years of the bond example.

FIGURE 2.2   Compound and Simple Interest at 24% per year for 20 Years

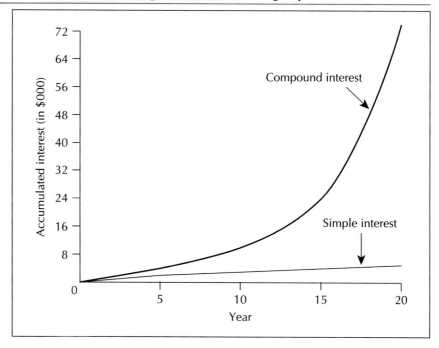

The conventional approach for computing interest is the compound interest method rather than simple interest. Simple interest is rarely used, except perhaps as an intuitive (yet incorrect!) way of thinking of compound interest. We mention simple interest primarily to contrast it with compound interest and to indicate that the difference between the two methods can be large.

2.4 Effective and Nominal Interest Rates

Interest rates may be stated for some period, like a year, while the computation of interest is based on shorter compounding sub-periods like months. In this section we consider the relation between the *nominal* interest rate that is stated for the full period and the *effective* interest rate that results from the compounding based on the sub-periods. This relation between nominal and effective interest rates must be understood to answer questions like this one: How would you choose between two investments, one bearing 12% per year interest, compounded yearly, with another with 1% per month interest, compounded monthly? Are they the same?

Suppose that a time period is divided into m equal sub-periods. Let there be stated a **nominal interest rate**, r, for the full period. By convention, for nominal interest, the interest rate for each sub-period is calculated as $i_s = \frac{r}{m}$. For example, a nominal interest rate of 18% per year, compounded monthly, is the same as $\frac{.18}{12} = 0.015$ or 1.5% per month.

What is the **effective interest rate**, i_e, for the full period that will yield the same amount as compounding at the end of each sub-period, i_s? If we compound interest every sub-period, we have

$$F = P(1 + i_s)^m$$

We want to find the effective interest rate, i_e, that yields the same future amount F at the end of the full period from the present amount P. Set

$$P(1 + i_s)^m = P(1 + i_e)$$

Then

$$(1 + i_s)^m = 1 + i_e$$
$$i_e = (1 + i_s)^m - 1 \tag{2.3}$$

Note that Equation (2.3) allows the conversion between the interest rate over a smaller compounding period, i_s, and the effective interest rate over a larger period, i_e, by using the number of smaller periods, m, in the larger period.

EXAMPLE 2.4

What interest rate per year, compounded yearly, is equivalent to 1% interest per month, compounded monthly?

Since the month is the shorter compounding period, we let $i_s = 0.01$ and $m = 12$. Then i_e refers to the effective interest rate per year. Substitution into Equation 2.3 then gives

$$i_e = (1 + i_s)^m - 1$$
$$= (1 + 0.01)^{12} - 1$$
$$= 0.126825$$
$$\approx 0.127 \text{ or } 12.7\%$$

An interest rate of 1% per month, compounded monthly, is equivalent to an effective rate of approximately 12.7% per year, compounded yearly. The answer to our previously posed question is that an investment bearing 12% per year interest, compounded yearly, pays less than an investment bearing 1% per month interest, compounded monthly.

Interest rates are normally given as nominal rates. We may get the effective (yearly) rate by substituting $i_s = \frac{r}{m}$ into Equation (2.3). We then obtain a direct means of computing an effective interest rate, given a nominal rate and the number of compounding periods per year:

$$i_e = \left(1 + \frac{r}{m}\right)^m - 1 \tag{2.4}$$

This formula is suitable only for converting from a nominal rate r to an annual effective rate. If the effective rate desired is for a period longer than a year, then Equation (2.3) must be used.

EXAMPLE 2.5

Leona the loan shark lends money to clients at the rate of 5% interest *per week*! What is the nominal interest rate for these loans? What is the effective annual interest rate?

The nominal interest rate is 5% × 52 = 260%. The effective yearly interest rate can be found by substitution into Equation (2.3):

$$i_e = (1 + 0.05)^{52} - 1 = 11.6$$

Leona charges an effective annual interest rate of about 1160% on her loans.

EXAMPLE 2.6

The Cardex Credit Card Company charges a nominal 24% interest on overdue accounts, compounded daily. What is the effective interest rate?

Assuming that there are 365 days per year, we can calculate the interest rate per day using either Equation (2.3) with $i_s = \frac{r}{m} = \frac{0.24}{365} = 0.0006575$ or by the use of Equation (2.4) directly. The effective interest rate (per year) is

$$i_e = (1 + 0.0006575)^{365} - 1$$
$$= 0.271 \text{ or } 27.1\%$$

With a nominal rate of 24% compounded daily, the Cardex Credit Card Company is actually charging an effective rate of about 27.1% per year.

Although there are laws which may require that the effective interest rate be disclosed for loans and investments, it is still very common for nominal interest rates to be quoted. Since the nominal rate will be less than the effective rate whenever the number of compounding periods per year exceeds one, there is an advantage to quoting loans using the nominal rates, since it makes the loan look more attractive. This is particularly true when interest rates are high and compounding occurs frequently.

2.5 | Continuous Compounding

As has been seen, compounding can be done yearly, quarterly, monthly, or daily. The periods can be made even smaller, as small as desired; the main disadvantage in having very small periods is having to do more calculations. If the period is made infinitesimally small, we say that interest is compounded *continuously*. There are situations where very frequent compounding makes sense. For instance, an improvement in material handling may reduce downtime on machinery. There will be benefits in the form of increased output that may be used immediately. If there are several additional runs a day, there will be benefits several times a day. Another example is trading on the stock market. Personal and corporate investments are often in the form of mutual funds. Mutual funds represent a changing set of stocks and bonds, where transactions occur very frequently, often many times a day.

A formula for **continuous compounding** can be developed from Equation (2.3) by allowing the number of compounding periods per year to become infinitely large:

$$i_e = \lim_{m \to \infty} \left(1 + \frac{r}{m}\right)^m - 1$$

By noting that

$$\lim_{m \to \infty} \left(1 + \frac{r}{m}\right)^m = e^r$$

we get

$$i_e = e^r - 1 \qquad\qquad (2.5)$$

EXAMPLE 2.7

Cash flow at the Arctic Oil Company is continuously reinvested. An investment in a new data logging system is expected to return a nominal 40% interest, compounded continuously. What is the effective interest rate earned by this investment?

The nominal interest rate is given as $r = 0.40$. From Equation (2.5),

$$i_e = e^{0.4} - 1$$
$$= 1.492 - 1 = 0.492 \text{ or } 49.2\%$$

The effective interest rate earned on this investment is about 49.2%.

FIGURE 2.3   **Growth in Value of $1 at 30% Interest, at Various Compounding Periods**

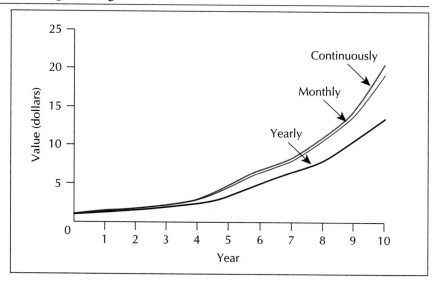

Although continuous compounding makes sense in some circumstances, it is rarely used. As with effective interest and nominal interest, in the days before calculators and computers, calculations involving continuous compounding were difficult to do. Consequently, discrete compounding is, by convention, the norm. As illustrated in Figure 2.3, the difference between continuous compounding and discrete compounding is relatively insignificant, even at a fairly high interest rate.

2.6 Cash Flow Diagrams

Sometimes a set of cash flows can be sufficiently complicated that it is useful to have a graphical representation. A **cash flow diagram** is a chart that summarizes the timing and magnitude of cash flows as they occur over time.

A cash flow diagram is actually a graph, although the vertical axis is not shown explicitly. The horizontal (X) axis represents time, measured in periods, and the vertical (Y) axis represents the size and direction of the cash flows. Individual cash flows are indicated by arrows pointing up or down from the horizontal axis, as indicated in Figure 2.4. The arrows that point up represent positive cash flows, or receipts. The downward pointing arrows represent negative cash flows, or disbursements. See Close-Up 2.2 for some comments on the beginning and ending of periods.

FIGURE 2.4   Cash Flow Diagram

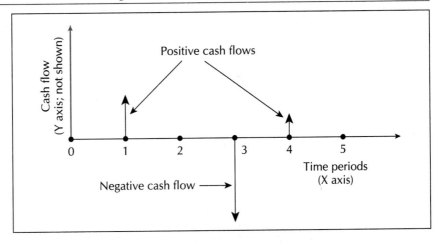

EXAMPLE 2.8

Consider Ashok, a recent university graduate who is trying to summarize typical cash flows for each month. His monthly income is $2200, received at the end of each month. Out of this he pays for rent, food, entertainment, telephone charges, and a credit card bill for all other purchases. Rent is $700 per month (including utilities), due at the end of each month. Weekly food and entertainment expenses total roughly $120, a typical telephone bill is $40 (due at the end of the first week in the month), and his credit card purchases average $300. Credit card payments are due at the end of the second week of each month.

Figure 2.5 shows the timing and amount of the disbursements and the single receipt over a typical month. It is assumed that there are exactly four weeks in a month, and it is now just past the end of the month. Each arrow, which represents a cash flow, is labelled with the amount of the receipt or disbursement.

When two or more cash flows occur in the same time period, the amounts may be shown individually, as in Figure 2.5, or in summary form, as in Figure 2.6. The level of detail used depends on personal choice and the amount of information the diagram is intended to convey.

FIGURE 2.5   **Cash Flow Diagram for Example 2.8**

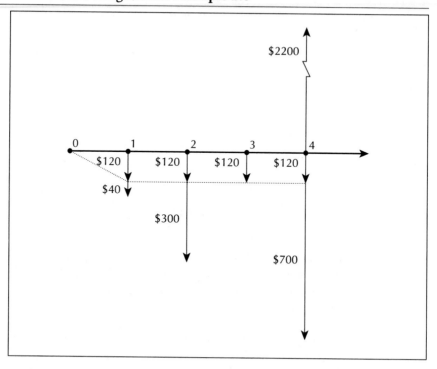

FIGURE 2.6   **Cash Flow Diagram for Example 2.8 in Summary Form**

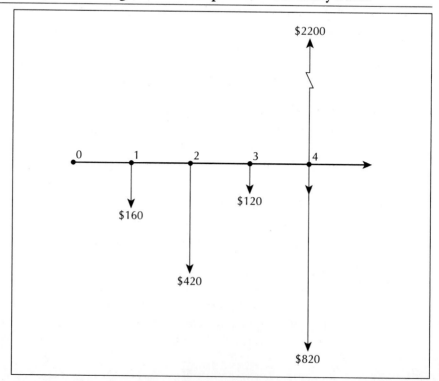

We suggest that the reader make a practice of using cash flow diagrams when working on a problem with cash flows that occur at different times. Just going through the steps in setting up a cash flow diagram can make the problem structure clearer. Seeing the pattern of cash flows in the completed diagram gives a "feel" for the problem.

2.7 Equivalence

We started this chapter by pointing out that many engineering decisions involve costs and benefits that occur at different times. Making these decisions requires that the costs and benefits at different times be compared.

To make these comparisons, we must be able to say that certain values at different times are *equivalent*. To understand the concept of **equivalence**, note that, if a cost at the beginning of a period has a greater value than a benefit at the end of the period, there must be some smaller cost at the beginning of the period that would be equivalent to the benefit at the end, or there must be some larger benefit at the end that would be equivalent to the cost at the beginning.

What is the concept of equivalence that underlies comparisons of costs and benefits at different times? In this section we distinguish three concepts of equivalence that may underlie comparisons of costs and benefits at different times.

With **mathematical equivalence**, equivalence is a consequence of the mathematical relationship between time and money. This is the form of equivalence used in $F = P(1 + i)^N$.

With **decisional equivalence**, equivalence is a consequence of indifference on the part of a decision maker among available choices.

With **market equivalence**, equivalence is a consequence of the ability to exchange one cash flow for another at zero cost.

Although the mathematics governing money is the same regardless of which form of equivalence is most appropriate for a given situation, it can be important to be aware of what assumptions must be made for the mathematical operations to be meaningful.

2.7.1 Mathematical Equivalence

Mathematical equivalence is simply a mathematical relationship. It says that two cash flows, P_t, at time t, and F_{t+N}, at time $t + N$, are equivalent with respect to the interest rate, i, if $F = P(1 + i)^N$. Notice that if F_{t+N+M} (where M is a second number of periods) is equivalent to P_t then

$$F_{t+N+M} = P_t(1 + i)^{M+N}$$
$$F_{t+N+M} = F_{t+N}(1 + i)^M$$

so that F_{t+N} and F_{t+N+M} are equivalent to each other. The fact that mathematical equivalence has this property permits complex comparisons to be made among many values.

2.7.2 Decisional Equivalence

For any individual, two cash flows, P_t at time t and F_{t+N} at time $t + N$, are equivalent if the individual is indifferent between the two. Here, the interest rate relating P_t and F_{t+N} can be calculated from the decision that the cash flows are equivalent, as opposed to mathematical equivalence, in which the interest rate determines whether the cash flows are equivalent. This can be illustrated best through an example.

EXAMPLE 2.9

Bildmet is an extruder of aluminum shapes used in construction. The company buys aluminum from Alpure, an outfit that recovers aluminum from scrap. When Bildmet's purchasing manager, Greta Kehl, called in an order for 1000 kilograms of metal on August 15, she was told that Alpure was having production difficulties and was running behind schedule. Alpure's manager, Masaaki Sawada, said that he could ship the order immediately if Bildmet required it. If Alpure shipped Bildmet's order, they would not be able to fill an order for another user whom Mr. Sawada was anxious to impress with Alpure's reliability. Mr. Sawada suggested that, if Ms. Kehl would wait a week until August 22, he would show his appreciation by shipping 1100 kilograms then at the same cost to Bildmet as 1000 kilograms now. In either case, payment would be due at the end of the month. Should Ms. Kehl accept Alpure's offer?

The rate of exchange, 1100 kg to 1000 kg, may be written as $(1 + 0.1)$ to 1 where the $0.1 = 10\%$ is an interest rate for the one-week period. (This is equivalent to an effective interest rate of more than 14 000% per year!) Whether or not Ms. Kehl accepts the offer from Alpure depends on her situation. There is some chance of Bildmet's running out of metal if they don't get supplied for a week. This would require Ms. Kehl to do some scrambling to find other sources of metal in order to ship to its own customers on time. Ms. Kehl would prefer the 1000 kilograms on the fifteenth to 1000 kilograms on the twenty-second. But there is some minimum amount, larger than 1000 kilograms, that she would accept on the twenty-second in exchange for 1000 kilograms on the fifteenth. This amount would take into account both the measurable costs and also unmeasurable costs, such as inconvenience and anxiety.

Let the minimum rate at which Ms. Kehl would be willing to make the exchange be one kilogram on the fifteenth for $(1 + x)$ kilograms on the twenty-second. In this case, if $x < 10\%$, Ms. Kehl should accept Alpure's offer of 1100 kilograms on the twenty-second.

In Example 2.9, the aluminum is a capital good that can be used productively by Bildmet. There is value in that use, and that value can be measured by Greta's willingness to postpone receiving the aluminum. It can be seen that interest is not necessarily a function of exchanges of money at different points in time. However, money is a convenient measure of the worth of a variety of goods, and so interest is usually expressed in terms of money.

2.7.3 Market Equivalence

Market equivalence is based on the idea that there is a market for money that permits cash flows in the future to be exchanged for cash flows in the present, and vice versa. Converting a future cash flow, F, to a present cash flow, P, is called borrowing money, while converting P to F is called lending or investing money. The market equivalence of two cash flows P and F means that they can be exchanged, one for the other, at zero cost.

The interest rate associated with an individual's borrowing money is usually a lot higher than the interest rate applied when that individual lends money. For example, the interest rate a bank pays on deposits is lower than what it charges to lend money to clients. The difference between these interest rates provides the bank with income. This means that, for an individual, market equivalence does not exist. An individual can exchange a present worth for a future worth by investing money but, if he or she were to try to borrow against that future worth to obtain money now, the resulting present worth would be less than the original amount invested. Moreover, each time either borrowing or lending occurred, transaction costs (the fees charged or cost incurred) would further diminish the capital.

EXAMPLE 2.10

This morning, Averill bought a $5000 one-year guaranteed investment certificate (GIC) at his local bank. It has an effective interest rate of 7% per year. At the end of a year, the GIC will be worth $5350. On the way home from the bank, Averill unexpectedly discovered a valuable piece of art he had been seeking for some time. He wanted to buy it, but all his spare capital was "tied up" in the GIC. So he went back to the bank again, this time to negotiate a one-year loan for $5000, the cost of the piece of art. He figured that, if the loan came due at the same time as the GIC, he would simply pay off the loan with the proceeds of the GIC.

Unfortunately, Averill found out that the bank charges 10% effective interest per year on loans. With the proceeds from the GIC of $5350 one year from now, the amount the bank would give him today is only $5350/1.1 = $4864 (roughly), less any fees applicable to the loan. Averill has discovered that, for him, market equivalence does not hold. He cannot exchange $5000 today for $5350 one year from now, and vice versa, at zero cost.

Large companies with good records have opportunities that differ from those of individuals. Large companies borrow and invest money in so many ways, both internally and externally, that the interest rates for borrowing and for lending are very close to being the same, and also the transaction costs are negligible. They can shift funds from the future to the present by raising new money or by avoiding investment in a marginal project that would earn only the rate that they pay on new money. They can shift funds from the present to the future by undertaking an additional project or investing externally.

How large is large? Established businesses of almost any size, and even individuals with some wealth and good credit, can acquire cash and invest at about the same interest rate, provided that the amounts are small relative to their total assets. For these companies and individuals, market equivalence is a reasonable model. Assuming market equivalence makes calculations easier and still generally results in good decisions.

For most of the remainder of the book, we will be making two broad assumptions with respect to equivalence: first, that market equivalence holds, and, second, that decisional equivalence can be expressed entirely in monetary terms. If these two assumptions are reasonably valid, mathematical equivalence can be used as an accurate model of how costs and benefits relate to one another over time. In several sections of the book, when we cover how firms raise capital and how to incorporate non-monetary aspects of a situation into a decision, we will discuss the validity of these two assumptions. In the meantime, however, mathematical equivalence is used to relate cash flows which occur at different points in time.

CANADIAN CORPORATE CASE 2.1

Canada Trust's Powerline Account

Canada Trust is a consumer financial services company headquartered in London, Ontario. It offers a "Powerline" line of credit which allows customers to borrow money with the ease of using a chequing account. One form is referred to as a "secured" line of credit. In this case, a valuable asset, usually the customer's home, is used to guarantee the loan. It is thus a form of mortgage where the amount borrowed can freely vary up to some maximum amount.

Each monthly statement displays the interest rate used to calculate that month's interest. The February 1996 statement contained the following information:

Interest is calculated at an annual rate of 7.50% (0.616% per 30-day month, or 0.02054 per day).

Although the printed information does not use the terms *nominal* or *effective*, or define the compounding period, these points can easily be deduced. Noting that 7.50/365 = 0.02054 and that 0.02054 × 30 = 0.616, it is clear that the quoted annual rate is nominal, and the compounding period is daily. The actual effective interest rate is $(1 + 0.0002054)^{365} - 1 = 7.784\%$.

REVIEW PROBLEMS

▌Review Problem 2.1

Atsushi has had $800 stashed under his mattress for 30 years. How much money has he lost by not putting it in a bank account at 8% annual compound interest all these years?

> **Answer**
>
> Since Atsushi has kept the $800 under his mattress, he has not earned any interest over the 30 years. Had he put the money into an interest-bearing account, he would have had far more today. We can think of the $800 as a present amount and the amount in 30 years as the future amount.
>
> Given: $P = \$800$
>
> $i = 0.08$ per year
>
> $N = 30$ years
>
> Formula: $F = P(1 + i)^N$
>
> $= \$800(1 + 0.08)^{30}$
>
> $= \$8050.13$
>
> Atsushi would have $8050.13 in the bank account today had he deposited his $800 at 8% annual compound interest. Instead, he has only $800. He has suffered an opportunity cost of $8050.13 − $800 = $7250.13 by not investing the money.

▌Review Problem 2.2

You want to buy a new computer, but you are $1000 short of the amount you need. Your aunt has agreed to lend you the $1000 you need now, provided you pay her $1200 two years from now. She compounds interest monthly. Another place from which you can borrow $1000 is the bank. There is, however, a loan processing fee of $20, which will be included in the loan amount. The bank is expecting to receive $1220 two years from now based on monthly compounding of interest

(a) What monthly rate is your aunt charging you for the loan? What is the bank changing?

> **Answer**
>
> *Your aunt*
>
> Given: $P = \$1000$
>
> $F = \$1200$
>
> $N = 24$ months (since compounding is done monthly)

Formula: $F = P(1 + i)^N$

The formula $F = P(1 + i)^N$ must be solved in terms of i to answer the question.

$$i = \sqrt[N]{F/P} - 1$$
$$= \sqrt[24]{\$1200/\$1000} - 1$$
$$= 0.007626$$

Your aunt is charging interest at a rate of approximately 0.76% per month.

The bank

Given: $P = \$1020$ (since the fee is included in the loan amount)

   $F = \$1220$

   $N = 24$ months (since compounding is done monthly)

$$i = \sqrt[N]{F/P} - 1$$
$$= \sqrt[24]{\$1220/\$1020} - 1$$
$$= 0.007488$$

The bank is charging interest at a rate of approximately 0.75% per month.

(b) What effective annual rate is your aunt charging? What is the bank charging?

   Answer

The effective annual rate can be found with the formula $i_e = (1 + r/m)^m - 1$, where r is the nominal rate per year and m is the number of compounding periods per year. Since the number of compounding periods per year is 12, notice that r/m is simply the interest rate charged per month.

Your aunt

   $i = 0.007626$ per month

Then

$$i_e = (1 + r/m)^m - 1$$
$$= (1 + 0.007626)^{12} - 1$$
$$= 0.095445$$

The effective annual rate your aunt is charging is approximately 9.54%.

The bank

   $i = 0.007488$ per month

Then

$$i_e = (1 + r/m)^m - 1$$
$$= (1 + 0.007488)^{12} - 1$$
$$= 0.09365$$

The effective annual rate for the bank is approximately 9.37%.

(c) Would you prefer to borrow from your aunt or from the bank?

Answer

The bank appears to be charging a lower interest rate than does your aunt. This can be concluded by comparing the two monthly rates or the effective annual rates the two charge. If you were to base your decision only upon who charged the lower interest rate, you would pick the bank, despite the fact they have a fee. However, although you are borrowing $1020 from the bank, because of the fee you are getting only $1000, since the bank immediately gets its $20. The cost of money for you from the bank is better calculated as:

Given: $P = \$1000$

$F = \$1220$

$N = 24$ months (since compounding is done monthly)

$i = \sqrt[N]{F/P} - 1$

$= \sqrt[24]{\$1220/\$1000} - 1$

$= 0.00832$

From this point of view, the bank is charging interest at a rate of approximately 0.83% per month, and you would be better off borrowing from your aunt.

■ Review Problem 2.3

At the end of four years, you would like to have $5000 in a bank account to purchase a used car. What you need to know is how much to deposit in the bank account now. The account pays daily interest. Create a spreadsheet and plot the necessary deposit today as a function of interest rate. Consider nominal interest rates ranging from 5% to 15% per year, and assume that there are 365 days per year.

Answer

From the formula $F = P(1 + i)^N$, we have $\$5000 = P(1 + i)^{365 \times 4}$. This gives

$$P = \$5000 \times \frac{1}{(1 + i)^{365 \times 4}}$$

Table 2.3 is an excerpt from a sample spreadsheet. It shows the necessary deposit to accumulate $5000 over four years at a variety of interest rates. The following is the calculation for cell B2:

$$\$5000 \times \cfrac{1}{\left[1 + \left(\cfrac{A2}{365}\right)\right]^{365 \times 4}}$$

The specific implementation of this formula will vary, depending on the particular spreadsheet program used. Figure 2.7 is a diagram of the necessary deposits plotted against interest rates.

TABLE 2.3: Necessary Deposits for a Range of Interest Rates

	Interest Rate (%)	Necessary Deposit ($)
1	0.05	4094
2	0.06	3933
3	0.07	3779
4	0.08	3631
5	0.09	3489
6	0.10	3352
7	0.11	3220
8	0.12	3094
9	0.13	2973
10	0.14	2856
11	0.15	2744
12		

FIGURE 2.7   Graph for Review Problem 2.3

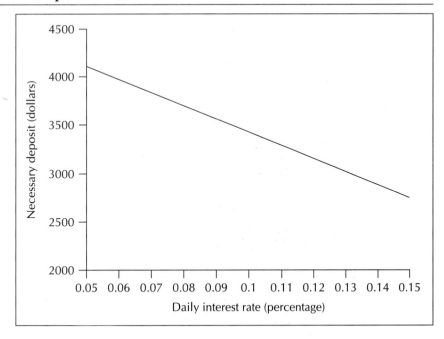

SUMMARY

This chapter has provided an introduction to interest, interest rate terminology, and interest rate conventions. Through a series of examples, the mechanics of working with simple and compound interest, nominal and effective interest rates, and continuous compounding were illustrated. Cash flow diagrams were introduced in order to represent graphically monetary transactions at various points in time. The final part of the chapter contained a discussion of various forms of cash flow equivalence: mathematical, decisional, and market equivalence. With the assumption that mathematical equivalence can be used as an accurate model of how costs and benefits relate to one another over time, we now move on to Chapter 3, in which equivalence formulas for a variety of cash flow patterns are presented.

Engineering Economics in Action, Part 2B: You Just Have to Know When

Naomi and Terry were looking at the steel orders for the J-class line. Terry thought money could be saved by ordering in advance. "Now look at this," Terry said. In the three months ending last December, we ordered steel for a total cost of $1 600 000. If we had bought this steel at the beginning of July, it would have cost only $1 400 000. That's a savings of $200 000!"

"Good observation, Terry, but I don't think buying in advance is the right thing to do. If you think about it, the rate of return on our $1 400 000 would be 200 000/1 400 000 or about 14.3% over six months."

"Yes, but that's over 30% effective interest, isn't it? I'll bet we only make 10% or 12% for money we keep in the bank."

"That's true, but the money we would use to buy the steel in advance we don't have sitting in the bank collecting interest. It would have to come from somewhere else, either money we borrow from the bank, at about 14% plus administrative costs, or from our shareholders."

"But it's still a good idea, right?"

"Well, you are right and you are wrong. Mathematically, you could probably show the advantage of buying a six-month supply in advance. But we wouldn't do it for two reasons. The first one has to do with where the money comes from. If we had to pay for six months of steel in advance, we would have a capital requirement beyond what we could cover through normal cash flows. I'm not sure the bank would even lend us that much money, so we would probably have to raise it through equity, that is, selling more shares in the company. This would cost a lot, and throw all your calculations way off."

"Just because it's such a large amount of money?"

"That's right. Our regular calculations are based on the assumption that the capital requirements don't take an extraordinary effort."

"You said there were two reasons. What's the other one?"

"The other reason is that we just wouldn't do it."

"Huh?"

"We just wouldn't do it. Right now the steel company's taking the risk — if we can't pay, they are in trouble. If we buy in advance, it's the other way around — if our widget orders dropped, we would be stuck with some pretty expensive raw materials. We would also have the problem of where to store the steel, and other practical difficulties. It makes sense mathematically, but I'm pretty sure we just wouldn't do it."

Terry looked a little dejected. Naomi continued, "But your figures make sense. The first thing to do is find out why we are carrying that account so long before we pay it off. The second thing to do is see if we can't get that price break, retroactively. We are good customers, and I'll bet we can convince them to give us the price break anyhow, without changing our ordering pattern. Let's talk to Clem about it."

"But, Naomi, why use the mathematical calculations at all, if they don't work?"

"But they do work, Terry. You just have to know when."

PROBLEMS

2.1 Using 12% simple interest per year, how much interest will be owed on a loan of $500 at the end of two years?

2.2 If a sum of $3000 is borrowed for six months at 9% simple interest per year, what is the total amount due (principal and interest) at the end of six months?

2.3 What principal amount will yield $150 in interest at the end of three months when the interest rate is 1% simple interest per month?

2.4 If $2400 interest is paid on a two-year simple-interest loan of $12 000, what is the interest rate per year?

2.5 Simple interest of $190.67 is owed on a loan of $550 after four years and four months. What is the annual interest rate?

2.6 How much will be in a bank account at the end of five years if $2000 is invested today at 12% interest per annum, compounded yearly?

2.7 How much is accumulated in each of these savings plans over two years?

(a) Deposit $1000 today at 10% compounded annually.

(b) Deposit $900 today at 12% compounded monthly.

2.8 Greg wants to have $50 000 in five years. The bank is offering five-year investment certificates that pay 8% nominal interest, compounded quarterly. How much money should he invest in the certificates to reach his goal?

2.9 Greg wants to have $50 000 in five years. He has $20 000 today to invest. The bank is offering five-year investment certificates that pay interest compounded quarterly. What is the minimum nominal interest rate he would have to receive to reach his goal?

2.10 Greg wants to have $50 000 in five years. He will invest $20 000 today in investment certificates that pay 8% nominal interest, compounded quarterly. How long will it take him to reach his goal?

2.11 Greg will invest $20 000 today in five-year investment certificates that pay 8% nominal interest, compounded quarterly. How much money will this be in five years?

2.12 You bought an antique car three years ago for $50 000. Today it is worth $65 000.

(a) What annual interest rate did you earn if interest is compounded yearly?

(b) What monthly interest rate did you earn if interest is compounded monthly?

2.13 You have a bank deposit now worth $5000. How long will it take for your deposit to be worth more than $8000 if

(a) the account pays 5% actual interest every half year, and is compounded?

(b) the account pays 5% nominal interest, compounded semi-annually?

2.14 Some time ago, you put $500 into a bank account for a "rainy day." Since then, the bank has been paying you 1% per month, compounded monthly. Today, you checked the balance, and found it to be $708.31. How long ago did you first deposit the $500?

2.15 (a) If you put $1000 in a bank account today that pays 10% interest per year, how much money could be withdrawn 20 years from now?

(b) If you put $1000 in a bank account today that pays 10% *simple* interest per year, how much money could be withdrawn 20 years from now?

2.16 How long will it take any sum to double itself,

(a) with an 11% simple interest rate?

(b) with an 11% interest rate, compounded annually?

(c) with an 11% interest rate, compounded continuously?

2.17 Compute the effective annual interest rate on each of these investments:

(a) 25% nominal interest, compounded semi-annually

(b) 25% nominal interest, compounded quarterly

(c) 25% nominal interest, compounded continuously

2.18 For a 15% effective annual interest rate, what is the nominal interest rate if

(a) interest is compounded monthly?

(b) interest is compounded daily (assume 365 days per year)?

(c) interest is compounded continuously?

2.19 The Bank of Edmonton advertises savings account interest as 6% compounded daily. What is the effective interest rate?

2.20 The Bank of Kitchener is offering a new savings account that pays a nominal 7.99% interest, compounded continuously. Will your money earn more in this account than in a daily interest account that pays 8%?

2.21 You are comparing two investments. The first pays 1% interest per month, compounded monthly, and the second pays 6% interest per six months, compounded every six months.

(a) What is the effective semi-annual interest rate for each investment?

(b) What is the effective annual interest rate for each investment?

(c) Based on interest rate, which investment do you prefer? Does your decision depend on whether you make the comparison based on an effective six-month rate or an effective one-year rate?

2.22 Dieter now has $6000. In three months, he will receive a cheque for $2000. He must pay $900 at the end of each month (starting exactly one month from now). Draw a single cash flow diagram illustrating all of these payments for a total of six monthly periods. Include his cash on hand as a payment at time 0.

2.23 Margaret is considering an investment that will cost her $500 today. It will pay her $100 at the end of each of the next 12 months, and cost her another $300 one year from today. Illustrate these cash flows in two cash flow diagrams. The first should show each cash flow element separately, and the second should show only the net cash flows in each period.

2.24 Heddy is considering a project that will cost her $20 000 today. It will pay her $10 000 at the end of each of the next 12 months, and cost her another $15 000 at the end of each quarter. An extra $10 000 will be received at the end of the project, one year from now. Illustrate these cash flows in two cash flow diagrams. The first should show each cash flow element separately, and the second should show only the net cash flow in each period.

2.25 You are indifferent between receiving $100 today and $110 one year from now. The bank pays you 6% interest on deposits and charges you 8% for loans. Name the three types of equivalence and comment (one sentence for each) on whether or not each exists for this situation and why.

2.26 Using a spreadsheet, construct graphs for the loan described in (a) below.

(a) Plot the amount owed (principal plus interest) on a simple interest loan of $100 for N years for $N = 1, 2, \ldots 10$. On the same graph, plot the amount owed on a compound interest loan of $100 for N years for $N = 1, 2, \ldots 10$. The interest rate is 6% per year for each loan.

(b) Repeat part (a), but use an interest rate of 18%. Observe the dramatic effect compounding has on the amount owed at the higher interest rate.

2.27 **(a)** At 12% interest per annum, how long will it take for a penny to become a million dollars? How long will it take at 18%?

(b) Show the growth in values on a spreadsheet using ten-year time intervals.

2.28 Use a spreadsheet to determine how long it will take for a $100 deposit to double in value for each of the following interest rates and compounding periods. For each, plot the size of the deposit over time, for as many periods as necessary for the original sum to double.

(a) 8% per year, compounded monthly

(b) 11% per year, compounded semi-annually

(c) 12% per year, compounded continuously

2.29 Construct a graph showing how the effective interest rate for the following nominal rates increases as the compounding period becomes shorter and shorter. Consider a range of compounding periods of your choice from daily compounding to annual compounding.

(a) 6% per year

(b) 10% per year

(c) 20% per year

2.30 Today, an investment you made three years ago has matured and is now worth $3000. It was a three-year deposit which bore an interest rate of 10% per year, compounded monthly. You knew at the time that you took a risk in making such an investment because interest rates vary over time and you "locked in" at 10% for three years.

(a) How much was your initial deposit? Plot the value of your investment over the three-year period.

(b) Looking back over the past three years, interest rates for similar one-year investments did indeed vary. The interest rates were 8% the first year, 10% the second, and 14% the third. Plot the value of your initial deposit over time as if you had invested at this set of rates, rather than for a constant 10% rate. Did you lose out by having locked into the 10% investment? If so, by how much?

C H A P T E R

3

Cash Flow Analysis

Engineering Economics in Action, Part 3A: Apples and Oranges

3.1   Introduction

3.2   Timing of Cash Flows and Modelling

3.3   Compound Interest Factors for Discrete Compounding

3.4   Compound Interest Factors for Single Disbursements or Receipts

3.5   Compound Interest Factors for Annuities

3.6   Conversion Factor for Arithmetic Gradient Series

3.7   Conversion Factor for Geometric Gradient Series

3.8   Non-Standard Annuities and Gradients

3.9   Present Worth Computations When $N \to \infty$

Canadian Corporate Case 3.1: A New Distribution Station for Kitchener-Wilmot Hydro

Review Problems

Summary

Engineering Economics in Action, Part 3B: No Free Lunch

Problems

Appendix 3A: Continuous Compounding and Continuous Cash Flows

Appendix 3B: Derivation of Discrete Compound Interest Factors

3B.1   Compound Amount Factor

3B.2   Present Worth Factor

3B.3   Sinking Fund Factor

3B.4   Uniform Series Compound Amount Factor

3B.5   Capital Recovery Factor

3B.6   Series Present Worth Factor

3B.7   Arithmetic and Geometric Gradients

Engineering Economics in Action, Part 3A: Apples and Oranges

The flyer was slick, all right. The information was laid out so anybody could see that leasing palletizing equipment through the Provincial Finance Company (PFC) made much more sense than buying it. It was something Naomi could copy right into her report to Clem.

Naomi had been asked to check out options for automating part of the Shipping Department. Parts were to be stacked and bound on plastic pallets for loading on trucks to be sent to one of Canadian Widget's sister companies. The saleswoman for the company whose equipment seemed most suitable for Canadian Widget's needs included the leasing flyer with her quote.

Naomi looked at the figures again. They seemed to make sense, but there was something that didn't seem right to her. For one thing, if it was cheaper to lease, why didn't everybody lease everything? She knew that some things, like automobiles and airplanes, are often leased instead of bought, but generally companies buy assets. Second, where was the money coming from to give the finance company a profit? If the seller was getting the same amount, and the buyer was paying less, how could PFC make money?

"Got a recommendation on that palletizer yet, Naomi?" Clem's voice was cheery as he suddenly appeared at her doorway. Naomi knew that the Shipping Department was the focus of Clem's attention right now and he wanted to get some improvements in place as soon as possible.

"Yes, I do. There's really only one that will do the job, and it does it well at a good price. There is something I'm trying to figure out, though. Christine sent me some information about leasing it instead of buying it, and I'm trying to figure out where the catch is. There has got to be one, but I can't see it right now."

"O.K., let me give you a hint: apples and oranges. You can't add them. Now, let's get the paperwork started for that palletizer. The shipping department is just too much of a bottleneck." Clem disappeared from her door as quickly as he had arrived, leaving Naomi musing to herself.

"Apples and ORANGES? APPLES and oranges? Ahh... apples and oranges, of course!"

3.1 Introduction

Chapter 2 showed that interest is the basis for determining whether or not different patterns of cash flows are equivalent. Rather than make comparisons of patterns of cash flows from first principles, it is usually easier to use functions that define *mathematical* equivalence among certain common cash flow patterns. These functions are called **compound interest factors**. We discuss a number of these common cash flow patterns along with their associated compound interest factors in this chapter. These compound interest factors are used throughout the remainder of the book. It is, therefore, particularly important to understand their use before proceeding to subsequent chapters.

This chapter opens with an explanation of how cash flow patterns that engineers commonly use are simplified approximations of complex reality. Next, we discuss four simple, discrete cash flow patterns and the compound interest factors that relate them to each other. There is then a brief discussion of the case in which the number of time periods considered is so large that it is treated as though the relevant cash flows continued indefinitely. Appendix 3A discusses modelling cash flow patterns when the interval between disbursements or receipts is short enough that we may view the flows as being continuous.

3.2 Timing of Cash Flows and Modelling

The actual timing of cash flows can be very complicated and irregular. Unless some simple approximation is used, comparisons of different cash flow sequences will be very difficult and impractical. Consider, for example, the cash flows generated by a relatively simple operation like a service station that sells gasoline and supplies, and also services cars. Some cash flows, like sales of gasoline and minor supplies, will be almost continuous during the time the station is open. Other flows, like receipts for the servicing of cars, will be on a daily basis. Disbursements for wages may be on a weekly basis. Some disbursements, like those for a manager's salary and for purchases of gasoline and supplies, may be monthly. Disbursements for insurance and taxes may be quarterly or semi-annual. Other receipts and disbursements, like receipts for major repairs or disbursements for used parts, may be irregular.

An analyst trying to make a comparison of two projects with different, irregular timings of cash flows might have to record each of the flows of the projects. He or she would then, on a one-by-one basis, find summary equivalent values like present worth that would be used in the comparison. This activity would be very time consuming and tedious if it could be done, but it probably could not be done because the data necessary would not exist. If the projects were potential, rather than actual, the cash flows would have to be predicted. This could not be done with great precision for either size or timing of the flows. Even if the analysis were of the past performances of ongoing operations, it is unlikely that it would be worthwhile to maintain a data bank that contained the exact timing of all cash flows.

Because of the difficulties of making precise calculations of complex and irregular cash flows, engineers usually work with fairly simple models of cash flow patterns. The most common type of model assumes that all cash flows and all compounding of cash flows occur at the ends of conventionally defined periods like months or years. Models that make this assumption are called **discrete models**. In some cases, analysts use models that contain the assumption of continuity of compounding or of cash flows and compounding; such models are called **continuous models**. Whether the analyst uses discrete modelling or continuous modelling, the model is usually an approximation. Cash flows do not occur only at the ends of conventionally defined periods, nor are they actually continuous. We shall emphasize discrete models throughout the book because they are the more common, and because they are more readily understood by persons of varied backgrounds. Discrete cash flow models are discussed in the main body of this chapter, and continuous models are presented in Appendix 3A, at the end of this chapter.

3.3 Compound Interest Factors for Discrete Compounding

Compound interest factors are formulas that define mathematical equivalence for specific common cash flow patterns. The compound interest factors permit cash flow analysis to be done more conveniently because tables or spreadsheet functions can be used instead of using complicated formulas. This section presents compound interest factors for four discrete cash flow patterns that are commonly used to model the timing of receipts and disbursements in engineering economic analysis. The four patterns are:

1. A single disbursement or receipt
2. A set of equal disbursements or receipts over a sequence of periods, referred to as an **annuity**
3. A set of disbursements or receipts that change by a constant *amount* from one period to the next in a sequence of periods, referred to as an **arithmetic gradient series**
4. A set of disbursements or receipts that change by a constant *proportion* from one period to the next in a sequence of periods, referred to as a **geometric gradient series**

The principle of discrete compounding requires several assumptions:

1. Compounding periods are of equal length.
2. Each disbursement and receipt occurs at the end of a period. A payment at time zero can be considered to occur at the end of period -1.
3. Annuities and gradients coincide with the ends of sequential periods. (Section 3.8 suggests several methods for dealing with annuities and gradients that do not coincide with the ends of sequential periods.)

Mathematical derivations of six of the compound interest factors are given in Appendix 3B at the end of this chapter.

3.4 Compound Interest Factors for Single Disbursements or Receipts

There are many situations in which a single disbursement or receipt is an appropriate model of cash flows. For example, the salvage value of production equipment with a limited service life will be a single receipt at some future date. An investment today to be redeemed at some future date is another example.

Figure 3.1 illustrates the general form of a single disbursement or receipt. There are two commonly used factors that relate a single cash flow in one period to another single cash flow in a different period. They are the *compound amount factor* and the *present worth factor*.

The **compound amount factor**, denoted by $(F/P,i,N)$, gives the future amount, F, that is equivalent to a present amount, P, when the interest rate is i and the number of periods is N. The value of the compound amount factor is easily seen as coming from Equation (2.1), the compound interest equation, which relates present and future values,

$$F = P(1 + i)^N$$

In the symbolic convention used for compound interest factors, this is written

$$F = P(1 + i)^N = P(F/P,i,N)$$

so that the compound amount factor is

$$(F/P,i,N) = (1 + i)^N$$

A handy way of thinking of the notation is (reading from left to right): "What is F, given P, i, and N?"

FIGURE 3.1   Single receipt at end of period N

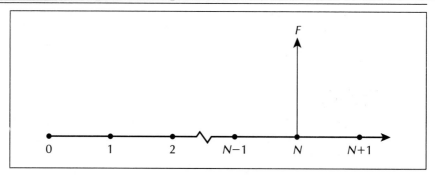

The compound amount factor is useful in determining the future value of an investment made today if the number of periods and the interest rate are known.

The **present worth factor**, denoted by $(P/F,i,N)$, gives the present amount, P, that is equivalent to a future amount, F, when the interest rate is i and the number of periods is N. The present worth factor is the inverse of the compound amount factor, $(F/P,i,N)$. That is, while the compound amount factor gives the future amount, F, that is equivalent to a present amount, P, the present worth factor goes in the other direction. It gives the present worth, P, of a future amount, F. Since $(F/P,i,N) = (1 + i)^N$,

$$(P/F, i,N) = \frac{1}{(1 + i)^N}$$

The compound amount factor and the present worth factor are fundamental to engineering economic analysis. Their most basic use is to convert a single cash flow which occurs at one point in time to an equivalent cash flow at another point in time. When comparing several individual cash flows which occur at different points in time, an analyst would apply the compound amount factor or the present worth factor, as necessary, to determine the equivalent cash flows at a common reference point in time. In this way, each of the cash flows is stated as an amount at one particular time. Example 3.1 illustrates this process.

Although the compound amount factor and the present worth factor are relatively easy to calculate, some of the other factors discussed in this chapter are more complicated, and it is therefore desirable to have an easier way to determine their values. The compound interest factors are sometimes available as functions in calculators and spreadsheets, but often these functions are provided in an awkward format that makes them relatively difficult to use. They can, however, be fairly easily programmed in a calculator or spreadsheet.

A traditional but still useful method for determining the value of a compound interest factor is to use tables. Appendix A at the back of this book lists values for all the compound interest factors for a selection of interest rates for discrete compounding periods. The desired compound interest factor can be determined by looking in the appropriate table.

EXAMPLE 3.1

How much money will be in a bank account at the end of 15 years if $100 is invested today and the nominal interest rate is 8% compounded semi-annually?

Since a present amount is given and a future amount is to be calculated, the appropriate factor to use is the compound amount factor, $(F/P,i,N)$. There are several ways of choosing i and N to solve this problem. The first solution method is to observe that, since interest is compounded semi-annually, the number of compounding periods, N, is 30. The interest rate per six-month period is 4%. Then

$$F = \$100(F/P, 4\%, 30)$$
$$= \$100(1 + 0.04)^{30}$$
$$= \$324.34$$

The bank account will hold $324.34 at the end of 15 years.

Alternatively, we can obtain the same results by using the interest factor tables.

$$F = \$100(3.2434) \quad \text{(from Appendix A)}$$
$$F = \$324.34$$

A second solution to the problem is to calculate the *effective* yearly interest rate and then compound over 15 years at this rate. Recall from Equation (2.4) that the effective interest rate per year is

$$i_e = \left(1 + \frac{r}{m}\right)^m - 1$$

where i_e = the effective annual interest rate
$\quad r$ = the nominal rate per year
$\quad m$ = the number of periods in a year

$$i_e = (1 + 0.08/2)^2 - 1 = 0.0816$$

where $r = 0.08$
$\quad m = 2$

When the effective yearly rate for each of 15 years is applied to the future worth computation, the future worth is

$$F = P(F/P,i,N)$$

$$F = P(1 + i)^N$$

$$F = \$100(1 + 0.0816)^{15}$$

$$= \$324.34$$

Once again, we conclude that the balance will be $324.34.

3.5 Compound Interest Factors for Annuities

The next four factors involve a series of uniform receipts or disbursements that start at the end of the first period and continue over N periods, as illustrated in Figure 3.2. This pattern of cash flows is called an annuity. Mortgage or lease payments and maintenance contract fees are examples of the annuity cash flow pattern. Annuities may also be used to model series of cash flows that fluctuate over time around some average value. Here the average value would be the constant uniform cash flow. This would be done if the fluctuations were unknown or deemed to be unimportant for the problem.

The **sinking fund factor**, denoted by $(A/F,i,N)$, gives the size, A, of a repeated receipt or disbursement that is equivalent to a future amount, F, if the interest rate is i and the number of periods is N. The name of the factor comes from the term **sinking fund**. A sinking fund is an interest-bearing account into which regular deposits are made in order to accumulate some amount. This amount may be used, for example, to replace a plant or equipment at the end of its useful live.

FIGURE 3.2   Annuity over N periods

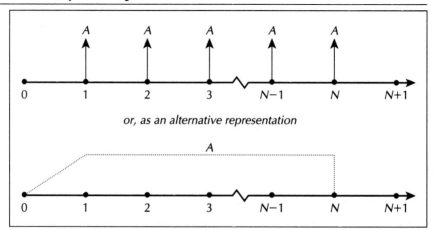

The equation for the sinking fund factor can be found by decomposing the series of disbursements or receipts made at times $1, 2, \ldots, N$, and summing to produce a total future value. The formula for the sinking fund factor is

$$(A/F,i,N) = \frac{i}{(1 + i)^N - 1}$$

The sinking fund factor is commonly used to determine how much has to be set aside or saved per period to accumulate an amount F at the end of N periods at an interest rate i. The amount F might be used, for example, to purchase new or replacement equipment, to pay for renovations, or to cover capacity expansion costs. In more general terms, the sinking fund factor allows us to convert a single future amount into a series of equal-sized payments, made over N equally spaced intervals, with the use of a given interest rate i.

The **uniform series compound amount factor**, denoted by $(F/A,i,N)$, gives the future value, F, that is equivalent to a series of equal-sized receipts or disbursements, A, when the interest rate is i and the number of periods is N. Since the uniform series compound amount factor is the inverse of the sinking fund factor,

$$(F/A,i,N) = \frac{(1 + i)^N - 1}{i}$$

The **capital recovery factor**, denoted by $(A/P,i,N)$, gives the value, A, of the equal periodic payments or receipts that is equivalent to a present amount, P, when the interest rate is i and the number of periods is N. The capital recovery factor is easily derived from the sinking fund factor and the compound amount factor:

$$(A/P,i,N) = (A/F,i,N)(F/P,i,N)$$

$$= \frac{i}{(1 + i)^N - 1}(1 + i)^N$$

$$(A/P,i,N) = \frac{i(1 + i)^N}{(1 + i)^N - 1}$$

The capital recovery factor can be used to find out, for example, how much money must be saved over N future periods to "recover" a capital investment of P today. The capital recovery factor for the purchase cost of something is sometimes combined with the sinking fund factor for its salvage value after N years to compose the *capital recovery formula*. See Close-Up 3.1.

CLOSE-UP 3.1   CAPITAL RECOVERY FORMULA

Industrial equipment and other assets are often purchased at a cost of P on the basis that they will incur savings of A per period for the firm. At the end of their useful life, they will be sold for some salvage value S. The expression to determine A for a given P and S combines the capital recovery factor (for P) with the sinking fund factor (for S):

$$A = P(A/P,i,N) - S(A/F,i,N)$$

Since

$$(A/F,i,N) = \frac{i}{(1 + i)^N - 1} = \frac{i}{(1 + i)^N - 1} + i - i$$

$$= \frac{i}{(1 + i)^N - 1} + \frac{i[(1 + i)^N - 1]}{(1 + i)^N - 1} - i$$

$$= \frac{i + i(1 + i)^N - i}{(1 + i)^N - 1} - i = \frac{i(1 + i)^N}{(1 + i)^N - 1} - i$$

$$= (A/P,i,N) - i$$

then

$$A = P(A/P,i,N) - S[(A/P,i,N) - i]$$
$$A = (P - S)(A/P,i,N) + Si$$

This is the capital recovery formula, which can be used to calculate the savings necessary to justify a capital purchase of cost P and salvage value S after N periods at interest rate i.

The capital recovery formula is also used to determine an annual amount which captures the loss in value of an asset over the time it is owned. Chapter 7 treats this use of the capital recovery formula more fully.

The **series present worth factor**, denoted by $(P/A,i,N)$, gives the present amount, P, that is equivalent to an annuity with disbursements or receipts in the amount, A, where the interest rate is i and the number of periods is N. It is the reciprocal of the capital recovery factor:

$$(P/A,i,N) = \frac{(1 + i)^N - 1}{i(1 + i)^N}$$

EXAMPLE 3.2

The Inuvik Go-Kart Club has decided to build a clubhouse and track five years from now. It must accumulate $50 000 by the end of five years by setting aside a uniform amount from its dues at the end of each year. If the interest rate is 10%, how much must be set aside each year?

Since the problem requires that we calculate an annuity amount given a future value, the solution can be obtained using the sinking fund factor where $i = 10\%$, $F = \$50\ 000$, $N = 5$, and A is unknown.

$$A = \$50\ 000(A/F, 10\%, 5)$$
$$= \$50\ 000(0.1638)$$
$$= \$8190.00$$

The Go-Kart Club must set aside $8190 at the end of each year to accumulate $50 000 in five years.

EXAMPLE 3.3

A car loan requires 30 monthly payments of $199.00, starting *today*. At an annual rate of 12% compounded monthly, how much money is being lent?

This cash flow pattern is referred to as an **annuity due**. It differs from a standard annuity in that the first of the N payments occurs at time 0 (now) rather than at the end of the first time period. Annuity dues are uncommon—not often will one make the first payment on a loan on the date the loan is received! Unless otherwise stated, it is reasonable to assume that any annuity starts at the end of the first period.

Two simple methods of analyzing an annuity due will be used for this example.

Method 1. Count the first payment as a present worth and the next 29 payments as an annuity:

$$P = \$199 + A(P/A,i,N)$$

where $A = \$199$, $i = 12\%/12 = 1\%$, and $N = 29$

$$P = \$199 + \$199(P/A, 1\%, 29)$$
$$= \$199 + \$199(25.066)$$
$$= \$199 + \$4988.13$$
$$= \$5187.13$$

The present worth of the loan is the current payment, $199.00, plus the present worth of the subsequent 29 payments, $4988.13, a total of about $5187.

Method 2. Determine the present worth of a standard annuity at time −1, and then find its worth at time 0 (now). The worth at time −1 is

$$P_{-1} = A(P/A,i,N)$$
$$= \$199(P/A, 1\%, 30)$$
$$= \$199(25.807)$$
$$= \$5135.79$$

Then the present worth now (time 0) is

$$P_0 = P_{-1}(F/P,i,N)$$
$$= \$5135.79(F/P,1\%,1)$$
$$= \$5135.79(1.01)$$
$$= \$5187.15$$

The second method gives the same result as the first, allowing a small margin for the effects of rounding.

It is worth noting here that although it is natural to think about the symbol P as meaning a cash flow at time 0, the present, and F as meaning a cash flow in the future, in fact these symbols can be more general in meaning. As illustrated in the last example, we can consider any point in time to be the "present" for calculation purposes, and similarly any point in time to be the "future," provided P is some point in time earlier than F. This observation gives us substantial flexibility in analyzing cash flows.

EXAMPLE 3.4

Clarence bought a house for \$94 000 in 1982. He made a \$14 000 down payment and negotiated a mortgage from the previous owner for the balance. Clarence agreed to pay the previous owner \$2000 per month at 12% nominal interest, compounded monthly. How long did it take him to pay back the mortgage?

Clarence borrowed only \$80 000, since he made a \$14 000 down payment. The \$2000 payments form an annuity over N months where N is unknown. The interest rate per month is 1%. We must find the value of N such that

$$P = A(P/A,i,N) = A\left(\frac{(1 + i)^N - 1}{i(1 + i)^N}\right)$$

or, alternatively, the value of N such that

$$A = P(A/P,i,N) = P\left(\frac{i(1 + i)^N}{(1 + i)^N - 1}\right)$$

where $P = 80\ 000$, $A = 2000$, and $i = 0.01$

By substituting the known quantities into either expression, some manipulation is required to find N. For illustration, the capital recovery factor has been used.

$$A = P\left(\frac{i(1 + i)^N}{(1 + i)^N - 1}\right)$$

$$\$2000 = \$80\,000\left(\frac{0.01(1.01)^N}{1.01^N - 1}\right)$$

$$2.5 = \frac{(1.01)^N}{(1.01)^N - 1}$$

$$2.5/1.5 = (1.01)^N$$

$$N[ln(1.01)] = ln(2.5/1.5)$$

$$N = 51.34 \text{ months}$$

It will take Clarence four years and four months to pay off the mortgage. He will make 51 full payments of $2000 and will be left with only a fraction of a full payment for his fifty-second and last monthly instalment. Problem 3.24 on page 81 asks what his final payment will be. Note also that mortgages can be confusing because of the different terms used. See Close-Up 3.2.

CLOSE-UP 3.2   CANADIAN MORTGAGES

Canadian mortgages can be a little confusing because of the terms used. The interest rate is a nominal rate, usually compounded monthly. The **amortization period** is the duration over which the original loan is calculated to be repaid. The **term** is the duration over which the loan agreement is valid.

For example, Salim has just bought a house for $135 000. He paid $25 000 down, and the rest of the cost has been obtained from a mortgage. The mortgage has a nominal interest rate of 9.5% compounded monthly with a 20-year amortization period. The term of the mortgage is three years. What are Salim's monthly payments? How much does he owe after three years?

Salim's monthly payments can be calculated as

$$A = (\$135\,000 - \$25\,000)(A/P, 9.5/12\%, [20 \times 12])$$

$$= \$110\,000(A/P, 0.7917\%, 240)$$

$$= \$110\,000(0.00932)$$

$$= \$1025.2$$

Salim's monthly payments would be about \$1025.20. After three years he would have to renegotiate his mortgage at whatever was the current interest rate at that time. The amount owed would be

$$F = \$110\ 000(F/P, 9.5/12\%, 36) - \$1025.2(F/A, 9.5/12\%, 36)$$
$$= \$110\ 000(1.3283) - \$1025.2(41.47)$$
$$= \$103\ 598$$

After three years, Salim still owes \$103 598.

In Example 3.4, it was possible to use the formula for the compound interest factor to solve for the unknown quantity directly. It is not always possible to do this when the number of periods or the interest rate is unknown. We can proceed in several ways. One possibility is to determine the unknown value by trial and error with a spreadsheet. Another approach is to find the nearest values using tables, and then to interpolate linearly to determine an approximate value. Some calculators will perform the interpolation automatically. See Close-Up 3.3 and Figure 3.3 for a reminder of how linear interpolation works.

FIGURE 3.3   Linear Interpolation

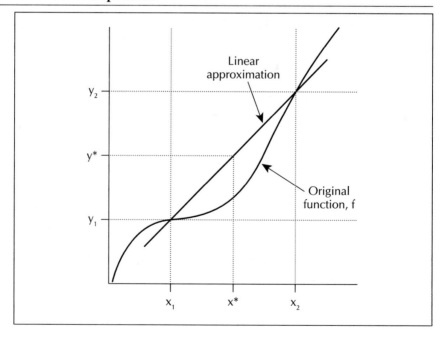

> ### CLOSE-UP 3.3 LINEAR INTERPOLATION
>
> Linear interpolation is the process of approximating a complicated function as a straight line in order to estimate a value for the independent variable based on two sample pairs of independent and dependent variables and an instance of the dependent variable. For example, the function f in Figure 3.3 relates the dependent variable y to the independent variable x. Two sample points (x_1, y_1) and (x_2, y_2) are known, but the actual shape of f is not. An estimate of the value for x^* can be made by drawing a straight line between (x_1, y_1) and (x_2, y_2).
>
> Because the line between (x_1, y_1) and (x_2, y_2) is assumed to be straight, the following ratios must be equal:
>
> $$\frac{x^* - x_1}{x_2 - x_1} = \frac{y^* - y_1}{y_2 - y_1}$$
>
> Isolating the x^* gives the linear interpolation formula:
>
> $$x^* = x_1 + (x_2 - x_1)\left[\frac{y^* - y_1}{y_2 - y_1}\right]$$

EXAMPLE 3.5

Clarence paid off an $80 000 mortgage completely in 48 months. He paid $2000 per month, and at the end of the first year made an extra payment of $7000. What interest rate was he charged on the mortgage?

Using the series present worth factor and the present worth factor, this can be formulated for an unknown interest rate:

$80\ 000 = \$2000(P/A, i, 48) + \$7000(P/F, i, 12)$

$2(P/A, i, 48) + 7(P/F, i, 12) = 80$

$$2\left[\frac{(1 + i)^{48} - 1}{i(1 + i)^{48}}\right] + 7\left[\frac{1}{(1 + i)^{12}}\right] = 80 \tag{3.1}$$

Solving such an equation directly is generally not possible. However, using a spreadsheet as illustrated in Table 3.1 can establish some close values for the left-hand side of Equation (3.1), and a similar process can be done using either tables or a calculator. Using a spreadsheet program or calculator, trials can establish a value for the unknown interest rate to the desired number of significant digits.

TABLE 3.1 Trials to Determine an Unknown Interest Rate

Interest rate i	$2(P/A, i, 48) + 7(P/F, i, 12)$
0.5%	91.7540
0.6%	89.7128
0.7%	87.7350
0.8%	85.8185
0.9%	83.9608
1.0%	82.1601
1.1%	80.4141
1.2%	78.7209
1.3%	77.0787
1.4%	75.4855
1.5%	73.9398

Once the approximate values for the interest rate are found, linear interpolation can be used to find a more precise answer. For instance, working from the values of the interest rate which give the LHS (left-hand side) value closest to the RHS (right-hand side) value of 80, which are 1.1% and 1.2%,

$$i = 1.1 + (1.2 - 1.1)\left[\frac{80 - 80.4141}{78.7209 - 80.4141}\right]$$

$$i = 1.1 + 0.02 = 1.12\% \text{ per month}$$

The nominal interest rate was $1.12 \times 12 = 13.44\%$
The effective interest rate was $(1.0112)^{12} - 1 = 14.30\%$.

Another interesting application of compound interest factors is calculating the value of a bond. See Close-Up 3.4.

CLOSE-UP 3.4 BONDS

Bonds are investments that provide an annuity and a future value in return for a cost today. They have a *par* or *face* value, which is the amount for which they can be redeemed after a certain period of time. They also have a *coupon rate*, meaning that they pay the bearer an annuity, usually semi-annually, calculated as a percentage of the face value. For example, a coupon rate of 10% on a bond with an $8000 face value would pay an annuity of $400 each six months. Bonds can sell at more or less than the face value, depending on how buyers perceive them as investments.

To calculate the worth of a bond today, sum together the present worth of the face value (a future amount) and the coupons (an annuity) at an appropriate interest rate. For example, if money can earn 12% compounded semi-annually, a bond maturing in 15 years with a face value of $5000 and a coupon rate of 7% is today worth

$$P = \$5000(P/F, 6\%, 30) + (\$5000 \times .07/2)\,(P/A, 6\%, 30)$$

$$= \$5000(0.17411) + \$175(13.765)$$

$$= \$3279.43$$

The bond is worth about $3279 today.

3.6 Conversion Factor for Arithmetic Gradient Series

An **arithmetic gradient series** is a series of receipts or disbursements that start at zero at the end of the first period and then increase by a constant *amount* from period to period. Figure 3.4 illustrates an arithmetic gradient series of receipts. Figure 3.5 shows an arithmetic gradient series of disbursements. As an example, we may model a pattern of increasing operating costs for an aging machine as an arithmetic gradient series if the costs are increasing by (approximately) the same amount each period. Note carefully that the first non-zero cash flow of a gradient occurs at the end of the *second* compounding period, not the first.

The sum of an annuity plus an arithmetic gradient series is a common pattern. The annuity is a base to which the arithmetic gradient series is added. This is shown in Figure 3.6. A constant-amount increase to a base level of receipts may occur where the increase in receipts is due to adding capacity and where the ability to add capacity is limited. For example, a company that specializes in outfitting warehouses for grocery chains can expand by adding work crews. But the crews must be trained

FIGURE 3.4   Arithmetic Gradient Series of Receipts

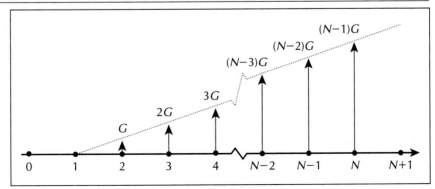

FIGURE 3.5 **Arithmetic Gradient Series of Disbursements**

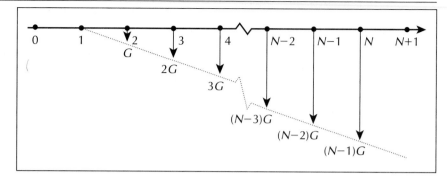

by managers who have time to train only one crew member every six months. Hence, we would have a base amount and a constant amount of growth in cash flows each period.

The **arithmetic gradient to annuity conversion factor**, denoted by $(A/G,i,N)$, gives the value of an annuity, A, that is equivalent to an arithmetic gradient series where the constant increase in receipts or disbursements is G per period, the interest rate is i, and the number of periods is N. That is, the arithmetic gradient series, $0G, 1G, 2G, \ldots, (N-1)G$ is given and the uniform cash flow, A, over N periods is found. Problem 3.20, in the problems section of this chapter, asks the reader to show that the equation for the arithmetic gradient to annuity factor is

$$(A/G,i,N) = \left(\frac{1}{i} - \frac{N}{(1+i)^N - 1} \right)$$

There is often a base annuity A' associated with a gradient, as illustrated in Figure 3.6. To determine the uniform series equivalent to the *total* cash flow, the base annuity A' must be included to give the overall annuity:

FIGURE 3.6 **Arithmetic Gradient Series with Base Annuity**

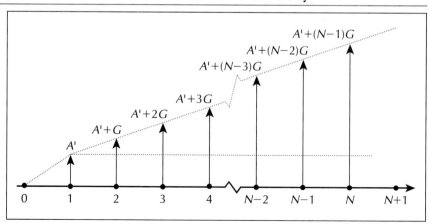

$$A_{tot} = A' + G(A/G,i,N)$$

EXAMPLE 3.6

Susan Ng owns an eight-year-old Jetta automobile. She wants to find the present worth of repair bills over the four years that she expects to keep the car. Susan has the car in for repairs every six months. Repair costs are expected to increase by $50 every six months over the next four years, starting with $500 six months from now, $550 six months later, and so on. What is the present worth of the repair costs over the next four years if the interest rate is 12% compounded monthly?

First, observe that there will be $N = 8$ repair bills over four years and that the base annuity payment, A', is $500. The arithmetic gradient component of the bills, G, is $50, and hence the arithmetic gradient series is 0, 50, 100, and so on. The present worth of the repair bills can be obtained in a two-step process:

Step 1. Find the total uniform annuity, A_{tot}, equivalent to the sum of the base annuity, $A' = 500, and the arithmetic gradient series with $G = 50 over $N = 8$ periods.

Step 2. Find the present worth of A_{tot}, using the series present worth factor.

The 12% nominal interest rate, compounded monthly, is 1% per month. The effective interest rate per six month period is

$$i_{6month} = (1 + 0.12/12)^6 - 1 = 0.06152 \text{ or } 6.152\%$$

Step 1

$$A_{tot} = A' + G(A/G,i,N)$$

$$= \$500 + \$50\left(\frac{1}{i} - \frac{N}{(1 + i)^N - 1}\right)$$

$$= \$500 + \$50\left(\frac{1}{0.06152} - \frac{8}{(1.06152)^8 - 1}\right)$$

$$= \$659.38$$

Step 2

$$P = A_{tot}(P/A,i,N) = A_{tot}\left(\frac{(1 + i)^N - 1}{i(1 + i)^N}\right)$$

$$= \$659.38\left(\frac{(1.06152)^8 - 1}{0.06152(1.06152)^8}\right)$$

$$= \$4070.14$$

The present worth of the repair costs is about $4070.

3.7 Conversion Factor for Geometric Gradient Series

A geometric gradient series is a series of cash flows that increase or decrease by a constant *percentage* each period. The geometric gradient series may be used to model inflation or deflation, productivity improvement or degradation, and growth or shrinkage of market size, as well as many other phenomena.

In a geometric series, the base value of the series is A and the "growth" rate in the series (the rate of increase or decrease) is referred to as g. The terms in such a series are given by A, $A(1 + g)$, $A(1 + g)^2$, ..., $A(1 + g)^{N-1}$ at the ends of periods 1, 2, 3, ..., N, respectively. If the rate of growth, g, is positive, the terms are increasing in value. If the rate of growth, g, is negative, the terms are decreasing. Figure 3.7 shows a series of receipts where g is positive. Figure 3.8 shows a series of receipts where g is negative.

The **geometric gradient to present worth conversion factor**, denoted by $(P/A,g,i,N)$, gives the present worth, P, that is equivalent to a geometric gradient series where the base receipt or disbursement is A, and where the rate of growth is g, the interest rate is i, and the number of periods is N.

The present worth of a geometric series is

$$P = \frac{A}{1 + i} + \frac{A(1 + g)}{(1 + i)^2} + \ldots + \frac{A(1 + g)^{N-1}}{(1 + i)^N}$$

FIGURE 3.7   Geometric Gradient Series for Receipts with Positive Growth

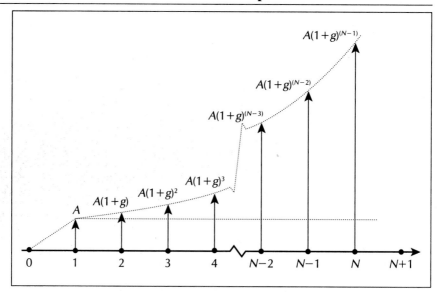

where A = the base amount
$ g$ = the rate of growth
$ i$ = the interest rate
$ N$ = the number of periods
$ P$ = the present worth

We can define a **growth adjusted interest rate**, $i°$, as

$$i° = \frac{1 + i}{1 + g} - 1$$

so that

$$\frac{1}{1 + i°} = \frac{1 + g}{1 + i}$$

Then the geometric gradient series to present worth conversion factor is given by

$$(P/A,g,i,N) = \frac{(P/A,i°,N)}{1 + g} \text{ or}$$

$$(P/A,g,i,N) = \left(\frac{(1 + i°)^N - 1}{i°(1 + i°)^N}\right)\frac{1}{1 + g}$$

Care must be taken in using the geometric gradient to present worth conversion factor. Four cases may be distinguished.

1. $i > g > 0$. *Growth is positive, but less than the rate of interest.* The growth adjusted interest rate, $i°$, is positive. Tables or functions built into software may be used to get the conversion factor.

2. $g < 0$. *Growth is negative.* In other words, the series is decreasing. The growth adjusted interest rate, $i°$, is positive. Tables or functions built into software may be used to get the conversion factor.

3. $g > i > 0$. *Growth is positive and greater than the interest rate.* The growth adjusted interest rate, $i°$, is negative. It is necessary to compute the conversion factor directly from the formula.

4. $g = i > 0$. *Growth is positive and exactly equal to the interest rate.* The growth adjusted interest rate $i° = 0$. As with any case where the interest rate is zero, the present worth of the series with constant terms, $A/(1 + g)$, is simply the sum of all the N terms

$$P = N\left(\frac{A}{1 + g}\right)$$

FIGURE 3.8   **Geometric Gradient Series for Receipts with Negative Growth**

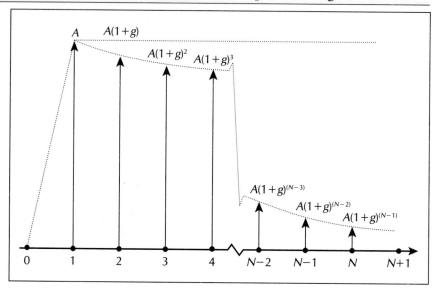

EXAMPLE 3.7

Tru-Test is in the business of assembling and packaging automotive and marine testing equipment to be sold through retailers to "do-it-your-selfers" and small repair shops. One of their products is tire pressure gauges. This operation has some excess capacity. Tru-Test is considering using this excess capacity to add engine compression gauges to their line. They can sell engine pressure gauges to retailers for $8 per gauge. They expect to be able to produce about 1000 gauges in the first month of production. They also expect that, as the workers learn how to do the work more efficiently, productivity will rise by 0.25% per month for the first two years. In other words, each month's output of gauges will be 0.25% more than the previous month's. The interest rate is 1.5% per month. All gauges are sold in the month in which they are produced, and receipts from sales are at the end of each month. What is the present worth of the sales of the engine pressure gauges in the first two years?

We first get the growth adjusted interest rate, i°.

$$i^\circ = \frac{1 + i}{1 + g} - 1 = \frac{1.015}{1.0025} - 1 = 0.01247$$

$$i^\circ \cong 1.25\%$$

We then make use of the geometric gradient to present worth conversion factor with the uniform cash flow $A = \$8000$, the growth rate $g = 0.0025$, the growth adjusted interest rate $i^\circ = 0.0125$, and the number of periods $N = 24$.

$$P = A(P/A,g,i,N) = A\left(\frac{(P/A,i^\circ,N)}{1 + g}\right)$$

$$P = \$8000\left(\frac{(P/A, 1.25\%, 24)}{1.0025}\right)$$

From the interest rate tables we get

$$P = \$8000\left(\frac{20.624}{1.0025}\right)$$

$$P = \$164\ 580$$

The present worth of sales of engine compression gauges over the two-year period would be about $165 000. Recall that we worked with an *approximate* growth-adjusted interest rate of 1.25% when the correct rate was a bit less than 1.25%. This means that $164 580 is a slight understatement of the present worth.

3.8   Non-Standard Annuities and Gradients

As discussed in Section 3.3, the standard assumption for annuities and gradients is that the payment period and compounding period are the same. If they are not, the formulas given in this chapter cannot be applied directly. There are three methods for dealing with this situation:

1. Treat each cash flow in the annuity or gradient individually. This is most useful when the annuity or gradient series is not large.

2. Convert the non-standard annuity or gradient to standard form by changing the compounding period.

3. Convert the non-standard annuity to standard form by finding an equivalent standard annuity for the compounding period. This method cannot be used for gradients.

EXAMPLE 3.8

How much is accumulated over 20 years in a fund that pays 4% interest, compounded yearly, if $1000 is deposited at the end of every fourth year? The cash flow diagram for this set of payments is shown in Figure 3.9.

Method 1: Consider the annuities as separate future payments.

Formula: $F = P(F/P,i\%,N)$
Known values: $P = \$1000$, $i = 0.04$, $N = 16, 12, 8, 4$, and 0

FIGURE 3.9   **Non-standard Annuity for Example 3.8**

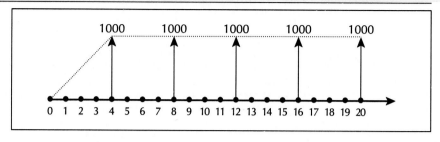

Year	Future Value		
4	$1000(*F/P*, 4%, 16)	= $!000(1.8729)	= $1873
8	$1000(*F/P*, 4%, 12)	= $1000(1.6010)	= $1601
12	$1000(*F/P*, 4%, 8)	= $1000(1.3685)	= $1369
16	$1000(*F/P*, 4%, 4)	= $!000(1.1698)	= $1170
20	$1000		= $1000
	Total future value		= $7013

About $7013 is accumulated over the 20 years.

Method 2: Convert the compounding period from yearly to every four years. This can be done with the effective interest rate formula.

$$i_e = (1 + 0.04)^4 - 1$$
$$= 16.99\%$$

The future value is then

$$F = \$1000(F/A, 16.99\%, 5) = \$1000 \ (7.013)$$
$$= \$7013$$

Method 3: Convert the annuity to an equivalent yearly annuity. This can be done by considering the first payment as a future value over the first four-year period, and finding the equivalent annuity over that period, using the sinking fund factor:

$$A = \$1000(A/F, 4\%, 4)$$
$$= \$1000(0.23549)$$
$$= \$235.49$$

In other words, a $1000 deposit at the end of the four years is equivalent to four equal deposits of $235.49 at the end of each of the four years. This yearly annuity is accumulated over the 20 years.

$$F = \$235.49(F/A, 4\%, 20)$$
$$= \$235.49(29.777)$$
$$= \$7012$$

Note that each method produces the same amount, allowing for rounding. When you have a choice in methods as in this example, your choice will depend on what you find convenient, or what is the most efficient computationally.

3.9 Present Worth Computations When $N \to \infty$

We have until now assumed that the cash flows of a project occur over some fixed, finite number of periods. For long lived projects it may be reasonable to model the cash flows as though they continued indefinitely. The present worth of an infinitely long uniform series of cash flows is called the **capitalized value** of the series. We can get the capitalized value of a series by allowing the number of periods, N, in the series present worth factor to go to infinity:

$$P = \lim_{N \to \infty} A(P/A,i,N)$$

$$= A \lim_{N \to \infty} \left(\frac{(1+i)^N - 1}{i(1+i)^N} \right)$$

$$= A \lim_{N \to \infty} \left(\frac{1 - \dfrac{1}{(1+i)^N}}{i} \right)$$

$$= \frac{A}{i}$$

EXAMPLE 3.9

The town of South Battleford is considering building a by-pass for truck traffic around the downtown commercial area. The by-pass will provide to merchants, shoppers, and others benefits that have an estimated value of $500 000 per year. Maintenance costs will be $125 000 per year. If the by-pass is properly maintained, it will provide benefits for a very long time. The actual life of the by-pass will depend on factors like future economic conditions that cannot be forecast at the time the by-pass is being considered. It is, therefore, reasonable to model the flow of benefits as though they continued indefinitely. If the interest rate is 10%, what is the present worth of benefits minus maintenance costs?

$$P = \frac{A}{i} = \frac{\$500\ 000 - \$125\ 000}{0.1} = \$3\ 750\ 000$$

The present worth of benefits net of maintenance costs is $3 750 000.

CANADIAN CORPORATE CASE 3.1

A New Distribution Station for Kitchener-Wilmot Hydro

Kitchener-Wilmot Hydro provides electricity to the City of Kitchener, Ontario, and nearby Wilmot Township as a regulated monopoly. It purchases power from the provincial utility Ontario Hydro and distributes it to homes and industries in these areas.

Recently, the utility undertook an investigation of the locations and capacities of the distribution stations in Wilmot Township. These distribution stations are essentially transformers which reduce voltage from 27.6 kV (thousand volts), which is efficient for long-distance distribution, to 8.3 kV, which is better for local distribution. Near each user, it is further transformed to 120 V or 600 V.

A particular problem was distribution station (DS) #5, located northwest of the town of St. Agatha. This station had old technology that required upgrading to match the other distribution stations. Three alternatives were identified. In short, they were:

1. Upgrade DS#5.

2. Build a new distribution station at the town of Philipsburg, using the salvaged transformer from former DS#5.

3. Build a new distribution station at the town of New Prussia, using the salvaged transformer from former DS#5.

Data were gathered concerning current and projected usage and costs for the three alternatives. A present worth analysis was done, using a discount factor (interest rate) of 10%. The least expensive choice turned out to be alternative 1, which was recommended for implementation.

REVIEW PROBLEMS

Review Problem 3.1

The benefits of a revised production schedule for a seasonal manufacturer will not be realized until the peak summer months. Net savings will be $1100, $1200, $1300, $1400, and $1500 at the ends of months 5, 6, 7, 8, and 9, respectively. It is now the beginning of month 1. Assume 365 days per year, 30 days per month. What is the present worth of the savings if nominal interest is

(a) 12% per year, compounded monthly?

(b) 12% per year, compounded daily?

Answer

(a) $A = \$1100$

$G = \$100$

$i = 0.12/12 = 0.01$ per month $= 1\%$

$$\text{PW(end of period 4)} = (P/A, 1\%, 5)[\$1100 + \$100(A/G, 1\%, 5)]$$
$$= 4.8528[\$1100 + \$100(1.9801)]$$
$$= 6298.98$$

$$\text{PW(at time 0)} \quad = \text{PW(end of period 4)}(P/F, 1\%, 4)$$
$$= \$6298.98/(1.01)^4 = \$6053.20$$

The present worth is about $6053.

(b) Effective interest rate $i = (1 + 0.12/365)^{30} - 1 = 0.0099102$

$$\text{PW(at time 0)} \ = \text{PW(end of period 4)}(P/F, i, 4)$$
$$= (P/A, i, 5)[\$1100 + \$100(A/G, i, 5)](P/F, i, 4)$$
$$= \$4.8547[\$1100 + \$100(1.98023)](0.9613)$$
$$= \$6057.80$$

The present worth is about $6058.

▮ Review Problem 3.2

It is January 1 of this year. You are starting your new job tomorrow, having just finished your engineering degree at the end of last term. Your take-home pay for this year will be $36 000. It will be paid to you in equal amounts at the end of each month, starting at the end of January. There is a cost-of-living clause in your contract that says that each subsequent January you will get an increase of 3% in your yearly salary (i.e., your take-home pay for next year will be $1.03 \times \$36\ 000$). In addition to your salary, a wealthy relative regularly sends you a $2000 birthday present at the end of each June.

Recognizing that you are not likely to have any government pension, you have decided to start saving 10% of your monthly salary and 50% of your birthday present for your retirement. Interest is 1% per month, compounded monthly.

How much will you have saved at the end of five years?

▮ Answer ▮

Yearly pay is a geometric gradient; convert your monthly salary into a yearly amount by the use of an effective yearly rate. The birthday present can be dealt with separately.

Salary: The future worth of the salary at the end of the first year is

$$\text{FW(salary, year 1)} = \$3000(F/A, 1\%, 12) = \$38\ 040.00$$

This forms the base of the geometric gradient; all subsequent years increase by 3% per year. Savings are 10% of salary, which implies that $A = \$3804.00$.

$$A = \$3804.00 \qquad g = 0.03$$

Effective yearly interest rate $i_e = (1 + 0.01)^{12} - 1 = 0.1268$ per year

$$i^\circ = \frac{1 + i_e}{1 + g} - 1 = \frac{1 + 0.1268}{1 + 0.03} - 1 = 0.093981$$

PW(gradient) $= A\ (P/A,\ i^\circ,\ 5)/(1 + g) = \$3804(3.8498)/1.03$
$$= \$14\ 218$$

FW(gradient, end of five years) $=$ PW(gradient)$(F/P,i_e,\ 5)$
$$= \$14\ 218(1.1268)^5 = \$25\ 827$$

Birthday present: The present arrives in the middle of each year. To get the total value of the five gifts, we can find the present worth of an annuity of five payments of \$2000(0.5) as of six months prior to employment:

PW(-6 months$) = \$2000(0.5)(P/A,\ i_e,\ 5) = \$3544.90$

The future worth [$(5 \times 12) + 6 =$] 66 months later is

FW(end of five years) $= \$3544.9(1.01)^{66} = \$6836$

Total amount saved $= \$6836 + \$25\ 827 = \$32\ 663$

■ Review Problem 3.3

The Easy Loan Company advertises a "10%" loan. You need to borrow \$1000, and the deal you are offered is the following: You pay \$1100 (\$1000 plus \$100 interest) in 11 equal \$100 amounts, starting one month from today. In addition, there is a \$25 administration fee for the loan, payable immediately, and a processing fee of \$10 per payment. Furthermore, there is a \$20 non-optional closing fee to be included in the last payment. Recognizing fees as a form of interest payment, what is the actual effective interest rate?

Answer

Since the \$25 administration fee is paid immediately, you are only getting \$975. The remaining payments amount to an annuity of \$110 per month, plus a \$20 future payment 11 months from now.

Formulas: $P = A(P/A,i,N),\ P = F(P/F,i,N)$

Known values: $P = \$975,\ A = \$110,\ F = \$20,\ N = 11$

$\$975 = \$110(P/A,\ i,\ 11) + \$20(P/F,\ i,\ 11)$

At $i = 4\%$

$\$110(P/A,\ 4\%,\ 11) + \$20(P/F,\ 4\%,\ 11)$
$= \$110(8.7603) + \$20(0.64958)$
$= \$976.62$

At $i = 5\%$

$\$110(P/A, 5\%, 11) + \$20(P/F, 5\%, 11)$
$= \$110(8.3062) + \$20(0.58469)$
$= \$925.37$

Linearly interpolating gives

$i = 4 + (5 - 4) (975 - 976.62)/(925.37 - 976.62)$
$= 4.03$

The effective interest rate is then

$i = (1 + 0.0403)^{12} - 1$
$= 60.69\%$ per annum (!)

Although the loan is advertised as a "10%" loan, the actual effective rate is over 60%.

Review Problem 3.4

Ming wants to retire as soon as she has enough money invested in a special bank account (paying 14% interest, compounded annually) to provide her with an annual income of $25 000. She is able to save $10 000 per year, and the account now holds $5000. If she just turned 20, and expects to die in 50 years, how old will she be when she retires? There should be no money left when she turns 70.

Answer

Let Ming's retirement age be $20 + x$ so that

$\$5000(F/P, 14\%, x) + \$10\,000(F/A, 14\%, x)$
$= \$25\,000(P/A, 14\%, 50 - x)$

Dividing both sides by 5000,

$(F/P, 14\%, x) + 2(F/A, 14\%, x) - 5(P/A, 14\%, 50 - x) = 0$

At $x = 5$

$(F/P, 14\%, 5) + 2(F/A, 14\%, 5) - 5(P/A, 14\%, 45)$
$= (1.9254) + 2(6.6100) - 5(7.1232) = -20.4706$

At $x = 10$

$(F/P, 14\%, 10) + 2(F/A, 14\%, 10) - 5(P/A, 14\%, 40)$
$= (3.37071) + 2(19.337) - 5(7.1050) = 6.5197$

Linearly interpolating,

$x = 5 + 5 \times (20.4706)/(6.5197 + 20.4706)$
$= 8.8$

Ming can retire at age $20 + 8.8 = 28.8$ years.

SUMMARY

In Chapter 3 we considered ways of modelling patterns of cash flows that enable easy comparisons of the worths of projects. The emphasis was on discrete models. Four basic patterns of discrete cash flows were considered:

1. Flows at a single point
2. Flows that are constant over time
3. Flows that grow or decrease at a constant arithmetic rate
4. Flows that grow or decrease at a constant geometric rate

TABLE 3.2   Summary of Useful Formulas for Discrete Models

Name	Symbol and Formula
Compound amount factor	$(F/P,i,N) = (1 + i)^N$
Present worth factor	$(P/F,i,N) = \dfrac{1}{(1 + i)^N}$
Sinking fund factor	$(A/F,i,N) = \dfrac{i}{(1 + i)^N - 1}$
Uniform series compound amount factor	$(F/A,i,N) = \dfrac{(1 + i)^N - 1}{i}$
Capital recovery factor	$(A/P,i,N) = \dfrac{i(1 + i)^N}{(1 + i)^N - 1}$
Series present worth factor	$(P/A,i,N) = \dfrac{(1 + i)^N - 1}{i(1 + i)^N}$
Arithmetic gradient to annuity conversion factor	$(A/G,i,N) = \left(\dfrac{1}{i} - \dfrac{N}{(1 + i)^N - 1}\right)$
Geometric gradient to present worth conversion factor	$(P/A,g,i,N) = \dfrac{(P/A,i^\circ,N)}{1 + g}$ $(P/A,g,i,N) = \left(\dfrac{(1 + i^\circ)^N - 1}{i^\circ(1 + i^\circ)^N}\right)\dfrac{1}{1 + g}$ $i^\circ = \dfrac{1 + i}{1 + g} - 1$
Capitalized value formula	$P = \dfrac{A}{i}$
Capitalized recovery formula	$A = (P - S)(A/P,i,N) + S_i$

Compound interest factors were presented that defined mathematical equivalence among the basic patterns of cash flows. A list of these factors with their names, symbols, and formulas appears in Table 3.2. The chapter also addressed the issue of how to analyze non-standard annuities and gradients as well as the idea of capital recovery and capitalized value.

For those who are interested in continuous compounding and continuous cash flows, Appendix 3A contains a summary of relevant notation and interest factors.

Engineering Economics in Action, Part 3B: No Free Lunch

This time it was Naomi who stuck her head in Clem's doorway. "Here's the recommendation on the shipping palletizer. Oh, and thanks for the hint on the leasing figures. It cleared up my confusion right away."

"No problem. What did you figure out?" Clem had his 'mentor' expression on his face, so Naomi knew he was expecting a clear explanation of the trick used by the leasing company.

"Well, as you hinted, they were adding apples and oranges. They listed the various costs for each choice over time, including interest charges, taxes, and so on. But then, for the final comparison, they added up these costs. When they added, leasing was cheaper."

"So what's wrong with that?" Clem prompted.

"They're adding apples and oranges. We're used to thinking of money as being just money, without remembering that money always has a 'when' associated with it. If you add money at different points in time, you might as well be adding apples and oranges; you have a number but it doesn't mean anything. In order to compare leasing with buying, you first have to change the cash flows into the same money, that is, at the same point in time. That's a little harder to do, especially when there's a complicated set of cash flows."

"So were you able to do it?"

"Yes. I identified various components of the cash flows as annuities, gradients, and present and future worths. Then I converted all of these to a present worth for each alternative and summed them. This is the correct way to compare them. If you do that, buying is cheaper, even when borrowing money to do so. And of course it has to be—that leasing company has to pay for those slick brochures somehow. There's no free lunch."

Clem nodded. "I think you've covered it. Mind you, there are some circumstances where leasing is worthwhile. For example, we lease our company cars to save us the time and trouble of reselling them when we're finished with them. Leasing can be good when it's hard to raise the capital for very large purchases, too. But almost always, buying is better. And you know, it amazes me how easy it is to fall for simplistic cash flow calculations that fail to take into account the time value of money. I've even seen articles in the newspaper quoting accountants who make the same mistake, and you'd think they would know better."

"Engineers can make that mistake, too, Clem. I almost did."

PROBLEMS

3.1 How much money will be in a bank account at the end of 15 years if $100 is deposited today and the interest rate is 8% compounded annually?

3.2 How much should you invest today at 12% interest to accumulate $1 000 000 in 30 years?

3.3 Morris paid $500 a month for 20 years to pay off the mortgage on his house. If his down payment was $5000 and the interest rate was 6% compounded monthly, how much did the house cost?

3.4 An investment pays $10 000 per year every five years, starting in seven years, for a total of four payments. If interest is 9%, how much is this investment worth today?

3.5 An industrial juicer costs $45 000. It will be used for five years and then sold to a remarketer for $25 000. If interest is 50%, what net yearly savings are needed to justify its purchase?

3.6 Fred wants to save up for a car. How much must he put in his bank account each month to save $10 000 in two years if the bank pays 6% interest compounded monthly?

3.7 It is May 1. You have just bought $2000 worth of furniture. You will pay for it in 24 equal monthly payments, starting at the end of May next year. Interest is 6% nominal per year, compounded monthly. How much will your payments be?

3.8 What is the present worth of the total of 20 payments, occurring at the end of every four months (the first payment is in four months), which are $400, $500, $600, increasing arithmetically? Interest is 12% nominal per year, compounded continuously.

3.9 What is the total value of the sum of the present worths of all the payments and receipts mentioned in Problem 2.22, at an interest rate of 0.5% per month?

3.10 How much is accumulated in each of the following savings plans over two years?

(a) $40 at the end of each month for 24 months at 12% compounded monthly

(b) $30 at the end of the first month, $31 at the end of the second month, and so forth, increasing by $1 per month, at 12% compounded monthly.

3.11 What interest rate will result in $5000 seven years from now, starting with $2300 today?

3.12 Refer back to the Inuvik Go-Kart problem of Example 3.2. The club members determined that it is possible to set aside only $7000 each year, and that they will have to put off building the clubhouse until they have saved the $50 000 necessary. How long will it take to save a total of $50 000, assuming that the interest rate is 10%? (*Hint:* Use logarithms to simplify the sinking fund factor.)

3.13 Gwen just bought a satellite dish, which provides her with exactly the same service as cable TV. The dish cost $2000, and the cable service she has now cancelled cost her $40 per month. How long will it take her to recoup her investment in the dish, if she can earn 12% interest, compounded annually, on her money?

3.14 A lottery prize pays $1000 at the end of the first year, $2000 the second, $3000 the third, and so on for 20 years. If there is only one prize in the lottery, 10 000 tickets are sold, and you can invest your money elsewhere at 15% interest, how much is each ticket worth, on average?

3.15 Joseph and three other friends bought a $110 000 house close to the university at the end of August last year. At that time they put down a deposit of $10 000 and took out a mortgage for the balance. Their mortgage payments are due at the end of each month (September 30, last year, was the date of the first payment) and are based on the assumption that Joseph and friends will take 20 years to pay off the debt. Annual nominal interest is 12%, compounded monthly. It is now February. Joseph and friends have made all their fall-term payments and have just made the January 31 payment for this year. How much do they still owe?

3.16 A new software package is expected to improve productivity at Saskatoon Insurance. However, because of training and implementation costs, savings are not expected to occur until the third year of operation. At that time, savings of $10 000 are expected, increasing by $1000 per year for the following five years. After this time (eight years from implementation), the software will be abandoned with no scrap value. How much is the software worth today, at 15% interest?

3.17 Clem is saving for a car, in a bank account that pays 12% interest, compounded monthly. The balance is now $2400. Clem will be saving $120 per month from his salary, and once every four months (starting in four months) he adds $200 in dividends from an investment. Bank fees, currently $10 per month, are expected to increase by $1 per month henceforth. How much will Clem have saved in two years?

3.18 Yogajothi is thinking of investing in a rental house. The total cost to purchase the house, including legal fees and taxes, is $115 000. All but $15 000 of this amount will be mortgaged. He will pay $800 per month in mortgage payments. At the end of two years, he will sell the house, and at that time expects to clear $20 000 after paying off the remaining mortgage principal (in other words, he will pay off all his debts for the house, and still have $20 000 left). Rents will earn him $1000 per month for the first year, and $1200 per month for the second year. The house is in fairly good condition now so that he doesn't expect to have any maintenance costs for the first six months. For the seventh month, Yogajothi has budgeted $200. This figure will be increased by $20 per month thereafter (e.g., the expected month 7 expense will be $200, month 8, $220, month 9, $240, etc.). If interest is 6% compounded monthly, what is the present worth of this investment? Given that Yogajothi's estimates of revenue and expenses are correct, should Yogajothi buy the house?

3.19 You have been paying off a mortgage in quarterly payments at a 24% nominal annual rate, compounded quarterly. Your bank is now offering an alternative payment plan, so you have a choice of two methods—continuing to pay as before, or switching to the new plan. Under the new plan, you would make monthly payments, 30% of the size of your current payments. The interest rate would be 24% nominal, compounded monthly. The time until the end of the mortgage would not change, regardless of the method chosen.

(a) Which plan would you choose, given that you naturally wish to minimize the level of your payment costs? (*Hint:* Look at the costs over a three-month period.)

(b) Under which plan would you be paying a higher effective yearly interest rate?

3.20 Derive the arithmetic gradient conversion to a uniform series formula. (*Hint:* Convert each period's gradient amount to its future value, and then look for a substitution from the other compound amount factors.)

3.21 Derive the geometric gradient to present worth conversion factor. (*Hint:* Divide and multiply the present worth of a geometric series by [1 + g] and then substitute in the growth adjusted interest rate.)

3.22 Reginald is expecting steady growth of 10% per year in profits from his new company. All profits are going to be invested at 20% interest. If profits for this year (at the end of the year) total $100 000, how much will be saved at the end of 10 years?

3.23 Reginald is expecting steady growth in profits from his new company of 20% per year. All profits are going to be invested at 10% interest. If profits for this year (at the end of the year) total $100 000, how much will be saved at the end of 10 years?

3.24 In Example 3.4, Clarence bought a $94 000 house with a $14 000 down payment and took out a mortgage for the remaining $80 000 at 12% nominal interest, compounded monthly. We determined that he would make 51 $2000 payments and then a final payment. What is his final payment?

3.25 A new wave soldering machine is expected to save Yukon Circuit Boards $15 000 per year through reduced labour costs and increased quality. The device will have a life of eight years, and have no salvage value after this time. If the company can generally expect to get 12% return on its capital, how much could it afford to pay for the wave soldering machine?

3.26 Gail has won a lottery that pays her $100 000 at the end of this year, $110 000 at the end of next year, $120 000 the following year, and so on, for 30 years. Leon has offered Gail $2 500 000 today in exchange for all the money she will receive. If Gail can get 8% interest on her savings, is this a good deal?

3.27 Gail has won a lottery that pays her $100 000 at the end of this year, and increases by 10% per year thereafter for 30 years. Leon has offered Gail $2 500 000 today in exchange for all the money she will receive. If Gail can get 8% interest on her savings, is this a good deal?

3.28 Tina has saved up $20 000 from her summer jobs. Rather than work for a living, she plans to buy an annuity from a trust company and become a beachcomber in Fiji. An annuity will pay her a certain amount each month for the rest of her life, and is calculated at 7% interest, compounded monthly, over Tina's 55 remaining years. Tina calculates that she needs at least $5 per day to live in Fiji, and she needs $1200 for air fare. Can she retire now? How much would she have available to spend each day?

3.29 The Regional Municipality of Kitchener is studying a water supply plan for the tri-city and surrounding area to the end of year 2040. To satisfy the water demand, one suggestion is to construct a pipeline from one of the Great Lakes. Construction would start in 2000 and take five years at a cost of $20 million per year. The cost of maintenance and repairs starts after completion of construction and for the first year is $2 million, increasing by 1% per year thereafter. At an interest rate of 6%, what is the present worth of this project?

Assume that all cash flows take place at year-end. Consider the present to be the end of 1995 / beginning of 1996. Assume that there is no salvage value at the end of year 2040.

3.30 Clem has a $50 000 loan. The interest rate offered is 8% compounded annually, and the repayment period is 15 years. Payments are to be received in equal instalments at the end of each year. Construct a spreadsheet (you must use a spreadsheet program) similar to the sample below that shows the amount received each year, the portion that is interest, the portion that is unrecovered capital, and the amount that is outstanding (i.e., unrecovered). Also, compute the total recovered capital which must equal the original capital amount; this can serve as a check on your solution. Design the spreadsheet so that the capital amount and the interest rate can be changed by updating only one cell for each. Construct:

(a) the completed spreadsheet for the amount, interest rate, and repayment period indicated

(b) the same spreadsheet, but for $75 000 at 10% interest (same repayment period)

(c) a listing showing the formulas used

Sample Capital Recovery Calculations				
Capital amount		$50 000.00		
Annual interest rate		8.00%		
Number of years to repay		15		
Payment Periods	**Annual Payment**	**Interest Received**	**Recovered Capital**	**Unrecovered Capital**
0				$ 50 000.00
1	$ 5 841.48	$ 4 000.00	$ 1 841.48	$ 48 158.52
2				
.				
.				
15				0.00
Total			50 000.00	

3.31 A software genius has been offered $10 000 per year for the next five years and then $20 000 per year for the following 10 years for the rights to his new video game. At 9% interest, how much is this worth today?

3.32 A bank offers a personal loan called "The Eight Per Cent Plan." The bank adds 8% to the amount borrowed; the borrower pays back one-twelfth of this total at the end of each month for a year. On a loan of

$500, the monthly payment is 540/12 = $45. There is also an administrative fee of $45, payable now. What is the actual effective interest rate on a $500 loan?

3.33 This year's electrical engineering class has decided to save up for a class party. Each of the 90 people in the class is to contribute $0.25 per day which will be placed in a daily interest (7 days a week, 365 days a year) savings account that pays a nominal 8% interest. Contributions will be made *five* days a week, Monday through Friday, beginning on Monday. The money is put into the account at the beginning of each day, and thus earns interest for the day. The class party is in 14 weeks (a full 14 weeks of payments will be made), and the money will be withdrawn on the Monday morning of the fifteenth week. How much will be saved, assuming everybody makes payments on time?

3.34 Coastal Shipping is setting aside capital to fund an expansion project. Funds earmarked for the project will accumulate at the rate of $50 000 per month until the project is completed. The project will take two years to complete. Once the project starts, costs will be incurred monthly at the rate of $150 000 per month over 24 months. Coastal currently has $250 000 saved. What is the minimum number of months they will have to wait before they can start if money is worth 18% nominal, compounded monthly? Assume that:

(a) Cash flows are all at the ends of months.

(b) The first $50 000 savings occurs one month from today.

(c) The first $150 000 payment occurs one month after the start of the project.

(d) The project must start at the beginning of a month.

3.35 A company is about to invest in a joint venture research and development project with another company. The project is expected to last eight years, but yearly payments the company makes will begin immediately (i.e., a payment is made today, and the last payment is eight years from today). Salaries will account for $40 000 of each payment. The remainder of each payment will cover equipment costs and facility overhead. The initial (immediate) equipment and facility cost is $26 000. Each subsequent year the figure will drop by $3000 until a cost of $14 000 is reached, after which the costs will remain constant until the end of the project.

(a) Draw a cash flow diagram to illustrate the cash flows for this situation.

(b) At an interest rate of 7%, what is the total future worth of all project payments at the end of the eight years?

TABLE 3A.1   Compound Interest Formulas for Discrete Cash Flow with Continuous Compounding

Name	Symbol and Formula
Compound amount factor	$(F/P,r,N) = e^{rN}$
Present worth factor	$(P/F,r,N) = \dfrac{1}{e^{rN}}$
Sinking fund factor	$(A/F,r,N) = \dfrac{e^r - 1}{e^{rN} - 1}$
Uniform series compound amount factor	$(F/A,r,N) = \dfrac{e^{rN} - 1}{e^r - 1}$
Capital recovery factor	$(A/P,r,N) = \dfrac{(e^r - 1)e^{rN}}{e^{rN} - 1}$
Series present worth factor	$(P/A,r,N) = \dfrac{e^{rN} - 1}{(e^r - 1)e^{rN}}$
Arithmetic gradient to annuity conversion factor	$(A/G,r,N) = \left(\dfrac{1}{e^r - 1} - \dfrac{N}{e^{rN} - 1}\right)$

EXAMPLE 3A.1

Yoram Gershon is saving to buy a new sound system. He plans to deposit $100 each month for the next 24 months in the Bank of Montrose. The nominal interest rate at the Bank of Montrose is 0.5% per month, compounded continuously. How much will Yoram have at the end of the 24 months?

We start by getting the uniform series compound amount factor for continuous compounding. Recall that the factor for discrete compounding is

$$(F/A,i,N) = \frac{(1 + i)^N - 1}{i}$$

Substituting $e^r - 1$ for i and e^{rN} for $(1 + i)^N$ gives the series compound amount, when compounding is continuous, as

$$(F/A,r,N) = \left(\frac{e^{rN} - 1}{e^r - 1}\right)$$

The amount Yoram will have at the end of 24 months, F, is given by

$$F = 100\left(\frac{e^{(0.005)24} - 1}{e^{0.005} - 1}\right)$$

$$F = 100\left(\frac{1.127497 - 1}{1.00501 - 1}\right)$$

$$F = 2544.85$$

Yoram will have about $2545 saved at the end of the 24 months.

The formulas for *continuous cash flows with continuous compounding* are derived using integral calculus. The continuous *series present worth* factor, denoted by $(P/\bar{A},r,T)$, for a continuous flow, $\bar{A}$, over a period length, T, where the nominal interest rate is r, is given by

$$P = \bar{A}\left(\frac{e^{rT} - 1}{re^{rT}}\right)$$

so that

$$(P/\bar{A},r,T) = \left(\frac{e^{rT} - 1}{re^{rT}}\right)$$

It is then easy to derive the formula for the continuous *uniform series compound amount factor*, denoted by $(F/\bar{A},r,T)$, by multiplying the series present worth factor by e^{rT} to get the future worth of a present value, P.

$$(F/\bar{A},r,T) = \frac{e^{rT} - 1}{r}$$

We can get the continuous *capital recovery* factor, denoted by $(\bar{A}/P,r,T)$, as the inverse of the continuous series present worth factor. The continuous *sinking fund* factor $(F/\bar{A},r,T)$ is the inverse of continuous uniform series compound amount factor. A summary of the formulas for continuous cash flow and continuous compounding is shown in Table 3A.2. Tables of values for these formulas are available in Appendix C.

TABLE 3A.2   Compound Interest Formulas for Continuous Cash Flow with Continuous Compounding

Name	Symbol and Formula
Sinking fund factor	$(\bar{A}/F,r,T) = \dfrac{r}{e^{rT} - 1}$
Uniform series compound amount factor	$(F/\bar{A},r,T) = \dfrac{e^{rT} - 1}{r}$
Capital recovery factor	$(\bar{A}/P,r,T) = \dfrac{re^{rT}}{e^{rT} - 1}$
Series present worth factor	$(P/\bar{A},r,T) = \dfrac{e^{rT} - 1}{re^{rT}}$

EXAMPLE 3A.2

Savings from a new widget grinder are estimated to be $10 000 per year. The grinder will last 20 years and will have no scrap value at the end of that time. Assume that the savings are generated as a continuous flow. The *effective* interest rate is 15% compounded continuously. What is the present worth of the savings?

From the problem statement, we know that $\bar{A} = 10\ 000$, $i = 0.15$, and $T = 20$. From the relation $i = e^r - 1$, for $i = 0.15$ the interest rate to apply for continuously compounding is $r = 0.13976$. The present worth computations are

$$P = \bar{A}\ (P/\bar{A}, r, T)$$

$$= \$10\ 000 \left(\frac{e^{(0.13976)20} - 1}{(0.13976)e^{(0.13976)20}} \right)$$

$$= \$67\ 180.00$$

The present worth of the savings is $67 180. Note that if we had used discrete compounding factors for the present worth computations we would have obtained a lower value.

$$P = A(P/A, i, N)$$

$$= \$10\ 000(6.2593)$$

$$= \$62\ 593$$

Review Problem 3A.1 for Appendix 3A

Mr. Big is thinking of buying the MQM Grand Hotel in Las Vegas. The hotel has continuous net receipts totalling $120 000 000 per year (Vegas hotels run 24 hours per day). This money could be immediately reinvested in Mr. Big's many other ventures, all of which earn a nominal 10% interest. The hotel will likely be out of style in about eight years, and could then be sold for about $200 000 000. What is the maximum Mr. Big should pay for the hotel today?

Answer

$$P = \$120\ 000\ 000(P/\bar{A}, 10\%, 8) + \$200\ 000\ 000e^{-(0.1)(8)}$$

$$= \$120\ 000\ 000\ \frac{e^{(0.1)(8)} - 1}{(0.1)e^{(0.1)(8)}} + \$200\ 000\ 000e^{-(0.1)(8)}$$

$$= \$701\ 184\ 547$$

Mr. Big should not pay more than about $700 000 000.

PROBLEMS

3A.1 An investment in new data logging technology is expected to generate extra revenue continuously for Calgary Petroleum Services. The initial cost is $300 000, but extra revenues total $75 000 per year. If the effective interest rate is 10% compounded continuously, does the present worth of the savings over five years exceed the original purchase cost? By how much does one exceed the other?

3A.2 Desmond earns $25 000 continuously over a year from an investment that pays 8% nominal interest, compounded continuously. How much money does he have at the end of the year?

3A.3 Gina intently plays the stock market, so that any capital she has can be considered to be compounding continuously. At the end of 1993, Gina had $10 000. How much did she have at the beginning of 1993, if she earned a nominal interest rate of 18%?

3A.4 Gina (from the previous problem) has earned a nominal interest rate of 18% on the stock market every year since she started with an initial investment of $100. What year did she start investing?

APPENDIX 3B: Derivation of Discrete Compound Interest Factors

This appendix derives six of the discrete compound interest factors presented in this chapter. All of them can be derived from the compound interest equation

$$F = P(1 + i)^N$$

3B.1 Compound Amount Factor

In the symbolic convention used for compound interest factors, the compound interest equation can be written

$$F = P(1 + i)^N = P(F/P,i,N)$$

so that the compound amount factor is

$$(F/P,i,N) = (1 + i)^N \tag{3B.1}$$

3B.2 Present Worth Factor

The present worth factor, $(P/F,i,N)$, converts a future amount F to a present amount P:

$$P = F(P/F,i,N)$$

$$\Rightarrow F = P\left(\frac{1}{(P/F,i,N)}\right)$$

Thus the present worth factor is the reciprocal of the compound amount factor. From Equation (3B.1),

$$(P/F,i,N) = \frac{1}{(1 + i)^N}$$

3B.3 Sinking Fund Factor

If a series of payments A follows the pattern of a standard annuity of N payments in length, then the future value of the payment in the jth period, from Equation (3B.1), is:

$$F = A(1 + i)^{N-j}$$

The future value of all of the annuity payments is then

$$F = A(1 + i)^{N-1} + A(1 + i)^{N-2} + \ldots + A(1 + i)^1 + A$$

Factoring out the annuity amount gives

$$F = A[(1 + i)^{N-1} + (1 + i)^{N-2} + \ldots + (1 + i)^1 + 1] \qquad (3B.2)$$

Multiplying Equation (3B.2) by $(1 + i)$ gives

$$F(1+i) = A[(1 + i)^{N-1} + (1 + i)^{N-2} + \ldots + (1 + i)^1 + 1] (1 + i)$$

$$F(1+i) = A[(1 + i)^N + (1 + i)^{N-1} + \ldots + (1 + i)^2 + (1 + i)] \quad (3B.3)$$

Subtracting Equation (3B.2) from Equation (3B.3) gives

$$F(1+i) - F = A[(1 + i)^N - 1]$$

$$Fi = A[(1 + i)^N - 1]$$

$$A = F\left[\frac{i}{(1 + i)^N - 1}\right]$$

Thus the sinking fund factor is given by

$$(A/F,i,N) = \frac{i}{(1 + i)^N - 1} \qquad (3B.4)$$

3B.4 Uniform Series Compound Amount Factor

The uniform series compound amount factor, $(F/A, i, N)$, converts an annuity A into a future amount F:

$$F = A(F/A,i,N)$$

$$\Rightarrow A = F\left(\frac{1}{(F/A,i,N)}\right)$$

Thus the uniform series compound amount factor is the reciprocal of the sinking fund factor. From Equation (3B.4),

$$(F/A,i,N) = \frac{(1 + i)^N - 1}{i}$$

3B.5 Capital Recovery Factor

If a series of payments A follows the pattern of a standard annuity of N payments in length, then the present value of the payment in the jth period is

$$P = A\frac{1}{(1 + i)^j}$$

The present value of the total of all the annuity payments is

$$P = A\left(\frac{1}{(1 + i)}\right) + A\left(\frac{1}{(1 + i)^2}\right) + \ldots + A\left(\frac{1}{(1 + i)^{N-1}}\right)$$

$$+ A\left(\frac{1}{(1 + i)^N}\right)$$

Factoring out the annuity amount gives

$$P = A\left[\left(\frac{1}{(1 + i)}\right) + \left(\frac{1}{(1 + i)^2}\right) + \ldots + \left(\frac{1}{(1 + i)^{N-1}}\right) + \left(\frac{1}{(1 + i)^N}\right)\right]$$

$$(3B.5)$$

Multiplying both sides of Equation (3B.5) by $(1 + i)$ gives

$$P(1 + i) = A\left[1 + \left(\frac{1}{(1 + i)}\right) + \ldots + \left(\frac{1}{(1 + i)^{N-2}}\right) + \left(\frac{1}{(1 + i)^{N-1}}\right)\right]$$

$$(3B.6)$$

Subtracting Equation (3B.5) from Equation (3B.6) gives

$$Pi = A\left[1 - \left(\frac{1}{(1 + i)^N}\right)\right]$$

$$P = A\left[\frac{(1 + i)^N - 1}{i(1 + i)^N}\right]$$

$$A = P\left[\frac{i(1 + i)^N}{(1 + i)^N - 1}\right]$$

Thus the capital recovery factor is given by

$$(A/P,i,N) = \frac{i(1 + i)^N}{(1 + i)^N - 1} \tag{3B.7}$$

3B.6 Series Present Worth Factor

The series present worth factor, $(P/A,i,N)$, converts an annuity A into a present amount P:

$$P = A(P/A,i,N)$$

$$\Rightarrow A = P\left(\frac{1}{(P/A,i,N)}\right)$$

Thus the uniform series compound amount factor is the reciprocal of the sinking fund factor. From Equation (3B.7),

$$(P/A,i,N) = \frac{(1 + i)^N - 1}{i(1 + i)^N}$$

3B.7 Arithmetic and Geometric Gradients

The derivation of the arithmetic gradient to annuity conversion factor and the geometric gradient to present worth conversion factor are left as problems for the student. See problems 3.20 and 3.21.

Comparison Methods Part 1

Engineering Economics in Action, Part 4A: What's Best?

4.1 Introduction

4.2 Relations Among Projects

4.3 Minimum Acceptable Rate of Return (MARR)

4.4 Present Worth (*PW*) and Annual Worth (*AW*) Comparisons

    4.4.1 Present Worth for Independent Projects

    4.4.2 Present Worth for Mutually Exclusive Projects

    4.4.3 Annual Worth Comparisons

    4.4.4 Comparisons of Alternatives with Unequal Lives

4.5 Payback Period

Canadian Corporate Case 4.1: Rockwell International of Canada

Review Problems

Summary

Engineering Economics in Action, Part 4B: Doing It Right

Problems

Appendix 4A: The MARR and the Cost of Capital

4A.1 Risk and the Cost of Capital

4A.2 Company Size and Sources of Capital

Engineering Economics in Action, Part 4A: What's Best?

Naomi waved hello as she breezed by Carole Brown, the receptionist, on her way in from the parking lot one Monday morning. She stopped as Carole caught her eye. "Clem wants to see you right away. Good morning."

After a moment of socializing, Clem got right to the point. "I have a job for you. Put aside the vehicle-life project for a couple of days."

"O.K., but you wanted a report by Friday."

"This is more important. You know that drop forging hammer in the South Shop? The beast is about 50 years old. I don't remember the exact age. We got it used four years ago. We were having quality control problems with the parts we were buying on contract and decided to bring production in-house. Stinson Brothers sold it to us cheap when they upgraded their forging operation. Fundamentally the machine is still sound, but the guides are worn out. The production people are spending too much time fiddling with it instead of turning out parts. Something has to be done. I have to make a recommendation to Ed Burns and Anna Kulkowski, who are going to be making decisions on investments for the next quarter. I'd like you to handle it." Ed Burns was the manager of manufacturing, and Anna Kulkowski was, among other things, the president of Canadian Widgets.

"What's the time frame?" Naomi asked. She was shifting job priorities in her mind and deciding what she would need to postpone.

"I want a report by tomorrow morning. I'd like to have a chance to review what you've done and submit a recommendation to Burns and Kulkowski for their Wednesday meeting." Clem sat back and gave Naomi his best big smile.

Naomi's return smile was a bit weak, as she was preoccupied with trying to sort out where to begin.

Clem laughed and continued with, "It's really not so bad. Dave Sullivan has done most of the work. But he's away and can't finish. His father-in-law had a heart attack on Friday, and he and Helena have gone to Florida to see him."

"What's involved?" asked Naomi.

"Not much, really. Dave has estimated all the cash flows. He's put everything on a spreadsheet. Essentially, there are three major possibilities. We can refurbish and upgrade the existing machine. We can get a manually operated mechanical press that will use less energy and be a lot quieter. Or we can go for an automated counterblow machine.

"Since there is going to be downtime while we are changing the unit, we might also want to replace the material-handling equipment at the same time. If we get the automated press, there is the possibility of going whole hog and integrating material handling with the press. But even if we automate, we could stay with a separate material-handling setup.

"Basically, you're looking at a fairly small first cost to upgrade the current beast, versus a large first cost for the automated equipment. But, if you take the high first cost route, you will get big savings down the road. All you have to do is decide what's best."

4.1   Introduction

The essential idea of investing is to give up something valuable now for the expectation of receiving something of greater value later. An investment may be thought of as an exchange of resources now for an expected flow of benefits in the future. Business firms, other organizations, and individuals all have opportunities to make such exchanges. A company may be able to use funds to install equipment that will reduce labour costs in the future. These funds might otherwise have been used on another project or returned to the shareholders or owners. An individual may be able to study to become an engineer. Studying requires that time be given up that could have been used to earn money or to travel. The benefit of study, though, is the expectation of a good income from an interesting job in the future.

Not all investment opportunities *should* be taken. The company considering a labour-saving investment may find that the value of the savings is less than the cost of installing the equipment. Not all investment opportunities *can* be taken. The person spending the next four years studying engineering cannot also spend that time getting a degree in business.

Engineers play a major role in making decisions about investment opportunities. In many cases, they are the ones who estimate the expected costs of and returns from an investment. They then must decide whether the expected returns outweigh the costs to see if the opportunity is potentially acceptable. They may also have to examine competing investment opportunities to see which is best. Engineers frequently refer to investment opportunities as **projects**. Throughout the rest of this text, the term "project" will be used to mean "investment opportunity."

In this chapter and in Chapter 5, we deal with methods of evaluating and comparing projects, sometimes called **comparison methods**. We start in this chapter with a scheme for classifying groups of projects. This classification system permits the appropriate use of any of the comparison methods. We then turn to a consideration of several widely used methods for evaluating opportunities. The **present worth method** compares projects by looking at the present worth of all cash flows associated with the projects. The **annual worth method** is similar, but converts all cash flows to a uniform series i.e., an annuity. The **payback period method** estimates how long it takes to "pay back" an investment. The study of comparison methods is continued in Chapter 5, which deals with the internal rate of return.

We have made six assumptions about all the situations presented in this chapter and in Chapter 5:

1. We have assumed that costs and benefits are always measurable in terms of money. In reality, costs and benefits need not be measurable in terms of money. For example, providing safe working conditions has many benefits, including improvement of worker

morale. However, it would be difficult to express the value of improved worker morale objectively in dollars and cents. Such other benefits as the pleasure gained from appreciating beautiful design may not be measurable quantitatively. We shall consider qualitative criteria and multiple objectives in Chapter 12.

2. We have assumed that future cash flows are known with certainty. In reality, future cash flows can only be estimated. Usually the further into the future we try to forecast, the less certain our estimates become. We look at methods of assessing the impact of this uncertainty in Chapter 10.

3. We have assumed that cash flows are unaffected by inflation or deflation. In reality, the purchasing power of money typically declines over time. We shall consider how inflation affects decision making in Chapter 9.

4. Unless otherwise stated, we have assumed that sufficient funds are available to implement all projects. In reality, cash constraints on investments may be very important, especially for new enterprises with limited ability to raise capital. We look at methods of raising capital in the appendix to this chapter.

5. We have assumed that taxes are not applicable. In reality, taxes are pervasive. We shall show how to include taxes in the decision-making process in Chapter 8.

6. Unless otherwise stated, we shall assume that all investments have a cash outflow at the start. These outflows are called *first costs*. We also assume that projects with first costs have cash inflows after the first costs that are at least as great in total as the first costs. In reality, some projects have cash inflows at the start, but involve a commitment of cash outflows at a later period. For example, a consulting engineer may receive an advance payment from a client, a cash inflow, to cover some of the costs of a project, but to complete the project the engineer will have to make disbursements over the project's life. We shall consider evaluation of such projects in Section 5.3.4 of Chapter 5.

4.2 Relations Among Projects

Companies and individuals are often faced with a large number of investment opportunities at the same time. Relations among these opportunities can range from the simple to the complex. We can distinguish three types of connections among projects that cover all the possibilities. Projects may be

(1) independent,

(2) mutually exclusive, or

(3) related but not mutually exclusive.

The simplest relation between projects occurs when they are **independent**. Two projects are independent if the expected costs and the expected benefits of each of the projects do not depend on whether or not the other one is chosen. A student considering the purchase of a vacuum cleaner and the purchase of a personal computer would probably find that the expected costs and benefits of the computer did not depend on whether he or she bought the vacuum cleaner. Similarly, the benefits and costs of the vacuum cleaner would be the same, whether or not the computer was purchased. If there are more than two projects under consideration, they are said to be independent if all possible pairs of projects in the set are independent. When two or more projects are independent, evaluation is simple. Consider each opportunity one at a time, and accept or reject it on its own merits.

Projects are **mutually exclusive** if, in the process of choosing one, all the other alternatives are excluded. In other words, two projects are mutually exclusive if it is impossible to do both or it clearly would not make sense to do both. For example, suppose Bismuth Realty Company wants to develop downtown office space on a specific piece of land. They are considering two potential projects. The first is a low-rise poured-concrete building. The second is a high-rise steel-frame structure with the same capacity as the low-rise building, but it has a small park at the entrance. It is impossible for Bismuth to have both buildings on the same site.

As another example, consider a student about to invest in a computer printer. She can get an ink-jet printer or a laser printer, but it would not make sense to get both. She would consider the options to be mutually exclusive.

The third class of projects consists of those that are **related but not mutually exclusive**. For pairs of projects in this category, the expected costs and benefits of one project depend on whether the other one is chosen. For example, Klamath Petroleum may be considering a service station at Fourth Avenue and Main Street as well as one at Twelfth and Main. The costs and benefits from either station will clearly depend on whether or not the other is built, but it may be possible, and may make sense, to have both stations.

Evaluation of related but not mutually exclusive projects can be simplified by combining them into exhaustive, mutually exclusive sets. For example, the two projects being considered by Klamath can be put into four mutually exclusive sets:

1. Neither station — the "do nothing" option
2. Just the station at Fourth and Main
3. Just the station at Twelfth and Main
4. Both stations

In general, n related projects can be put into 2^n sets including the "do nothing" option. Once the related projects are put into mutually exclusive sets, the analyst treats these sets as the alternatives. We can make 2^n mutually exclusive sets with n related projects by noting that for any single set there are exactly two possibilities for each project. The project may be *in* or *out* of that set. To get the total number of sets, we multiply the n twos to get 2^n. In the Klamath example, there were two possibilities for the station at Fourth and Main — accept or reject. These are combined with the two possibilities for the station at Twelfth and Main, to give the four sets that we listed.

A special case of related projects is where one project is *contingent* on another. Consider the case where project A could be done alone, or A and B could be done together, but B could not be done by itself. Project B is then contingent on Project A because it cannot be taken unless A is taken first. For example, the Athens and Manchester Development Company is considering building a shopping mall on the outskirts of Moncton. They are also considering building a parking garage to avoid long outdoor walks by patrons. Clearly, they would not build the parking garage unless they were also building the mall.

Sometimes two or more projects are mutually exclusive, not because of physical restrictions, but because of resource constraints. Usually the constraint is financial. For example, Bismuth may be considering two office buildings at different sites, where the expected costs and benefits of the two are unrelated, but Bismuth may be able to finance only one building. The two office-building projects would then be mutually exclusive because of financial constraints. If there are more than two projects, then all of the sets of projects that meet the budget form a mutually exclusive set of alternatives.

When there are several related projects, say four or five, the number of logically possible combinations becomes quite large. If there are four related projects, there are $2^4 = 16$ mutually exclusive sets, including the "do-nothing" alternative. If there are five related projects, the number of alternatives doubles to 32. A good way to keep track of these alternatives is to construct a table with all possible combinations of projects. The potential projects are in rows. The alternatives, which are sets of projects, are in columns. An x in a cell indicates that a project is in the alternative represented by that column. Not all logical combinations of projects represent feasible alternatives, as seen in the special cases of contingent alternatives or budget constraints. A last row, below the potential-project rows, indicates whether or not the sets are feasible alternatives.

EXAMPLE 4.1

The Small Street residential association wants to improve their district. Four ideas for renovation projects have been proposed: (1) converting part of the roadway to gardens, (2) adding old-fashioned light standards, (3) replacing the pavement with cobblestones, and (4) making the street one-way. However, there are a number of restrictions. The residential association can afford to do only two of the first three projects together. Also, gardens are possible only if the street is one-way. Finally, old-fashioned light standards would look out of place unless the pavement was replaced with cobblestones. The residential association feels it must do something. They do not want simply to leave things the way they are. What mutually exclusive alternatives are possible?

Since the association does not want to "do nothing," only 15 (i.e., $2^4 - 1$) alternatives will be considered. These are shown in Table 4.1.

TABLE 4.1 Potential Alternatives for the Small Street Renovation

Potential Alternative	1	2	3	4	5	6	7	8	9	10	11	12	13	14	15
Gardens	x	x	x	x	x	x	x	x							
Lights	x	x	x	x					x	x	x	x			
Cobblestones	x	x			x	x			x	x			x	x	
One-way	x		x		x		x		x		x		x		x
Feasible?	No	No	No	No	Yes	No	Yes	No	Yes	Yes	No	No	Yes	Yes	Yes

The result is that there are seven feasible mutually exclusive alternatives:

1. One-way street with gardens and cobblestones (alternative 5)
2. One-way street with gardens (alternative 7)
3. One-way street with old-fashioned lights and cobblestones (alternative 9)
4. Two-way street with old fashioned lights and cobblestones (alternative 10)
5. One-way street with cobblestones (alternative 13)
6. Two-way street with cobblestones (alternative 14)
7. One-way street (alternative 15)

To summarize our investigation of possible relations among projects, we have a threefold classification system: (1) independent projects, (2) mutually exclusive projects, and (3) related but not mutually exclusive projects. We can, however, arrange related projects into mutually exclusive sets and treat the sets as mutually exclusive alternatives. This reduces the system to two categories, independent and mutually exclusive. (See Figure 4.1.) Therefore, in the remainder of this chapter we consider only independent and mutually exclusive projects.

FIGURE 4.1 **Possible Relations Among Projects and How to Treat Them**

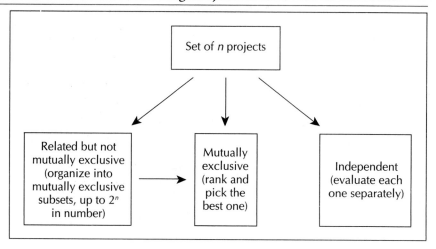

4.3 Minimum Acceptable Rate of Return (MARR)

A company evaluating projects will set for itself a lower limit for investment acceptability known as the **minimum acceptable rate of return (MARR)**. The MARR is an interest rate that must be earned for any project to be accepted. Projects that earn at least the MARR are desirable, since this means that the money is earning at least as much as can be earned elsewhere. Projects that earn less than the MARR are not desirable, since investing money in these projects denies the opportunity to use the money more profitably elsewhere.

The MARR can also be viewed as the rate of return required to get investors to invest in a business. If a company accepts projects that earn less than the MARR, investors will not be willing to put money into the company. This minimum return required to induce investors to invest in the company is the company's **cost of capital**. Methods for determining the cost of capital are presented in Appendix 4A.

The MARR is thus an opportunity cost in two senses. First, investors have investment opportunities outside any given company. Investing in a given company implies foregoing the opportunity of investing elsewhere. Second, once a company sets a MARR, investing in a given project implies giving up the opportunity of using company funds to invest in other projects that pay at least the MARR.

We shall show in this chapter and in Chapter 5 how the MARR is used in calculations involving the present worth, annual worth, or internal rate of return to evaluate projects. Henceforth, it is assumed that a value for the MARR has been supplied.

4.4 Present Worth (PW) and Annual Worth (AW) Comparisons

The present worth (PW) comparison method and the annual worth (AW) comparison method are based on finding a comparable basis of evaluation of projects in monetary units. With the present worth method, the analyst compares project A and project B by computing the present worths of the two projects at the MARR. The preferred project is the one with the greater present worth. The value of any company can be considered to be the present worth of all of its projects. Therefore, choosing projects with the greatest present worth maximizes the value of the company. With the annual worth method, the analyst compares projects A and B by transforming all disbursements and receipts of the two projects to uniform series at the MARR. The preferred project is the one with the greater annual worth. One can also speak of *present cost* and *annual cost*. See Close-Up 4.1.

CLOSE-UP 4.1   PRESENT COST AND ANNUAL COST

Sometimes mutually exclusive projects are compared in terms of present cost or annual cost. That is, the best project is the one with minimum cost as opposed to maximum worth. Two conditions should hold for this to be valid. 1. All projects have the same major benefit. 2. The estimated value of the major benefit clearly outweighs the projects' costs, even if that estimate is imprecise. Therefore, the "do nothing" option is rejected. The value of the major benefit is ignored in further calculations since it is the same for all projects. We choose the project with the lowest cost, considering secondary benefits as offsets to costs.

4.4.1 Present Worth for Independent Projects

The alternative to investing money in an independent project is to "do nothing." Doing nothing doesn't mean that the money is not used productively. In fact, it would be used for some other project, earning interest at a rate at least equal to the MARR. However, the present worth of any money invested at the MARR is zero, since the present worth of future receipts would exactly offset the current disbursement. Consequently, if an independent project has a present worth greater than zero, it is acceptable. If an independent project has a present worth less than zero, it is unacceptable. If an independent project has a present worth of exactly zero, it is considered *marginally* acceptable.

EXAMPLE 4.2

Steve Chen, a third-year electrical engineering student at Seaforth University, has noticed that the networked personal computers provided

The present worth of the cost savings is about $3000 greater than the $15 000 first cost. Therefore, the project is worth implementing.

4.4.2 Present Worth for Mutually Exclusive Projects

It is very easy to use the present worth method to choose the best project among a set of mutually exclusive projects when the service lives are the same. One just computes the present worth of each project using the MARR. The project with the greatest present worth is the preferred project because it is the one with the greatest profit.

EXAMPLE 4.4

Fly-by-Night Aircraft must purchase a new lathe. It is considering four lathes, each of which has a life of 10 years with no scrap value.

Lathe	1	2	3	4
First cost	$100 000	$150 000	$200 000	$255 000
Annual savings	25 000	34 000	46 000	55 000

Given a MARR of 15%, which alternative should be taken?

The present worths are:

Lathe 1:   PW = − $100 000 + $25 000($P/A$, 15%, 10)
$$= − \$100\ 000 + \$25\ 000(5.0187) = \$25\ 468$$

Lathe 2:   PW = − $150 000 + $34 000($P/A$, 15%, 10)
$$= − \$150\ 000 + \$34\ 000(5.0187) = \$20\ 636$$

Lathe 3:   PW = − $200 000 + $46 000($P/A$, 15%, 10)
$$= − \$200\ 000 + \$46\ 000(5.0187) = \$30\ 860$$

Lathe 4:   PW = − $255 000 + $55 000($P/A$, 15%, 10)
$$= − \$155\ 000 + \$55\ 000(5.0187) = \$21\ 029$$

Lathe 3 has the greatest present worth, and is therefore the preferred alternative.

4.4.3 Annual Worth Comparisons

Annual worth comparisons are essentially the same as present worth comparisons, except that all disbursements and receipts are transformed to a uniform series at the MARR, rather than to the present worth. Any present worth P can be converted to an annuity A by the capital recovery factor ($A/P,i,N$). Therefore, a comparison of two projects *that have the same life* by the present worth and annual worth methods will always indicate the same preferred alternative. Note that, although the method is called annual worth, the uniform series is not necessarily on a yearly basis.

Present worth comparisons make sense because they compare the worth today of each alternative, but annual worth comparisons can sometimes be more easily grasped mentally. For example, to say that operating an automobile over five years has a present cost of $20 000 is less meaningful than saying that it will cost about $5300 per year for each of the following five years.

Sometimes there is no clear justification for preferring either the present worth method or the annual worth method. Then it is reasonable to use the one that requires less conversion. For example, if most receipts or costs are given as annuities or gradients, one can more easily perform an annual worth comparison. Sometimes it can be useful to compare projects on the basis of future worths. See Close-Up 4.2.

CLOSE-UP 4.2   FUTURE WORTH

Sometimes it may be desirable to compare projects with the **future worth method**, on the basis of the future worth of each project. This is most likely to be true for cases where money is being saved for some future expense.

For example, two investment plans are being compared to see which accumulates more money for retirement. Plan A consists of a payment of $10 000 today and then $2000 per year over 20 years. Plan B is $3000 per year over 20 years. Interest for both plans is 10%. Rather than convert these cash flows to either present worth or annual worth, it is sensible to compare the future worths of the plans, since the actual dollar value in 20 years has particular meaning.

$$FW_A = \$10\ 000(F/P, 10\%, 20) + \$2000(F/A, 10\%, 20)$$
$$= \$10\ 000(6.7275) + \$2000(57.275)$$
$$= \$181\ 825$$
$$FW_B = \$3000(F/A, 10\%, 20)$$
$$= \$3000(57.275)$$
$$= \$171\ 825$$

Plan A is the better choice. It will accumulate to $181 825 over the next 20 years.

EXAMPLE 4.5

Sweat University is considering two alternative types of bleachers for a new athletic stadium:

Alternative 1: Concrete bleachers. The first cost is $350 000. The expected life of the concrete bleachers is 90 years and the annual upkeep costs are $2500.

Alternative 2: Wooden bleachers on earth fill. The first cost of $200 000 consists of $100 000 for earth fill and $100 000 for the wooden bleachers. The annual painting costs are $5000. The wooden bleachers must be replaced every 30 years at a cost of $100 000. The earth fill will last the entire 90 years.

One of the two alternatives will be chosen. It is assumed that the receipts and other benefits of the stadium are the same for both construction methods. Therefore, the greatest net benefit is obtained by choosing the alternative with the lower cost. The University uses a MARR of 7%. Which of the two alternatives is better?

For this example, let us base the analysis on annual worth. Since both alternatives have a life of 90 years, we shall get the equivalent annual costs over 90 years for both at an interest rate of 7%.

Alternative 1: Concrete bleachers

The equivalent annual cost over the 90-year life span of the concrete bleachers is

$$AW = \$350\,000(A/P, 7\%, 90) + \$2500$$

$$= \$350\,000(0.07016) + \$2500$$

$$= \$27\,056 \text{ per year}$$

$$\cong \$27\,000 \text{ per year}$$

Alternative 2: Wooden bleachers on earth fill

The total annual costs can be broken into three components: A_1 (for the earth fill), A_2 (for the bleachers), and A_3 (for the painting).

The equivalent annual cost of the earth fill is

$$AW_1 = \$100\,000(A/P, 7\%, 90)$$

The equivalent annual cost of the bleachers is easy to determine. The first set of bleachers is put in at the start of the project, the second set at the end of 30 years, and the third set at the end of 60 years, but the cost of the bleachers is the same at each installation. Therefore, we need to get only the cost of the first installation.

$$AW_2 = \$100\,000(A/P, 7\%, 30)$$

The last expense is for annual painting:

$$AW_3 = \$5000$$

The total equivalent annual cost for alternative 2, wooden bleachers on earth fill, is the sum of AW_1, AW_2, and AW_3:

$$AW = AW_1 + AW_2 + AW_3$$

$$= \$100\ 000[(A/P, 7\%, 90) + (A/P, 7\%, 30)] + \$5000$$

$$= \$100\ 000(0.07016 + 0.08059) + \$5000$$

$$= \$20\ 075$$

$$\cong \$20\ 000$$

The concrete bleachers have an equivalent annual cost of about $7000 more than the wooden ones. Therefore, the wooden bleachers are the better choice.

4.4.4 Comparison of Alternatives with Unequal Lives

When making present worth comparisons, we must always use the same time period in order to take into account the full benefits and costs of each alternative. If the lives of the alternatives are not the same, we can transform them to equal lives with one of the following two methods:

1. Repeat the *service life* of each alternative to arrive at a common time period for all alternatives. Here we assume that each alternative can be repeated with the same costs and benefits in the future — an assumption known as **repeated lives**. Usually we use the *least common multiple* of the lives of the various alternatives. Sometimes it is convenient to assume that the lives of the various alternatives are repeated indefinitely. Note that the assumption of repeated lives may not be valid where it is reasonable to expect technological improvements.

2. Adopt a specified **study period** — a time period that is given for the analysis. To set an appropriate study period, a company will usually take into account the time of required service, or the length of time they can be relatively certain of their forecasts. The study period method necessitates an additional assumption about *salvage value* whenever the life of one of the alternatives exceeds that of the given study period. Arriving at a reliable estimate of salvage value may be difficult sometimes.

Because they rest on different assumptions, the repeated lives and the study period methods can lead to different conclusions when applied to a particular project choice.

EXAMPLE 4.6

A mechanical engineer has decided to introduce automated material-handling equipment for a production line. She must choose between two alternatives, building the equipment or buying the equipment off the shelf. Each alternative has a different service life and a different set of costs.

Alternative 1: Build custom automated material-handling equipment.

First cost	$15 000
Labour	$ 3 300 per year
Power	$ 400 per year
Maintenance	$ 2 400 per year
Taxes and insurance	$ 300 per year
Service life	10 years

Alternative 2: Buy off-the-shelf standard automated material-handling equipment.

First cost	$25 000
Labour	$ 1 450 per year
Power	$ 600 per year
Maintenance	$ 3 075 per year
Taxes and insurance	$ 500 per year
Service life	15 years

If the MARR is 9%, which alternative is better?

The present worth of the custom system over its 10-year life is

$$
\begin{aligned}
PW(1) &= -\$15\,000 - (\$3300 + \$400 + \$2400 + \$300) \\
&\quad (P/A, 9\%, 10) \\
&= -\$15\,000 - \$6400(6.4176) \\
&= -\$56\,073 \\
&\cong -\$56\,100
\end{aligned}
$$

The present worth of the off-the-shelf system over its 15-year life is:

$$
\begin{aligned}
PW(2) &= -\$25\,000 - (\$1450 + \$600 + \$3075 + \$500) \\
&\quad (P/A, 9\%, 15) \\
&= -\$25\,000 - \$5625(8.0606) \\
&= -\$70\,341 \\
&\cong -\$70\,300
\end{aligned}
$$

The custom system has a lower cost for its 10-year life than the off-the-shelf system for its 15-year life, but it would be *wrong* to conclude from these calculations that the custom system should be preferred. The custom system yields benefits for only 10 years, whereas the off-the-shelf system lasts 15 years. It would be surprising if the cost of 15 years of benefits were not higher than the cost of 10 years of benefits. A fair comparison of the costs can be made only if equal lives are compared.

Let us apply the *repeated lives method*. If each alternative is repeated enough times, there will be a point in time where their service lives are simultaneously completed. This will happen first at the time equal to the *least common multiple* of the service lives. The least common multiple of 10 years and 15 years is 30 years. Alternative 1 will be repeated twice (after 10 years and after 20 years), while alternative 2 will be repeated once (after 15 years) during the 30-year period. At the end of 30 years, both alternatives will be completed simultaneously. See Figure 4.3.

With the same time period of 30 years for both alternatives, we can now compare present worths.

Alternative 1: Build custom automated material-handling equipment and repeat twice.

$$PW(1) = -\$15\ 000 - \$15\ 000(P/F, 9\%, 10) - \$15\ 000(P/F, 9\%, 20)$$
$$- (\$3300 + \$400 + \$2400 + \$300)(P/A, 9\%, 30)$$
$$= -\$15\ 000 - \$15\ 000(0.42241) - \$15\ 000(0.17843)$$
$$- \$6400(10.273)$$
$$= -\$89\ 760$$
$$\cong -\$89\ 800$$

Alternative 2: Buy off-the-shelf standard automated material-handling equipment and repeat once.

$$PW(2) = -\$25\ 000 - \$25\ 000(P/F, 9\%, 15)$$
$$- (\$1450 + \$600 + \$3075 + \$500)(P/A, 9\%, 30)$$
$$= -\$25\ 000 - \$25\ 000(0.27454) - \$5625(10.273)$$
$$= -\$89\ 649$$
$$\cong -\$89\ 600$$

Using the repeated lives method, we find little difference between the alternatives.

FIGURE 4.3   Least Common Multiple of the Service Lives

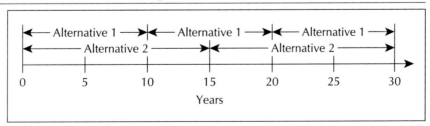

An annual worth comparison can also be done over a period of time equal to the least common multiple of the service lives by multiplying each of these present worths by the capital recovery factor for 30 years.

$$AW(1) = -\$89\ 760(A/P, 9\%, 30)$$
$$= -\$89\ 760(0.09734)$$
$$= -\$8737$$
$$\cong -\$8700$$

$$AW(2) = -\$89\ 649(A/P, 9\%, 30)$$
$$= -\$89\ 649(0.09734)$$
$$= -\$8726$$
$$\cong -\$8700$$

As we would expect, there is again little difference in the annual cost between the alternatives. However, if an annual worth comparison is done, there is a more convenient approach if it can be assumed that the alternatives are repeated indefinitely. Since the annual costs of an alternative remain the same no matter how many times it is repeated, it is not necessary to determine the least common multiple of the service lives. The annual worth of each alternative can be assessed for whatever time period is most convenient for each alternative.

Alternative 1: Build custom automated material-handling equipment.

$$AW(1) = -\$15\ 000(A/P, 9\%, 10) - \$6400$$
$$= -\$15\ 000(0.15582) - \$6400$$
$$= -\$8737$$
$$\cong -\$8700$$

Alternative 2: Buy off-the-shelf standard automated material-handling equipment.

$$AW(2) = -\$25\ 000(A/P, 9\%, 15) - \$5625$$
$$= -\$25\ 000(0.12406) - \$5625$$
$$= -\$8726$$
$$\cong -\$8700$$

If it cannot be assumed that the alternatives can be repeated to permit a calculation over the least common multiple of their service lives, then it is necessary to use the *study period method*.

Suppose that the given study period is 10 years, because the engineer is uncertain about costs past that time. The service life of the off-the-shelf system (15 years) is greater than the study period (10 years).

Therefore, we have to make an assumption about the salvage value of the off-the-shelf system after 10 years. Suppose the engineer judges that its salvage value will be $5000. We can now proceed with the comparison.

Alternative 1: Build custom automated material-handling equipment (10-year study period).

$$PW(1) = -\$15\,000 - (\$3300 + \$400 + \$2400 + \$300)(P/A, 9\%, 10)$$
$$= -\$15\,000 - \$6400(6.4176)$$
$$= -\$56\,073$$
$$\cong -\$56\,100$$

Alternative 2: Buy off-the-shelf standard automated material-handling equipment (10-year study period).

$$PW(2) = -\$25\,000 - (\$1450 + \$600 + \$3075 + \$500)(P/A, 9\%, 10)$$
$$\qquad + \$5000(P/F, 9\%, 10)$$
$$= -\$25\,000 - \$5625(6.4176) + \$5000(0.42241)$$
$$= -\$58\,987$$
$$\cong -\$59\,000$$

Using the study period method of comparison, alternative 1 has the smaller present cost and is, therefore, preferred.

Note that here the study period method gives a different answer than the repeated lives method gives. The study period method is often sensitive to the chosen salvage value. A larger salvage value tends to make an alternative with a life longer than the study period more attractive, and a smaller value tends to make it less attractive.

In some instances, it may be difficult to arrive at a reliable estimate of salvage value. Given the sensitivity of the study period method to the salvage value estimate, the analyst may be uncertain about the validity of the results. One way of circumventing this problem is to avoid estimating the salvage value at the outset. Instead we calculate what salvage value would make the alternatives equal in value. Then we decide whether the actual salvage value will be above or below the break-even value found. Applying this approach to our example, we set $PW(2) = PW(1)$ so that

$$PW(2) = -\$25\,000 - \$5625(6.4176) + S(0.42241)$$
$$= -\$56\,100$$

where S is the salvage value.

Solving for S, we find $S \cong \$12\,100$. Is a reasonable estimate of the salvage value above or below $12 100? If it is above $12 100, then we conclude that the off-the-shelf system is the preferred choice. If it is below $12 100, then we conclude that the custom system is preferable.

The study period can also be used for the annual worth method if the assumption of being able to indefinitely repeat the choice of alternatives is not justified.

EXAMPLE 4.7

Joan is renting an apartment while on a one-year assignment in a distant city. The apartment does not have a refrigerator. She can rent one for a $100 deposit (returned in a year) and $15 per month (paid at the end of each month). Alternatively, she can buy a used refrigerator for $300, which she would sell in a year when she leaves. For how much would Joan have to be able to sell the used refrigerator in one year when she leaves, in order to be better off buying the used refrigerator than renting one? Interest is at 6% nominal, compounded monthly.

Let S stand for the unknown salvage value (i.e., the amount Joan will be able to sell the refrigerator for in a year). We then equate the present worth of the rental alternative with the present worth of the purchase alternative for the one-year study period:

$$- \$100 - \$15(P/A, 0.5\%, 12) + \$100(P/F, 0.5\%, 12)$$
$$= - \$300 + S(P/F, 0.5\%, 12)$$
$$- \$100 - \$15(11.616) + \$100(0.94192)$$
$$= - \$300 + S(0.94192)$$
$$S = \$127.35$$

If Joan can sell the used refrigerator for more than about $127 after one year's use, she is better off buying it rather than renting one.

4.5   Payback Period

The simplest method for judging the economic viability of projects is the payback period method. It is a rough measure of the time it takes for an investment to pay for itself. More precisely, the **payback period** is the number of years it takes for an investment to be recouped when the interest rate is assumed to be zero. It is usually calculated as follows:

$$\text{Payback period} = \frac{\text{First cost}}{\text{Annual savings}}$$

For example, if a first cost of $20 000 yielded a return of $8000 per year, then the payback period would be 2.5 years (i.e., $20 000/$8000).

If the annual savings are not constant, we can calculate the payback period by deducting each years of savings from the first cost until the first cost is recovered. The number of years of savings required to do this is the payback period. For example, suppose the saving from a $20 000 first cost is $5000 the first year, increasing by $1000 each year thereafter. By adding the annual savings one year at a time, we see that it would take a little less than four years to pay back the first cost ($5000 + $6000 + $7000 + $8000 = $26 000). The payback period would then be stated as either four years (if we assume that the $8000 is received at the end of the fourth year) or 3.25 years (if we assume that the $8000 is received during the fourth year).

According to the payback period method of comparison, the project with the shorter payback period is the preferred investment. A company may have a policy of rejecting projects for which the payback period exceeds some preset number of years. The length of the maximum payback period depends on the type of project and the company's financial situation. If the company expects a cash constraint in the near future, or if a project's returns are highly uncertain after more than a few periods, the company will set a maximum payback period that is relatively short. As a rule of thumb, a payback period of two years is often considered acceptable, while one of more than four years is unacceptable. Accordingly, government grant programs often target projects with payback periods of between two and four years on the rationale that in this range the grant can justify economically feasible projects that a company with limited cash flow would otherwise be unwilling to undertake.

The payback period need not, and perhaps should not, be used as the sole criterion for evaluating projects. It is a rough method of comparison and possesses some glaring weaknesses (as we shall discuss below). Nevertheless, the payback period method can be used effectively as a preliminary filter. All projects with paybacks within the minimum would then be evaluated, using either rate of return methods or present/annual worth methods.

EXAMPLE 4.8

A new packaging machine will save the Greene Cheese Company $3000 per year in reduced spoilage, $1000 per year in packaging material, and $2500 per year in labour. The new machine will have additional expenses of $700 per year in maintenance and $200 per year in energy. If it costs $20 000 to purchase, what is its payback period? Assume that the savings are earned throughout the year, not just at year end.

$$\text{Payback period} = \$20\ 000/[(\$3000 + \$1000 + \$2500) - (\$700 + \$200)]$$

$$= \$20\ 000/\$5600 = 3.6 \text{ years}$$

If Greene Cheese had a maximum payback period of less than 3.6 years, the project would be rejected.

EXAMPLE 4.9

Monster Meats is considering a plant expansion. Net positive cash flows resulting from a $5 000 000 initial investment are $1 000 000 next year, and $3 000 000 per year thereafter. What is the payback period for this project?

Decrementing the initial $5 000 000 investment by the savings one year at a time, we have

$$\$5\ 000\ 000 = \$1\ 000\ 000 + \$3\ 000\ 000 + \tfrac{1}{3}(\$3\ 000\ 000)$$

This gives a payback period of $2\tfrac{1}{3}$ years.

CLOSE-UP 4.3 DISCOUNTED PAYBACK PERIOD

In a discounted payback period calculation, the present worth of each year's savings is subtracted from the first cost until the first cost is diminished to zero. The number of years of savings required to do this is the discounted payback period. The main disadvantages of using a discounted payback period include the more complicated calculations and the need for an interest rate.

For instance, in Example 4.8, the Greene Cheese Company had an investment of $20 000 recouped by net savings of $5600 per year. If interest were at 10%, the present worth of savings would be:

Year	Present Worth	Cumulative
Year 1	$5600(P/F, 10%, 1) = $5600(0.90909) = $5091	$ 5 091
Year 2	$5600(P/F, 10%, 2) = $5600(0.82645) = $4628	$ 9 719
Year 3	$5600(P/F, 10%, 3) = $5600(0.75131) = $4207	$13 926
Year 4	$5600(P/F, 10%, 4) = $5600(0.68301) = $3825	$17 751
Year 5	$5600(P/F, 10%, 5) = $5600(0.62092) = $3477	$21 228

Thus the discounted payback period is over 4.5 years, compared with 3.6 years calculated for the standard payback period.

The payback period method has four main advantages:

1. It is very easy to understand. One of the goals of engineering decision making is to communicate the reasons for a decision to managers or clients with a variety of backgrounds. The reasons behind the payback period and its conclusions are very easy to explain.

2. The payback period is very easy to calculate. It can usually be done without even using a calculator, so projects can be very quickly assessed.

3. It accounts for the need to recover capital quickly. Cash flow is almost always a problem for small- to medium-sized companies. Even large companies sometimes can't tie up their money in long-term projects.

4. The future is unknown. The future benefits from an investment
    may be estimated imprecisely. It may not make much sense to
    use precise methods like present worth on numbers that are
    imprecise to start with. A rule of thumb like the payback period
    may be good enough for most purposes.

But the payback period method has three important disadvantages:

1. It discriminates against long-term projects. No houses or highways
    would ever be built if they had to pay themselves off in two years.

2. It ignores the effect of the timing of cash flows within the pay-
    back period. It disregards interest rates and takes no account of
    the time value of money. (Occasionally, a discounted payback
    period is used to overcome this disadvantage. See Close-Up 4.3.)

3. It ignores the expected service life. It disregards the benefits that
    accrue after the end of the payback period.

The following example illustrates how the payback period method
can ignore future cash flows.

EXAMPLE 4.10

Self Defence Systems is going to upgrade their paper-shredding facility.
They have a choice between two models. Model 007, with a first cost of
$50 000 and a service life of seven years, would save them $10 000 per
year. Model MX, with a first cost of $10 000 and an expected service life
of 20 years, would save them $1500 per year. If the company's MARR is
8%, which model is the better buy?

Using payback period as the sole criterion

Model 007: Payback period = $50 000/$10 000 = 5 years

Model MX: Payback period = $10 000/$1500 = 6.6 years

It appears that the 007 model is better.

Using annual worth

Model 007: AW = $- $50 000(A/P, 8\%, 7) + $10 000 = 396.5

Model MX: AW = $- $10 000(A/P, 8\%, 20) + $1500 = 481.5

Here, the model MX is substantially better.

The difference in the results from the two comparison methods is that
the payback period method has ignored the benefits of the models that
occur after the models have paid themselves off. This is illustrated in Figure
4.4. For model MX, about 14 years of benefits have been omitted, whereas
for model 007, only two years of benefits have been left out.

CANADIAN CORPORATE CASE 4.1

Rockwell International of Canada

The Light Vehicle Division of Rockwell International of Canada makes seat-slide assemblies for the automotive industry. They have two major classifications for investment opportunities. Investments are made in developing new products to be manufactured and sold, and are also made in new machines to improve production. The overall approach to assessing whether or not an investment should be made depends on the nature of the project.

In evaluating new products, they consider the following:

1. *Marketing strategy:* Does it fit the business plan for the company?
2. *Work force:* How will it affect human resources?
3. *Margins:* The product should generate appropriate profits.
4. *Cash flow:* Positive cash flow is expected within two years.

In evaluating new machines, they consider the following:

1. *Cash flow:* Positive cash flow is expected within a limited time period.
2. *Quality issues:* For issues of quality, justification is based on cost avoidance rather than positive cash flow.
3. *Cost avoidance:* Savings should pay back an investment within one year.

FIGURE 4.4   Flows Ignored by the Payback Period

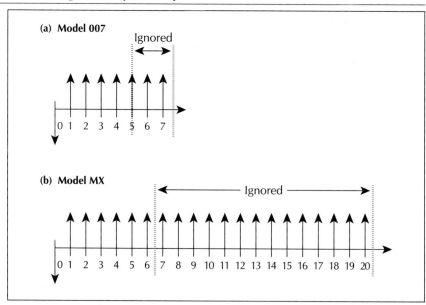

REVIEW PROBLEMS

Review Problem 4.1

Tilson Dairies operates several cheese plants. The plants are all old and in need of renovation. Tilson's engineers have developed plans to renovate all the plants. Each project would have a positive present worth at the company's MARR. Tilson has $3.5 million available to invest in these projects. The following facts about the potential renovation projects are available:

Plant	First Cost	Present Worth
A	$0.8 million	$1.1 million
B	$1.2 million	$1.7 million
C	$1.4 million	$1.8 million
D	$2.0 million	$2.7 million

Which projects should Tilson accept?

Answer

Table 4.2 shows the possible mutually exclusive projects that Tilson can consider.

TABLE 4.2   Mutually Exclusive Projects for Tilson Dairies

Project	Total First Cost	Total Present Worth	Feasibility
Do nothing	$0.0 million	$0.0 million	Feasible
A	$0.8 million	$1.1 million	Feasible
B	$1.2 million	$1.7 million	Feasible
C	$1.4 million	$1.8 million	Feasible
D	$2.0 million	$2.7 million	Feasible
A and B	$2.0 million	$2.8 million	Feasible
A and C	$2.2 million	$2.9 million	Feasible
A and D	$2.8 million	$3.8 million	Feasible
B and C	$2.6 million	$3.5 million	Feasible
B and D	$3.2 million	$4.4 million	Feasible
C and D	$3.4 million	$4.5 million	Feasible
A, B, and C	$3.4 million	$4.6 million	Feasible
A, B, and D	$4.0 million	$5.5 million	Not feasible
A, C, and D	$4.2 million	$5.6 million	Not feasible
B, C, and D	$4.6 million	$6.2 million	Not feasible
A, B, C and D	$5.4 million	$7.3 million	Not feasible

Tilson should accept projects A, B, and C. They have a combined present worth of $4.6 million. Other feasible combinations that come close to using all available funds are B and D with a total present worth of $4.4 million, and C and D with a total present worth of $4.5 million.

Note that it is not necessary to consider explicitly the "leftovers" of the $3.5 million budget when comparing the present worths. The assumption is that any leftover part of the budget will be invested and provide interest at the MARR, resulting in a zero present worth for that part. Therefore, it is best to choose the combination of projects that has the largest total present worth and stays within the budget constraint.

Review Problem 4.2

City engineers are considering two plans for municipal aqueduct tunnels. They are to decide between the two, using an interest rate of 8%.

Plan A is a full-capacity tunnel that will meet the needs of the city forever. Its cost is $3 000 000 now, and $100 000 every 10 years for lining repairs.

Plan B involves building a half-capacity tunnel now and a second half-capacity tunnel in 20 years, when the extra capacity will be needed. Each of the half-capacity tunnels costs $2 000 000. Maintenance costs for each tunnel are $80 000 every 10 years. There is also an additional $15 000 per tunnel per year required to pay for extra pumping costs caused by greater friction in the smaller tunnels.

(a) Which alternative is preferred? Use a present worth comparison.

(b) Which alternative is preferred? Use an annual worth comparison.

Answer

(a) *Plan A: Full-Capacity Tunnel*

First, the $100 000 paid at the end of 10 years can be thought of as a future amount which has an equivalent annuity.

$$AW = \$100\ 000(A/F, 8\%, 10) = \$100\ 000(0.06903) = \$6903$$

Thus, at 8% interest, $100 000 every 10 years is equivalent to $6903 every year.

Since the tunnel will have (approximately) an infinite life, the present cost of the lining repairs can be found using the capitalized cost formula, giving a total cost of

$$PW(\text{Plan A}) = \$3\ 000\ 000 + \$6903/0.08 = \$3\ 086\ 288$$

Plan B: Half-Capacity Tunnels

For the first tunnel, the equivalent annuity for the maintenance and pumping costs is

$$AW = \$15\ 000 + \$80\ 000(0.06903) = \$20\ 522$$

The present cost is then found with the capitalized cost formula, giving a total cost of

PW1 = $2 000 000 + $20 522/0.08 = $2 256 525

Now, for the second tunnel, basically the same calculation is used, except that the present worth calculated must be discounted by 20 years at 8%, since the second tunnel will be built 20 years in the future.

PW2 = {$2 000 000 + [$15 000 + $80 000(0.06903)]/0.08}(P/F, 8%, 20)
    = $2 256 525(0.21455) = $484 137

P(Plan B) = P1 + P2 = $2 256 530 + $484 140 = $2 740 662

Consequently, the two half-capacity aqueducts are economically preferable.

(b) *Plan A: Full-Capacity Tunnel*

First, the $100 000 paid at the end of 10 years can be thought of as a future amount which has an equivalent annuity of

AW = $100 000(A/F, 8%, 10) = $100 000(0.06903) = $6903

Thus, at 8% interest, $100 000 every 10 years is equivalent to $6903 every year.

Since the tunnel will have (approximately) an infinite life, an annuity equivalent to the initial cost can be found using the capitalized cost formula, giving a total annual cost of

AW(Plan A) = $3 000 000(0.08) + $6903 = $246 903

Plan B: Half Capacity Tunnels

For the first tunnel, the equivalent annuity for the maintenance and pumping costs is

AW_{mp} = $15 000 + $80 000(0.06903) = $20 522

The annual equivalent of the initial cost is then found with the capitalized cost formula, giving a total cost of

AW1 = $2 000 000(0.08) + $20 522 = $180 522

Now, for the second tunnel, basically the same calculation is used, except that the annuity must be discounted by 20 years at 8%, since the second tunnel will be built 20 years in the future.

AW2 = AW1(P/F, 8%, 20)
    = $180 522(0.21455) = $38 731

AW(Plan B) = AW1 + AW2 = $180 522 + $38 731 = $219 253

Consequently, the two half-capacity aqueducts are economically preferable.

Review Problem 4.3

Constantine Fernando, an engineer at Corner Brook Manufacturing, has a $100 000 budget for plant improvements. He has identified four mutually exclusive investments, all of five years duration, which have the cash flows shown in Table 4.3. For each alternative, he wants to determine the payback period and the present worth. For his recommendation report, he will order the alternatives from most preferred to least preferred in each case. Corner Brook Manufacturing uses an 8% MARR for such decisions.

TABLE 4.3   Cash Flows for Review Problem 4.3

Alternative	Cash Flow at the End of Each Year					
	0	1	2	3	4	5
A	$100 000	$25 000	$25 000	$25 000	$25 000	$25 000
B	100 000	5 000	10 000	20 000	40 000	80 000
C	100 000	50 000	50 000	10 000	0	0
D	100 000	0	0	0	0	1 000 000

Answer

The payback period can be found by decrementing yearly. The payback periods for the alternatives are then

A: 4 years

B: 4.3125 or 5 years

C: 2 years

D: 4.1 or 5 years

The order of the alternatives from most preferred to least preferred using the payback period method with yearly decrementing is: C, A, D, B.
    The present worth computations for each alternative are:

A: $PW = -\$100\ 000 + \$25\ 000(P/A, 8\%, 5) = -\$100\ 000$

   $+ \$25\ 000(3.9926)$

   $= -\$185$

B: $PW = -\$100\ 000 + \$5000(P/F, 8\%, 1) + \$10\ 000(P/F, 8\%, 2)$

   $+ \$20\ 000(P/F, 8\%, 3) + \$40\ 000(P/F, 8\%, 4)$

   $+ \$80\ 000(P/F, 8\%, 5)$

   $= -\$100\ 000 + \$5000(0.92593) + \$10\ 000(0.85734)$

   $+ \$20\ 000(0.79383) + \$40\ 000(0.73503) + \$80\ 000(0.68059)$

   $= \$12\ 982$

C: PW $= -\$100\ 000 + \$50\ 000(P/F, 8\%, 1) + \$50\ 000(P/F, 8\%, 2)$

$+ \$10\ 000(P/F, 8\%, 3)$

$= -\$100\ 000 + \$50\ 000(0.92593) + \$50\ 000(0.85734)$

$+ \$10\ 000(0.79283)$

$= -\$2908$

D: PW $= -\$100\ 000 + \$1\ 000\ 000(P/F, 8\%, 5)$

$= -\$100\ 000 + \$1\ 000\ 000(0.68059)$

$= \$580\ 590$

The order of the alternatives from most preferred to least preferred using the present worth method is: D, B, A, C.

SUMMARY

This chapter discussed relations among projects, and the present worth, annual worth, and payback period methods for evaluating projects. The discussion of relations among projects started with three classes of relations, (1) independent, (2) mutually exclusive, and (3) related but not mutually exclusive. We then showed how the third class of projects, those that are related but not mutually exclusive, could be combined into sets of mutually exclusive projects. This enabled us to limit the discussion to the first two classes, independent and mutually exclusive. Independent projects are considered one at a time. They are either accepted or rejected. Only the best of a set of mutually exclusive projects is chosen.

The present worth method compares projects on the basis of converting all cash flows for the project to a present worth. An independent project is acceptable if its present worth is greater than zero. The mutually exclusive project with the highest present worth should be taken. Projects with unequal lives must be compared by assuming that the projects are repeated or by specifying a study period. Annual worth is similar to present worth, except that the cash flows are converted to a uniform series. The annual worth method may be more meaningful, and also does not require more complicated calculations when the projects have different service lives.

The payback period is a rule-of-thumb method that calculates the length of time it takes to pay back an initial investment. It is inaccurate but very easy to calculate.

Engineering Economics in Action, Part 4B: Doing It Right

Naomi stopped for coffee on her way back from Clem's office. She needed time to think about how to decide which potential forge shop investments were best. She wasn't sure that she knew what "best" meant. She got down her engineering economics text and looked at the table of contents. There were a couple of chapters on comparison methods that seemed to be what she wanted. She sat down with the coffee in her right hand and the text on her lap, and hoped for an uninterrupted hour.

One read through the chapters was enough to remind Naomi of the main relevant ideas that she had learned in school. The first thing she had to do was decide whether the investments were independent or not. They clearly were not independent. It would not make sense to refurbish the current forging hammer and replace it with a mechanical press. Where potential investments were not independent, it was easiest to form mutually exclusive combinations as investment options. Naomi came up with seven options. She ranked the options by first cost, starting with the one with the lowest cost:

1. Refurbish the current machine.

2. Refurbish the current machine plus replace the material-handling equipment.

3. Buy a manually operated mechanical press.

4. Buy a manual mechanical press plus replace the material-handling equipment.

5. Buy an automated mechanical press.

6. Buy an automated mechanical press plus replace the material-handling equipment.

7. Buy an automated mechanical press plus integrate with the material-handling equipment.

At this point, Naomi wasn't sure what to do next. There were different ways of comparing the options.

Naomi wanted a break from thinking about theory. She decided to take a look at Dave Sullivan's diskette. She started up her computer and put in the diskette. One of the files was called "Naomi." In it Dave apologized for dumping the work on her and invited Naomi to call him in Florida if she needed help. Naomi decided to call him. The phone was answered by Dave's wife, Helena. After telling Naomi that her father was out of intensive care and was in good spirits, Helena turned the phone over to Dave.

"Hi, Naomi. How's it going?"

"Well, I'm trying to finish off the forge project that you started. And I'm taking you up on your offer to consult."

"You have my attention. What's the problem?"

"Well, I've gotten started. I have formed seven mutually exclusive combinations of potential investments." Naomi went on to explain her selection of alternatives.

"That sounds right, Naomi. I like the way you've organized that. Now, how are you going to make the choice?"

"I've just reread the present worth, annual worth, and payback period stuff, and of those three, present worth makes the most sense to me. I can just compare the present worths of the cash flows for each alternative, and the one whose present worth is highest is the best one. Annual worth is the same, but I don't see any good reason in this case to look at the costs on an annual basis."

"What about internal rate of return?"

> *"Well, actually, Dave, I haven't reviewed IRR yet. I'll need it, will I?"*
> *"You will. Have a look at it, and also remember that your recommendation is for Burns and Kulkowski. Think about how they will be looking at your information."*
> *"Thanks, Dave. I appreciate your help."*
> *"No problem. This first one is important for you; let's make sure we do it right."*

PROBLEMS

4.1 IQ Computer assembles PC workstations at its plant just outside St. Catharines, Ontario. Their current X-terminal station is nearing the end of its marketing life, and it is time to start production of one or more new products. The data for several candidates are shown below.

	Potential Product			
	A	**B**	**C**	**D**
Research and development costs	$120 000	$60 000	$150 000	$75 000
Lead time	1 year	2 years	1 year	2 years
Resource draw	60%	50%	40%	30%

The maximum budget for research and development is $300 000. A minimum of $200 000 should be spent on these projects. It is desirable to spread out the introduction of new products, so, if two products are to be developed together, they should have different lead times. Resource draw refers to the labour and space that are available to the new products; it cannot exceed 100%.

Based on the above information, determine the set of feasible mutually exclusive alternative projects that IQ Computers should consider.

4.2 The Alabama Alabaster Marble Company (AAM) is considering opening three new quarries. One, designated T, is in Tusksarelooser County; a second, L, is in Lefant County; the third, M, is in Marxbro County. Marble is shipped mainly within a 500 kilometre range of its quarry because of its weight. The market within this range is limited. The returns that AAM can expect from any of the quarries depends on how many quarries AAM opens. Therefore, these potential projects are related.

(a) Construct a set of mutually exclusive alternatives from these three potential projects.

(b) The Lefant County quarry has very rich deposits of marble. This makes the use of mechanized cutter-loaders a reasonable investment at this quarry. Such loaders would not be considered at the other quarries. Construct a set of mutually exclusive alternatives from the set of quarry projects augmented by the potential mechanized cutter-loader project.

(c) AAM has decided to invest no more than $2.5 million in the potential quarries. The first costs are as follows:

Project	First Cost
T quarry	$0.9 million
L quarry	$1.4 million
M quarry	$1.0 million
Cutter-loader	$0.4 million

Construct a set of mutually exclusive alternatives that are feasible, given the investment limitation.

4.3 Chatham Automotive has $100 000 to invest in internal projects. The choices are:

Project	Cost
1. Line improvements	$20 000
2. New manual tester	30 000
3. New automatic tester	60 000
4. Overhauling press	50 000

Only one tester will be bought and the press will not need overhauling if the line improvements are not made. What mutually exclusive project combinations are available?

4.4 The intersection of King and Main Streets needs widening and improvement. The possibilities include:

1. Widening King

2. Widening Main

3. Left turn lane on King

4. Left turn lane on Main

5. Stoplights

6. Stoplights with advanced green for Main

7. Stoplights with advanced green for King

A left turn lane can be installed only if the street in question is widened. Left turn lanes are necessary on each street that has stoplights installed with an advanced green. The city cannot afford to widen both streets. How many mutually exclusive projects are there?

4.5 Nabil is considering buying a house while he is at university. The house costs $100 000 today. Renting out part of the house and living in the rest over his five years at school will net, after expenses, $1000 per month. He estimates that he will sell the house after five years for $105 000. If Nabil's MARR is 18%, compounded monthly, should he buy the house?

4.6 A software genius is selling the rights to a new video game he has just developed. Two companies have offered him contracts. The first contract offers $10 000 at the end of each year for the next five years, and then $20 000 per year for the following 10 years. The second offers ten payments, starting with $10 000 at the end of the first year, $13 000 at the end of the second, and so forth, increasing by $3000 each year (i.e., the tenth payment is $10 000 + 9 × $3000). Assume the genius uses a MARR of 9%. Which contract should the genius choose? Use a present worth comparison.

4.7 Sam is considering buying a new lawnmower. He has a choice between a "Lawn Guy" mower or a Bargain Joe's "Clip Job" mower. Sam has a MARR of 5%. The salvage value of each mower at the end of its service life is zero.

	Lawn Guy	Clip Job
First cost	$350	$120
Life	10 years	4 years
Annual gas	$60	$40
Annual maintenance	$30	$60

(a) Determine which alternative is preferable. Use a present worth comparison and the least common multiple of the service lives.

(b) For a four-year study period, what salvage value for the Lawn Guy mower would result in its being the preferred choice? What salvage value for the Lawn Guy would result in the Clip Job being the preferred choice?

4.8 Water supply for an irrigation system can be obtained from a stream in some nearby mountains. Two alternatives are being considered, both of which have essentially infinite lives, provided proper maintenance is performed. The first is a concrete reservoir with a steel pipe system and the second is an earthen dam with a wooden aqueduct. Below are the costs associated with each.

	Concrete reservoir	Earthen dam
First cost	$500 000	$200 000
Annual maintenance costs	2 000	12 000
Replacing the wood portion of the aqueduct each 15 years	N/A	100 000

Compare the present worths of the two alternatives, using an interest rate of 8%. Which alternative should be chosen?

4.9 PCB Electronix needs to expand its capacity. It has two feasible alternatives under consideration. Both alternatives will have essentially infinite lives.

Alternative 1: Construct a new building of 200 000 square feet now. The first cost will be $2 000 000. Annual maintenance costs will be $10 000. In addition, the building will need to be painted every 15 years (starting in 15 years) at a cost of $15 000.

Alternative 2: Construct a new building of 125 000 square feet now and an additional 75 000 square feet in 10 years. The first cost of the 125 000 square foot building will be $1 250 000. The annual maintenance costs will be $5000 for the first 10 years (that is, until the addition is built). The 75 000 square foot addition will have a first cost of $1 000 000. Annual maintenance costs of the renovated building (the original building and the addition) will be $11 000. The renovated building will cost $15 000 to repaint every 15 years (starting 15 years after the addition is done).

Carry out an annual worth comparison of the two alternatives. Which is preferred if the MARR is 15%?

4.10 Westmount Waxworks is considering buying a new wax melter for their line of replicas of statues of government leaders. They have two choices of supplier, Finedetail and Simplicity. Their proposals are as follows:

	Finedetail	Simplicity
Expected life	7 years	10 years
First cost	$200 000	$350 000
Maintenance	$10 000/year + $0.05/unit	$20 000/year + $0.01/unit
Labour	$1.25/unit	$0.50/unit
Other costs	$6500/year + $0.95/unit	$15 500/year + $0.55/unit
Salvage value	$5000	$20 000

Management thinks they will sell about 30 000 replicas per year if there is stability in world governments. If the world becomes very unsettled so that there are frequent overturns of governments, sales may be as high as 200 000 units a year. Westmount Waxworks uses a MARR of 15% for equipment projects.

(a) Who is the preferred supplier if sales are 30 000 units per year? Use an annual worth comparison.

(b) Who is the preferred supplier if sales are 200 000 units per year? Use an annual worth comparison.

(c) How sensitive is the choice of supplier to sales levels? Experiment with sales levels between 30 000 and 200 000 units per year. At what sales level will the costs of the two melters be equal?

4.11 The City of Inuvik is installing a new swimming pool in the downtown recreation centre. There are two designs under consideration, both of which are to be permanent (i.e., lasting forever). The first design is for a reinforced concrete pool which has a first cost of $1 500 000. Every 10 years the inner surface of the pool would have to be refinished and painted at a cost of $200 000.

The second design consists of a metal frame and a plastic liner, which would have an initial cost of $500 000. For this alternative, the plastic liner must be replaced every five years at a cost of $100 000, and every 15 years the metal frame would need replacement at a cost of $150 000. Extra insurance of $5000 per year is required for the plastic liner (to cover repair costs if the liner leaks). The city's cost of long-term funds is 5%.

Determine which swimming pool design has the lower present cost.

4.12 Sam is buying a refrigerator. He has two choices. A used one, at $475, should last him about three years. A new one, at $1250, would likely last eight years. Both have a scrap value of $0. The interest rate is 8%.

(a) Which refrigerator has lower cost? (Use a present worth analysis with repeated lives. Assume operating costs are the same.)

(b) If Sam knew that he could resell the new refrigerator after three years for $1000, would this change the answer? (Use a present worth analysis with a three-year study period. Assume operating costs are the same.)

4.13 Val is considering purchasing a display panel to allow her to project her notebook computer through an overhead projector. One model, the XJ3, costs $4500 new, while another, the Y19, sells for $3200. Val figures that the XJ3 will last about three years, at which point it could be sold for $1000, while the Y19 will last for only two years and will also be sold for $1000. Both panels give similar service, except that the Y19 is not suitable for client presentations. If she buys the Y19, about four times a year she will have to rent one similar to the XJ3, at a total year-end cost of about $300. Using present worth and the least common multiple of the service lives, determine which display panel Val should buy. Val's MARR is 10%.

4.14 For problem 4.13, Val has determined that the salvage value of the XJ3 after two years of service is $1900. Which display panel is the better choice, based on present worth with a two-year study period?

4.15 Sam is considering buying a $24 000 car. After five years, he will be able to sell the car for $8000. Gas costs will be $2000 per year, insurance $600 per year, and parking $600 per year, and maintenance costs for the first year are $1000, rising by $400 per year thereafter.

The alternative is for Sam to take taxis everywhere. This will cost an estimated $6000 per year. Sam will rent a car each year at a total cost (to year-end) of $600 for the family vacation, if he has no car. If Sam values money at 11% annual interest, should he buy the car? Use an annual worth comparison method.

4.16 A new gizmo costs $10 000. Maintenance costs $2000 per year, and labour savings are $6567 per year. What is its payback period?

4.17 The Biltmore Garage has lights in places that are difficult to reach. Management estimates that it costs about $2 to change a bulb. Standard 100 watt bulbs are now used. These have an expected life of 1000 hours. Standard bulbs cost $1. A long-life bulb that requires 90 watts for the same effective level of light is available. Long-life bulbs cost $3. The bulbs that are difficult to reach are in use for about 500 hours a month. Electricity costs $0.08/kilowatt-hour payable at the end of each month. Biltmore uses a 12% MARR (1% per month) for projects involving supplies.

(a) What minimum life for the long-life bulb would make its cost lower?

(b) If the cost of changing bulbs is ignored, what is the minimum life for the long-life bulb for them to have lower cost?

(c) If the solutions are obtained by linear interpolation of the capital recovery factor, will the approximations understate or overstate the required life?

4.18 A chemical recovery system costs $30 000 and saves $5280 each year of its seven-year life. The salvage value is estimated at $7500. The MARR is 9%. What is the net annual benefit or cost of purchasing the chemical recovery system? Use the capital recovery formula.

4.19 Savings of $5600 per year can be achieved through either a $14 000 machine (A) with a seven-year service life and a $2000 salvage value, or a $25 000 machine (B) with a ten-year service life and a $10 000 salvage value. If the MARR is 9%, which machine is a better choice, and for what annual benefit or cost? Use annual worth and the capital recovery formula.

4.20 **(a)** Ridgely Custom Metal Products (RCMP) must purchase a new tube bender. There are two models:

Model	First Cost	Economic Life	Yearly Net Savings	Salvage Value
T	$100 000	5 years	$50 000	$20 000
A	150 000	5 years	60 000	30 000

RCMP's MARR is 11%. Using the *present worth* method, which tube bender should they buy?

(b) RCMP has discovered a third alternative, which has been added to the table below:

Model	First Cost	Economic Life	Yearly Net Savings	Salvage Value
T	$100 000	5 years	$50 000	$ 20 000
A	150 000	5 years	60 000	30 000
X	200 000	3 years	75 000	100 000

Now which tube bender should they buy?

4.21 RCMP [see Problem 4.20 (b)] can forecast demand for its products for only three years in advance. The salvage value after three years is $40 000 for model T and $80 000 for model A. Using the *study period* method, which of the three alternatives is best?

4.22 Using the *annual worth* method, which of the three tube benders should RCMP buy? The MARR is 11%. Use the data from Problem 4.20 (b).

4.23 What is the payback period for each of the three alternatives from the RCMP problem? Use the data from Problem 4.20 (b).

4.24 Data for two independent investment opportunities are shown below.

	Machine A	Machine B
Initial cost	$15 000	$20 000
Revenues (annual)	$ 9 000	$11 000
Costs (annual)	$ 6 000	$ 8 000
Scrap value	$ 1 000	$ 2 000
Service life	5 years	10 years

(a) For a MARR of 8%, should either, both, or neither machine be purchased? Use the annual worth method.

(b) For a MARR of 8%, should either, both, or neither machine be purchased? Use the present worth method.

(c) What are the payback periods for these machines? Should either, both, or neither machine be purchased, based on the payback periods? The required payback period for investments of this type is three years.

4.25 Xaviera is comparing two mutually exclusive projects, A and B, that have the same initial investment and the same present worth over their service lives. Wolfgang points out that, using the annual worth method, A is clearly better than B. What can be said about the service lives for the two projects?

4.26 Two plans have been proposed for accumulating money for capital projects at Thunder Bay Lighting. One idea is to put aside $10 000 per year, independent of growth. The second is to start with a smaller amount, $8000 per year, but increase this in proportion to the expected company growth. The money will accumulate interest at 10%, and the company is expected to grow about 5% per year. Which plan will accumulate more money in 10 years?

4.27 Crystal City Environmental Services is evaluating two alternative methods of disposing of municipal waste. The first involves developing a landfill site near the city. Costs of the site include $1 000 000 start-up costs, $100 000 close-down costs 30 years from now, and operating costs of $20 000 per year. Starting in 10 years, it is expected that there will be revenues from user fees of $30 000 per year. The alternative is to ship the waste out of the province. A United States firm will agree to a long-term contract to dispose of the waste for $130 000 per year. Using the *annual worth* method, which alternative is economically preferred for a MARR of 11%? Would this likely be the actual preferred choice?

4.28 Peterborough Auto Parts is considering investing in a new forming line for their grille assemblies. For a five-year study period, the cash flows for two separate designs are shown below. Create a spreadsheet which will calculate the present worths for each project for a variable MARR. Through trial and error, establish the MARR at which the present worths of the two projects are exactly the same.

| Cash Flows for Grille Assembly Project ($) | | | | | | |
| Year | Automated Line | | | Manual Line | | |
	Disburse-ments	Receipts	Net Cash Flow	Disburse-ments	Receipts	Net Cash Flow
0	$1 500 000	$ 0	– $1 500 000	$1 000 000	$ 0	– $1 000 000
1	50 000	300 000	250 000	20 000	200 000	180 000
2	60 000	300 000	240 000	25 000	200 000	175 000
3	70 000	300 000	230 000	30 000	200 000	170 000
4	80 000	300 000	220 000	35 000	200 000	165 000
5	90 000	800 000	710 000	40 000	200 000	160 000

4.29 Derek has two choices for a heat-loss prevention system for the shipping doors at Kirkland Manufacturing. He can isolate the shipping department from the rest of the plant, or he can curtain off each shipping door separately. Isolation consists of building a permanent wall around the shipping area. It will cost $60 000 and will save $10 000 in heating costs per year. Plastic curtains around each shipping door will have a total cost of about $5000, but will have to be replaced about once every two years. Savings in heating costs for installing the curtains will be about $3000 per year. Use the payback period method to determine which alternative is better. Comment on the use of the payback period for making this decision.

4.30 Assuming that the wall built to isolate the shipping department in prolem 4.29 will last forever, and that the curtains have zero salvage value, compare the annual worths of the two alternatives. The MARR for Kirkland Manufacturing is 11%. Which alternative is better?

APPENDIX 4A: The MARR and the Cost of Capital

For a business to survive, it must be able to earn a high enough return to induce investors to put money into the company. The rate of return required to get investors to invest in a business is that business's **cost of capital**. A company's cost of capital is its minimum acceptable rate of return for projects, its MARR. This appendix reviews how the cost of capital is determined. We first look at the relation between risk and the cost of capital. Next, we discuss sources of capital for large businesses and small businesses.

4A.1 Risk and the Cost of Capital

There are two main forms of investment in a company, *debt* and *equity*. Investors in a company's debt are lending money to the company. The loans are contracts that give lenders rights to repayment of their loans, and to interest at predetermined interest rates. Investors in a company's equity are the owners of the company. They hold rights to the residual after all contractual payments, including those to lenders, are made.

Investing in equity is more risky than investing in debt. Equity owners are paid only if the company first meets its contractual obligations to lenders. This higher risk means that equity owners require an expectation of a greater return on average than the interest rate paid to debt holders. Consider a simple case in which a company has three possible performance levels — weak results, normal results, and strong results. Investors do not know which level will actually occur. Each level is equally probable. To keep the example simple, we assume that all after-tax income is paid to equity holders as dividends so that there is no growth. The data are shown in Table 4A.1.

TABLE 4A.1

	Possible Performance Levels		
	Weak Results	Normal Results	Strong Results
Net operating income ($/year)[1]	40 000	100 000	160 000
Interest payment ($/year)	10 000	10 000	10 000
Net income before tax ($/year)	30 000	90 000	150 000
Tax at 40% ($/year)	12 000	36 000	60 000
After-tax income = Dividends ($/year)	18 000	54 000	90 000
Debt ($)	100 000		
Value of shares ($)	327 273		

[1] Net operating income per year is revenue per year minus cost per year.

We see that, no matter what happens, lenders will get a return of 10%:

$$\left(0.1 = \frac{10\ 000}{100\ 000}\right)$$

Owners get one of three possible returns:

$$5.5\%\ \left(0.055 = \frac{18\ 000}{327\ 273}\right),$$

$$16.5\%\ \left(0.165 = \frac{54\ 000}{327\ 273}\right),\ \text{or}$$

$$27.5\%\ \left(0.275 = \frac{90\ 000}{327\ 273}\right)$$

These three possibilities average out to 16.5%. If things are good, owners do better than lenders. If things are bad, owners do worse. But their average return is greater than returns to lenders.

The lower rate of return to lenders means that companies would like to get their capital with debt. However, reliance on debt is limited for two reasons.

1. If a company increases the share of capital from debt, it increases the chance that it will not be able to meet the contractual obligations to lenders. This means the company will be bankrupt. Bankruptcy may lead to reorganizing the company or possibly closing the company. In either case, bankruptcy costs may be high.

2. Lenders are aware of the dangers of high reliance on debt and will, therefore, limit the amount they lend to the company.

4A.2 Company Size and Sources of Capital

Large well-known companies, like Dofasco or Molson Breweries, can secure capital both by borrowing and by selling ownership shares. Large companies will seek ratios of debt to equity that balance the marginal advantages and disadvantages of debt financing. Their being well-known means that there will be ready markets for their shares as well as any debt instruments, like bonds, they may issue. Well-known companies can raise additional capital in their desired proportions of debt and equity. Or they can reduce their capital by repaying loans and buying back shares while keeping debt and equity at their desired proportions.

The cost of capital for large well-known companies is a weighted average of the costs of borrowing and of selling shares. The weights are the fractions of total capital that come from the different sources. The cost of capital is called the **weighted average cost of capital**. If market conditions do not change, a large company that seeks to raise a moderate amount of additional capital can do so at a stable cost of capital. This cost of capital is that company's MARR. We can compute the after-tax cost of capital for the example shown in Table 4A.1.

Weighted average cost of capital

$$= 0.1\left(\frac{100\ 000}{427\ 273}\right) + 0.165\left(\frac{327\ 273}{427\ 273}\right) = 0.150$$

This company has a cost of capital of about 15%.

The cost of capital for small companies will be greater than for large well-known companies. As well, the cost will depend on the amounts small companies seek to raise. Most investors in large companies will not be willing to invest in unknown small companies. At start-up, a small company may rely entirely on the capital of the owners and their friends and relatives. Here the cost of capital is the opportunity cost for the investors. The only alternative available to the owners may be bank deposits or publicly traded securities. This cost will be moderate.

If a new company seeks to grow more rapidly than the owners' investment plus cash flow permits, more funds will be needed. The next source of capital with the lowest cost is usually a bank loan. Bank loans will be limited because banks are usually not willing to lend more than some fraction of the amount an owner puts into a business. If a small company needs more capital than is available from the owners or from bank loans, the company will have to sell new shares of the company.

There are two major sources of new equity investments for small companies. One of these sources is venture capitalists. Venture capitalists are investors who specialize in investing in new companies. The cost of evaluating new companies is usually high. The risk of investing in them is also high. Together, these factors usually lead venture capitalists to want to put enough money into a small company to enable the venture capitalist to control the company.

The second source of additional equity capital for small companies is selling shares through stock exchanges, like the Vancouver Stock Exchange or the Alberta Stock Exchange. These exchanges specialize in small, speculative companies. In either case, new equity investment is usually very expensive. Studies have shown that venture capitalists typically require the expectation of at least a 35% rate of return after tax. Raising funds on a stock exchange is usually even more expensive than getting funding from a venture capitalist.

CHAPTER

5

Comparison Methods Part 2

Engineering Economics in Action, Part 5A: What's Best? Revisited

5.1   Introduction

5.2   The Internal Rate of Return

5.3   Internal Rate of Return Comparisons

      5.3.1   IRR for Independent Projects

      5.3.2   IRR for Mutually Exclusive Projects

      5.3.3   Multiple IRRs

      5.3.4   External Rate of Return Methods

      5.3.5   When to Use the ERR

5.4   Rate of Return and Present/Annual Worth Methods Compared

      5.4.1   Equivalence of Rate of Return and Present/Annual Worth Methods

      5.4.2   Why Choose One Method over the Other?

Canadian Corporate Case 5.1: Air Canada Supply and Stores

Review Problems

Summary

Engineering Economics in Action, Part 5B: The Invisible Hand

Problems

Appendix 5A: Tests for Multiple IRRs

Engineering Economics in Action, Part 5A: What's Best? Revisited

C*lem had said, "I have to make a recommendation to Ed Burns and Anna Kulkowski for their Wednesday meeting on this forging hammer in the South Shop. I'd like you to handle it." Dave Sullivan, who had started the project, had gone to Florida to see his sick father-in-law. Naomi welcomed the opportunity, but she still had to figure out exactly what to recommend.*

Naomi looked carefully at the list of seven mutually exclusive alternatives for replacing or refurbishing the machine. Present worth could tell her which of the seven was "best," but present worth was just one of several comparison methods. Which of the comparison methods was best for choosing which of the alternatives was best?

Dave would help more, if she asked him. In fact, he could no doubt tell her exactly what to do, if she wanted. But this one she knew she could handle, and it was a matter of pride to do it herself. Opening her engineering economics textbook, she read on.

5.1 Introduction

In Chapter 4, we showed how to structure projects so that they were either independent or mutually exclusive. The present worth, annual worth, and payback period methods for evaluating projects were also introduced. This chapter continues on the theme of comparing projects by presenting a commonly used but somewhat more complicated comparison method called the *internal rate of return*, or IRR.

Although the IRR method is widely used, all of the comparison methods have value in particular circumstances. Selecting the method to use is also covered in this chapter. It is also shown that the present worth, annual worth, and IRR methods all result in the same recommendations for the same problem. We close this chapter with a chart summarizing the strengths and weaknesses of the four comparison methods presented in Chapters 4 and 5.

5.2 The Internal Rate of Return

Investments are undertaken with the expectation of a return in the form of future earnings. One way to measure the return from an investment is as a rate of return per dollar invested, or in other words as an interest rate. The rate of return usually calculated for a project is known as the *internal rate of return (IRR)*. The adjective "internal" refers to the fact that the internal rate of return depends only on the cash flows due to the investment. The internal rate of return is that interest rate at which a project just breaks even. The meaning of the IRR is most easily seen with a simple example.

EXAMPLE 5.1

Suppose $100 is invested today in a project that returns $110 in one year. We can calculate the IRR by finding the interest rate at which $100 now is equivalent to $110 at the end of one year:

$$P = F(P/F, i^*, 1)$$

$$\$100 = \$110(P/F, i^*, 1)$$

$$\$100 = \frac{\$110}{1 + i^*}$$

where i^* is the internal rate of return.

Solving this equation gives a rate of return of 10%. In a simple example like this, the process of finding an internal rate of return is finding the interest rate that makes the present worth of benefits equal to the first cost. This interest rate is the IRR.

Of course, cash flows associated with a project will usually be more complicated than in the example above. A more formal definition of the IRR is: The **internal rate of return (IRR)** on an investment is that interest rate, i^*, such that, when all cash flows associated with the project are discounted at i^*, the present worth of the cash inflows equals the present worth of the cash outflows. That is, the project just breaks even. An equation that expresses this is

$$\sum_{t=0}^{T} (R_t - D_t)(1 + i^*)^{-t} = 0 \tag{5.1}$$

where

R_t = the cash inflow (receipts) in period t
D_t = the cash outflow (disbursements) in period t
T = the number of time periods
i^* = the internal rate of return

Since Equation (5.1) can also be expressed as

$$\sum_{t=0}^{T} R_t(1 + i^*)^{-t} = \sum_{t=0}^{T} D_t(1 + i^*)^{-t}$$

it can be seen that, in order to calculate the IRR, one sets the disbursements equal to the receipts and solves for the unknown interest rate. For this to be done, the disbursements and receipts must be comparable, as a present worth, a uniform series, or a future worth. That is, use

PW(disbursements) = PW(receipts) and solve for the unknown i^*,

AW(disbursements) = AW(receipts) and solve for the unknown i^*, or

FW(disbursements) = FW(receipts) and solve for the unknown i^*.

The IRR is usually positive, but can be negative as well. A negative IRR means that the project is losing money rather than earning it.

To avoid complex calculations, we usually solve the equations for the IRR by means of trial and error. A spreadsheet provides a quick way to perform a trial and error calculation; most spreadsheet programs also include a built-in IRR function.

EXAMPLE 5.2

Clem is considering buying a tuxedo. It would cost $500, but would save him $160 per year in rental charges over its five-year life. What is the IRR for this investment?

As illustrated in Figure 5.1, Clem's initial cash outflow for the purchase would be $500. This is an up-front outlay relative to continuing to rent tuxedos. The investment would create a saving of $160 per year over the five-year life of the tuxedo. These savings can be viewed as a series of receipts relative to rentals. The IRR of Clem's investment can

FIGURE 5.1   Clem's Tuxedo

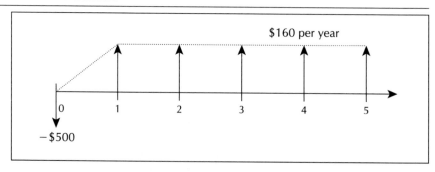

be found by determining what interest rate makes the present worth of the disbursements equal to the present worth of the cash inflows.

Present worth of disbursements = $500

Present worth of receipts   = $160(P/A, i*, 5)

Setting the two equal,

$$\$500 = \$160(P/A, i^*, 5)$$
$$(P/A, i^*, 5) = \$500/\$160$$
$$= 3.125$$

From the interest rate tables, we find that

$$(P/A, 15\%, 5) = 3.3521$$
$$(P/A, 20\%, 5) = 2.9906$$

Interpolating between (P/A, 15%, 5) and (P/A, 20%, 5) gives

$$i^* = 15\% + (5\%)[(3.125 - 3.3521)/(2.9906 - 3.3521)]$$
$$= 18.14\%$$

An alternative way to get the IRR for this problem is to convert all cash outflows and inflows to equivalent annuities over the five-year period. This will yield the same result as when present worth was used.

Annuity equivalent to the disbursements = $500(A/P, i*, 5)

Annuity equivalent to the receipts = $160

Again, setting the two equal,

$$\$500(A/P, i^*, 5) = \$160$$
$$(A/P, i^*, 5) = \$160/\$500$$
$$= 0.32$$

From the interest rate tables,

$$(A/P, 15\%, 5) = 0.29832$$
$$(A/P, 20\%, 5) = 0.33438$$

An interpolation gives

$$i^* = 15\% + 5\%[(0.32 - 0.29832)/(0.33438 - 0.29832)]$$

$$= 18.01\%$$

$$i^* \cong 18.0\%$$

Note that there is a slight difference in the answers, depending on whether the disbursements and receipts were compared as present worths or as annuities. This difference is due to the small error induced by the linear interpolation.

5.3 Internal Rate of Return Comparisons

In this section, we show how the internal rate of return can be used to decide whether or not a project should be accepted. We first show how to use the IRR to evaluate independent projects. Then we show how to use the IRR to decide which of a group of mutually exclusive alternatives to accept. We then show that it is possible for a project to have more than one IRR. Finally, we show how to handle this difficulty by using an *external rate of return*.

5.3.1 IRR for Independent Projects

For independent projects, the basic principle is to invest in any project that has an IRR equal to or exceeding the MARR. Note that projects with IRR = MARR have a marginally acceptable rate of return (by definition of the MARR).

EXAMPLE 5.3

The High Society Baked Bean Co. is considering a new canner. The canner costs $120 000, and will have a scrap value of $5000 after its 10-year life. Given expected increases in sales, the total savings due to the new canner, compared with continuing with the current operation, will be $15 000 the first year, increasing by $5000 each year thereafter. Total extra costs due to the more complex equipment will be $10 000 per year. The MARR for High Society is 12%. Should they invest in the new canner?

The cash inflows and outflows for this problem are summarized in Figure 5.2. We need to compute the internal rate of return in order to decide if High Society should buy the canner. There are several ways we can do this. In this problem, equating annual outflows and receipts appears to be the easiest approach, because most of the cash flows are already stated on a yearly basis.

$$\$5000(A/F, i^*, 10) + \$15\,000 + \$5000(A/G, i^*, 10)$$
$$- \$120\,000(A/P, i^*, 10) - \$10\,000 = 0$$

FIGURE 5.2   High Society Baked Bean Canner

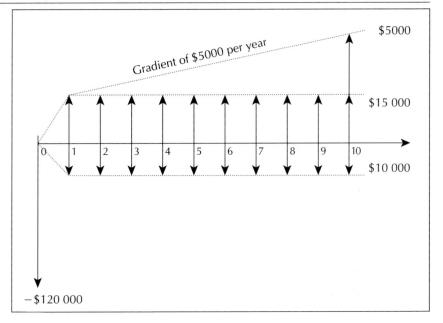

Dividing by 5000,

$$(A/F, i^*, 10) + 1 + (A/G, i^*, 10) - 24(A/P, i^*, 10) = 0$$

The IRR can be found by trial and error alone, by trial and error and linear interpolation, or by a spreadsheet IRR function. A trial and error process is particularly easy using a spreadsheet, so this is often the best approach. A good starting point for the trial and error process is at zero interest. A graph derived from the spreadsheet shown in Figure 5.3 indicates that the IRR is between 13% and 14%. This may be good enough for a decision, since it exceeds the MARR of 12%.

If finer precision is required, there are two ways to proceed. One way is to use a finer grid, for example, one that covers 13% to 14%. The other way is to interpolate between 13% and 14%. We shall first use the interest rate factors from the tables to show that the IRR is indeed between 13% and 14%. Next we shall interpolate between 13% and 14%.

First, at $i = 13\%$

$$0.05429 + 1 + 3.5161 - 24(0.18429) = 0.1474$$

The result is a bit too high. A higher interest rate will reduce the annual worth of the benefits more than the annual worth of the costs, since the benefits are spread over the life of the project while most of the costs are early in the life of the project.

FIGURE 5.3   **Estimating the IRR for Example 5.3**

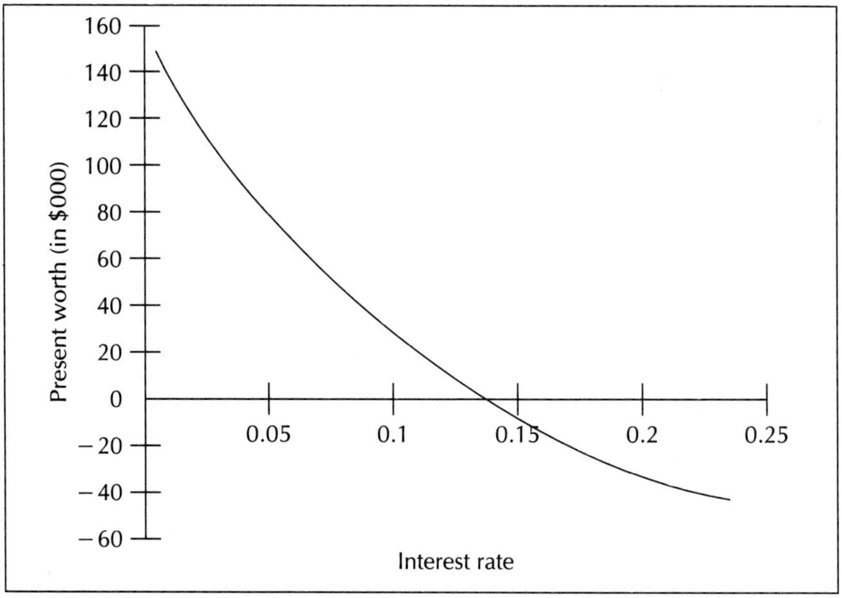

At $i = 14\%$

$$0.05171 + 1 + 3.4489 - 24(0.19171) = -0.1004$$

This confirms that the IRR of the investment is between 13% and 14%. A good approximation to the IRR can be found by linearly interpolating:

$$i^* = 13\% + (-0.1474)/(-0.1004 - 0.1474)$$

$$\cong 13.6\%$$

The IRR for the investment is approximately 13.6%. Since this is greater than the MARR of 12%, the company should buy the new canner. Note again that it was not actually necessary to determine where in the range of 13% to 14% the IRR fell. It was enough to demonstrate that it was 12% or more.

In summary, if there are several independent projects, the IRR for each is calculated separately, and those having an IRR equalling or exceeding the MARR should be chosen.

5.3.2 IRR for Mutually Exclusive Projects

Choice among mutually exclusive projects using the IRR is a bit more involved. Some insight into the complicating factors can be obtained with an example that involves two mutually exclusive alternatives.

EXAMPLE 5.4

Monster Meats can buy a new meat slicer system for $50 000 that they estimate will save them $11 000 per year in labour and operating costs. The same system with an automatic loader is $68 000, and will save approximately $14 000 per year. The life of either system is thought to be eight years. Monster Meats has three feasible alternatives:

Alternative	First Cost	Annual Savings
"Do nothing"	$ 0	$ 0
Meat slicer alone	50 000	11 000
Meat slicer with automatic loader	68 000	14 000

Monster Meats uses a MARR of 12% for this type of project. Which alternative is better?

We first consider the system without the loader. Its IRR is 14.5%, which exceeds the MARR of 12%. This can be seen by solving for i in

$$- \$50\ 000 + \$11\ 000(P/A, i^*, 8) = 0$$

$$(P/A, i^*, 8) = \$50\ 000/\$11\ 000$$

$$(P/A, i^*, 8) = 4.545$$

From the interest rate tables, or by trial and error with a spreadsheet,

$$(P/A, 14\%, 8) = 4.6388$$

$$(P/A, 15\%, 8) = 4.4873$$

By interpolation or further trial and error,

$$i^* \cong 14.5\%$$

The slicer alone is thus economically justified.

We now consider the system with the slicer and loader. Its IRR is 12.5%, which may be seen by solving for i in

$$- \$68\ 000 + \$14\ 000(P/A, i^*, 8) = 0$$

$$(P/A, i^*, 8) = \$68\ 000/\$14\ 000$$

$$(P/A, i^*, 8) = 4.857$$

$$(P/A, 12\%, 8) = 4.9676$$

$$(P/A, 13\%, 8) = 4.7987$$

$$i^* \cong 12.5\%$$

The IRR of the meat slicer and automatic loader is about 12.5%, which on the surface appears to meet the 12% MARR requirement. But, on the incremental investment, Monster Meats would be earning only 7%. This may be seen by looking at the IRR on the *extra*, or *incremental*, $18 000 spent on the loader.

$$- (\$68\ 000 - \$50\ 000) + (\$14\ 000 - \$11\ 000)(P/A, i^*, 8) = 0$$
$$- \$18\ 000 + \$3000(P/A, i^*, 8) = 0$$
$$(P/A, i^*, 8) = \$18\ 000/\$3000$$
$$(P/A, i^*, 8) = 6$$
$$i^* \cong 7\%$$

This is less than the MARR; therefore, Monster Meats should not buy the automated loader.

When the IRR was calculated for the system including the loader, the surplus return on investment earned by the slicer alone essentially subsidized the loader. The slicer investment made enough of a return so that, even when it was coupled with the money-losing loader, the whole machine still seemed to be a good buy. In fact, the extra $18 000 would be better spent on some other project at the MARR or higher. The relation between the potential projects is shown in Figure 5.4.

The fundamental principle illustrated here is that, to use the IRR to compare two mutually exclusive alternatives properly, not only must both of the alternatives exceed the MARR, but also the *incremental* investment is relevant. When there are more than two alternatives, it is necessary to have a systematic means of determining which pairs of comparisons to make. A diagram showing the procedure is given in Figure 5.5.

The first step in the process is to order the alternatives from the smallest first cost to the largest first cost. Start with the alternative with the smallest first cost. If one of the alternatives *must* be selected, then the one with the smallest first cost becomes what is referred to as the *current best alternative* (denoted by an A in Figure 5.5).

FIGURE 5.4   Monster Meats

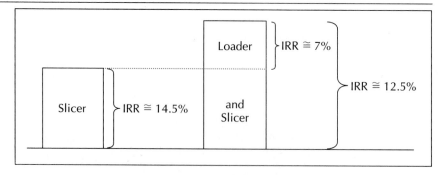

FIGURE 5.5   Flowchart for Comparing Mutually Exclusive Alternatives

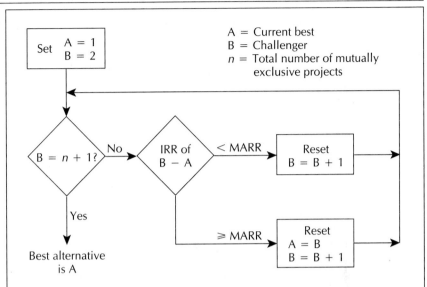

If, on the other hand, it is *not* necessary to select an alternative, then check to see if the IRR for the alternative with the smallest first cost exceeds the MARR. If this alternative *does* exceed the MARR, it is acceptable and becomes the current best alternative. If the alternative with the lowest first cost is not acceptable, exclude it from further consideration and move on to evaluate the IRR of the alternative with the second lowest first cost. As before, if this alternative is acceptable, it becomes the current best. If it is not acceptable, it is excluded from further consideration. The search for an acceptable alternative continues until either an acceptable alternative is found or all alternatives have been put aside because their IRRs are less than the MARR. If there is an acceptable alternative, it becomes the current best alternative, A. If there is no acceptable alternative, the process ends, and none of the projects should be implemented.

The alternatives that remain in the analysis will be the current best, A, as well as the alternatives with first costs higher than A's. Assume that *n* projects remain and that they are ranked from 1 (the current best) to *n*, in increasing order of first costs. The analysis now moves to looking at the IRR of the incremental investments of alternatives that have a higher first cost than A. The current best is "challenged" by the project ranked second. One of two things occurs:

1. The incremental investment to implement the challenger does not have an IRR at least equal to the MARR. In this case, the challenger is excluded from further consideration and the current best is challenged by the investment that is ranked third.

2. The incremental investment to implement the challenger has an IRR at least as high as the MARR. In this case, the challenger replaces the current best. It then is challenged by the alternative ranked third.

The process then continues with the next alternative challenging the current best until all alternatives have been compared. In Figure 5.5, this is indicated by showing B = n + 1, implying that the process is complete because there are then no more challengers to the current best alternative. The current best alternative remaining at the end of the process is then selected.

In the next section, the issue of multiple IRRs is discussed, and methods for identifying and eliminating them are given. Note that the process described in Figure 5.5 requires that a single IRR (or ERR, as discussed later) be determined for each incremental investment. If there are multiple IRRs, they must be eliminated at *each* increment of investment.

EXAMPLE 5.5 (Reprise of Example 4.4)

Fly-by-Night Aircraft must purchase a new lathe. It is considering one of four new lathes, each of which has a life of 10 years with no scrap value:

Lathe	1	2	3	4
First cost	$100 000	$150 000	$200 000	$255 000
Annual savings	25 000	34 000	46 000	55 000

Given a MARR of 15%, which alternative should be chosen?

The alternatives have already been ordered from lathe 1, which has the smallest first cost, to lathe 4, which has the greatest first cost. Next is the search for the initial current best alternative. This begins by calculating the IRR for alternative 1. The interest rate at which the present worth of the first cost is equal to the present worth of the savings is calculated as follows:

$100 000 = $25 000(P/A, i^*, 10)$

$(P/A, i^*, 10) = 4$

An approximate IRR is obtained by trial and error with a spreadsheet.

$i^* \cong 21.4\%$

Since the IRR of lathe 1 exceeds the MARR, alternative 1 is acceptable and, therefore, becomes the current best alternative, A. The current best alternative and the remaining alternatives with higher first costs are then retained for the "challenger" analysis. The first challenger, lathe 2, has the next highest first cost compared with the current best. The next step is to see if the incremental investment from lathe 1 to lathe 2 is justified. This is done by finding the IRR on the incremental investment:

[$150 000 − $100 000] − [$34 000 − $25 000]$(P/A, i^*, 10)$ = 0,
or [$150 000 − $34 000$(P/A, i^*, 10)$] − [$100 000 − $25 000$
$(P/A, i^*, 10)$] = 0

$(P/A, i^*, 10)$ = $50 000/$9000 = 5.556

An approximate IRR is obtained by trial and error.

$i^* \cong 12.4\%$

Since the IRR of the incremental investment falls below the MARR, lathe 2 fails the challenge to become the current best alternative. The reader can verify that lathe 2 alone has an IRR of approximately 18.7%. Even so, lathe 2 is not considered a viable alternative. In other words, the incremental investment of $50 000 could be put to better use elsewhere. Lathe 1 remains the current best, A, and the next challenger is lathe 3.

As before, the incremental IRR is the interest rate at which the present worth of lathe 3 less the present worth of lathe 1 is 0:

[$200 000 − $46 000$(P/A, i^*, 10)$] − [$100 000 − $25 000$
$(P/A, i^*, 10)$] = 0

$(P/A, i^*, 10)$ = $100 000/$21 000 = 4.762

An approximate IRR is obtained by trial and error.

$i^* \cong 16.4\%$

The IRR on the incremental investment exceeds the MARR, and therefore lathe 3 is preferred to lathe 1. Lathe 3 now becomes the current best. The new challenger is lathe 4. The IRR on the incremental investment is

[$255 000 − $55 000$(P/A, i^*, 10)$] − [$200 000 − $46 000$
$(P/A, i^*, 10)$] = 0

$(P/A, i^*, 10)$ = $55 000/$9000 = 6.11

$i^* \cong 10.1\%$

The additional investment from lathe 3 to lathe 4 is not justified. The reader can verify that the IRR of lathe 4 alone is about 17%. Once again, we have a challenger with an IRR greater than the MARR, but it fails as a challenger because the incremental investment from the current best does not have an IRR at least equal to the MARR. The current best remains lathe 3. There are no new challengers, and so the best overall alternative is lathe 3.

5.3.3 Multiple IRRs

A problem with implementing the internal rate of return method is that there may be multiple internal rates of return. Consider the following example.

EXAMPLE 5.6

A project pays $1000 today, costs $5000 a year from now, and pays $6000 in two years. (See Figure 5.6.) What is its IRR?

Equating the present worths of disbursements and receipts and solving for the IRR gives the following:

$$\$1000 - \$5000(P/F, i^*, 1) + \$6000(P/F, i^*, 2) = 0$$

Recalling that $(P/F, i^*, N)$ stands for $\dfrac{1}{(1 + i^*)^N}$, we have

$$1 - \frac{5}{1 + i^*} + \frac{6}{(1 + i^*)^2} = 0$$

$$(1 + i^*)^2 - 5(1 + i^*) + 6 = 0$$

$$(1 + 2i^* + i^*) - 5i^* + 1 = 0$$

$$i^* - 3i^* + 2 = 0$$

$$(i^* - 1)(i^* - 2) = 0$$

The roots of this equation are $i^*_1 = 1$ and $i^*_2 = 2$. In other words, this project has two IRRs: 100% and 200%!

FIGURE 5.6   Multiple IRR Example

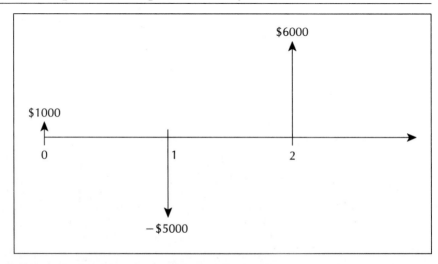

The multiple internal rates of return problem may be stated more generally. Consider a project that has cash flows over T periods. The **net cash flow**, A_t, associated with period t is the difference between cash inflows and outflows for the period (i.e., $A_t = R_t - D_t$ where R_t is cash inflow in period t, and D_t is cash outflow in period t). We set the present worth of the net cash flows over the entire life of the project equal to zero to find the IRR(s). We have

$$A_0 + A_1(1 + i)^{-1} + A_2(1 + i)^{-2} + \ldots + A_T(1 + i)^{-T} = 0 \quad (5.2)$$

Any value of i that solves Equation (5.2) is an internal rate of return for that project. That there may be multiple solutions to Equation (5.2) can be seen if we rewrite the equation as

$$A_0 + A_1 x + A_2 x^2 + \ldots + A_T x^T = 0 \quad (5.3)$$

where x is $(1 + i)^{-1}$.

Solving the Tth degree polynomial of Equation (5.3) is the same as solving for the internal rates of return in Equation (5.2). In general, when finding the roots of Equation (5.3), there may be as many solutions for x as there are sign changes in the coefficients, the As. Thus, there may be as many IRRs as there are sign changes in the As.

We can see the meaning of multiple roots most easily with the concept of **project balance**. Let the sequence of net cash flows for a T period project be $A_0, A_1, A_2, \ldots, A_T$. A project balance, B_t, is the cumulative future value of net cash flows, compounded at some interest rate, i', up to the end of period t. That is, the project balances for this project, using i', are given by

$$B_0 = A_0$$
$$B_1 = A_0(1 + i') + A_1$$
$$B_2 = A_0(1 + i')^2 + A_1(1 + i') + A_2$$

.

.

.

$$B_T = A_0(1 + i')^T + A_1(1 + i')^{T-1} + \ldots + A_2$$

Table 5.1 shows the project balances at the end of each year for both 100% and 200% interest rates for the project in Example 5.6. The project starts with a cash inflow of $1000. At a 100% interest rate, the $1000 increases to $2000 over the first year. At the end of the first year, there is a $5000 disbursement, leaving a negative project balance of $3000. At 100% interest, this negative balance increases to $6000 over the second year. This negative $6000 is offset exactly by the $6000 inflow. This makes the project balance zero at the end of the second year. The project balance at the end of the project is the future worth of all the cash flows in the project. When the future worth at the end of the project life is zero, the present worth is also zero. This verifies that the 100% IRR is correct.

Now consider the 200% interest rate. Over the first year, the $1000 inflow increases to $3000. At the end of the first year, $5000 is paid out, leaving a negative project balance of $2000. This negative balance grows at 200% to $6000 over the second year. This is offset exactly by the $6000 inflow so that the project balance is zero at the end of the second year. This verifies that the 200% IRR is also correct!

TABLE 5.1   Project Balances for Example 5.6

End of Year	At $i = 100\%$	At $i = 200\%$
0	$1000	$1000
1	$1000(1 + 1) − $5000 $$= -\$3000$$	$1000(1 + 2) − $5000 $$= -\$2000$$
2	− $3000(1 + 1) + $6000 $$= 0$$	− $2000(1 + 2) + $6000 $$= 0$$

Looking at Table 5.1, it's actually fairly obvious that an important assumption is being made about the initial $1000 received. *The IRR computation implicitly assumes that the $1000 is invested during the first period at either 100% or 200%, one of the two IRRs.* During the first period, the project is not an investment. The project balance is positive. The project is *providing* money, not using it. This money is not reinvested immediately in the project. It is simply cash on hand. The $1000 must be invested elsewhere for one year if it is to earn any return. It is unlikely that the $1000 provided by the project in this example would be invested in something else at 100% or 200%. More likely, it would be invested at a rate at or near the company's MARR.

5.3.4 External Rate of Return Methods

To resolve the multiple IRR difficulty, we need to consider what return is earned by money associated with a project that is not invested in the project. The usual assumption is that the funds are invested elsewhere and earn an *explicit rate of return* equal to the MARR. This makes sense, because when there is cash on hand that is not invested in the project under study it will be used elsewhere. These funds would, by definition, gain interest at a rate at least equal to the MARR. The **external rate of return (ERR)**, denoted by i_e^*, is the rate of return on a project where any cash flows that are not invested in the project are assumed to earn interest at a predetermined explicit rate (usually the MARR). For a given explicit rate of return, a project can have only one value for its ERR.

It is possible to calculate a precise ERR that is comparable to the IRRs of other projects using an explicit interest rate exactly when necessary. Because the cash flows of Example 5.6 are fairly simple, let us use them to illustrate how to calculate the ERR precisely.

EXAMPLE 5.6 Revisited (ERR)

A project pays $1000 today, costs $5000 a year from now, and pays $6000 in two years. What is its rate of return? Assume that the MARR is 25%.

The first $1000 is not invested immediately in the project. Therefore, we assume that it is invested outside the project for one year at the MARR. Thus, the cumulative cash flow for year 1 is

$$\$1000(F/P, 25\%, 1) - \$5000 = \$1250 - \$5000 = -\$3750$$

With this calculation, we transform the cash-flow diagram representing this problem from that in Figure 5.7(a) to that in Figure 5.7(b). These cash flows provide a single (precise) ERR, as follows:

$$-\$3750 + \$6000(P/F, i_e^*, 1) = 0$$

$$(P/F, i_e^*, 1) = \$3750/\$6000 = 0.625$$

$$\frac{1}{1+i_e^*} = 0.625$$

$$1+i_e^* = \frac{1}{0.625} = 1.6$$

$$i_e^* = 0.6$$

$$ERR = 60\%$$

FIGURE 5.7   Multiple IRR Solved

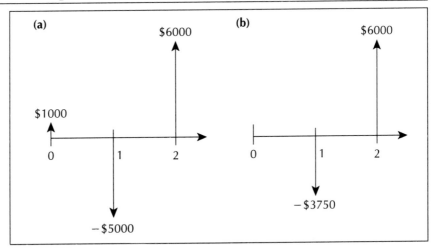

In general, computing a precise ERR can be a complex procedure because of the difficulty in determining exactly when the explicit interest rate should be applied. Project balances have to be computed for trial ERRs to do such a calculation. In periods in which project balances are positive for the trial ERR, the project is a source of funds. These funds would have to be invested outside the project at the MARR. During periods when the project balance is negative for the trial ERR, any receipts would be invested in the project and will typically yield more than the MARR. Whether the project balances are negative or positive will depend on the trial ERRs. This implies that the calculation process requires much experimenting with trial ERRs before an ERR that makes the future worth zero is found. A more convenient, but approximate, method is to use the following procedure:

1. Take all *net* receipts forward at the MARR to the time of the last cash flow.
2. Take all *net* disbursements forward at an unknown interest rate, i^*_{ea}, also to the time of the last cash flow.
3. Equate the future value of the receipts from 1 to the future value of the disbursements from 2 and solve for i^*_{ea}.
4. The value for i^*_{ea} is the approximate ERR for the project.

EXAMPLE 5.6   Revisited Again (An Approximate ERR)

To approximate the ERR, we compute the interest rate that gives a zero future worth at the end of the project when all receipts are brought forward at the MARR. In Example 5.6, the $1000 is thus assumed to be reinvested at the MARR for two years, the life of the project. The disbursements are taken forward to the end of the two years at an unknown interest rate, i^*_{ea}. With a MARR of 25%, the revised calculation is

$$\$1000(F/P, 25\%, 2) + \$6000 = \$5000(F/P, i^*_{ea}, 1)$$

$$(F/P, i^*_{ea}, 1) = [\$1000(1.5625) + \$6000]/\$5000$$

$$(F/P, i^*_{ea}, 1) = 1.5125$$

$$1 + i^*_{ea} = 1.5125$$

$$i^*_{ea} = 0.5125 \ or$$

$$i^*_{ea} = 51.25\%$$

$$ERR \cong 51\%$$

The ERR calculated using this method is an approximation, since *all* receipts, not just those that occur when the project balance is positive, are assumed to be invested at the MARR. Note that the precise value of 60% is different from the approximation of 51%. In practice, whenever the precise calculation of the ERR is difficult to do, the approximation is often used instead. Despite the fact that the precise ERR and the approximate ERR can differ, the approximate ERR will always give the correct decision. Whenever the precise ERR is above the MARR, the approximation will also be above the MARR. Whenever the precise ERR is below the MARR, the approximation will be below the MARR. It should be noted that, when the precise ERR is above the MARR, the error in the approximation is on the conservative side. This is because the approximate ERR is between the precise ERR and the MARR. Consequently, an acceptable project will earn *at least* the rate given by the approximate ERR. Therefore, even though an approximate ERR is inaccurate, it provides the correct decision as well as useful information about the return on an investment. It is also quite easy to calculate.

5.3.5 When to Use the ERR

The ERR (approximate or precise) must be used whenever there are multiple IRRs possible. Unfortunately, it can be difficult to know in advance whether there will be multiple IRRs. On the other hand, fortunately, most ordinary projects have a structure that precludes multiple IRRs.

Most projects consist of one or more periods of outflows at the start, followed only by one or more periods of inflows. Such projects are called **simple investments**. The cash flow diagram for a simple investment takes the general form shown in Figure 5.8. In terms of Equations (5.2) and (5.3), there is only one change of sign, from negative to positive in the As, the sequence of coefficients. Therefore, a simple investment always has a unique IRR. When checking for multiple IRRs, the first and easiest thing to do is see if the project is a simple investment. If it is a simple investment, we know there is a unique IRR and no further checking is required. If it is not a simple investment, then a more detailed examina-

FIGURE 5.8   The general form of simple investments

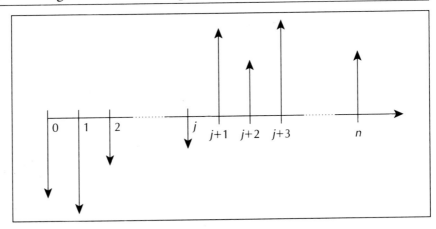

tion is required to determine if the ERR must be used. Appendix 5A shows a complete procedure for finding out if there are multiple IRRs possible in a project.

The approximate ERR can be used to evaluate any project, whether it is a simple investment or not. However, the approximate ERR will tend to be a less accurate rate than the IRR. The inaccuracy will tend to be similar for projects with cash flows of a similar structure, and either method will result in the same decision.

In general, it is desirable to compute an IRR wherever it is possible to do so, and to use an approximate ERR only when there may be multiple IRRs. In this way, the rate of return computations will be as accurate as possible.

5.4 Rate of Return and Present/Annual Worth Methods Compared

A comparison of rate of return and present/annual worth methods leads to two important conclusions:

1. The two sets of methods, when properly used, give the same decisions.

2. Each set of methods has its own advantages and disadvantages.

Let us consider each of these conclusions in more detail.

5.4.1 Equivalence of Rate of Return and Present/Annual Worth Methods

If an independent project has a unique IRR, the IRR method and the present worth method give the same conclusion. Consider Figure 5.9. It shows the present worth as a function of the interest rate for a project with a unique IRR. The maximum of the curve lies at the vertical axis (where the interest rate = 0) at the point given by the sum of all undiscounted net cash flows. (We assume that the sum of all the undiscounted net cash flows is positive.) As the interest rate increases, the present worth of all cash flows after the first cost decreases. Therefore, the present worth curve slopes down to the right. To determine what happens as the interest rate increases indefinitely, let us recall the general equation for present worth

$$PW(i) = \sum_{t=0}^{T} A_t(1 + i)^{-t} \tag{5.1}$$

where

i = the interest rate
A_t = the net cash flow in period t
T = the number of periods

Letting $i \to \infty$, we have

$$\lim_{i \to \infty} \frac{1}{(1 + i)^t} = 0$$

Therefore, as the interest rate becomes indefinitely large, all terms in Equation (5.1) approach zero except the first term (where $t = 0$), which remains at A_0. In Figure 5.9, this is shown by the asymptotic approach of the curve to the first cost, which, being negative, is below the horizontal axis.

The interest rate at which the curve crosses the horizontal axis (i^* in Figure 5.9), where the present worth is zero, is, by definition, the IRR.

To demonstrate the equivalence of the rate of return and the present/annual worth methods for decision making, let us consider possible values for the MARR. First, suppose the MARR $= i_1$, where $i_1 < i^*$. In Figure 5.9, this MARR would lie to the left of the IRR. From the graph we see that the present worth is positive at i_1. In other words, we have

IRR > MARR

and

PW > 0

Thus, in this case, both the IRR and PW methods lead to the same conclusion: Accept the project.

FIGURE 5.9   **Present Worth (PW) as a Function of Interest Rate (i) for a Simple Investment**

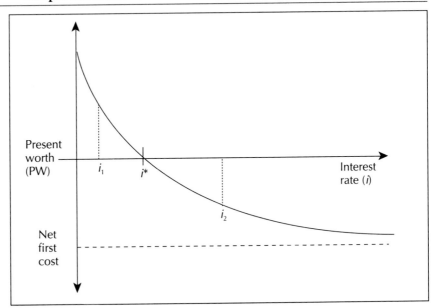

Second, suppose the MARR $= i_2$, where $i_2 > i^*$. In Figure 5.9, this MARR would lie to the right of the IRR. From the graph we see that, at i_2, the present worth is negative. Thus we have

IRR < MARR

and

PW < 0

Here, too, both the IRR and PW methods lead to the same conclusion: Reject the project.

Now consider two simple, mutually exclusive, projects, A and B, where the first cost of B is greater than the first cost of A. If the increment from A to B has a unique IRR, then we can readily demonstrate that the IRR and PW methods lead to the same decision. See Figure 5.10(a), which shows the present worths of projects A and B as a function of the interest rate. Since the first cost of B is greater than that of A, the curve for project B asymptotically approaches a lower present worth than does the curve for project A as the interest rate becomes indefinitely large, and thus the two curves must cross at some point.

To apply the IRR method, we must consider the increment (B to A). The present worth of the increment (B to A) will be zero where the two curves cross. This point of intersection is marked by the interest rate, i^*. We have plotted the curve for the increment (B to A) in Figure 5.10(b) to clarify the relationships.

Let us again deal with possible values of the MARR. First, suppose the MARR (i_1) is less than i^*. Then, as we see in Figure 5.10(b), the present worth of (B to A) is positive at i_1. That is, the following conditions hold:

IRR(B to A) > MARR

and

PW(B to A) > 0

Thus, according to both the IRR method and the PW method, project B is better than project A.

Second, suppose the MARR $= i_2$, where $i_2 > i^*$. Then we see from Figure 5.10(b) that the present worth of the increment (B to A) is negative at i_2. In other words, the following conditions hold:

IRR(B to A) < MARR

and

PW(B to A) < 0

Thus, according to both methods, project A is better than project B.

In a similar fashion, we could show that the approximate ERR method gives the same decisions as the PW method in those cases where there may be multiple IRRs.

FIGURE 5.10   Present Worth (PW) as a Function of Interest Rate (*i*) for Two Simple, Mutually Exclusive Projects

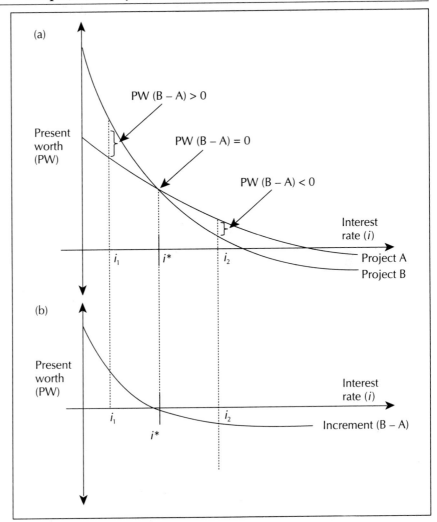

We already noted that the annual worth and present worth methods are equivalent. Therefore, by extension, our demonstration of the equivalence of the rate of return methods and the present worth methods means that the rate of return and the annual worth methods are also equivalent.

EXAMPLE 5.7

Bracebridge Enterprises operates a resort in the tourist area north of Toronto, Ontario. They are considering adding either a parasailing operation or canoe rentals to their other activities. Available space limits them to one of these two choices. The initial costs for parasailing will be $100 000, with net returns of $15 000 for the 15-year life of the project. Initial costs for canoeing will be $10 000, with net returns of $2000 for its 15-year life. Assume that both projects have a $0 salvage value after 15 years, and the MARR is 10%.

(a) Using present worth analysis, which alternative is better?

(b) Using IRR, which alternative is better?

The present worths of the two projects are calculated as follows:

$$PW_{para} = -\$100\ 000 + \$15\ 000(P/A, 10\%, 15)$$
$$= -\$100\ 000 + \$15\ 000(7.6061)$$
$$= \$14\ 091.50$$
$$PW_{can} = -\$10\ 000 + \$2000(P/A, 10\%, 15)$$
$$= -\$10\ 000 + \$2000(7.6061)$$
$$= \$5212.20$$

The parasailing venture has a higher present worth and is thus preferred.

The IRRs of the two projects are calculated as follows:

Parasailing

$$\$100\ 000 = \$15\ 000(P/A, i^*, 15)$$
$$(P/A, i^*, 15) = \$100\ 000/\$15\ 000 = 6.67 \Rightarrow i^*_{para} = 12.4\%$$

Canoeing

$$\$10\ 000 = \$2000(P/A, i^*, 15)$$
$$(P/A, i^*, 15) = 5 \Rightarrow i^*_{can} = 18.4\%$$

One might conclude that, because IRR_{can} is larger, Bracebridge Enterprises should invest in the canoeing project, but this is *wrong*. When done correctly, a present worth analysis and an IRR analysis will always agree. The error here is that the parasailing project can be assessed only by looking at the increment from the canoeing project. Check the IRR of the increment:

$$(\$100\ 000 - \$10\ 000) = (\$15\ 000 - \$2000)(P/A, i^*, 15)$$
$$(P/A, i^*, 15) = \$90\ 000/\$13\ 000 = 6.923 \Rightarrow i^*_{can-para} = 11.7\%$$

Since the increment from the canoeing project also exceeds the MARR, the larger parasailing project should be taken.

5.4.2 Why Choose One Method over the Other?

Although rate of return methods and present worth/annual worth methods give the same decisions, each set of methods has its own advantages and disadvantages. The choice of method may depend on the way the results are to be used and the sort of data the decision makers prefer to consider.

Rate of return methods state results in terms of *rates*. Many managers prefer rates to absolute figures. Rates facilitate direct comparisons of projects whose sizes are quite different. For example, a petroleum company comparing performance of a refining division and a distribution division would not look at the typical values of present worth for projects in the two divisions. A refining project may have first costs in the range of hundreds of *millions* of dollars. Distribution projects may have first costs in the range of hundreds of *thousands* of dollars. It would not be meaningful to compare the absolute profits between a refining project and a distribution project. The absolute profits of the refining projects will almost certainly be larger than those of the distribution projects. Expressing project performance in terms of rates of return permits understandable comparisons.

On the other hand, a present worth computation gives a direct measure of the profit provided by a project. A company's main goal is likely to be to earn profits for its owners. The present worth of a project states the contribution of a project toward that goal.

Present worth/annual worth methods are usually easier to apply than rate of return methods, but, given the ease of making the necessary computations with computers, there may be no need to avoid more complicated calculations. The method selected in each situation will depend on the characteristics of that situation, as illustrated in the following examples.

EXAMPLE 5.8

Each of the following scenarios suggests a best choice of comparison method:

1. Edward has his own small firm that will lease injection-moulding equipment to make polyethylene containers. He must decide on the specific model to lease. He has estimates of future monthly sales.

   The annual worth method makes sense here, because Edward's cash flows, including sales receipts and leasing expenses, will probably all be on a monthly basis. As a sole proprietor, Edward need not report his conclusions to others.

2. Ramesh works for a large power company and must assess the viability of locating a transformer station at various sites in the city. He is looking at the cost of the building lot, power lines,

and power losses for the various locations. He has fairly accurate data about costs and future demand for electricity.

As part of a large firm, Ramesh will probably be obliged to use a specific comparison method. This would probably be IRR. A power company makes many large and small investments, and the IRR method allows them to be compared fairly. Ramesh has the data necessary for the IRR calculations.

3. Sehdev must buy a relatively inexpensive log splitter for his agricultural firm. There are several different types that require a higher or lower degree of manual assistance. He has only rough estimates of how this machine will affect future cash flows.

   This relatively inexpensive purchase is a good candidate for the payback period method. The fact that it is inexpensive means that extensive data gathering and analysis are probably not warranted. Also, since future cash flows are relatively uncertain, there is no justification for using a particularly precise comparison method.

4. Ziva will be living in Inuvik for six months, testing her company's equipment under hostile weather conditions. She needs a field office and must determine which of the following choices is economically best: (1) renting space in an industrial building; (2) buying and outfitting a trailer; (3) renting a hotel room for the purpose.

   For this decision, a present worth analysis would be appropriate. The cash flows for each of the alternatives are of different types, and bringing them to present worth would be a fair way to compare them. It would also provide an accurate estimate to Ziva's firm of the expected cost of the remote office for planning purposes.

CANADIAN CORPORATE CASE 5.1

Air Canada Supply and Stores

Air Canada's Supply and Stores facility in Dorval, Quebec, is the main maintenance base for the airline. The facility houses over 140 000 parts worth $200 million, and supplies service and replacement parts for Air Canada's operations. To improve the use of the existing warehouse space and to increase the efficiency of the parts-picking process, two automated storage and retrieval systems (AS/RS) were installed. Each AS/RS system consists of many aisles of stacked parts storage bins, several cranes used for parts retrieval, and a conveyor loop to transport the parts to the requesting workstation. Both AS/RS systems were configured so that the parts needed most often were stored in positions that would facilitate fast retrieval.

The warehousing software that controls the storage systems communicates with the Air Canada inventory control system and has boosted efficiency by prioritizing the parts-picking sequence. The priorities range from "aircraft-on-ground with passengers aboard" to requests for forms or stationery. Other improvements with the use of the AS/RS systems have been increased accuracy of parts counting and reduced costs of inventory purchasing and holding. Air Canada reported that the increase in productivity due to the AS/RS system provided a 3.5 year payback period.

Source: Industrial Engineering, June 1994

REVIEW PROBLEMS

Review Problem 5.1

Weiping's consulting firm needs new quarters. A downtown office building is ideal. The company can either buy or lease it. To buy the office building will cost $6 000 000. If, on the other hand, the building is leased, the lease fee is $400 000 payable at the beginning of each year. In either case, the company must pay city taxes, maintenance, and utilities.

Weiping figures that the company needs the office space for only 15 years. Therefore, they will either sign a 15-year lease or buy the building. If they buy the building, they will then sell it after 15 years. The value of the building at that time is estimated to be $15 000 000.

What rate of return will Weiping's firm receive by buying the office building instead of leasing it?

Answer

The rate of return can be calculated as the IRR on the incremental investment necessary to buy the building rather than lease it.

The IRR on the incremental investment is found by solving for i^* in

($6 000 000 - $400 000) - $15 000 000(P/F, i^*, 15)
= $400 000(P/A, i^*, 14)

$4(P/A, i^*, 14) + 150(P/F, i^*, 15) = 56$

For $i^* = 11\%$, the result is

$4(P/A, 11\%, 14) + 150(P/F, 11\%, 15)$
$= 4(6.9819) + 150(0.20900)$
$= 59.2781$

For $i^* = 12\%$,

$4(P/A, 12\%, 14) + 150(P/F, 12\%, 15)$
$= 4(6.6282) + 150(0.1827)$
$= 53.9171$

A linear interpolation between 11% and 12% gives the IRR

$$i^* = 11\% + (59.2781 - 56)/(59.2781 - 53.9171) = 11.6115\%$$

By investing their money in buying the building rather than leasing, Weiping's firm is earning an IRR of about 11.6% .

Review Problem 5.2

The Real S. Tate Company is considering investing in one of four rental properties. Real S. Tate will rent out whatever property they buy for four years and then sell it at the end of that period. The following data concerning the properties are available:

Rental Property	Purchase Price	Net Annual Rental Income	Sales Price at the End of Four Years
1	$100 000	$ 7 200	$100 000
2	120 000	9 600	130 000
3	150 000	10 800	160 000
4	200 000	12 000	230 000

Based on the purchase prices, rental incomes, and sale prices at the end of the four years, answer the following questions:

(a) Which property, if any, should Tate invest in? Real S. Tate uses a MARR of 8% for projects of this type.

(b) Construct a graph which depicts the present worth of each alternative as a function of interest rates ranging from 0% to 20%. (A spreadsheet would be helpful in answering this part of the problem.)

(c) From your graph, determine for what range of interest rates is your choice in part (a) the best investment. If the MARR were 9%, which rental property would be the best investment? Comment on the sensitivity of your choice to the MARR used by the Real S. Tate Company.

Answer

(a) First, a current best alternative must be found. The properties are already ordered on the basis of first cost, so the IRR on property 1 is given by:

$$- \$100\ 000 + \$100\ 000(P/F, i^*, 4) + \$7200(P/A, i^*, 4) = 0$$

The IRR of property 1 is 7.2%. Because this is less than the MARR of 8%, property 1 is discarded from further consideration. The IRR for property 2, the alternative with the next highest first cost, is found by solving for i^* in

$$-\ \$120\ 000 + \$130\ 000(P/F, i^*, 4) + \$9600(P/A, i^*, 4) = 0$$

The interest rate that solves the above equation is 9.8%. Since an IRR of 9.8% exceeds the MARR, property 2 becomes the current best alternative. Now the incremental investments over and above the first cost of property 2 are analyzed. First, property 3 challenges the current best. The IRR in the incremental investment to property 3 is

$$(-\ \$150\ 000 + \$120\ 000) + (\$160\ 000 - \$130\ 000)(P/F, i^*, 4)$$
$$+\ (\$10\ 800 - \$9600)(P/A, i^*, 4) = 0$$

$$-\ \$30\ 000 + \$30\ 000(P/F, i^*, 4) + \$1200(P/A, i^*, 4) = 0$$

This gives an IRR of only 4%, which is below the MARR. Property 2 remains the current best alternative and property 3 is discarded. Next, property 4 challenges the current best. The IRR on the incremental investment from property 2 to property 4 is

$$(-\ \$200\ 000 + \$120\ 000) + (\$230\ 000 - \$130\ 000)(P/F, i^*, 4)$$
$$+\ (\$12\ 000 - \$9600)(P/A, i^*, 4) = 0$$

$$-\ \$80\ 000 + \$100\ 000(P/F, i^*, 4) + \$2400(P/A, i^*, 4) = 0$$

The IRR on the incremental investment is 8.5%, which is above the MARR. Property 4 becomes the current best choice. Since there are no further challengers, the choice based on IRR is the current best, property 4.

(b) The graph for part (b) is shown in Figure 5.11.

(c) From the graph, one can see that, provided the MARR is between 0% and 8.5% , property 4 is the best alternative. This is the range of interest rates over which property 4 has the largest present worth.

FIGURE 5.11   Present Worths for Review Problem 5.2

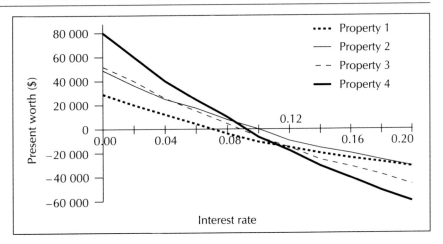

If the MARR is 9%, the best alternative is property 2. This can be seen by going back to the original IRR computations and observing that the results of the analysis are essentially the same, except that the incremental investment from property 2 to property 4 no longer has a return exceeding the MARR. This can be confirmed from the diagram (Figure 5.11) as well, since the property with the largest present worth at 9% is property 2.

With respect to sensitivity analysis, the graph shows that, for a MARR between 0% and 8.5%, property 4 is the best choice and, for a MARR between 8.5% and 9.8%, property 2 is the best choice. If the MARR is above 9.8%, no property has an acceptable return on investment, and the "do nothing" alternative would be chosen.

Review Problem 5.3

You are in the process of arranging a marketing contract for a new browser that will allow easy access to the "web" (the World Wide Web). It still needs more development, so your contract will pay you $5000 today to finish the prototype. You will then get royalties of $10 000 at the end of each of the second and third years. At the end of each of the first and fourth years, you will be required to do $20 000 and $10 000 in upgrades, respectively. What is the (approximate) ERR on this project, assuming a MARR of 20%? Should you accept the contract ?

Answer

To calculate the approximate ERR, set

FW(receipts @ MARR) = FW(disbursements @ ERR)

$5000(F/P, 20%, 4) + $10 000(F/P, 20%, 2) +
$10 000(F/P, 20%, 1) = $20 000(F/P, i_{ea}^*, 3) + $10 000

$5000(2.0736) + $10 000(1.44) + $10 000(1.2) =
$20 000(F/P, i_{ea}^*, 3) + $10 000

$(F/P, i, 3) = 1.3384$

At ERR = 10%, $(F/P, i, 3) = 1.3310$

At ERR = 11%, $(F/P, i, 3) = 1.3676$

Interpolating:

$i_{ea}^* = 10\% + (1.3384 - 1.3310)(11 - 10)/(1.3676 - 1.3310) =$
$10\% + 0.0074/0.0366 = 10.2022\%$

The (approximate) ERR is 10.2%. Since this is below the MARR of 20%, the contract should not be accepted.

SUMMARY

This chapter presented the IRR method for evaluating projects, and also discussed the relationship among the present worth, annual worth, payback period, and IRR methods.

The IRR method consists of determining the rate of return for a sequence of cash flows. For an independent project, the calculated IRR is compared with a MARR, and if it is equal to or exceeds the MARR it is an acceptable project. To determine the best project of several mutually exclusive ones, it is necessary to determine the IRR of each increment of investment.

The IRR selection procedure is complicated by the possibility of having more than one rate of return because of a cash flow structure that, over the course of a project, requires that capital eventually invested in the project at some point be invested externally. Under such circumstances, it is necessary to calculate an ERR.

The present worth and annual worth methods are closely related, and both give results identical to those of the IRR method. Rate of return measures are readily understandable, especially when comparing projects of unequal sizes, whereas present/annual worth measures give an explicit expression of the profit contribution of a project. The main advantage of the payback period method is that it is easy to implement and understand, and takes into account the need to have capital recovered quickly. A summary of the advantages and disadvantages of each of the evaluation methods is given in Table 5.2.

TABLE 5.2   Advantages and Disadvantages of Comparison Methods

Method	Advantages	Disadvantages
IRR	Facilitates comparisons of projects of different sizes Commonly used	Relatively difficult to calculate Multiple IRRs may exist
Present worth	Gives explicit measure of profit contribution	Difficult to compare projects of different sizes
Annual worth	Annual cash flows may have familiar meanings to decision makers	Difficult to compare projects of different sizes
Payback period	Very easy to calculate Commonly used Takes into account the need to have capital recovered quickly	Discriminates against long-term projects Ignores time value of money Ignores the expected service life

Engineering Economics in Action, Part 5B: The Invisible Hand

"Hello." Dave's voice was clear enough over the phone that he could have been in his office down the hall, but Naomi could tell from his relaxed tone that the office was not on his mind.

"Hi, Dave, it's Naomi. Can I bend your ear about that drop forge project again?"

"Oh, hi, Naomi. Sure, what have you got?"

"Well, as I see it, IRR has got to be the way to go. Of course, present worth or annual worth will give the same answer, but I'm sure Ed Burns and Anna Kulkowski would prefer IRR. They have to compare potential investments across different parts of the organization. It's kind of hard to compare net present worths of investments in information systems where you rarely get above a first cost of $25 000 with forge investments where you can easily get up to a few hundred thousand first cost. And, as I said before, the drop forge operation isn't one in which the annual cost has any particular significance."

There was a short pause. Naomi suddenly regretted speaking as if she was so sure of herself — but, darn it, she was sure on this one.

"Exactly right," Dave replied. Naomi could feel an invisible hand pat her on the back. "So how exactly would you proceed?"

"Well, I have the options ranked by first cost. The first one is just refurbishing the existing machine. There is no test on that one unless we are willing to stop making our own parts, and Clem told me that was out . . ."

Dave interjected with, "You don't mean that you're automatically going to refurbish the existing machine do you?"

"No, no. The simple refurbishing option is the base. I then go to the next option which is to refurbish the drop forging hammer and replace the material-handling system. I compare this with the just refurbish option by looking at the incremental first cost. I will check to see if the additional first cost has an IRR of at least 15% after tax, which, Clem tells me, is the minimum acceptable rate of return. If the incremental first cost has an IRR of at least 15%, the combination of refurbishing and replacing the material-handling system is better than just refurbishing. I then consider the next option, which is to buy the manually oper-ated mechanical press with no change in material handling. I look at the incre-mental investment here and see if its IRR is at least 15%. To go back a step, if the IRR of replacing material handling plus refurbishing the old machine did not pay off at 15%, I would have rejected that and compared the manually operated mechanical press with the first option, just refurbishing the old machine. I then work my way, option by option, up to the seventh. How does that sound?"

"Well, that sounds great, as far as it goes. Have you checked for problems with multiple IRRs?"

"Well, so far each set of cash flows has been a simple investment, but I will be careful."

"I would also compute payback periods for them in case we are having cash flow problems. They may not necessarily take an option, even if its incremental IRR is above their 15% MARR, if the payback is too long."

> *Naomi considered this for a second. "One other question, Dave. What should I do about intangibles?"*
> *"You mean the noise from the forging hammer?"*
> *"Yes. It's important, but you can't evaluate it in dollars and cents."*
> *"Just remind them of it in your report. If they want a more formal analysis, they'll come back to you."*
> *"Thanks, Dave. You've been a big help."*
> *As Naomi hung up the phone, she couldn't help smiling ruefully to herself. She had ignored the payback period altogether — after all, it didn't take either interest or service life into account. "I guess that's what they call practical experience," she said to herself as she got out her calculator.*

PROBLEMS

5.1 What is the IRR for a $1000 investment that returns $200 at the end of each of the next

(a) 7 years?

(b) 6 years?

(c) 100 years?

(d) 2 years?

5.2 New windows are expected to save $400 per year in energy costs over their 30-year life for Nottawasaga Fabricating. At an initial cost of $8000 and zero salvage value, are they a good investment? NF's MARR is 8%.

5.3 An advertising campaign will cost $2 000 000 for planning and $400 000 in each of the next six years. It is expected to increase revenues permanently by $400 000 per year. Additional revenues will be gained in the pattern of an arithmetic gradient with $200 000 in the first year, declining by $50 000 per year to zero in the fifth year. What is the IRR of this investment? If the company's MARR is 12%, is this a good investment?

5.4 Aline has three contracts from which to choose. The first contract will require an outlay of $100 000, but will return $150 000 one year from now. The second contract requires an outlay of $200 000, and will return $300 000 one year from now. The third contract requires an outlay of $250 000, and will return $355 000 one year from now. Only one contract can be accepted. If her MARR is 20%, which one should she choose?

5.5 Antigonish Footwear can invest in one of two different automated clicker cutters. The first, A, has a $10 000 first cost. A similar one with many extra features, B, has a $40 000 first cost. A will save $5000 per year over the cutter now in use. B will save $15 000 per year. Each clicker cutter will last five years. If the MARR is 10%, which alternative is better? Use an IRR comparison.

5.6 PCB Electronix must buy a piece of equipment to place electronic components on the printed circuit boards it assembles. The proposed equipment has a 10-year life with no scrap value.

The supplier has given PCB several purchase alternatives. The first is to purchase the equipment for $850 000. The second is to pay for the equipment in 10 equal instalments of $135 000 each, starting one year from now. The third is to pay $200 000 now and $95 000 at the end of each year for the next 10 years.

(a) Which alternative should PCB choose if their MARR is 11% per year? Use an IRR comparison approach.

(b) Below what MARR does it make sense for PCB to buy the equipment now for $850 000?

5.7 The following table summarizes information for four projects:

Project	First Cost	IRR on Overall Investment	IRR on Increments of Investment Compared with Project		
			1	2	3
1	$100 000	19%			
2	175 000	15%	9%		
3	200 000	18%	17%	23%	
4	250 000	16%	12%	17%	13%

The data can be interpreted in the following way: The IRR on the incremental investment between project 4 and project 3 is 13%.

(a) If the projects are independent, which projects should be undertaken if the MARR is 16%?

(b) If the projects are mutually exclusive, which project should be undertaken if the MARR is 15%? Indicate what logic you have used.

(c) If the projects are mutually exclusive, which project should be undertaken if the MARR is 17%? Indicate what logic you have used.

5.8 There are several mutually exclusive ways Rimouski Dairy can meet a requirement for a filling machine for their creamer line. One choice is to buy a machine. This would cost $65 000 and last for six years with a salvage value of $10 000. Alternatively, they could contract with a packaging supplier to get a machine free. In this case, the extra costs for packaging supplies would amount to $15 000 per year over the six-year life (after which the supplier gets the machine back with no salvage value for Rimouski). The third alternative is to buy a used machine for $30 000 with zero salvage value after six years. The used machine has extra maintenance costs of $3000 in the first year, increasing by $2500 per year. In all cases, there are installation costs of $6000 and revenues of $20 000 per year. Using the IRR method, determine which is the best alternative. The MARR is 10%.

5.9 Project X has an IRR of 16% and a first cost of $20 000. Project Y has an IRR of 17% and a first cost of $18 000. The MARR is 15%. What can be said about which (if either) of the two projects should be undertaken?

5.10 Sam has an opportunity to buy a bond with a face value of $10 000 and a coupon rate of 14%, payable semi-annually.

(a) If the bond matures in five years and Sam can buy one now for $3500, what is his IRR for this investment?

(b) If his MARR for this type of investment is 20%, should he buy the bond?

5.11 The following cash flows result from a potential construction contract for Estevan Engineering:

(a) Receipts of $500 000 at the start of the contract, and $1 200 000 at the end of the fourth year

(b) Expenditures at the end of the first year of $400 000 and at the end of the second year of $900 000

(c) A net cash flow of $0 at the end of the third year

Using an appropriate rate of return method, for a MARR of 25% should Estevan Engineering accept this project?

5.12 Sam has entered into an agreement to develop and maintain a computer program for symbolic mathematics. Under the terms of the agreement, he will pay $90 000 in royalties to the investor at the end of the fifth, tenth, and fifteenth years, with the investor paying Sam $45 000 now, and then $65 000 at the end of the twelfth year.

Sam's MARR for this type of investment is 20%. Calculate the ERR of this project. Should he accept this agreement, based on these disbursements and receipts alone? Are you sure that the ERR you calculated is the only ERR? Why? Are you sure that your recommendation to Sam is correct? Justify your answer.

5.13 Yee Swian has received an advance of $2000 on a software program she is writing. She will spend $12 000 this year writing it (consider the money to have been spent at the end of year 1), and then receive $10 000 at the end of the second year. The MARR is 12%.

(a) What is the IRR for this project? Does the result make sense?

(b) What is the true ERR?

(c) What is the approximate ERR?

5.14 Zhe develops truss analysis software for civil engineers. He has the opportunity to contract with at most one of two clients who have approached him with development proposals. One contract pays him $15 000 immediately, and then $22 000 at the end of the project three years from now. The other possibility pays $20 000 now and $5000 at the end of each of the three years. In either case, his expenses will be $10 000 per year. For a MARR of 10%, which project should Zhe accept? Use an appropriate rate of return method.

5.15 The following table summarizes cash flows for a project:

Year	Cash Flow at End of Year
0	−$5000
1	3000
2	4000
3	−1000

(a) Write out the expression you need to solve to find the IRR(s) for this set of cash flows. Do not solve.

(b) What is the maximum number of solutions for the IRR that could be found in part (a)? Explain your answer in one sentence.

(c) You have found that an IRR of 14.58% solves the expression in part (a). Compute the project balances for each year.

(d) Can you tell (without further computations) if there is a unique IRR from this set of cash flows? Explain in one sentence.

5.16 Orillia Properties makes its decisions using the payback period method. For renovation decisions, the minimum acceptable payback period is five years. Renovation projects are characterized by an immediate investment of P dollars which is recouped as an annuity of A dollars per year over 20 years. They are considering changing to the IRR method for such decisions. If they changed to the IRR method, what MARR would result in exactly the same decisions as their current policy using payback period?

5.17 Six mutually exclusive projects, A, B, C, D, E, and F, are being considered. They have been ordered by first costs so that project A has the smallest first cost, F the largest. The data in the table below applies to these projects. The data can be interpreted as follows: The IRR on the incremental investment between project D and project C is 6%. Which project should be chosen?

Project	IRR on Overall Investment	IRR on Increments of Investment Compared with Project				
		A	B	C	D	E
A	20%					
B	15%	12%				
C	24%	30%	35%			
D	16%	18%	22%	6%		
E	17%	16%	19%	15%	16%	
F	21%	20%	21%	19%	18%	11%

5.18 Three mutually exclusive designs for a by-pass are under consideration. The by-pass has a 10-year life. The first design incurs a cost of $1.2 million for a net savings of $300 000 per annum. The second has a cost of $1.5 million for a net savings of $400 000 per annum. The third has a cost of $2.1 million for a net savings of $500 000 per annum. For each of the alternatives, what range of values for the MARR results in its being chosen? It is not necessary that any be chosen.

5.19 Development projects done by Produits Trois Rivières are subsidized by a government grant program. The program pays 30% of the total cost of the project (costs summed without discounting, i.e., the interest rate is zero), half at the beginning of the project and half at the end, up to a maximum of $100 000. There are two projects being considered. One is a customized checkweigher for cheese products, and the other is an automated production scheduling system. Each project has a service life of five years. Costs and benefits for both projects, not including grant income, are shown below. Only one can be done, and the grant money is certain. PTR has a MARR of 15% for projects of this type. Using an appropriate rate of return method, which project should be chosen?

Checkweigher

First cost	$30 000
Yearly costs	5 000
Yearly benefits	14 000
Salvage value	8 000

Scheduler

First cost	$10 000
Yearly costs	12 000
Yearly benefits	17 000
Salvage value	0

5.20 Jacob is considering the replacement of the heating system for his building. There are three alternatives. All are natural gas fired furnaces, but they vary in energy efficiency. Model A is leased at a cost of $500 per year over a 10-year study period. There are installation charges of $500, and no salvage value. It is expected to provide energy savings of $200 per year. Model B is purchased for a total cost of $3600, including installation. It has a salvage value of $1000 after 10 years of service, and is expected to provide energy savings of $500 per year. Model C is also purchased, for a total cost of $8000, including installation. However, half of this cost is paid now, and the other half is paid at the end of two years. It has a salvage value of $1000 after 10 years, and is expected to provide energy savings of $1000 per year. For a MARR of 12% and using a rate of return method, which heating system should be installed? One model must be chosen.

5.21 Calgary Cartage leases trucks to service its shipping contracts. Larger trucks have cheaper operating costs if there is sufficient business, but are more expensive if they are not full. CC has estimates of monthly shipping demand. What comparison method(s) would be appropriate for choosing which trucks to lease?

5.22 The bottom flaps of shipping cartons for Yonge Auto Parts are fastened with industrial staples. Yonge needs to buy a new stapler. What comparison method(s) would be appropriate for choosing which stapler to buy?

5.23 Joan runs a dog kennel. She is considering installing a heating system for the interior runs which will allow her to operate all year. What comparison method(s) would be appropriate for choosing which heating system to buy?

5.24 A large Canadian food company is considering replacing a scale on its packaging line with a more accurate one. What comparison method(s) would be appropriate for choosing which scale to buy?

5.25 Mona runs a one-person company producing custom paints for hobbyists. She is considering buying printing equipment to produce her own labels. What comparison method(s) would be appropriate for choosing which equipment to buy?

5.26 Peter is the president of a rapidly growing company. There are dozens of important things to do, and cash flow is tight. What comparison method(s) would be appropriate for Peter to make acquisition decisions?

5.27 Lemuel is an engineer working for Ontario Hydro. He must compare several routes for transmission lines from the Darlington nuclear plant to new industrial parks north of Toronto. What comparison method(s) is he likely to use?

5.28 Vicky runs a music store that has been suffering from thefts. She is considering installing a magnetic tag system. What comparison method(s) would be best for her to use to choose among competing leased systems?

5.29 Thanh's company is growing very fast and has a hard time meeting its orders. An opportunity to purchase additional production equipment has arisen. What comparison method(s) would Thanh use to justify to her manager that the equipment purchase was prudent?

APPENDIX 5A: Tests for Multiple IRRs

When the IRR method is used to evaluate projects, we have to test for multiple IRRs. If there are undetected multiple IRRs, an IRR might be calculated that seems correct, but is in error. We consider three tests for multiple IRRs, forming essentially a three-step procedure. In the first test, the signs of the cash flows are examined to see if the project is a *simple investment*. In the second test, the present worth of the project is plotted against the interest rate to search for interest rates at which the present value is zero. In the third test, project balances are calculated. Each test *can* have a definitive outcome: (1) There is definitely a unique IRR, or (2) There definitely are two or more IRRs. But each test *may* have an outcome that is consistent with either a single, unique IRR, or with multiple IRRs. The tests are applied sequentially. The second test is applied only if the outcome of the first test is not clear. The third test is applied only if the outcomes of the first two are not clear. Even after all three tests have been applied, there are still three possible outcomes:

1. There is definitely a unique IRR.
2. There are definitely multiple IRRs because two or more IRRs have been found.
3. The test outcomes are ambiguous. A unique IRR or multiple IRRs are both possible.

Recall that most projects consist of one or more periods of outflows at the start, followed only by one or more periods of inflows; these are called simple investments. Although simple investments guarantee a single IRR, a project that is not simple may have a single IRR or multiple IRRs. Some investment projects have large cash outflows during their lives or at the ends of their lives that cause net cash flows to be negative after years of positive net cash flows. For example, a project that involves the construction of a manufacturing plant may involve a planned expansion of the plant requiring a large expenditure some years after its initial operation. As another example, a nuclear electricity plant may have planned large cash outflows for disposal of spent fuel at the end of its life. Such a project may have a unique IRR, but it may also have multiple IRRs. Consequently we must examine such projects further.

Where a project is not simple, we go to a second test. The second test consists of making a graph plotting present worth against interest rate. Points at which the present worth crosses or just touches the interest-rate axis (i.e., where present worth = 0) are IRRs. (We assume that there is at least one IRR.) If there are more than one such point, we know that there are more than one IRR. A convenient way to produce such a graph is using a spreadsheet. Table 5.3 was obtained by computing the present worth of the cash flows in Example 5.6 for a variety of interest rates. Figure 5.12 shows the graph of the values in Table 5.3.

EXAMPLE 5A.1 (Example 5.6 Restated)

A project pays $1000 today, costs $5000 a year from now, and pays $6000 in two years. What is its IRR?

TABLE 5.3   The Spreadsheet Cells Used to Construct Figure 5.13

Interest Rate, i	Present Worth
0.6	218.8
0.8	74.1
1.0	0.0
1.2	−33.1
1.4	−41.7
1.6	−35.5
1.8	−20.4
2.0	0.0
2.2	23.4
2.4	48.4

While finding multiple IRRs in a plot ensures that the project does indeed have multiple IRRs, failure to find multiple IRRs does not necessarily mean that multiple IRRs do not exist. *Any* plot will cover only a finite set of points. There may be values of the interest rate for which the present worth of the project is zero that are not in the range of interest rates used.

Where the project is not simple and a plot does not show multiple IRRs, we apply the third test. The third test entails calculating the project balances. As we mentioned earlier, project balances refer to the cumulative net cash flows at the end of each time period. For an IRR to be unique, there should be no time when the project balances, computed using that IRR, are positive. This means that there is no extra cash not reinvested in the project. This is a sufficient condition for there to be a unique IRR. (Recall that it is the cash generated by a project, but not reinvested in the project, that creates the possibility of multiple IRRs.)

FIGURE 5.12   Illustration of two IRRs for Example 5A.1

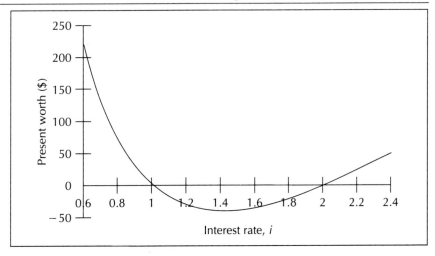

We now present three examples. All three examples involve projects that are not simple investments. In the first, a plot shows multiple IRRs. In the second the plot shows only a single IRR. This is inconclusive, so project balances are computed. None of the project balances is positive, so we know that there is a single IRR. In the third example, the plot shows only one IRR, so the project balances are computed. One of these is positive, so the results of all tests are inconclusive.

EXAMPLE 5A.2

Wellington Woods are considering buying land that they will log for three years. In the second year, they expect to develop the area that they clear as a residential subdivision that will entail considerable costs. Thus, in the second year, the net cash flow will be negative. In the third year, they expect to sell the developed land at a profit. The net cash flows that are expected for the project are:

End of Year	Cash Flow
0	−$100 000
1	440 000
2	− 639 000
3	306 000

The negative net cash flow in the second period implies that this is not a simple project. Therefore, we apply the second test. We plot the present worth against interest rates to search for IRRs. (See Figure 5.13.)

FIGURE 5.13 **Wellington Woods Present Worth**

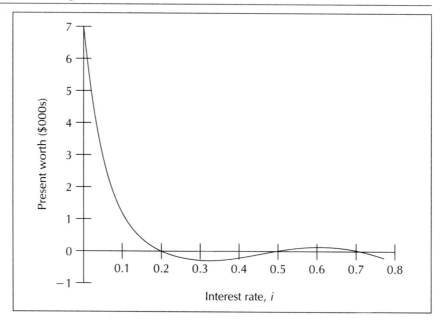

At 0% interest, the present worth is a small positive amount, $7000. The present worth is then 0 at 20%, 50%, and 70%. Each of these values is an IRR. The spreadsheet cells that were used for the plot are shown in Table 5.4.

In this example, a moderately fine grid of two percentage points was used. Depending on the problem, the analyst may wish to use a finer or coarser grid.

The correct decision in this case can be obtained by the approximate ERR method. Suppose the MARR is 15%; then the approximate ERR is the interest rate that makes the future worth of outlays equal to the future worth of receipts when the receipts earn 15%. In other words, the approximate ERR is the value of i that solves

$$\$100\,000(1+i)^3 + \$639\,000(1+i) = \$440\,000(1.15)^2 + \$306\,000$$

$$\$100\,000(1+i)^3 + \$639\,000(1+i) = \$887\,900$$

Try 15% for i_{ea}^*. Using the tables for the left-hand side of the above equation, we have

$$\$100\,000(F/P, 15\%, 3) + \$639\,000(F/P, 15\%, 1)$$
$$= \$100\,000(1.5208) + \$639\,000(1.15)$$

$$= \$887\,000 < \$887\,900$$

Thus, the approximate ERR is slightly above 15%. The project is (marginally) acceptable by this calculation, because the approximate ERR, which is a conservative estimate of the correct ERR, is above the MARR.

TABLE 5.4   Spreadsheet Cells Used to Generate Figure 5.14

Interest Rate	Present Worth	Interest Rate	Present Worth	Interest Rate	Present Worth
0%	$7000.00	28%	− 352.48	56%	$ 79.65
2%	5536.33	30%	− 364.13	58%	92.49
4%	4318.39	32%	− 356.87	60%	97.66
6%	3310.12	34%	− 335.15	62%	94.84
8%	2480.57	36%	− 302.77	64%	83.79
10%	1803.16	38%	− 263.01	66%	64.36
12%	1255.01	40%	− 218.66	68%	36.44
14%	816.45	42%	− 172.11	70%	0.00
16%	470.50	44%	− 125.39	72%	− 44.96
18%	202.55	46%	− 80.20	74%	− 98.41
20%	0.00	48%	− 38.00	76%	− 160.24
22%	− 148.03	50%	0.00	78%	− 230.36
24%	− 250.91	52%	32.80		
26%	− 316.74	54%	59.58		

EXAMPLE 5A.3

Investment in a new office coffeemaker has the following effects:
1. There is a three-month rental fee of $40 for the equipment, payable immediately and in three months.
2. A rebate of $30 from the supplier is given immediately for an exclusive six-month contract.
3. Supplies will cost $20 per month, payable at the beginning of each month.
4. Income from sales will be $30 per month, received at the end of each month.

Will there be more than one IRR for this problem?

We apply the first test by calculating net cash flows for each time period. The net cash flows for this project are as follows:

End of Month	Receipts	Disbursements	Net Cash Flow
0	+ $30	− $40 + (− $20)	− $30
1	+ 30	− 20	+ 10
2	+ 30	− 20	+ 10
3	+ 30	− 40 + (− 20)	− 30
4	+ 30	− 20	+ 10
5	+ 30	− 20	+ 10
6	+ 30	0	+ 30

As illustrated in Figure 5.14, the net cash flows for this problem do not follow the pattern of a simple investment. Therefore, there may be more than one IRR for this problem. Accordingly, we apply the second test.

FIGURE 5.14   Net Cash Flows for the Coffeemaker

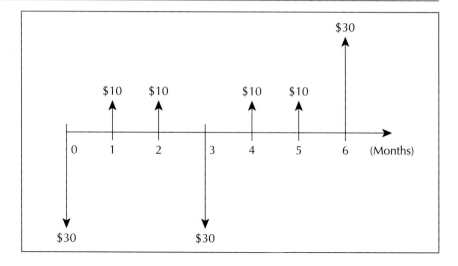

A plot of present worth against the interest rate is shown in Figure 5.15. The plot starts with a zero interest rate where the present worth is just the arithmetic sum of all the net cash flows over the project's life. This is a positive $10. The present worth as a function of the interest rate decreases as the interest rate increases from zero. The plot continues down, and passes through the interest-rate axis at about 5.8%. There is only one IRR in the range plotted. We need to apply the third test by computing project balances at the 5.8% interest rate.

FIGURE 5.15   IRR for New Coffeemaker

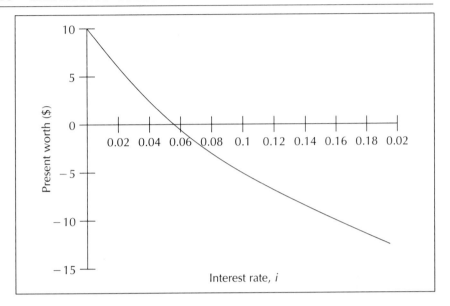

The project balances at the 5.8% interest rate are as follows:

Month	Project Balance
0	$B_0 = -\$30$
1	$B_1 = -\$30.0(1.058) + \$10 = -\$21.7$
2	$B_2 = -\$21.7(1.058) + \$10 = -\$13.0$
3	$B_3 = -\$13.0(1.058) - \$30 = -\$43.7$
4	$B_4 = -\$43.7(1.058) + \$10 = -\$36.3$
5	$B_5 = -\$36.3(1.058) + \$10 = -\$28.4$
6	$B_6 = -\$28.4(1.058) + \$30 = \$0$

Since all project balances are negative or zero, we know that this investment has only one IRR. It is 5.8% per month or about 69.3% per year.

EXAMPLE 5A.4

Green Woods, like Wellington Woods, are considering buying land that they will log for three years. In the second year, they also expect to develop the area that they have logged as a residential subdivision, which again will entail considerable costs. Thus, in the second year, the net cash flow will be negative. In the third year, they expect to sell the developed land at a profit. But Green Woods expect to do much better than Wellington

Woods in the sale of the land. The net cash flows that are expected for the project are:

Year	Cash Flow
0	−$100 000
1	455 000
2	− 667 500
3	650 000

The negative net cash flow in the second period implies that this is not a simple project. We now plot the present worth against interest rate. See Figure 5.16. At zero interest rate, the present worth is a positive $337 500. The present worth falls as the interest rate rises. It crosses the interest-rate axis at about 206.4%. There are no further crossings of the interest-rate axis in the range plotted, but since this is not conclusive we compute project balances.

FIGURE 5.16 Present Worths for Example 5A.4

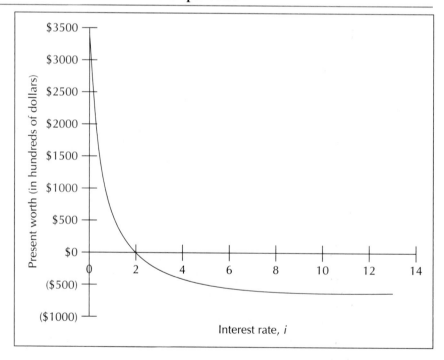

Year	Project Balance
0	$B_0 = -\$100\ 000$
1	$B_1 = -\$100\ 000(3.064) + \$455\ 000 = \$148\ 600$
2	$B_2 = -\$148\ 600(3.064) - \$667\ 500 = -\$2\ 121\ 900$
3	$B_3 = -\$2\ 121\ 900(3.064) + \$650\ 000 = -\$1500$

We note that the project balance is positive at the end of the first period. This means that a unique IRR is *not* guaranteed. We have gone as far as the three tests can take us. On the basis of the three tests, there may be only the single IRR that we have found, 206.4%, or there may be multiple IRRs.

In this case, we use the approximate ERR to get a decision. Suppose the MARR is 30%. The approximate ERR, then, is the interest rate that makes the future worth of outlays equal to the future worth of receipts when the receipts earn 30%. That is, the approximate ERR is the value of i that solves the following:

$$\$100\ 000(1 + i)^3 + \$667\ 500(1 + i) = \$455\ 000(1.3)^2 + \$650\ 000$$

Trial and error with a spreadsheet gives the approximate ERR as $i_{ea}^* \cong 57\%$. This is above the MARR of 30%. Therefore, the investment is acceptable.

It is possible, using the precise ERR, to determine that the IRR that we got with the plot of present worth against the interest rate, 206.4%, is, in fact, unique. The precise ERR equals the IRR in this case. Computation of the precise ERR may be cumbersome, and we do not cover this computation in this book. Notice, however, that we got the same decision using the approximate ERR as we would have obtained with the precise ERR. Also note that the approximate ERR is a conservative estimate of the precise ERR, which is equal to the unique IRR.

To summarize, we have discussed three tests that are to be applied sequentially, as shown in Figure 5.17. The first and easiest test to apply is to see if a project is a simple investment. If it is a simple investment, there is a single IRR, and the correct decision can be obtained by the IRR method. If the project is not a simple investment, we apply the second test, which is to plot the project's present worth against the interest rate. If the plot shows at least two IRRs, we know that there is not a unique IRR, and the correct decision can be obtained with the approximate ERR method. If a plot does not show multiple IRRs, we next compute project balances using the IRR found from the plot. If none of the project balances is positive, the IRR is unique, and the correct decision can be obtained with the IRR method. If one or more of the project balances are positive, we don't know whether or not there is a unique IRR. Accordingly, we use the approximate ERR method which always will yield a correct decision.

FIGURE 5.17   Tests for Multiple IRR

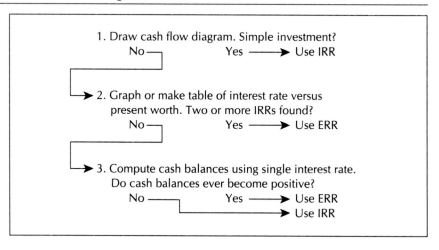

PROBLEMS

5A.1 A five-year construction project for Wawa Engineering receives staged payments in years 2 and 5. The resulting net cash flows are as follows:

Year	Cash Flow
0	−$300 000
1	− 500 000
2	700 000
3	− 400 000
4	− 100 000
5	900 000

The MARR for Wawa Engineering is 15%.

(a) Is this a simple project?

(b) Plot the present worth of the project against interest rates from 0% to 100%. How many times is the interest-rate axis crossed? How many IRRs are there?

(c) Calculate project balances over the five-year life of the project. Can we conclude that the IRR(s) observed in (b) is (are) the only IRR(s)? If so, should the project be accepted?

(d) Calculate the approximate ERR for this project. Should the project be accepted?

5A.2 For the cash flows associated with the projects below, determine whether there is a unique IRR, using the project balances method.

| | Project | | |
End of Period	1	2	3
0	−$3000	−$1500	$ 600
1	900	7000	− 2000
2	900	− 9000	500
3	900	2900	500
4	900	500	1000

5A.3 A mining opportunity in a third-world country has the following cash flows:

(a) $10 000 000 is received at time 0 as an advance against expenses.

(b) Costs in the first year are $20 000 000, and in the second year $10 000 000.

(c) Over years 3 to 10, annual revenues of $5 000 000 are expected.

After 10 years, the site reverts to government ownership. MARR is 30%.

(a) Is this a simple project?

(b) Plot the present worth of the project against interest rates from 0% to 100%. How many times is the interest-rate axis crossed? How many IRRs are there?

(c) Calculate project balances over the 10-year life of the project. Can we conclude that the IRR(s) observed in (b) is (are) the only IRR(s)? If so, should the project be accepted?

(d) Calculate the approximate ERR for this project. Should the project be accepted?

(e) Calculate the exact ERR for this project. Should the project be accepted?

Depreciation and Financial Accounting

Engineering Economics in Action, Part 6A: The Pit Bull

6.1 Introduction

6.2 Depreciation and Depreciation Accounting

    6.2.1 Reasons for Depreciation

    6.2.2 Value of an Asset

    6.2.3 Straight-Line Depreciation

    6.2.4 Declining-Balance Depreciation

6.3 Elements of Financial Accounting

    6.3.1 Measuring the Performance of a Firm

    6.3.2 The Balance Sheet

    6.3.3 The Income Statement

    6.3.4 The Statement of Changes in Financial Position

    6.3.5 Estimated Values in Financial Statements

    6.3.6 Financial Ratio Analysis

    6.3.7 Financial Ratios

Canadian Corporate Case 6.1: Capital Expenditure or Business Expense?

Review Problems

Summary

Engineering Economics in Action, Part 6B: Usually the Truth

Problems

Engineering Economics in Action, Part 6A: The Pit Bull

Naomi liked to think of Terry as a pit bull. Terry had this endearing habit of finding some detail that irked him, and not letting go of it until he was satisfied that things were done properly. Naomi had seen this several times in the months they had worked together. Terry would sink his teeth into some quirk of Canadian Widgets' operating procedures and, just like a fighting dog, not let go until the fight was over.

This time, it was about the disposal of some computing equipment. Papers in hand, he quietly approached Naomi and earnestly started to explain his concern. "Naomi, I don't know what Bill Fisher is doing, but something's definitely not right here. Look at this."

Terry displayed two documents to Naomi. One was an accounting statement showing the book value of various equipment, including some CAD/CAM computers that had been sold for scrap the previous week. The other was a copy of a sales receipt from a local salvage firm for that same equipment.

"I don't like casting aspersions on my fellow workers, but I really am afraid that Bill might be doing something wrong." Bill Fisher was the buyer responsible for capital equipment at Canadian Widgets, and also disposed of surplus assets. "You know the CAD/CAM workstations they had in Engineering Design? Well, they were replaced recently, and sold. Here is the problem. They were only three years old, and our own accounting department estimated their value as about $5000 each." Terry's finger pointed to the evidence on the accounting statement. "But here," his finger moving to the guilty figure on the sales receipt, "they were actually sold for $300 each!" Terry sat back in his chair. "How about that!"

Naomi smiled. Unfortunately, she would have to pry his teeth out of this one. "Interesting observation, Terry. But you know, I think it's probably O.K. Let me explain."

6.1 Introduction

Engineering projects often involve an investment in equipment, buildings, or other assets which are put to productive use. As time passes, these assets lose value, or depreciate. The first part of this chapter is concerned with the concept of depreciation and several methods that are commonly used to model depreciation. Depreciation is taken into account when a firm states the value of its assets in its financial statements, as seen in the second half of this chapter. It also forms an important part of the decisions of when to replace an aging asset and when to make cyclic replacements, as will be seen in Chapter 7, and has an important impact on taxation, as we will see in Chapter 8.

With the growth in importance of small technology-based enterprises, many engineers have taken on broad managerial responsibilities that include financial accounting. Financial accounting is concerned with recording and organizing the financial data of businesses. The data cover both *flows over time*, like revenues and expenses, and *levels*, like an enterprise's resources and the claims on those resources at a given date. Even engineers who do not have broad managerial responsibilities need to know the elements of financial accounting to understand the enterprises with which they work.

In the second part of this chapter, we explain three basic financial statements used to summarize the financial dimensions of a business. We then explain how these statements can be used to make inferences about the financial health of the firm.

6.2 Depreciation and Depreciation Accounting

6.2.1 Reasons for Depreciation

An asset starts to lose value as soon as it is purchased. A car bought for $20 000 today may be worth $18 000 next week, $15 000 next year, and $1000 in 10 years. This loss in value, called **depreciation**, occurs for several reasons.

Use-related physical loss: As something is used, parts wear out. An automobile engine has a limited life span because the metal parts within it wear out. This is one reason why a car diminishes in value over time. Often, use-related physical loss is measured with respect to *units of production*, such as thousands of kilometres for a car, hours of use for a light bulb, or thousands of cycles for a punch press.

Time-related physical loss: Even if something is not used, there can be a physical loss over time. This can be due to environmental factors affecting the asset or to endogenous physical factors. For example, an unused car can rust and thus lose value over time. Time-related physical loss is expressed in units of time, such as a 10-year-old car or a 40-year-old sewage treatment plant.

Functional loss: Losses can occur without any physical changes. For example, a car can lose value over time because styles change so that it is no longer fashionable. Other examples of causes of loss of value include legislative changes, such as for pollution control or safety devices, and technical changes. Functional loss is usually expressed simply in terms of the particular unsatisfied function.

6.2.2 Value of an Asset

Models of depreciation can be used to estimate the loss in value of an asset over time, and also to determine the remaining value of the asset at any point in time. This remaining value has several names, depending on the circumstances.

Market value is usually taken as the actual value an asset can be sold for in an open market. Of course, the only way to determine the actual market value for anything is to sell it. Consequently, the term *market* *value* usually means an *estimate* of the market value. One way to make such an estimation is by using a depreciation model that reasonably captures the true loss in value of an asset.

Book value is the depreciated value of an asset, as calculated with a depreciation model, for accounting purposes. The book value may be more or less than market value. The depreciation model used to arrive at a book value might be controlled by regulation for some purposes, such as taxation, or simply by the desirability of an easy calculation scheme. There might be several different book values for the same asset, depending on the purpose and depreciation model applied. We shall see how book values are reported in financial statements later in this chapter.

Scrap value can be either the actual value of an asset at the end of its physical life (when it is broken up for the material value of its parts) or an estimate of the scrap value calculated using a depreciation model.

Salvage value can be either the actual value of an asset at the end of its useful life (when it is sold) or an estimate of the salvage value calculated using a depreciation model.

It is desirable to be able to construct a good model of depreciation in order to state a book value of an asset for a variety of reasons:

1. In order to make many managerial decisions, it is necessary to know the value of owned assets. For example, money may be borrowed with the firm's assets as collateral. In order to demonstrate to the lender that there is security for the loan, a credible estimate of the assets' value must be made. A depreciation model permits this to be done. The use of depreciation for this purpose is explored more thoroughly in the second part of this chapter.

2. One needs an estimate of the value of owned assets for planning purposes. In order to decide whether to keep an asset or replace it, you have to be able to judge how much it is worth. More than that, you have to be able to assess how much it will be worth at some time in the future. The impact of depreciation in replacement studies is covered in Chapter 7.

3. Government tax legislation requires that taxes be paid on company profits. Because there can be many ways of calculating profits, strict rules are made concerning how to calculate income and expenses. These rules include a particular scheme for determining depreciation expenses. This use of depreciation is discussed more thoroughly in Chapter 8.

To match the way in which certain assets depreciate, and also to meet regulatory or accuracy requirements, many different depreciation models have been developed over time. Of the large number of depreciation schemes available (see Close-Up 6.1), straight-line and declining-balance are certainly the most commonly used in Canada. Straight-line depreciation is popular primarily because it is particularly easy to make the calculations. The declining-balance method is required by Canadian tax law for determining corporate taxes, as is discussed in Chapter 8. In the United States, tax laws prior to 1954 required straight-line depreciation to be used, and between 1954 and 1981, several other methods were permitted. Under current United States law, things are more complicated, but the main depreciation methods used are also straight-line and declining-balance. Consequently, these are the only depreciation methods presented in detail in this book.

CLOSE-UP 6.1	DEPRECIATION METHODS
Method	*Description*
Straight-line	The book value of an asset diminishes by an equal *amount* each year.
Declining-balance	The book value of an asset diminishes by an equal *proportion* each year.
Sum-of-the-year's-digits	An accelerated method, like declining-balance, in which the actual depreciation is calculated by summing the digits corresponding to the years of life
Double-declining-balance	A declining-balance method in which the depreciation rate is calculated as 2/N for an asset with service life N years
150%-declining-balance	A declining-balance method in which the depreciation rate is calculated as 1.5/N for an asset with service life N years
Units-of-production	Depreciation is determined according to the proportion which some production unit is of the production capacity over the asset's service life.

6.2.3 Straight-Line Depreciation

The **straight-line method of depreciation** assumes that the rate of loss in value of an asset is constant over its useful life. This is illustrated in Figure 6.1 for an asset worth $1000 at the time of purchase, and $200 eight years later. Graphically, straight-line depreciation is determined by drawing a straight line between the first cost of the asset and its salvage or scrap value.

Algebraically, the assumption is that the rate of loss in asset value is constant, based on its original cost, and gives rise to a simple expression for the depreciation amount per period. We estimate the depreciation per period from the asset's current value and its estimated salvage value at the end of its useful life, N periods from now

$$D_{sl}(n) = \frac{P - S}{N} \qquad (6.1)$$

where

P = the purchase price or current market value

S = the salvage value after N periods

FIGURE 6.1   Book Value under Straight-Line Depreciation
($1000 Purchase and $200 Salvage Value after Eight Years)

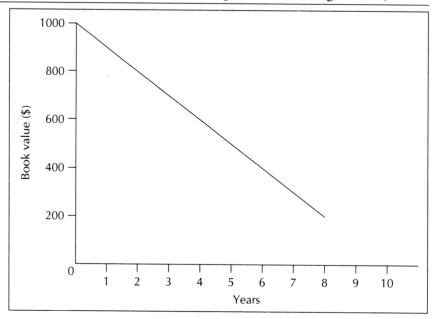

N = the useful life of the asset, in periods

$D_{sl}(n)$ = the depreciation amount for period n using the straight-line method

Similarly, the book value at the end of any particular period is easy to calculate:

$$BV_{sl}(n) = P - n\left[\frac{P - S}{N}\right] \tag{6.2}$$

where

$BV_{sl}(n)$ = the book value at the end of period n using straight-line depreciation

EXAMPLE 6.1

A laser cutting machine was purchased four years ago for $380 000. It will have a salvage value of $30 000 two years from now. If we believe a constant rate of depreciation is a reasonable means of approximating book value, what is its current book value?

From Equation (6.2), with $P = \$380\ 000$, $S = \$30\ 000$, $N = 6$, and $n = 4$,

$$BV_{sl}(4) = \$380\ 000 - 4\left[\frac{\$380\ 000 - \$30\ 000}{6}\right]$$

$$BV_{sl}(4) = \$146\ 667$$

The current book value for the cutting machine is \$146 667.

The straight-line depreciation method has the great advantage that it is very easy to calculate. It also is easy to understand and is in common use. The main problem with the method is that its assumption of a constant rate of loss in asset value is often not valid. Thus, book values calculated using straight-line depreciation will frequently be different from market values. For example, the loss in value of a car over its first year (say from \$20 000 to \$15 000) is clearly more than its loss in value over its fifth year (say from \$6000 to \$5000). The declining-balance method of depreciation covered in the next section allows for "faster" depreciation in earlier years of an asset's life.

6.2.4 Declining-Balance Depreciation

Declining-balance depreciation models the loss in value of an asset over a period as a constant proportion of the asset's current value. In other words, the depreciation amount in a particular period is a constant percentage (called the depreciation rate) of its closing book value from the previous period. The effect of various depreciation rates on estimated book values is illustrated in Figure 6.2.

FIGURE 6.2   Book Value under Declining-Balance Depreciation ($1000 Purchase with Various Depreciation Rates)

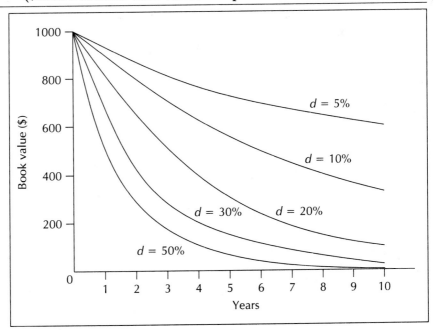

Algebraically, the depreciation charge for period n is simply the depreciation rate multiplied by the book value from the period $(n - 1)$. Noting that $BV_{db}(0) = P$,

$$D_{db}(n) = BV_{db}(n - 1) \times d \tag{6.3}$$

where

P	= the purchase price or current market value
d	= the depreciation rate
$D_{db}(n)$	= the depreciation amount in period n using the declining balance method
$BV_{db}(n)$	= the book value at the end of period n using the declining balance method

Similarly, the book value at the end of any particular period is easy to calculate, by noting that the remaining value after each period is $(1 - d)$ times the value at the end of the previous period.

$$BV_{db}(n) = P(1 - d)^n \tag{6.4}$$

In order to use the declining-balance method of depreciation, we must determine a reasonable depreciation rate. By using an asset's current value, P, and a salvage value, S, n periods from now, we can use Equation (6.4) to find the declining balance rate that relates P and S.

$$BV_{db}(n) = S = P(1 - d)^n$$

$$(1 - d) = \sqrt[n]{\frac{S}{P}} \tag{6.5}$$

$$d = 1 - \sqrt[n]{\frac{S}{P}}$$

EXAMPLE 6.2

Paquita wants to estimate the scrap value of a smokehouse twenty years after purchase. She feels that the depreciation is best represented using the declining-balance method, but she doesn't know what depreciation rate to use. She observes that the purchase price of the smokehouse was $245 000 three years ago, and an estimate of its current salvage value is $180 000.

What is a good estimate of the value of the smokehouse after 20 years?

From Equation (6.5),

$$d = 1 - \sqrt[n]{\frac{S}{P}}$$

$$d = 1 - \sqrt[3]{\frac{\$180\ 000}{\$245\ 000}}$$

$$d = 0.097663$$

Then, by using Equation (6.4), we have

$$BV_{db}(20) = \$245\ 000(1 - 0.097663)^{20}$$
$$= \$31\ 372$$

An estimate of the salvage value of the smokehouse after 20 years using the declining-balance method of depreciation is $31 372.

The declining-balance method has a number of useful features. For one thing, it matches the observable loss in value that many assets have over time. The rate of loss is expressed in one parameter, the depreciation rate. It is relatively easy to calculate, although perhaps not quite as easy as the straight-line method. In particular, it is required to be used in Canada for taxation purposes, as discussed in detail in Chapter 8.

EXAMPLE 6.3

Sherbrooke Data Services has purchased a new mass storage system for $250 000. It is expected to last six years, with a $10 000 salvage value. Using both the straight-line and declining-balance methods, determine the following:

(a) The depreciation amount during year 1
(b) The depreciation amount during year 6
(c) The book value at the end of year 4
(d) The accumulated depreciation at the end of year 4

This is an ideal application for a spreadsheet solution. Table 6.1 illustrates a spreadsheet that calculates the book value, depreciation charge, and accumulated depreciation for both depreciation methods over the six-year life of the system.

The depreciation amount for each year with the *straight-line* method is $40 000:

$$D_{sl}(n) = (\$250\ 000 - \$10\ 000)/6 = \$40\ 000$$

The depreciation rate for the *declining-balance* method is

$$d = 1 - \sqrt[n]{\frac{S}{P}} = 1 - \sqrt[6]{\frac{\$10\ 000}{\$250\ 000}} = 0.4152$$

The detailed calculation for each of the given questions is as follows:

(a) The depreciation amount during year 1

$$D_{sl}(1) = (\$250\ 000 - \$10\ 000)/6 = \$40\ 000$$

$$D_{db}(1) = BV_{db}(0)d = \$250\ 000(0.4152) = \$103\ 799.11$$

(b) The depreciation amount during year 6

$$D_{sl}(6) = D_{sl}(1) = \$40\ 000$$

$$D_{db}(6) = BV_{db}(5)d = \$250\ 000(0.5848)^5(0.4152) = \$7099.82$$

(c) The book value at the end of year 4

$$BV_{sl}(4) = \$250\ 000 - 4(\$250\ 000 - \$10\ 000)/6 = \$90\ 000$$

$$BV_{db}(4) = \$250\ 000(1 - 0.4152)^4 = \$29\ 240.17$$

(d) The accumulated depreciation at the end of year 4

Straight-line accumulated depreciation at the end of year 4 is

$$P - BV_{sl}(4) = \$160\ 000$$

Declining-balance accumulated depreciation at the end of year 4

$$P - BV_{db}(4) = \$220\ 759.83$$

Depreciation affects economic analyses in several ways. First, it allows us to estimate the value of an owned asset, as illustrated in the above examples. We shall see in the next part of this chapter how these values are reported in a firm's financial statements. Next, the capability of estimating the value of an asset is particularly useful in replacement studies, which is the topic of Chapter 7. Finally, in Chapter 8, we cover aspects of the Canadian tax system which affect decision making; in particular we look at the effect of depreciation expenses.

6.3 Elements of Financial Accounting

How well is a business doing? Can it survive an unforeseen temporary drop in cash flows? How does a business compare with others of its size in the industry? Answering these questions and others like them is part of the accounting function. The accounting function has two parts, financial accounting and management accounting. **Financial accounting** is concerned with recording and organizing the financial data of a business. **Management accounting** is concerned with the costs and benefits of the various activities of an enterprise. The goal of management accounting is to provide managers with information to help in decision making.

TABLE 6.1: Spreadsheet for Example 6.3

| Year | Straight-Line Depreciation | | |
	Depreciation Charge	Accumulated Depreciation	Book Value
0			$250 000
1	$40 000	$ 40 000	210 000
2	40 000	80 000	170 000
3	40 000	120 000	130 000
4	40 000	160 000	90 000
5	40 000	200 000	50 000
6	40 000	240 000	10 000

| Year | Declining-Balance Depreciation | | |
	Depreciation Charge	Accumulated Depreciation	Book Value
0			$250 000
1	$103 799	$103 799	146 201
2	60 702	164 501	85 499
3	35 499	200 000	50 000
4	20 760	220 760	29 240
5	12 140	232 900	17 100
6	7 100	240 000	10 000

Engineers have always played a major role in management account-ing, especially in a part of management accounting called *cost* accounting. They have not, for the most part, had significant responsibility for finan-cial accounting until recently. With the growth in importance of small technology-based enterprises, many engineers have taken on broad man-agerial responsibilities that include financial accounting. Even engineers who do not have broad managerial responsibilities need to know the ele-ments of financial accounting to understand the enterprises with which they work. Management accounting is not covered in this text because it is difficult to provide useful information without taking more than a sin-gle chapter. Instead, we focus on financial accounting.

The object of financial accounting is to provide information to internal management and interested external parties. Internally, management uses financial accounting information for processes such as budgeting, cash management, and management of long-term debt. External users include actual and potential investors and creditors who wish to make rational decisions about an enterprise. External users also include government agencies concerned with taxes and regulation.

Areas of interest to all these groups include an enterprise's revenues and expenses, and assets (resources held by the enterprise) and liabilities (claims on those resources).

In the next few sections, we discuss two basic summary financial statements that give information about these matters. These are

(a) the balance sheet, and

(b) the income statement.

These financial statements form the basis of a financial report, which is usually produced on a monthly, quarterly, or yearly basis. We also briefly discuss one additional financial statement, the statement of changes in financial position. It is useful for understanding the cash status of the firm.

Following the discussion of financial statements, we shall consider the use of information in these statements when making inferences about an enterprise's performance compared with industry standards and with its own performance over time.

6.3.1 Measuring the Performance of a Firm

The flow of money in a company is much like the flow of water in a network of pipes or the flow of electricity in an electrical circuit, as illustrated in Figure 6.3. In order to measure the performance of a water system, we need to determine the flow through the system and the pressure in the system. For an electrical circuit, the analogous parameters are current and voltage. Flow and current are referred to as *through variables*, and are measured with respect to time (flow is litres per second and current is amperes, which are coulombs per second). Pressure and voltage are referred to as *across variables*, and are measured at a point in time.

The flow of money in an organization is measured in a similar way with the income statement and balance sheet. The income statement represents a *through variable* because it summarizes revenues and expenses over a period of time. It is prepared by listing the revenues earned during a period and the expenses incurred during the same period, and by subtracting total expenses from total revenues, arriving at a net income. An income statement is always associated with a particular period of time, be it a month, quarter, or year.

FIGURE 6.3   **Through and Across Variables**

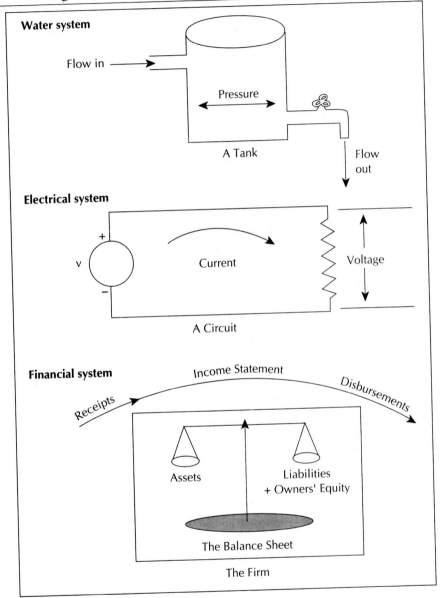

The balance sheet, in contrast to the income statement, is a snapshot of the financial position of a firm at a particular point in time, and so represents an *across variable*. The financial position is summarized by listing the assets of the firm, its liabilities (debts), and the equity of the owner or owners.

TABLE 6.8: Income Statements for Electco Electronics for Years Ended 1994, 1995, 1996

Electco Electronics Income Statements *(in thousands of dollars)*			
	1994	**1995**	**1996**
Revenues			
Sales	12 440	11 934	12 100
Total Revenues	12 440	11 934	12 100
Expenses			
Cost of goods sold (excluding depreciation)	10 100	10 879	11 200
Depreciation	692	554	443
Interest paid	346	344	341
Total Expenses	11 138	11 777	11 984
Profit before taxes	1 302	157	116
Taxes (at 40%)	521	63	46
Profit before extraordinary items	781	94	70
Extraordinary gains/losses	70		
Profit after taxes	851	94	70

The first two financial ratios we address are referred to as **liquidity ratios**. They help us evaluate the ability of a business to weather unforeseen fluctuations in cash flows. A company that does not have a reserve of cash, or other assets that can be converted to cash easily, may not be able to fulfil its short-term obligations.

A company's reserve of cash and assets easily converted to cash is called its working capital. **Working capital** is simply the difference between total current assets and total current liabilities:

Working capital = Current assets − Current liabilities

The adequacy of working capital is commonly measured with two ratios. The first, the **current ratio**, is the ratio of all current assets relative to all current liabilities. The current ratio may also be referred to as the **working capital ratio**.

$$\text{Current ratio} = \frac{\text{Current assets}}{\text{Current liabilities}}$$

Electco Electronics had a current ratio of $4314/$2489 = 1.73 in 1994. Ordinarily, a current ratio of 2 is considered adequate, although this determination may depend a great deal on the composition of current assets. It also may depend on industry standards. In the case of

6.5

Electco, the industry standard can be obtained from Table 6.5. It is $15 296/$9819 = 1.56. It would appear that Electco had a reasonable amount of liquidity in 1994, certainly more than the industry average.

A second ratio, the acid-test ratio, is more conservative than the current ratio. The **acid-test ratio** (also known as the **quick ratio**) is the ratio of quick assets to current liabilities:

$$\text{Acid-test ratio} = \frac{\text{Quick assets}}{\text{Current liabilities}}$$

The acid-test ratio recognizes that some current assets, for example, inventory and prepaid expenses, may be more difficult than others to turn into cash. *Quick assets* are cash, accounts receivable, notes receivable, and temporary investments in marketable securities—those current assets considered to be highly *liquid*.

The acid-test ratio for Electco for 1994 was ($431 + $2489)/$2489 = 1.17. Normally, an acid test ratio of 1 is considered adequate, as this indicates that a firm could meet all its current liabilities with the use of its *quick* current assets if it were necessary. Electco appears to meet this requirement.

The current ratio and the acid-test ratio provide important information about how liquid a firm is, or how well it is able to meet its current financial obligations. The extent to which a firm relies on debt for its operations can be captured by what are called **leverage** or **debt-management ratios**. An example of such a ratio is the **equity ratio**. It is the ratio of total owners' equity to total assets. The smaller this ratio, the more dependent the firm is on debt for its operations and the higher are the risks the company faces.

$$\begin{aligned}
\text{Equity ratio} &= \frac{\text{Total owners' equity}}{\text{Total liabilities} + \text{Total equity}} \\
&= \frac{\text{Total owners' equity}}{\text{Total assets}}
\end{aligned}$$

The equity ratio for Electco in 1994 was $3318/$8296 = 0.40 and the industry average was $12 190/$29 931 = 0.41. Electco has paid for roughly 60% of its assets with debt; the remaining 40% represents equity. This is very close to the industry average and would appear acceptable.

Another group of ratios is called **efficiency** or **asset-management ratios**. One such ratio looks at how efficiently a firm is using its resources to manage its inventories. This is reflected in the number of times that its inventories are replaced (or turned over) per year. The **inventory-turnover ratio** provides a measure of whether the firm has more or less inventory than normal.

$$\text{Inventory-turnover ratio} = \frac{\text{Sales}}{\text{Inventories}}$$

Electco's turnover ratio for 1994 was $12 440/$1244 = 10 turns per year. This is very close to the industry average of $44 153/$4060 = 10.86

turns per year. In 1994, Electco invested roughly the same amount in inventory per dollar of sales as the industry did, on average.

Two points should be observed about the inventory-turnover ratio. First, the sales amount in the numerator has been generated over a period of time, while the inventory amount in the denominator is for one point in time. A more accurate measure of inventory turns would be to approximate the average inventory over the period in which sales were generated.

A second point is that sales refer to market prices, while inventories are listed at cost. The result is that the inventory-turnover ratio as computed above will be an overstatement of the true turnover. It may be more reasonable to compute inventory turnover based on the ratio of cost of goods sold to inventories. Despite this observation, traditional financial analysis uses the sales to inventories ratio.

The next ratio gives evidence of how productively assets have been employed in producing a profit. The **return-on-total-assets** or **net-profit ratio** is an example of a **profitability ratio**:

Return-on-total-assets ratio

$$= \frac{\text{Profits after taxes (but before extraordinary items)}}{\text{Total assets}}$$

The industry average return on total assets for 1994 was $1242/ $29 931 = 0.0415, or 4.15%. Electco had a return on total assets of $781/ $8296 = 0.0941 or 9.41%, roughly twice the industry average. Note the comments on extraordinary items in Close-Up 6.2.

CLOSE-UP 6.2   EXTRAORDINARY ITEMS

Extraordinary items are gains and losses that do not typically result from a company's normal business activities, are not expected to occur regularly, and are not recurring factors in any evaluations of the ordinary operations of the business. Extraordinary items are reported separately from regular items and are listed net of applicable taxes.

Overall, Electco's performance in 1994 is very similar to that of the electronics equipment industry as a whole. The one exception is that Electco generated higher profits than the norm; it may have been extremely efficient in its operations that year.

The rosy profit picture painted for Electco in 1994 does not appear to extend into 1995 and 1996, as a trend analysis shows. Table 6.9 shows the financial ratios computed for 1995 and 1996 with those of 1994 and the industry standard of 1994.

For more convenient reference, we have summarized the five financial ratios we have dealt with and their definitions in Table 6.10.

Electco's return on total assets has dropped significantly over the three-year period. Though the current and quick ratios indicate that Electco should be able to meet its short-term liabilities, there has been a significant buildup of inventories over the period. Electco is not selling what it is manufacturing. This would explain the drop in Electco's inventory turns.

TABLE 6.9: 1994 Industry Standard Ratios and Financial Ratios for Electco Electronics for 1994, 1995, and 1996.

Financial Ratio	Industry Standard	Electco Electronics		
	1994	1994	1995	1996
Current ratio	1.56	1.73	1.88	1.90
Quick ratio		1.17	1.10	0.94
Equity ratio	0.41	0.40	0.39	0.38
Inventory-turnover ratio	10.67	10.00	5.87	4.08
Return-on-total-assets ratio	4.15%	9.41%	1.09%	0.76%

TABLE 6.10: A Summary of Financial Ratios and Definitions

Ratio	Definition	Comments
Current ratio	$\dfrac{\text{Current assets}}{\text{Current liabilities}}$	A liquidity ratio
Acid-test ratio	$\dfrac{\text{Quick assets}}{\text{Current liabilities}}$	A liquidity ratio (quick assets = current assets − inventories − prepaid items)
Equity ratio	$\dfrac{\text{Total equity}}{\text{Total assets}}$	A leverage ratio
Inventory-turn-over ratio	$\dfrac{\text{Sales}}{\text{Inventories}}$	An asset management ratio
Return-on-total-assets ratio	$\dfrac{\text{Profits after taxes}}{\text{Total assets}}$	A profitability ratio (excludes extraordinary items)

Coupled with rising inventory levels is a slight increase in the cost of goods sold over the three years. From the building and equipment figures in the balance sheet, we know that no major capital expenditures on new equipment have occurred during the period. Electco's equipment may be aging and need replacement, though further analysis of what is happening is necessary before any conclusions on this issue can be drawn.

A final observation is that Electco's accounts receivable seems to be growing over the three-year period. Since there may be risks associated with the possibility of bad debt, Electco should probably investigate the matter.

In summary, Electco's main problem appears to be a mismatch between production levels and sales levels. Other areas deserving attention are the increasing cost of goods sold and possible problems with accounts receivable collection. These matters need investigation if Electco is to recover from its current slump in profitability.

We close the section on financial ratios with some cautionary notes on their use. First, since financial statement figures are often approximations, we need to interpret the financial ratios accordingly. In addition, accounting practices vary from firm to firm and may lead to differences in ratio values. Wherever possible, look for explanations of how figures are derived in financial reports.

A second problem encountered in comparing a firm's financial ratios with an industry standard is that it may be difficult to determine what industry the firm best fits into. Furthermore, within each industry, large variations exist. In some cases, an analyst may construct a relevant "average" by searching out a small number of similar firms (in size and business type) that may be used to form a customized industry average.

Finally, it is important to recognize the effect of seasonality on the financial ratios calculated. Many firms have highly seasonal operations and natural high and low periods of activity. An analyst needs to judge these fluctuations in context. One solution to this problem is to adjust the data seasonally through the use of averages. Another is to collect financial data from several seasons so that any deviations from the normal pattern of activity can be picked up.

Despite our cautionary words on the use of financial ratios, they do provide a useful framework for analyzing the financial health of a firm and for answering many questions about its operations.

CANADIAN CORPORATE CASE 6.1

Capital Expenditure or Business Expense?

When a Calgary shopping centre began to experience considerable congestion on the roadways which provided access to the centre, it approached the local municipality to see if the roadways close to the mall could be improved. An agreement was struck with the municipality, and Oxford Shopping Centres Ltd. paid the municipality $450 050 to make the improvements in lieu of any increase in local tax rates which might have otherwise been charged by the municipality.

Was the $450 050 a business expense or a capital expenditure? The issue at hand was whether Oxford Shopping Centres Ltd. could claim the $450 050 as a current expense in the year in which it was paid, or whether the amount had to be amortized over a period of years, with only a fraction of the total amount claimed as an expense each year. The owners of the shopping centre argued that the aim was to increase the popularity of the mall and that the outlay related to the business as a whole rather than an improvement to the physical premises. With this logic, Oxford Shopping Centres Ltd. was allowed to claim the entire amount as an expense in the year in which it was paid.

REVIEW PROBLEMS

Review Problem 6.1

Joan is the sole proprietor of a small lawn care service. Last year, she purchased an eight-horsepower chipper-shredder to make mulch out of small tree branches and leaves. At the time it cost $760. She expects that the value of the chipper-shredder will decline by a constant amount each year over the next six years. At the end of six years, she thinks that it will have a salvage value of $100.

Construct a table that gives the book value of the chipper-shredder at the end of each year, for six years. Also indicate the accumulated depreciation at the end of each year. A spreadsheet may be helpful.

Answer

The depreciation amount for each year is

$$D_{sl}(n) = \frac{(P-S)}{N} = \frac{\$760 - \$100}{6} = \$110 \qquad n = 1, \ldots, 6$$

This is the requested table.

Year	Depreciation Amount	Book Value	Accumulated Depreciation
0		$760	
1	$110	650	$110
2	110	540	220
3	110	430	330
4	110	320	440
5	110	210	550
6	110	100	660

Review Problem 6.2

A three-year-old extruder used in making plastic yogurt cups has a current book value of $168 750. The declining-balance method of depreciation with a rate $d = 0.25$ is used to determine depreciation amounts. What was its original price? What will be its book value two years from now?

Answer

Let the original price of the extruder be P. The book value three years after purchase is $168 750. This means that the original price was

$$BV_{db}(3) = P(1 - d)^3$$
$$\$168\,750 = P(1 - 0.25)^3$$
$$P = \$400\,000$$

The original price was $400 000.

Two years from now, the book value will be the book value five years after purchase.

$$BV_{db}(5) = \$400\ 000(1 - 0.25)^5$$
$$= \$94\ 921.88$$

or

$$BV_{db}(3) = \$168\ 750(1 - 0.25)^2$$
$$= \$94\ 921.88$$

The book value two years from now will be $94 921.88.

Review Problem 6.3

You have been given the following data from the Fine Fishing Factory for the year ending December 31, 1996. Construct an income statement and a balance sheet from the data.

Accounts payable	$ 27 500
Accounts receivable	32 000
Advertising expense	2 500
Bad debts expense	1 100
Buildings, net	14 000
Cash	45 250
Common stock	125 000
Cost of goods sold	311 250
Depreciation expense, buildings	900
Government bonds	25 000
Income taxes	9 350
Insurance expense	600
Interest expense	500
Inventory, December 31, 1996	42 000
Land	25 000
Machinery, net	3 400
Mortgage due May 30, 1999	5 000
Office equipment, net	5 250
Office supplies expense	2 025
Other expenses	7 000
Prepaid expenses	3 000
Retained earnings	?
Salaries expense	69 025
Sales	421 400
Taxes payable	2 500
Wages payable	600

Answer

Solving this problem consists of sorting through the listed amounts and identifying which are balance sheet entries and which are income statement entries. Then, assets can be separated from liabilities and owners' equity, and revenues from expenses.

Fine Fishing Factory **Balance Sheet** **as of December 31, 1996**	
Assets	
Current Assets	
Cash	$ 45 250
Accounts receivable	32 000
Inventory, December 31, 1996	42 000
Prepaid expenses	3 000
Total Current Assets	$122 250
Long-Term Assets	
Land	25 000
Government bonds	25 000
Machinery, net	3 400
Office equipment, net	5 250
Buildings, net	14 000
Total Long-Term Assets	$ 72 650
Total Assets	**$194 900**
Liabilities	
Current Liabilities	
Accounts payable	$ 27 500
Taxes payable	2 500
Wages payable	600
Total Current Liabilities	$ 30 600
Long-Term Liabilities	
Mortgage due May 30, 1999	5 000
Total Long-Term Liabilities	$ 5 000
Total liabilities	**$ 35 600**
Owners' Equity	
Common stock	$125 000
Retained earnings	34 300
Total Owners' Equity	**$159 300**
Total Liabilities and Owners' Equity	**$194 900**

Fine Fishing Factory
Income Statement
for the Year Ending December 31, 1996

Revenues	
Sales	$421 400
Cost of goods sold	311 250
Net revenue from sales	$110 150
Expenses	
Salaries expense	69 025
Bad debts expense	1 100
Advertising expense	2 500
Interest expense	500
Insurance expense	600
Office supplies expense	2 025
Other expenses	7 000
Depreciation expense, buildings	900
Depreciation expense, office equipment	850
Total Expenses	$ 84 500
Profit before taxes	$ 25 650
Income taxes	9 350
Profit after taxes	**$ 16 300**

Review Problem 6.4

Perform a ratio analysis for the Major Electric Company using the balance sheet and income statement from sections 6.3.2 and 6.3.3. Industry standards for the ratios are as follows:

Ratio	Industry Standard
Current ratio	1.80
Acid-test ratio	0.92
Equity ratio	0.71
Inventory-turnover ratio	14.21
Return-on-total-assets ratio	7.91%

Answer

The ratio computations for Major Electric are:

$$\text{Current ratio} = \frac{\text{Current assets}}{\text{Current liabilities}} = \frac{\$801\ 000}{\$90\ 000} = 8.9$$

$$\text{Acid-test ratio} = \frac{\text{Quick assets}}{\text{Current liabilities}} = \frac{\$66\ 000}{\$90\ 000} = 0.73$$

$$\text{Equity ratio} = \frac{\text{Total equity}}{\text{Total assets}} = \frac{\$4\ 311\ 000}{\$5\ 401\ 000} = 0.7982 \approx 0.80$$

$$\text{Inventory-turnover ratio} = \frac{\text{Sales}}{\text{Inventories}} = \frac{\$7\ 536\ 000}{\$683\ 000}$$

$$= 11.03 \text{ turns per year}$$

$$\text{Return-on-total-assets ratio} = \frac{\text{profits after taxes}}{\text{total assets}} = \frac{\$304\ 200}{\$5\ 401\ 000} = 0.0563$$

$$\text{or } 5.63\% \text{ per year}$$

A summary of the ratio analysis results follows:

Ratio	Industry Standard	Major Electric
Current ratio	1.80	8.90
Acid-test ratio	0.92	0.73
Equity ratio	0.71	0.80
Inventory-turnover ratio	14.21	11.03
Return-on-total-assets ratio	7.91%	5.63%

Major Electric's current ratio is well above the industry average and well above the general guideline of 2. They appear to be quite liquid. However, the acid test ratio, with a value of 0.73, gives a slightly different view of Major Electric's liquidity. Most of Major Electric's current assets are inventory; thus, the current ratio is somewhat misleading. If we look at the acid test, Major Electric's quick assets are only 73% of their current liabilities. They may have a difficult time meeting their current debt obligations if they have unforeseen difficulties with their cash flows.

Major Electric's equity ratio of 0.80 indicates that it is not heavily reliant on debt and therefore is not at high risk of going bankrupt. Major Electric's inventory turns are lower than the industry norm, as is their return on total assets.

Taken together, Major Electric appears to be in reasonable financial shape. One matter they should probably investigate is that of why their inventories are so high. With lower inventories, they could improve their inventory turns as well as their return on total assets.

SUMMARY

This chapter opened with a discussion of the concept of depreciation and various reasons why assets lose value. Two popular depreciation models, straight-line and declining-balance, were then presented as methods commonly used to approximate book value of capital assets and depreciation amounts.

The second part of the chapter dealt with the elements of financial accounting. We first presented the two main financial statements: the balance sheet and the income statement. The statement of changes in financial position was also introduced as a means of identifying changes in cash available to the firm. Next, we showed how these statements can be used to assess the financial health of a firm through the use of ratios. Comparisons with industry norms and trend analysis are normally part of financial analysis. We closed with cautionary notes on the interpretation of the ratios.

The significance of the material in this chapter is twofold. First, it sets the groundwork for material in Chapters 7 and 8, replacement analysis and taxation. Second, and perhaps more importantly, it is increasingly necessary for all engineers to have an understanding of depreciation and financial accounting as they become more and more involved in decisions that affect the financial positions of the organizations in which they work.

Engineering Economics in Action, Part 6B: Usually the Truth

Terry had shown Naomi what he thought was evidence of wrongdoing by a fellow employee. Naomi said, "Interesting observation, Terry. But you know, I think it's probably O.K. Let me explain. The main problem is that you are looking at two kinds of evaluation here, book value and market value. The book value is an estimate of what an asset is worth, while the market value is what it sells for."

Terry nodded. "Yes, I know that. That's true about anything you sell. But this is different. We've got a $5000 estimate against a $300 sale. You can't tell me that our guess about the sales price can be that far out!"

"Yes, it can, and I'll tell you why. That book value is an estimate that has been calculated according to very particular rules. The Canadian tax rules require us to use a declining-balance depreciation method for almost all of our assets. They also specify which declining-balance rate to use, which they call the CCA, which stands for capital cost allowance. For most equipment it's 20%. Now, the reality is that things decline in value at different rates, and computers lose value really quickly. We could, for our own purposes, determine a book value for any asset that is a better estimate of its market value, but sometimes it's too much trouble to keep one set of figures for tax reasons and another for other purposes. So often everything is given a book value according to the tax rules, and consequently sometimes the difference between the book value and the market value can be a lot."

> "But surely the government can see that computers in particular don't match that 20% rate. Or are they just ripping us off?"
>
> "Well, they can see that. Until a few years ago, the CCA rate for computers was 20%. But because it was painfully obvious that this rate was too low, it was revised to be 30%. This is still too low, as you can see from the sale of our own computers, but it is better than it was."
>
> Terry smiled ruefully, "So our accounting statements don't really show the truth?"
>
> Naomi smiled back, "I guess not, if by 'truth' you mean market value. But usually they're close. Usually."

PROBLEMS

6.1 An asset costs $14 000 and has a scrap value of $3000 after seven years. Calculate its book value using straight-line depreciation:

(a) after one year

(b) after four years

(c) after seven years

6.2 An asset costs $14 000. At a depreciation rate of 20%, calculate its book value using declining-balance depreciation:

(a) after one year

(b) after four years

(c) after seven years

6.3 An asset costs $14 000 and has a scrap value of $3000 after seven years.

(a) What depreciation rate could be used to estimate the book value of the asset using the declining-balance method?

(b) Using this depreciation rate, what is the book value of the asset after four years?

6.4 Using a spreadsheet program, chart the book value of a $14 000 asset over a seven-year life using declining-balance depreciation ($d = 0.2$). On the same chart, show the book value of the $14 000 asset, using straight-line depreciation, with a scrap value of $3000 after seven years.

6.5 Using a spreadsheet program, chart the book value of a $150 000 asset for the first 10 years of its life at depreciation rates of 5%, 20%, and 30%.

6.6 A machine has a life of 30 years, costs $245 000, and has a salvage value of $10 000 using straight-line depreciation. What depreciation rate will result in the machine's having the same book value for both the declining-balance and straight-line methods in year 20?

6.7 A new press brake costs Medicine Hat Steel $780 000. It is expected to last 20 years, with a $60 000 salvage value. What rate of depreciation for the declining-balance method will produce a book value after 20 years that equals the salvage value of the press?

6.8 (a) Using straight-line depreciation, what is the book value after four years for an asset costing $150 000 that has a salvage value of $25 000 after 10 years? What is the depreciation charge during the fifth year?

(b) Using declining-balance depreciation with $d = 20\%$, what is the book value after four years for an asset costing $150 000? What is the depreciation charge during the fifth year?

(c) What is the depreciation rate using declining-balance for an asset costing $150 000 that has a salvage value of $25 000 after 10 years?

6.9 Julia must choose between two different designs for a safety enclosure, which will be in use indefinitely. Model A has a life of three years, a first cost of $8000, and maintenance of $1000 per year. Model B will last four years, has a first cost of $10 000, and has maintenance of $800 per year. A salvage value can be estimated for Model A using a depreciation rate of 40% and declining-balance depreciation, while a salvage value for Model B can be estimated using straight-line depreciation and the knowledge that after one year its salvage value will be $7500. Interest is at 14%. Using a present worth analysis, which design is better?

6.10 A company had net sales of $20 000 last month. From the balance sheet for the end of last month, and an income statement for the month, you have determined that the current ratio was 2.0, the acid-test ratio was 1.2, and the inventory turnover was 2 per month. What was the value of the company's current assets?

6.11 A potentially very large customer for Chicoutimi Metals wants to fully assess the financial health of the company in order to decide whether to commit to a long-term, high-volume relationship. You have been asked by the company president, Roch, to review the company's financial performance over the last three years and make a complete report to him. He will then select from your report information to present to the customer. Consequently, your report should be as thorough and honest as possible.

Research has revealed that in your industry (sheet metal products), the average value of the current ratio is 2.79, the equity ratio is 0.54, the inventory turnover is 4.9, and the net-profit ratio is 3.87. Beyond that information, you have access to only the balance sheet on page 221 and the income statement on page 222, and should make no further assumptions. Your report should be limited to the equivalent of about 300 words.

Chicoutimi Metals Consolidated Balance Sheets December 31, 1996, 1997, and 1998 *(in thousands of dollars)*			

Assets

	1998	1997	1996
Current Assets			
Cash	19	19	24
Accounts receivable	779	884	1 176
Inventories	3 563	3 155	2 722
	4 361	4 058	3 922
Fixed Assets			
Land	1 136	1 064	243
Buildings and equipment	2 386	4 682	2 801
	3 552	5 746	3 044
Other Assets	413	....	3
Total Assets	8 296	9 804	6 969

Liabilities and Owners' Equity

	1998	1997	1996
Current Liabilities			
Due to bank	1 431	1 929	2 040
Accounts payable	1 644	1 349	455
Wages payable	341	312	333
Income tax payable	562	362	147
Long-Term Debt	2 338	4 743	2 528
Total Liabilities	6 316	8 695	5 503
Owners' Equity			
Capital stock	1 194	1 191	1 091
Retained earnings	786	(82)	375
Total Owner's Equity	1 980	1 109	1 466
Total Liability and Owners' Equity	8 296	9 804	6 969

6.12 The Chicoutimi Metals income statement and balance sheets shown in problem 6.11 were in error. A piece of production equipment was sold for $100 000 cash in 1998 and was not accounted for. Which items on these statements must be changed, and (if known) by how much?

Chicoutimi Metals Income Statement for the years ending December 31, 1996, 1997, and 1998 (in thousands of dollars)			
	1998	1997	1996
Total revenue	9 355	9 961	8 470
Less: Costs	8 281	9 632	7 654
Net revenue	1 074	329	816
Less: Depreciation	447	431	398
Interest	412	334	426
Income taxes	117	21	156
Net income from operations	98	(457)	(164)
Add: Extraordinary item	770		(1 832)
Net income	868	(457)	(1 996)

6.13 The Chicoutimi Metals income statement and balance sheet shown in problem 6.11 were in error. An extra $100 000 in sales was made in 1998 and not accounted for. Only half of the payments for these sales have been received. Which items on these statements must be changed, and (if known) by how much?

6.14 At the end of last month, Estevan Manufacturing had $45 954 in the bank. They owed the bank, because of their mortgage, $224 000. They also had a working capital loan of $30 000. Their customers owed them $22 943, and they owed their suppliers $12 992. The company owned property worth $250 000. They had $123 000 in finished goods, $102 000 in raw materials, and $40 000 in work in progress. Their production equipment was worth $450 000 when new (partially paid for by a large government loan due to be paid back in three years) but had accumulated a total of $240 000 in depreciation, $34 000 worth last month.

The company has investors who put up $100 000 for their ownership. It has been reasonably profitable; this month the gross income from sales was $220 000, and the cost of the sales was only $40 000. Expenses were also relatively low; salaries were $45 000 last month, while the other expenses were depreciation, maintenance at $1500, advertising at $3400, and insurance at $300. In spite of $32 909 in accrued taxes (they pay taxes at 55%), the company had retained earnings of $135 000.

Using a spreadsheet program, construct a balance sheet (at the end of this month) and income statement (for this month) for Estevan Manufacturing. Should the company release some of its retained earnings through dividends at this time?

6.15 Brandon Industries bought land and built its plant 20 years ago. The depreciation on the building is calculated using the straight-line method, with a life of 30 years and a salvage value of $50 000. The land is not depreciating. The depreciation for the equipment, all of which was purchased at the same time the plant was constructed, is calculated using declining-balance at 20%. Brandon currently has two outstanding loans, one for $50 000 due December 31, this year, and another one for which the next payment is due in four years.

Brandon Industries Balance Sheet as of June 30, 1995		
Assets		
Cash		$ 350 000
Accounts receivable		2 820 000
Inventories		2 003 000
Prepaid services		160 000
Total Current Assets		
Long-Term Assets		
Building	$200 000	
Less accumulated depreciation		
Equipment	$480 000	
Less accumulated depreciation		
Land		540 000
Total Long-Term Assets		
Total Assets		
Liabilities and Owners' Equity		
Current Liabilities		
Accounts payable		$ 921 534
Accrued taxes		29 000
Total		
Long-Term Liabilities		
Mortgage		$1 200 000
		318 000
Total Long-Term Liabilities		
Total		
Owners' Equity		
Capital stock		$1 920 000
Total Owners' Equity		
Total Liabilities and Owners' Equity		

During April 1995, there was a flood in the building because a nearby river overflowed its banks after unusually heavy rain. Pumping out the water and cleaning up the basement and the first floor of the building took a week. Manufacturing was suspended during this period, and some inventory was damaged. Because of lack of adequate insurance, this unusual and unexpected event cost the company $100 000 net.

(a) Complete a copy of the balance sheet on page 223 and the income statement below, using any of the above information you feel necessary.

(b) Show how information from financial ratios can indicate whether Brandon Industries can manage an unusual and unexpected event such as the flood without threatening its existence as a viable business.

Brandon Industries
Income Statement for the Year Ended June 30, 1995

Income

Gross income from sales	$8 635 000	
Less _____	7 490 000	=========
Total income		
Depreciation		70 000
Interest paid		240 000
Other expenses		100 000
Total expenses		
Profit before taxes		
Taxes at 40%		
Profit after taxes		

6.16 Movit Manufacturing has the following alphabetized income statement and balance sheet entries from the year 1996. Construct an income statement and a balance sheet from the information given.

Accounts payable	$ 7 500
Accounts receivable	15 000
Accrued wages	2 850
Cash	2 100
Common shares	150
Contributed capital	3 000
Cost of goods sold	57 000
Current assets	

Current liabilities	
Deferred income taxes	2 250
Depreciation expense	750
General expense	8 100
GIC's	450
Income taxes	1 800
Interest expense	1 500
Inventories	18 000
Land	3 000
Less: Accumulated depreciation	10 950
Long-term assets	
Long-term bonds	4 350
Long-term liabilities	
Mortgage	9 450
Net income after taxes	2 700
Net income before taxes	4 500
Net plant and equipment	7 500
Net sales	76 500
Operating expenses	
Owners' equity	
Prepaid expenses	450
Selling expenses	4 650
Total assets	46 500
Total current assets	36 000
Total current liabilities	15 000
Total expenses	15 000
Total liabilities and owners' equity	46 500
Total long-term assets	10 500
Total long-term liabilities	16 050
Total owners' equity	15 450
Working capital loan	4 650

6.17 Calculate for Movit Manufacturing for 1996 the financial ratios listed in the table below. (See problem 6.16.) Using these ratios and those provided for 1994 and 1995, conduct a short analysis of Movit's financial health.

Movit Manufacturing Financial Ratios			
Ratio	1996	1995	1994
Current ratio		1.90	1.60
Acid-test ratio		0.90	0.75
Equity ratio		0.40	0.55
Inventory-turns ratio		7.00	12.00
Return-on-total-assets ratio		0.08	0.10

6.18 Léger Lites' balance sheets for year-ends 1996 and 1997 and their 1997 income statement follow. Construct a statement of changes in financial position for the year ended in 1997. Use the major headings given on page 227 to summarize the changes in financial position.

Léger Lites Company Comparative Balance Sheets for the years ending December 31, 1996 and 1997 *(in thousands of dollars)*		
	1996	**1997**
Assets		
Current Assets		
Cash	3 750	3 500
GIC's	750	750
Accounts receivable	21 250	25 000
Inventories	28 250	30 000
Prepaid expenses	500	750
Total Current Assets	54 500	60 000
Long-Term Assets		
Land	5 000	5 000
Plant and equipment	28 000	30 750
Less: Accumulated depreciation	17 000	18 250
Net Plant and Equipment	11 000	12 500
Total Long-Term Assets	16 000	17 500
Total Assets	70 500	77 500
Liabilities and Owner's Equity		
Current Liabilities		
Accounts payable	9 250	12 500
Accrued wages	2 250	4 750
Working capital loan	9 500	7 750
Total Current Liabilities	21 000	25 000
Long-Term Liabilities		
Deferred income taxes	3 500	3 750
Mortgage	16 500	15 750
Long term bonds	7 500	7 250
Total Long-Term Liabilities	27 500	26 750
Owners' Equity		
Common shares	250	250
Contributed capital	5 000	5 000
Retained earnings	16 750	20 500
Total Owners' Equity	22 000	25 750
Total Liabilities and Owners' Equity	70 500	77 500

Léger Lites **Income Statement** **for the Year Ended December 31, 1997** *(in thousands of dollars)*	
Net sales	127 500
Cost of goods sold	(95 000)
Gross profit	32 500
Operating expenses	
Selling expenses	7 750
Depreciation expense	1 250
General expense	13 500
Interest expense	2 500
Total expenses	25 000
Net income before taxes	7 500
Income taxes	3 000
Net income after taxes	4 500
Common dividends paid	750
Increase in retained earnings	3 750

(1) Cash from operating activities (Include all inflows and outflows.)

(2) Cash from financial activities (This includes new debt or debt repayment, and dividend payments.)

(3) Cash from investing activities (Sale or acquisition of assets)

(4) Total cash increase (decrease)

Check to verify that the total cash increase or decrease is consistent with the cash amounts which appear on Léger Lites' balance sheets for year-ends 1996 and 1997.

6.19 Refer back to the year-end balance sheets and income statements for Electco Electronics (Tables 6.7 and 6.8). Construct a statement of changes in financial position for the 1996 year-end. Include the following major sections in your statement:

(1) Cash from operating activities (Include all inflows and outflows.)

(2) Cash from financial activities (This includes new debt or debt repayment, and dividend payments.)

(3) Cash from investing activities (Sale or acquisition of assets)

(4) Total cash increase (decrease)

Check to verify that the total cash increase or decrease is consistent with the cash amounts which appear in Electco Electronics' balance sheets for year ends 1995 and 1996.

6.20 Fraser Phraser operates a small publishing company. He is interested in getting a loan for expanding his computer systems. The bank has asked Phraser to supply them with his financial statements from the past two years. His statements appear below. Comment on Phraser's financial position with regard to the loan, using a financial ratio analysis.

Fraser Phraser Company Comparative Balance Sheets for the Years Ending in 1995 and 1996 *(in thousands of dollars)*		
	1995	**1996**
Assets		
Current Assets		
Cash	22 500	1 250
Accounts receivable	31 250	40 000
Inventories	72 500	113 750
Total Current Assets	126 250	155 000
Long-Term Assets		
Land	50 000	65 000
Plant and equipment	175 000	250 000
Less: Accumulated depreciation	70 000	95 000
Net Plant and equipment	105 000	155 000
Total Long-Term Assets	155 000	220 000
Total Assets	281 250	375 000
Liabilities and Owners' Equity		
Current Liabilities		
Accounts payable	26 250	55 000
Working capital loan	42 500	117 500
Total Current Liabilities	68 750	172 500
Long-Term Liabilities		
Mortgage	71 875	57 375
Total Long-Term Liabilities	71 875	57 375
Owners' Equity		
Common shares	78 750	78 750
Retained earnings	61 875	66 375
Total Owners' Equity	140 625	145 125
Total Liabilities and Owners' Equity	281 250	375 000

Fraser Phraser Income Statements for Years Ending in 1995 and 1996 *(in thousands of dollars)*		
	1995	**1996**
Revenues		
Sales	156 250	200 000
Cost of goods sold	93 750	120 000
Net revenue from sales	62 500	80 000
Expenses		
Operating expenses	41 875	46 250
Depreciation expense	5 625	12 500
Interest expense	3 750	7 625
Total expenses	51 250	66 375
Profit before Taxes	11 250	13 625
Income taxes	5 625	6 813
Profit after Taxes	5 625	6 813

6.21 Complete a statement of changes in financial position for 1996 from the financial statements for Fraser Phraser from problem 6.20. Does this provide you with additional information for the bank with respect to its decision to give Phraser the loan?

6.22 A friend of yours is thinking of purchasing shares in Petit Ourson Ltée in the near future, and decided that it would be prudent to examine its financial statements for the past two years before making a phone call to his stockbroker. The statements are shown on pages 230 and 231.

Your friend has asked you to help him conduct a financial ratio analysis. Fill out the financial ratio information on a copy of the table below. After comparison with industry standards, what advice would you give your friend?

Petit Ourson Ltée Financial Ratios			
	Industry Norm	**1995**	**1996**
Current ratio	4.500		
Acid-test ratio	2.750		
Equity ratio	0.600		
Inventory-turns ratio	2.200		
Return-on-total-assets ratio	0.090		

	Petit Ourson Ltée. Comparative Balance Sheets for the Years Ending 1995 and 1996 (*in thousands of dollars*)	1995	1996
Assets			
Current Assets			
Cash		500	375
Accounts receivable		1 125	1 063
Inventories		1 375	1 563
Total Current Assets		3 000	3 000
Long-Term Assets			
Plant and equipment		5 500	6 500
Less: Accumulated depreciation		2 500	3 000
Net Plant and Equipment		3 000	3 500
Total Long-Term Assets		3 000	3 500
Total Assets		6 000	6 500
Liabilities and Owners' Equity			
Current Liabilities			
Accounts payable		500	375
Working capital loan		000	375
Total Current Liabilities		500	750
Long-Term Liabilities			
Bonds		1 500	1 500
Total Long-Term Liabilities		1 500	1 500
Owners' Equity			
Common shares		750	750
Contributed capital		1 500	1 500
Retained earnings		1 750	2 000
Total Owners' Equity		4 000	4 250
Total Liabilities and Owners' Equity		6 000	6 500

6.23 Construct an income statement and a balance sheet from the following scrambled entries for Paradise Pond Company from the years 1995 and 1996.

Petit Ourson Ltée Income Statements for the Years Ending in 1995 and 1996 *(in thousands of dollars)*		
	1995	**1996**
Revenues		
Sales	3 000	3 625
Cost of goods sold	1 750	2 125
Net revenue from sales	1 250	1 500
Expenses		
Operating expenses	75	100
Depreciation expense	550	500
Interest expense	125	150
Total expenses	750	750
Profit before Taxes	500	750
Income taxes	200	300
Profit after Taxes	300	450

	1995	**1996**
Accounts receivable	$ 675	$ 638
Less: Accumulated depreciation	1 500	1 800
Accounts payable	300	225
Bonds	900	900
Cash	300	225
Common shares	450	450
Contributed capital	900	900
Cost of goods sold	1 750	2 125
Depreciation expense	550	500
Income taxes	200	300
Interest expense	125	150
Inventories	825	938
Net plant and equipment	1 800	2 100
Net revenue from sales	1 250	1 500
Operating expenses	075	100
Plant and equipment	3 300	3 900
Profit after taxes	300	450
Profit before taxes	500	750
Retained earnings	1 050	1 200
Sales	3 000	3 625
Total assets	3 600	3 900
Total current assets	1 800	1 800
Total current liabilities	300	450
Total expenses	750	750
Total liabilities and owners' equity	3 600	3 900
Total long-term assets	1 800	2 100
Total long-term liabilities	900	900
Total owners' equity	2 400	2 550
Working capital loan	000	225

AN EXTENDED CASE

WELCOME TO THE REAL WORLD

A.1 Introduction

Clem looked up from his computer as Naomi walked into his office. "Hi, Naomi. Sit down. Just let me save this stuff."

After a few seconds Clem turned around showing a grin. "I'm working on our report for the last quarter's operations. Things went pretty well. We exceeded our targets on defect reductions, and on reducing overtime. And we shipped everything required—over 90% on time."

Naomi caught a bit of Clem's exuberance. "Sounds like a report you don't mind writing."

"Yeah, well, it was a team job. Everyone did good work. Talking about doing good work, I should have told you this before, but I didn't think about it at the right time. Ed Burns and Anna Kulkowski were really impressed with the report you did on the forge project."

Naomi leaned forward. "But they didn't follow my recommendation to get a new manual counterblow machine. I assumed there was something wrong with what I did."

"I read your report carefully before I sent it over to them. If there had been something wrong with it, you would have heard right away. Trust me. I'm not shy. It's just that we were a little short of cash at the time. We could stay in business with just fixing up the guides on the old forging hammer. And Burns and Kulkowski decided there were more important things to do with our money.

"If I didn't have confidence in you, you wouldn't be here this morning. I'm going to ask you and Dave Sullivan to look into an important strategic issue concerning whether or not we continue to buy small aluminum parts or whether we make them ourselves. We're just waiting for Dave to show up."

"O.K. Thanks, Clem. But please tell me next time if what I do is all right. I'm still finding my way around here."

"You're right. I guess that I'm still more of an engineer than a manager."

Voices carried into Clem's office from the corridor. "That sounds like Dave in the hall saying hello to Carole," Naomi observed. "It looks like we can get started."

Dave Sullivan came in with long strides and dropped into a chair. "Good morning, everybody. It is still morning, barely. Sorry to be late. What's up?"

Clem looked at Dave and started talking. "What's up is this. I want you and Naomi to look into our policy about buying or making small aluminum parts. We now use about 200 000 pieces a month. Most of these, like bolts and sleeves, are cold formed.

"Prabha Vaidyanathan has just done a market projection for us. If she's right, our demand for these parts will continue to grow. Unfortunately, she wasn't very precise about the *rate* of growth. Her estimate was for anything between 5% and 15% a year. We now contract this work out. But even if growth is only 5%, we may be at the level where it pays for us to start doing this work ourselves.

"You remember we had a couple of engineers from Hamilton Tools looking over our processes last week? Well, they've come back to us with an offer to sell us a cold former. They have two possibilities. One is a high-volume job that is a version of their Model E2. The other is a low-volume machine based on their Model E1.

"The E2 will do about 2000 pieces an hour, depending on the sizes of the parts and the number of change-overs we make. The E1 will do about 1000 pieces an hour."

Naomi asked, "About how many hours per year will these formers run?"

"Well, with our two shifts, I think we're talking about 3600 hours a year for either model."

Dave came in with, "Hold it. If my third grade arithmetic still works, that sounds like either 3.6 million or 7.2 million pieces a year. You say that we are using only 2.4 million pieces a year."

Clem answered with, "That's right. Ms. Vaidyanathan has an answer to that one. She says we can sell excess capacity until we need it ourselves. Again, unfortunately, she isn't very precise about what this means. We now pay about five cents a piece. Metal cost is in addition to that. We pay for that by weight. She says that we won't get as much as five cents because we don't have the market connections. But she says we should be able to find a broker so that we net somewhere between three cents and four cents a piece, again plus metal."

Naomi spoke. "That's a pretty wide range, Clem."

"I know. Prabha says that she couldn't do any better with the budget Burns and Kulkowski gave her. For another $5000, she says that she can narrow the range on *either* the growth rate or the potential prices for selling pieces from any excess capacity. Or, for about $7500, she could do both. I spoke to Anna Kulkowski about this. Anna says that they won't approve anything over $5000. One of the things I want you two to look at is whether or not it's necessary to get more information. If you do recommend spending on market research, it has to be for just one of either the selling price range or the growth rate.

"I have the proposal from Hamilton Tools here. It has information on the two formers. This is Wednesday. I'd like a report from you by Friday afternoon so that I can look at it over the weekend.

"Did I leave anything out?"

Naomi asked, "Are we still working with a 15% after-tax MARR?"

Clem hesitated. "This is just a first cut. Don't worry about details on taxes. We can do a more precise calculation before we actually make a decision. Just bump up the MARR to 25% before tax. That will about cover our 40% marginal tax rate."[1]

Dave asked, "What time frame should we use in our calculations?"

"Right. Use 10 years. Either of these models should last at least that long. But I wouldn't want to stretch Prabha's market projections beyond 10 years."

Dave stood up and announced, "It's about a quarter to one." He turned to Naomi. "Do you want to start on this over at the Grand China Restaurant? It's past the lunch rush, and we'll be able to talk while we eat. I think Clem will buy us lunch out of his budget."

Clem interjected. "All right, Dave. Just don't order the most expensive thing on the menu."

Naomi laughed. "I'm glad we have one big spender around here."

A.2 Problem Definition

About forty minutes later, Dave and Naomi were most of the way through their main courses. Dave suggested that they get started. He took a pad from his brief case and said that he would take notes. Naomi agreed to let him do that.

---

[1] Businesses in Canada and the United States are required to pay tax on their earnings. Determining the effect of taxes on after-tax earnings may involve extensive computation. Managers frequently approximate the effect of taxes on decisions by increasing the MARR. However, it is good practice to do precise calculations before actually making a decision.

Dave started with, "O.K. What are our options?"

"Well, I did a bit of arithmetic on my calculator while you were on the phone before lunch. It looks as though, even if the demand growth rate is only 5%, a single small former will not have enough capacity to see us through 10 years. This means that there are four options. The first is a sequence of two low capacity formers. The second is just a high capacity former. The third, which would kick in only if the growth rate is high, would be a sequence of three low capacity formers. The fourth is a low capacity and a high capacity. I'm not sure of the sequence for that."

Dave thought for a bit. "I don't think so. I assume that, even if we put in our own former, we could contract out requirements that our own shop couldn't handle. That might be the way to go. That is, you wouldn't want to add to capacity if there were only one year left in the 10-year horizon. There probably would not be enough unsatisfied output requirement to amortize the first cost of a second small former."

"That sounds as though there are a whole bunch of options. It looks like we're in for a couple of long nights." Naomi sounded dejected.

"Well, maybe not."

"Maybe not what?"

"Maybe we won't have to spend those long nights. I think we can look at just three options at the start. We could look at a sequence of two small formers. We could look at a small former followed by outsourcing when capacity is exhausted. And we could look at a large former, possibly followed by outsourcing if capacity is exhausted. If we can rule out the two-small-formers option, we can certainly rule out three small formers or a big former combined with a small one."

"Smart, Dave. How should we proceed?"

"Well, there are a couple of ways of doing this. But, given that we have only 10 years to look at, it's probably easiest to use a spreadsheet to develop cash flow sequences for the three options. The two options in which only a single machine is bought at time zero are pretty straightforward. The one with a sequence of two small formers is a bit more complicated. One of us can do the two easy ones. The other can do the sequence. For each option we need to look at, say, nine outcomes: three possible demand growth rates—5%, 10%, and 15%—times three possible prices—3¢, 3.5¢, and 4¢—for selling excess capacity. That should be enough to show us what's happening. What part do you want to do?"

"I'll take the hard one, the sequence of two. I'd like the practice. I'll let you check my analysis when I'm finished."

"O.K. That's fine. But notice that the two-low-capacity-formers sequence is not a simple investment, so let's stick with present worths at this stage. Also, we are going to have to make some decision about how we record the timing of the purchase of the second former if we run out of capacity during a year. I suggest that we assume that the second former is bought at the end of the year before we run out of capacity."

"O.K."

Dave continued with, "We need to put together a simple table on the specifications for these two machines. I'll do that, since you are doing the hard job with cash flows. "Why don't we go back to the plant. I'll make up the table. I'll get you a copy later this afternoon."

A.3 Crunch Time

Naomi was sitting in her office thinking about structuring the cash flows for the two-small-machine sequence. Dave knocked and came in. He handed Naomi a sheet of paper.

TABLE A.1: Specifications for the Two Formers

Characteristic	Model E1 (Small)		Model E2 (Large)		
First cost ($)	125 000		225 000		
Hourly running cost ($)	35.00		61.25		
Average number of pieces/hour	1 000		2 000		
Hours/year	3 600		3 600		
Depreciation	20%/year declining balance, for both models				
Market facts	Buying price—$0.05/piece plus cost of metal Selling price—$0.03 to $0.04 per piece plus metal Demand growth rate—5% to 15%				

"Here's the table, as promised. Shall we meet tomorrow morning to compare results?"

"O.K. What time?"

"Why don't we exchange results first thing in the morning and then meet about nine-thirty in my office?"

"That's fine. See you then."

Naomi then looked at Dave's table, shown in Table A.1.

A.4. Comparing Results

The next morning, Naomi knocked on Dave's door. Dave shouted an invitation to come in.

"What do you think, Naomi?"

"It looks as if the two-small-machine option is out. But I can't decide what to say about the other two options. At low growth rates and low prices for excess capacity, the small-machine option looks better. At high growth rates and high prices for excess capacity, the large-machine option looks better."

"Welcome to the real world, Naomi, where nothing is simple."

The two engineers talked for some time after that before they agreed on what should go into the report to Clem.

QUESTIONS

1. Construct cash flow tables and compute present worths for the three options for all nine combinations of prices and demand growth rates. Sample tables appear on page 236 as Tables A.2 and A.3.

2. Write a report to Clem concerning the project. The report should contain a tentative recommendation about which option looks best. It should also make a recommendation about what additional research, if any, should be done.

TABLE A.2: Cash Flows for the Option of Two E1 Models in Sequence

Growth = 10%; selling price = $0.035											
Year	0	1	2	3	4	5	6	7	8	9	10	PW(25%)
Running cost		-126 000	-126 000	-126 000	-126 000	-126 000	-219 975	-252 000	-252 000	-252 000	-252 000	
Saving	0	120 000	132 000	145 200	159 720	175 692	193 261	212 587	233 846	257 231	282 954	
Sales of excess	0	42 000	33 600	24 360	14 196	3 016	84 693	103 189	88 308	71 939	53 932	
Capital expenditures or salvage	-125 000	0	0	0	0	-125 000	0	0	0	0	543 382	
Net cash flow	-125 000	36 000	39 600	43 560	47 916	-72 292	57 978	63 776	70 154	77 169	139 268	13 039

TABLE A.3: Cash Flows for the Option of a Single E1 Model

Growth = 10%; selling price = $0.035											
Year	0	1	2	3	4	5	6	7	8	9	10	PW(25%)
Running cost	0	-126 000	-126 000	-126 000	-126 000	-126 000	-126 000	-126 000	-126 000	-126 000	-126 000	
Saving	0	120 000	132 000	145 200	159 720	175 692	180 000	180 000	180 000	180 000	180 000	
Sales of excess	0	42 000	33 600	24 360	14 196	3 016	0	0	0	0	0	
Capital expenditures or salvage	-125 000	0	0	0	0	0	0	0	0	0	13 422	
Net cash flow	-125 000	36 000	39 600	43 560	47 916	52 708	54 000	54 000	54 000	54 000	67 422	37 372

Replacement Decisions

Engineering Economics in Action, Part 7A: You Need the Facts

7.1   Introduction

7.2   Reasons for Replacement or Retirement

7.3   The Relevance of Capacity Costs

7.4   The Irrelevance of Sunk Costs

7.5   Economic Life and Cyclic Replacement

7.6   Challenger Is Different from Defender

      7.6.1   Sequence of Identical Challengers

      7.6.2   Challenger Is Not Repeated

Canadian Corporate Case 7.1: Canadians Holding on to Vehicles Longer

Review Problems

Summary

Engineering Economics in Action, Part 7B: Decision Time

Problems

Engineering Economics in Action, Part 7A: You Need the Facts

"You know the 5-stage progressive die that we use for the Admiral Motors rocker arm contract?" Naomi was speaking to Terry, her co-op student, one Tuesday afternoon. "Clem asked me to look into replacing it with a 10-stage progressive die that would reduce the hand finishing substantially. It's mostly a matter of labour cost saving, but there is likely to be some quality improvement with the 10-stage die as well. I would like you to come up with a ball-park estimate of the cost of switching to the 10-stage progressive die."

Terry asked, "Don't you have the cost from the supplier?"

"Yes, but not really," said Naomi. "The supplier is Hamilton Tools. They've given us a price for the machine, but there are a lot of other costs involved in replacing one production process with another."

"You mean things like putting the machine in place?" Terry asked.

"Well, there's that," responded Naomi. "But there is also a lot more. For example, we will lose production during the changeover. That's going to cost us something."

"Is that part of the cost of the 10-stage die?"

"It's part of the first cost of switching to the 10-stage die," Naomi said. "If we decide to go ahead with the 10-stage die and incur these costs, we'll never recover them — they are sunk. We have already incurred those costs for the 5-stage die and it's only two years old. It still has lots of life in it. If the first costs of the 10-stage die are large, it's going to be hard to make a cost justification for switching to the 10-stage die at this time."

"O.K. How do I go about this?" Terry asked.

Naomi sat back and chewed on her yellow pencil for about 15 seconds. She leaned forward and began. "Let's start with order of magnitude estimates of what it's going to cost to get the 10-stage die in place. If it looks as if there is no way that the 10-stage die is going to be cost effective now, we can just stop there."

"It sounds like a lot of fuzzy work," said Terry.

"Terry, I know you like to be working with mathematical models. I'm also sure that you can read the appropriate sections on replacement models in an engineering economics book. But none of those models is worth anything unless you have data to put in it. You need the models to know what information to look for. And once you have the information, you will make better decisions using the models. But you do need the facts."

7.1   Introduction

Survival of businesses in a competitive environment requires regular evaluation of the plant and equipment they use in production. As these assets age, they may not provide adequate quality, or their costs may become excessive. When plant or equipment is evaluated, one of four mutually exclusive choices will be made:

1. An existing asset may be kept in its current use without major change.

2. An existing asset may be overhauled so as to improve its performance.

3. An existing asset may be removed from use without replacement by another asset.

4. An existing asset may be replaced with another asset.

This chapter is concerned with methods of making choices about possible replacement of long-lived assets. While the comparison methods developed in Chapters 4 and 5 for choosing between alternatives are often used for making these choices, the issues of replacement deserve a separate chapter for several reasons. First, the relevant costs for making replacement decisions are not always obvious, since there are costs associated with taking the replaced assets out of service that should be considered. This was ignored in the studies in Chapters 4 and 5. Second, the service lives of assets were provided to the reader in Chapters 4 and 5. As seen in this chapter, the principles of replacement allow the calculation of these service lives. Third, assumptions about how an asset might be replaced in the future can affect a decision now. Some of these assumptions are implicit in the methods analysts use to make the choices. It is therefore important to be aware of these assumptions when making replacement decisions.

The chapter starts with a consideration of the reasons why a long-lived asset may be replaced. In the following section we consider the built-in cost advantage of existing assets. Then, the idea of the **economic life** of an asset is developed. This is the life that minimizes the average cost of using the asset. We then consider replacement of an asset with a new asset that is identical to the current asset. This is followed by a discussion of replacement with an asset that differs from the current asset.

We shall not consider the implications of taxes for replacement decisions in this chapter. This is postponed until Chapter 8. We shall assume in this chapter that no future price changes are expected. The effect of expected price changes on replacement decisions will be considered in Chapter 9.

7.2 Reasons for Replacement or Retirement

An existing asset is **retired** if it is removed from use without being replaced. This can happen if the service that the asset provides is no longer needed. Changes in customer demand, changes in production methods, or changes in technology may result in an asset's no longer being necessary. For example, the growth in the use of compact discs for audio recordings has led manufacturers of cassette tapes to retire production equipment since the service it provided is no longer needed.

If there is an ongoing need for the service an asset provides, at some point it will need *replacement*. Replacement becomes necessary if there is a cheaper way to get the service the asset provides, or if the service provided by the existing asset is no longer adequate.

There may be a cheaper way to get the service provided by the existing asset for several reasons. First, productive assets often deteriorate over time because of wearing out in use, or simply because of the effect of time. As a familiar example, an automobile becomes less valuable with age (older cars, unless they are collectors' cars, are worth less than newer cars with the same mileage) or if it has a high mileage (the kilometres driven reflect the wear on the vehicle). Similarly, production equipment may become less productive or more costly to operate over time. It is usually more expensive to maintain older assets. They need fixing more often, and parts may be harder to find and may cost more.

Technological or organizational change can also bring about cheaper methods of providing service than the method used by an existing asset. For example, the technological changes associated with the use of computers have improved productivity. Organizational changes, both within a company and in markets outside the company, can lead to lower-cost methods of production. A form of organizational change that has become very popular is the specialist company. These companies take on parts of the production activities of other companies. Their specialization may enable them to have lower costs than the companies can attain themselves. See Close-Up 7.1.

CLOSE-UP 7.1   SPECIALIST COMPANIES

Specialist companies concentrate on a limited range of very specialized products. They develop the expertise to produce these products at minimal cost. Larger firms often find it more economical to contract out production of low volume components instead of manufacturing the components themselves.

In some industries, the use of specialist companies is so pervasive that the companies apparently producing a product actually are simply assembling it; the manufacturing takes place at dozens or sometimes hundreds of supplier firms.

A good example of this is the automotive industry. In North America, auto makers support an extremely large network of specialist companies, linked by computer. A single specialist company might supply brake pads, for example, to all three major auto manufacturers. Producing brake pads in huge quantities, the specialist firm can refine its production process to extremes of efficiency and profitability.

The second major reason why a current asset may be replaced is inadequacy. An asset used in production can become inadequate because it has insufficient capacity to meet growing demand or because it no longer produces items of high enough quality. When the quantity of output demanded has increased, an existing asset may not be able to meet the higher demand. A company may have a choice between adding new capacity parallel to the existing capacity, or replacing the existing asset with a higher capacity asset, perhaps one with more advanced technology. If higher quality is required, there may be a choice between upgrading an existing piece of equipment or replacing it with equipment that will yield the higher quality. In either case, contracting out the work to a specialist is a possibility.

In summary, there are two main reasons for replacing an existing asset. First, an existing asset will be replaced if there is a cheaper way to get the service that the asset provides. This can occur because the asset ages or because of technological or organizational changes. Second, an existing asset will be replaced if the service it provides is inadequate in either quantity or quality.

7.3 The Relevance of Capacity Costs

When a decision is made to acquire a new asset, it is essentially a decision to purchase the capacity to perform tasks or produce output. **Capacity** is the ability to produce, often measured in units of production per time period. Although production requires capacity, it is also important to understand that just acquiring the capacity entails costs that are incurred whether or not there is actual production. Furthermore, a large portion of the capacity cost is incurred early in the life of the capacity. There are two main reasons for this:

1. Part of the cost of acquiring capacity is the depreciation expense incurred over time because the assets required for that capacity gradually lose their value. This depreciation expense is often called the **capital cost** of the asset. The largest portion of the capital costs typically occurs early in the lives of the assets.

2. Installing a new piece of equipment or new plant involves substantial up-front costs, called **installation costs**. These costs may include disruption of production, training of workers, and perhaps a reorganization of other processes. Installation costs are not reversible once the capacity has been put in place.

It is worth noting that the total cost of a new asset includes the installation costs and the cost of purchasing the asset. When we compute the capital costs of an asset over a period of time, the first cost (usually denoted by *P*), includes the installation costs. However, when we compute a salvage value for the asset as it ages, we do *not* include the installation costs as part of the depreciable value of the asset, since these costs are expended upon installation and cannot be recovered at a later time.

The large influence of capital costs associated with acquiring new capacity means that, once the capacity has been installed, the *incremental* cost of continuing to use that capacity during its planned life is relatively low. This gives an existing asset, the **defender**, a cost advantage during its planned life over a potential replacement, a **challenger**. This up-front weighting of capital costs also gives a defender a cost advantage over the alternative of contracting out the service performed by the asset, as illustrated by Example 7.1.

EXAMPLE 7.1

The Jiffy Printer Company produces printers for home use. Currently, they pay a custom moulder $0.25 per piece (excluding material costs) to produce parts for their printers. Demand is forecast to be 200 000 parts per year. Jiffy is considering installing an automated plastic moulding system to produce the parts themselves. The moulder itself costs $20 000 and the installation costs are estimated to be $5000. The expected life of the system is six years. Operating and maintenance costs are expected to be $30 000 in the first year and to rise at the rate of 5% per year. Jiffy estimates its capital costs with a declining-balance depreciation model with a rate of 40%, and uses a MARR of 15% for such investments.

In Jiffy's situation, the *defender* is the current technology: a subcontractor. The *challenger* is the automated plastic moulding system. In order to decide whether Jiffy is better off with the defender or the challenger, we need to compute the cost per piece of production with the moulder. We first find the present worth of the total cost associated with acquiring and using the moulder over its six-year life. We then convert the present cost into an equivalent annual amount, and then into a cost per piece.

The present worth of acquiring the moulder and using it over its six-year life is the sum of its installation costs, capital costs, and operating and maintenance costs:

$$PW(\text{moulder}) = PW(\text{capital}) + PW(\text{operating and maintenance})$$

The present worth of the capital cost of the moulding system is the loss in value of the asset over the six years over which it will be operated:

$$PW(\text{moulder}) = \$20\ 000 + \$5000 - BV_{db}(6)(P/F, 15\%, 6)$$
$$= \$25\ 000 - \$20\ 000(1 - 0.4)^6(0.4323)$$
$$= \$25\ 000 - \$933.12(0.4323)$$
$$= \$24\ 596.61$$

Finally, the present worth of operating and maintenance costs over the six-year life can be obtained using the geometric gradient to present worth conversion factor (see Section 3.7):

$$PW(\text{operating and maintenance}) = \frac{\$30\,000(P/A, i^\circ, 6)}{1+g}$$

The growth-adjusted interest rate, i°, is given by

$$i^\circ = \frac{1+i}{1+g} - 1 = \frac{1.15}{1.05} - 1 = 0.09524$$

With $g = 0.05$ and the series present worth formula, we get

$$PW(\text{operating and maintenance}) = \$30\,000(4.4167)/1.05$$
$$= \$126\,191.43$$

This gives a present worth of cost for the six-year planned life of the moulding system of $\$24\,596.61 + \$126\,191.43 = \$150\,788$.

To determine the costs on a per piece basis, we convert the present worth to an **equivalent annual cost (EAC)** and divide by the number of pieces per year. Notice that by converting to an equivalent annual cost we are assuming that all yearly payments occur at the end of each year. This is an approximation to the periodic costs associated with the moulder that are actually spread out over the year.

$$EAC(\text{moulder}) = \$150\,788(A/P, 15\%, 6)$$
$$= \$150\,788(0.2642)$$
$$= \$39\,838.20$$

Finally, the cost per piece is $\$39\,838.20/200\,000 = \$0.1992$

When the cost per piece of in-house production is compared with the $0.25 cost per piece of contracting out the work, it appears that Jiffy should replace the *defender* (contracting out) with in-house production (the challenger).

This example has illustrated the basic idea behind a replacement analysis when we are considering the purchase of a *new* asset as a replacement to current technology. The cost of the replacement must take into account the capital costs (including installation) and the operating and maintenance costs over the life of the new asset.

In the next section, we see how some costs are no longer relevant in the decision to replace an *existing* asset.

7.4 The Irrelevance of Sunk Costs

Once an asset has been installed and has been operating for some time, the costs of installation and all other costs incurred up to that time are no longer relevant to any decision to replace the current asset. These costs are called **sunk costs**. Only those costs that will be incurred in keeping and operating the asset from this time on are relevant. This is best illustrated with an example.

EXAMPLE 7.2

Two years have passed since the Jiffy Printer Company from Example 7.1 installed an automated moulding system to produce parts for their printers. At the time of installation, they expected to be producing about 200 000 pieces per year, which justified the investment. However, their actual production has turned out to be only about 150 000 pieces per year. Their cost per piece is $39 838.20/150 000 = $0.2656 rather than the $0.1992 they had expected. They estimate the market value of the moulder now at $7200. Maintenance costs do not depend, in this case, on the actual production rate. Should Jiffy sell the moulding system and go back to buying from the custom moulder at $0.25 per piece?

In the context of a replacement problem, Jiffy is looking at replacing the existing system (the defender) with a different technology (the challenger). Since Jiffy already has the moulder and has already expended considerable capital on putting it into place, it may be better for Jiffy to keep the current moulder for some time longer. Let us calculate the cost to Jiffy of keeping the moulding system one more year. This may not be the optimal length of time to continue to use the system, but if the cost is less than $0.25 per piece it is cheaper than retiring or replacing it now.

The reason that the cost of keeping the moulder an additional year is low is that the capital costs for the two-year-old system are now low compared with the costs of putting the capacity in place. The capital cost for the third year is simply the loss in value of the moulder over the third year. This is the difference between what Jiffy can get for the system now, at the end of the second year, and what they can get a year from now when the system will be three years old. Jiffy can get $7200 for the system now. Using the declining-balance depreciation rate of 40% to calculate a salvage value, we can determine the annual capital cost for keeping the moulder to the end of the third year. Applying the capital recovery formula from Chapter 3, the EAC for capital costs is

EAC(capital costs, third year)
$$= (P - S)(A/P, 15\%, 1) + Si$$
$$= [\$7200 - 0.6(\$7200)](1.15) + 0.6(\$7200)(0.15)$$
$$= \$3960$$

Recall that the operating and maintenance costs started at $30 000 and rose at 5% each year. The operating and maintenance costs for the third year are

EAC(operating and maintenance, third year) = $30 000(1.05)^2$
$$= \$33\ 075$$

The total annual cost of keeping the moulder for the third year is the sum of the capital costs and the operating and maintenance costs:

EAC(third year) = EAC(capital costs, third year)
                  + EAC(operating and maintenance, third year)
$$= \$3960 + \$33\ 075$$
$$= \$37\ 035$$

Dividing the annual costs for the third year by 150 000 gives us a cost per piece of $0.247 for moulding in-house during the third year. Not only is this lower than the average cost over a six-year life of the system, it is also lower than what the custom moulder charges. Similar computations would show that Jiffy could go two more years after the third year with in-house moulding. Only then would the increase in operating and maintenance costs cause total cost per piece to rise above $0.25. The computations for this are shown in Section 7.5.

We see that installing the automated moulding system was a mistake for Jiffy. The average lifetime costs for in-house moulding were greater than the cost of contracting out, but, once the system was installed, it was not optimal to go back to contracting out immediately. This is because the sunk costs for the initial period of use of an asset are disproportionately large as compared with the costs of using the asset once it is in place.

That a defender has a cost advantage over a challenger, or over contracting out during the planned life of the defender, is important. It means that if a defender is to be removed from service during its life for cost reasons, the average lifetime costs for the challenger or the costs of contracting out must be considerably lower than the average lifetime costs of the defender.

Just because well functioning defenders are not often retired for cost reasons does not mean that they will not be retired at all. Changes in markets or technology may make the quantity or quality of output produced by a defender inadequate. This can lead to their retirement or replacement even when they are functioning well.

7.5 Economic Life and Cyclic Replacement

All long-lived assets eventually require replacement. Consequently, the issue in replacement studies is not *whether* to replace an asset, but *when* to replace it. In this section we consider the case where there is an ongoing need for a service provided by an asset and where the asset technology is not changing rapidly. There are several assumptions made:

1. The defender and challenger are assumed to be technologically identical. It is also assumed that this constancy of technology remains for the company's entire planning horizon.

2. The lives of these identical assets are assumed to be short relative to the time horizon over which the assets are required.

3. Relative prices and interest rates are assumed to be constant over the company's time horizon.

These assumptions are quite restrictive. In fact, there are only a few cases where the assumptions strictly hold (cable used for electric power delivery is an example). Nonetheless, the idea of economic life of an asset is still useful to our understanding of replacement analysis.

The assumptions of constant technology and asset lives that are short relative to the time over which they are needed imply that we may model the replacement decision as being repeated an indefinitely large number of times. The objective is then to determine a minimum cost-lifetime for the assets, a lifetime that will be the same for all the assets in the sequence of replacements over the company's time horizon.

We have seen that the relevant costs associated with acquiring a new asset are the capital costs, installation costs (which are often pooled with the capital costs), and operating and maintenance costs. It is usually true that operating and maintenance costs of assets — plant or equipment — rise with the age of the asset. Offsetting increases in operating and maintenance costs is the fall in capital costs per year that usually occurs as the asset life is extended and the capital costs are spread over a greater number of years. The rise in operating and maintenance costs per year and the fall in capital costs per year as the life of an asset is extended work in opposite directions. In the early years of an asset's life, the capital costs per year (although decreasing) usually, but not always, dominate total yearly costs. As the asset ages, increasing operating and maintenance costs usually overtake the declining annual capital costs. This means that there is a lifetime that will minimize the *average* cost (adjusting for the time value of money) per year of owning and using long-lived assets. This is referred to as the **economic life** of the asset. These ideas are illustrated in Figure 7.1 where we see that the economic life of an asset is found at the point where the rate of increase in operating and maintenance costs per year equals the rate of fall in capital costs per year.

EXAMPLE 7.3

Refer back to Example 7.1 where the Jiffy Printer Company is considering the purchase of an automated moulding system based on an expected production level of 200 000 pieces per year. It is economically justified for them to purchase the system, as was shown in Example 7.1. Assuming that there will be an ongoing need for the moulder, and assuming that the technology does not change (i.e., no cheaper or better method will arise), how long should Jiffy keep a moulder before replacing it with a new model? In other words, what is the economic life of the automated moulding system?

FIGURE 7.1   Cost Components for Replacement Studies

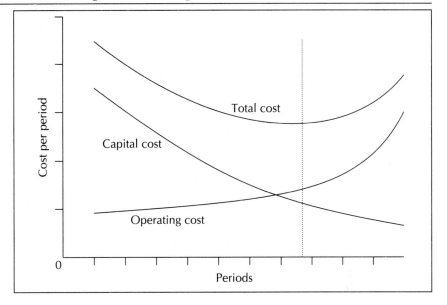

Determining the economic life of an asset is most easily done with a spreadsheet. Table 7.1 shows the development of the equivalent annual costs for the automated plastic moulding system of Example 7.1.

In the first column is the life of the asset, in years. The second column shows the salvage value of the moulding system as it ages. The equipment costs $20 000 originally, and as the system ages the value declines by 40% of current value each year, giving the estimated salvage values listed in Table 7.1. For example, the salvage value at the end of year 4 is

$$BV_{db}(4) = \$20\ 000(1 - 0.4)^4$$
$$= \$2592$$

The next column gives the equivalent annual capital costs if the asset is kept for n years, $n = 1, \ldots, 10$. This captures the loss in value of the asset over the time it is kept in service. As an example of the computations, the equivalent annual capital costs of keeping the moulding system for four years is

EAC(capital costs over four years)
$$= (P - S)(A/P, 15\%, 4) + Si$$
$$= (\$20\ 000 + \$5000 - \$2592)(0.35027) + \$2592(0.15)$$
$$= \$8237.55$$

Note that the installation costs have been included in the capital costs, as these are expenses incurred at the time the asset is originally put into service. Table 7.1 illustrates that the equivalent annual capital costs decline as the asset's life is extended.

TABLE 7.1 Computation of Total Equivalent Annual Costs of the Moulding System with MARR = 15%

Life in Years	Salvage Value	EAC Capital Costs	EAC Operating and Maintenance Costs	EAC Total
0	$20 000.00			
1	12 000.00	$16 750.00	$30 000.00	$46 750.00
2	7 200.00	12 029.07	30 697.67	42 726.74
3	4 320.00	9 705.36	31 382.29	41 087.65
4	2 592.00	8 237.55	32 052.47	40 290.02
5	1 555.20	7 227.23	32 706.94	39 934.17
6	933.12	6 499.33	33 344.56	39 843.88
7	559.87	5 958.42	33 964.28	39 922.70
8	335.92	5 546.78	34 565.20	40 111.98
9	201.55	5 227.34	35 146.55	40 373.89
10	120.93	4 975.35	35 707.69	40 683.04

Next, the equivalent annual operating and maintenance costs is found by converting the stream of operating and maintenance costs (which are increasing by 5% per year) into a stream of equal-sized annual amounts. Continuing with our sample calculations, the EAC of operating and maintenance costs when the moulding system is kept for four years is

EAC(operating and maintenance costs over four years)

$$= \$30\ 000\ (A/P, 15\%, 4)\ [(P/F, 15\%, 1) + (1.05)(P/F, 15\%, 2)$$
$$+ (1.05)^2(P/F, 15\%, 3) + (1.05)^3(P/F, 15\%, 4)]$$
$$= \$32\ 052.47$$

Notice that the equivalent annual operating and maintenance costs increase as the asset life of the moulding system increases.

Finally, we obtain the equivalent annual total cost of the moulding system by adding the equivalent annual capital costs and the equivalent annual operating and maintenance costs. This is shown in the last column of Table 7.1. We see that at a six-year life the declining equivalent annual installation and capital costs offset the increasing operating and maintenance costs. In other words, the economic life of the moulder is six years.

While it is *usually* true that capital cost per year falls with increasing life, it is not always true. Capital costs per year can rise at some point in the life of an asset if the decline in value of the asset is not smooth or if the asset requires a major overhaul.

If there is a large drop in value in some year during the asset's life, the cost of holding the asset over that year will be high. This will raise the cost of holding the asset in that year. Consider the following example.

EXAMPLE 7.4

An asset costs $50 000 to buy and install. The asset has a resale value of $40 000 after installation. It then declines in value by 20% per year until the fourth year when its value drops from over $20 000 to $5000 because of a predictable wearing out of a major component. Determine the equivalent annual capital cost of this asset for lives ranging from one to four years. The MARR is 15%.

The computations are summarized in Table 7.2. The first column gives the life of the asset, in years. The second gives the salvage value of the asset as it ages. The asset loses 20% of its previous year's value each year except the fourth, when its value drops to $5000. The last column summarizes the equivalent annual capital cost of the asset. Sample computations for the third and fourth years are

EAC(capital costs, three-year life)
$$= (P - S)(A/P,15\%,3) + Si$$
$$= (\$40\ 000 + \$10\ 000 - \$20\ 480)(0.43798) + \$20\ 480(0.15)$$
$$= \$16\ 001$$

EAC(capital costs, four-year life)
$$= (P - S)(A/P, 15\%, 4) + Si$$
$$= (\$40\ 000 + \$10\ 000 - \$5000)(0.35027) + \$5000(0.15)$$
$$= \$16\ 512$$

TABLE 7.2   EAC of Capital Costs for Example 7.4

Life in Years	Salvage Value	EAC Capital Costs
0	$40 000	
1	32 000	$25 500
2	25 600	18 849
3	20 480	16 001
4	5 000	16 512

The large drop in value in the fourth year means that there is a high cost of holding the asset in the fourth year. This is enough to raise the average capital cost per year.

In summary, when we replace one asset with another asset with an identical technology, it makes sense to speak of its economic life. This is the lifetime of an individual asset that will minimize the average cost per year of owning and using it. In the next section, we deal with the case where the challenger is different from the defender.

7.6 Challenger Is Different from Defender

In this section we explore a more common situation in which there is a challenger that is different from the defender. We distinguish between two such cases. In the first case we assume that, although the challenger is different from the defender, all succeeding challengers are identical to the first challenger. The next case is more general. We recognize that there will be challengers after the current challenger. We expect them to be better than the current challenger. We shall see that the solution to this problem is quite complex.

7.6.1 Sequence of Identical Challengers

The decision rule that minimizes cost in the case where a defender is faced by a challenger that is expected to be followed by a sequence of identical challengers is as follows:

1. Determine the economic life of the challenger and its associated equivalent annual cost.
2. Determine the cost of using the defender one more year. If the cost of using the defender one more year is less than the equivalent annual cost of installing and using the challenger over its economic life, then keep the defender at least one more year.
3. If the cost of using the defender one more year is greater than the cost of installing and using the challenger over its economic life, see if there is a life longer than one year over which the cost of using the defender is less than the cost of installing and using the challenger. If there is such a life (which will happen only under unusual circumstances), keep the defender for that remaining economic life. If there is no incremental life for the defender for which its cost per year is less than the cost of installing and using the challenger for its economic life, replace the defender immediately.

Consider this example concerning the potential replacement of a generator.

EXAMPLE 7.5

The Colossal Construction Company uses a generator to produce power at remote sites. The existing generator is now three years old. It cost $11 000 when purchased. Its current salvage value is $2400. This salvage value is expected to fall to $1400 next year and $980 the year after, and to continue declining at 30% of current value per year. Its operating and maintenance costs are now $2000 per year and are expected to rise by $500 per year.

New fuel-efficient generators have been developed, and Colossal is thinking of replacing their existing generator. It is expected that the new generator technology will be the best available for the foreseeable future. The new generator sells for $9500. Installation costs are negligible. Other data for the new generator are summarized in Table 7.3.

TABLE 7.3   Salvage Values and Operating Costs for New Generators

End of Year	Salvage Value	Operating Cost
0	$9 500	
1	8 000	$1 000
2	7 000	1 000
3	6 000	1 200
4	5 000	1 500
5	4 000	2 000
6	3 000	2 000
7	2 000	2 000
8	1 000	3 000

Should Colossal replace the existing generator with the new type? The MARR is 12%.

We first determine the economic life for the challenger. The calculations are shown in Table 7.4.

TABLE 7.4   Economic Life of the Generator

End of year	Salvage Value	Operating Costs	EAC
1	$8 000	$1 000	$3 640.00
2	7 000	1 000	3 319.25
3	6 000	1 200	3 236.50
4	5 000	1 500	3 233.07*
5	4 000	2 000	3 290.81
6	3 000	2 000	3 314.16
7	2 000	2 000	3 318.68
8	1 000	3 000	3 393.52

*Lowest annual cost

Sample calculations for the EAC of keeping the challenger for one, two, and three years are as follows:

$$EAC(1 \text{ year}) = (P - S)(A/P, 12\%, 1) + Si + \$1000$$
$$= (\$9500 - \$8000)(1.12) + \$8000(0.12) + \$1000$$
$$= \$3640$$

$$EAC(2 \text{ years}) = (P - S)(A/P, 12\%, 2) + Si + \$1000$$
$$= (\$9500 - \$7000)(0.5917) + \$7000(0.12) + \$1000$$
$$= \$3319.25$$

$$EAC(3 \text{ years}) = (P - S)(A/P, 12\%, 3) + Si + \$1000$$
$$+ \$200(A/F, 12\%, 3)$$
$$= (\$9500 - \$6000)(0.41635) + \$6000(0.12)$$
$$+ \$1000 + \$200(0.29635)$$
$$= \$3236.50$$

As the number of years increases, this approach for calculating the EAC becomes more difficult, especially since in this case the operating costs are neither a standard annuity nor an arithmetic gradient. An alternative is to calculate the present worths of the operating costs for each year. The EAC of the operating costs can found by applying the capital recovery factor to the sum of the present worths. This approach is particularly handy when using spreadsheets.

By either calculation, we see in Table 7.4 that the economic life of the generator is four years.

Next, to see if and when the defender should be replaced, we get the costs of keeping the defender for one more year. Using the capital recovery formula

EAC(keep defender 1 more year)

$$= EAC(\text{capital costs}) + EAC(\text{operating costs})$$
$$= (\$2400 - \$1400)(A/P, 12\%, 1) + \$1400(0.12) + \$2000$$
$$= \$3288$$

The equivalent annual cost of using the defender one more year is $3288. This is more than the yearly cost of installing and using the challenger over its economic life. We therefore see if there is a longer life for the defender for which its costs are lower than for the challenger. This can be done with a spreadsheet, as shown in Table 7.5.

We see that, for an additional life of two years, the defender has a lower cost per year than the challenger, when the challenger is kept over its economic life. Therefore, the defender should be kept for at least two more years. At this time, a new evaluation should be performed.

TABLE 7.5   Equivalent Annual Cost of Additional Life for the Defender

Additional Life in Years	Salvage Value	Operating Costs	EAC
0	$2400		
1	1400	$2000	$3288
2	980	2500	3194
3	686	3000	3258
4	480	3500	3369
5	336	4000	3500
6	235	4500	3641

7.6.2 Challenger Is Not Repeated

From this point we no longer assume that challengers are alike. We recognize that future challengers will be available and we expect them to be better than the current challenger. We must then decide if the defender is to be replaced by the current challenger. Furthermore, if it is to be replaced by the current challenger, when should the replacement occur? This problem is quite complex. The reason for the complexity is that, if we believe that challengers will be improving, we may be better off skipping the current challenger and waiting until the next improved challenger arrives. The difficulties are outlined in Example 7.6.

EXAMPLE 7.6

Rita is examining the possibility of replacing the kiln controllers at the Burnaby Insulators plant. She has information about the existing controllers and the best replacement on the market. She also has information about a new controller design that will be available in three years. Rita has a five-year time horizon for the problem. What replacement alternatives should Rita consider?

One way to determine the minimum cost over the five-year horizon is to determine the costs of all possible combinations of the defender and the two challengers. This is impossible, since the defender and challengers could replace one another at any time. However, it is reasonable to consider only the combinations of the period length of one year. Any period length could be used, but a year is a natural choice because investment decisions tend, by convention, to follow a yearly cycle. These combinations form a mutually exclusive set of investment opportunities (see Section 4.2). If there were no time horizon given in the problem, we would have had to assume one, again to limit the number of possible alternatives.

The possible decisions that need to be evaluated in this case are shown in Table 7.6.

TABLE 7.6   Possible Decisions for Burnaby Insulators

Decision	Defender Life in Years	First Challenger Life in Years	Second Challenger Life in Years
1	5	0	0
2	4	1	0
3	4	0	1
4	3	2	0
5	3	1	1
6	3	0	2
7	2	3	0
8	2	2	1
9	2	1	2
10	1	4	0
11	1	3	1
12	1	2	2
13	0	5	0
14	0	4	1
15	0	3	2

To choose among these possible decisions, we need information about the following for the defender and both challengers:

1. Costs of installing the challengers
2. Salvage values for different possible lives for all three kiln controllers
3. Operating and maintenance costs for all possible ages for all three

With this information, the minimum cost solution is obtained by computing the costs for all possible decisions. Since these are mutually exclusive projects, any of the comparison methods of Chapters 4 and 5 are appropriate, including present worth, annual worth, or IRR. The effects of sunk costs are already included in the enumeration of the various replacement possibilities, so looking at the benefits of keeping the defender is already automatically taken into account.

The difficulty with this approach is that the computational burden becomes great if the number of years in the time horizon is large. On the other hand, it is unlikely that under normal circumstances information about a future challenger will be available. In Example 7.6, Rita had knowledge about a controller that wouldn't be available for three years. In real life, even if somehow Rita had inside information on the supplier research and marketing plans, it is unlikely that she would be confident enough of events three years away to use the information with complete assurance. Normally, if the information were available, the challenger itself would be available, too. Consequently, in many cases it is reasonable to assume that challengers in the planning future will be identical to the current challenger, and the decision procedure to use is the simpler one presented in the previous section.

CANADIAN CORPORATE CASE 7.1

Canadians Holding on to Vehicles Longer

A typical Canadian motorist now drives a car at least five years old with close to 100 000 kilometres on it. Based on a survey done by the Canadian Automobile Association in 1995, people are keeping their cars longer because they're built better and last longer and fewer people can afford the cost of driving a new car.

One reason people are driving older cars is that the cost of repairs for old cars is not that much higher than for newer ones. The survey found that owners of 1992-model-year vehicles spent an average of $514 on repairs and maintenance in 1995, while owners of cars built in 1986 or earlier spent an average of $870.

Another reason why people are driving older cars is that the cost of car ownership goes down with the length of time you keep the vehicle. This is because you lose less on depreciation each year on an older car than on a newer one. For example, the $7715 average cost of driving a new 1995 Chevrolet Cavalier for the year is largely due to its large depreciation expense of $3500. The balance includes the cost of repairs, insurance, and gas. Older cars have lower depreciation expenses and thus cost less to keep on the road.

Source: Article by Michael Prentice, Adapted from the *Ottawa Citizen*
Appeared in the *Kitchener-Waterloo Record*, February 7, 1996.

REVIEW PROBLEMS

Review Problem 7.1

Kenwood Limousines runs a fleet of vans which ferry people from several outlying cities to a major international airport. New vans cost $45 000 each and depreciate at a declining-balance rate of 30% per year. Maintenance for each van is quite expensive, because they are in use 24 hours a day, seven days a week. Maintenance costs, which are about $3000 the first year, double each year the vehicle is in use. Given a MARR of 8%, what is the economic life of a van?

Answer

Table 7.7 shows the various components of this problem for replacement periods of from one to five years. It can be seen that the replacement period with the minimum equivalent annual cost is two years. Therefore, the economic life is two years.

TABLE 7.7   Summary Computations for Review Problem 7.1

Year	Salvage Value	Maintenance Costs	Equivalent Annual Costs		
			Capital	Operating	Total
0	$45 000				
1	31 500	$ 3 000	$17 100	$ 3 000	$20 100
2	22 050	6 000	14 634	4 442	19 076
3	15 435	12 000	12 707	6 770	19 477
4	10 805	24 000	11 189	10 594	21 783
5	7 563	48 000	9 981	16 970	26 951

As an example, the calculation for a three-year period is:

$$EAC(\text{capital costs}) = (\$45\ 000 - \$15\ 435)\,(A/P, 8\%, 3) \\ + \$15\ 435(0.08)$$
$$= \$29\ 565(0.38803) + \$15\ 435(0.08)$$
$$= \$12\ 707$$

$$EAC(\text{operating costs}) = [\$3000(F/P, 8\%, 2) + \$6000(F/P, 8\%, 1) \\ + \$12\ 000]\,(A/F, 8\%, 3)$$
$$= (\$3000(1.1664) + \$6000(1.08) \\ + \$12\ 000)(0.30804)$$
$$= \$6770$$

$$EAC(\text{total}) = EAC(\text{capital costs}) + EAC(\text{operating costs})$$
$$= \$12\ 707 + \$6770 = \$19\ 477$$

Review Problem 7.2

Canadian Widgets makes rocker arms for car engines. The manufacturing process consists of punching blanks from raw stock, forming the rocker arm in a five-stage progressive die, and finishing in a sequence of operations using hand tools. A recently developed 10-stage die can eliminate many of the finishing operations for a high volume rocker arm.

The existing five-stage die could be used for a different product, and in this case would have a salvage value of $20 000. Maintenance costs of the five-stage die will total $19 500 this year, and are expected to increase by $3500 per year. The 10-stage die will cost $89 000, and will incur maintenance costs of $4000 this year, increasing by $2700 per year thereafter. Both dies depreciate at a declining-balance rate of 20% per year. The net yearly benefit of the automation of the finishing operations is expected to be $16 000 per year. The MARR is 10%. Should the five-stage die be replaced?

Answer

Since there is no information about subsequent challengers, it is reasonable to assume that the 10-stage die would be repeated. The EAC of using the 10-stage die for various periods is shown in Table 7.8.

TABLE 7.8   EAC Computations for the Challenger in Review Problem 7.2

Life in Years	Salvage Value	Maintenance Costs	Equivalent Annual Costs		
			Capital	Maintenance	Total
0	$89 000				
1	71 200	$ 4 000	$26 700	$ 4 000	$30 700
2	56 960	6 700	24 157	5 286	29 443
3	45 568	9 400	22 021	6 529	28 550
4	36 454	12 100	20 222	7 729	27 951
5	29 164	14 800	18 701	8 887	27 589
6	23 331	17 500	17 411	10 004	27 415
7	18 665	20 200	16 314	11 079	27 393
8	14 932	22 900	15 377	12 113	27 490

A sample EAC computation for keeping the 10-stage die for two years is as follows:

EAC(capital costs, two-year life)

$$= (P - S)(A/P, 10\%, 2) + Si$$

$$= (\$89\,000 - \$56\,960)(0.57619) + \$56\,960(0.10)$$

$$= \$24\,157$$

EAC(operating costs, two-year life)

$$= [\$4000(F/P, 10\%, 1) + \$6700](A/F, 10\%, 2)$$

$$= [\$4000(1.1) + \$6700](0.47619)$$

$$= \$5286$$

EAC(total, two-year life) $= \$24\,157 + \$5286$

$$= \$29\,443$$

Completing similar computations for other lifetimes shows that the economic life of the 10-stage die is seven years and the associated equivalent annual costs are $27 393.

The next step in the replacement analysis is to consider the annual cost of the five-stage die (the defender) over the next year. This cost is to be compared with the economic life EAC of the 10-stage die, i.e., $27 393. Note that the cost analysis of the defender should include the benefits generated by the 10-stage die as an operating cost for the five-stage die as this $16 000 is a cost of *not* changing to the 10-stage die. The EAC of the capital and operating costs of keeping the defender one additional year are found as follows:

The salvage value of the five-stage die after one year is

$$\$20\,000(1 - 0.2) = \$16\,000$$

EAC(capital costs, one additional year)

$$= (P - S)(A/P, 10\%, 1) + Si$$

$$= (\$20\,000 - \$16\,000)(1.10) + \$16\,000(0.10)$$

$$= \$6000$$

EAC(operational costs, one additional year)

$$= \$3500 + \$16\,000$$

$$= \$19\,500$$

EAC(total, one additional year)

$$= \$19\,500 + \$6000$$

$$= \$25\,500$$

The five-stage die should not be replaced this year because the EAC of keeping it one additional year ($25 500) is less than the optimal EAC of the 10-stage die ($27 393). The knowledge that the five-stage die should not be replaced this year is usually sufficient for the immediate replacement decision. However, if a different challenger appears in the future, we would want to reassess the replacement decision.

It may also be desirable to estimate when in the future the defender might be replaced, even if it is not being replaced now. This can be done by calculating the equivalent annual cost of keeping the defender additional years until the time we can determine when it should be replaced. Table 7.9 summarizes those calculations for additional years of operating the five-stage die.

TABLE 7.9   EAC Computations for Keeping the Defender Additional Years

Additional Life in Years	Salvage Value	Operating Costs	Equivalent Annual Costs		
			Capital	Operating	Total
0	$20 000				
1	16 000	$19 500	$6 000	$19 500	$25 500
2	12 800	23 000	5 429	21 167	26 595
3	10 240	26 500	4 949	22 778	27 727
4	8 192	30 000	4 544	24 334	28 878
5	6 554	33 500	4 202	25 836	30 038
6	5 243	37 000	3 913	27 283	31 196
7	4 194	40 500	3 666	28 677	32 343
8	3 355	44 000	3 455	30 018	33 473

As an example of the computations, the EAC of keeping the defender for two additional years is calculated as

Salvage value of five-stage die after two years:
$$\$16\,000(1 - 0.2) = \$12\,800$$

EAC(capital costs, two additional years)
$$= (P - S)(A/P, 10\%, 2) + Si$$
$$= (\$20\,000 - \$12\,800)(0.57619) + \$12\,800(0.10)$$
$$= \$5248.57$$

EAC(operating costs, two additional years)
$$= [\$19\,500(F/F, 10\%, 1) + (\$16\,000 + \$7000)](A/F, 10\%, 2)$$
$$= [\$19\,500(1.1) + \$23\,000](0.47619)$$
$$= \$21\,167$$

EAC(total, two additional years)
$$= \$5429 + \$21\,167 = \$26\,595$$

Continuing calculations in this manner will predict that the defender should be replaced at the end of the second year, given that the challenger remains the same during this time. This is because the EAC of keeping the defender for two years is less than the optimal EAC of the 10-stage die, but keeping the defender three years or more is more costly.

■ Review Problem 7.3

Avril bought a computer three years ago for $3000, which she can now sell on the open market for $300. The local Mr. Computer store will sell her a new HAL computer for $4000, including the new accounting package she wants. Her own computer will probably last another two years, and then would be worthless. The new computer would have a salvage value of $300 at the end of its economic life of five years. The net benefits to Avril of the new accounting package and other features of the new computer amount to $800 per year. An additional feature is that Mr. Computer will give Avril a $500 trade-in on her current computer. Interest is 15%. What should Avril do?

Answer

There are a couple of things to note about this problem. First, the cost of the new computer should be taken as $3800 rather than $4000. This is because, although the price was quoted as $4000, the dealer was willing to give Avril a $500 trade-in on a used computer that had a market value of only $300. This amounts to discounting the price of the new computer to $3800. Similarly, the used computer should be taken to be worth $300, and not $500. The $500 figure does not represent the market value of the used computer, but rather the value of the used computer combined with the discount on the new computer. One must sometimes be careful to extract from the available information the best estimates of the values and costs for the various components of a replacement study.

First, we need to determine the EAC of the challenger over its economic life. We are told that the economic life is five years and hence the EAC computations are as follows:

$$\text{EAC(capital costs)} = (\$3800 - \$300)(A/P, 15\%, 5) + \$300(0.15)$$
$$= \$3500(0.29832) + \$45$$
$$= \$1089$$

$$\text{EAC(operating costs)} = \$0$$

$$\text{EAC(challenger, total)} = \$1089$$

Now we need to check the equivalent annual cost of keeping the existing computer one additional year. A salvage value for the computer for one year was not given. However, we can check to see if the EAC for the defender over two years is less than for the challenger. If it is, this is sufficient to retain the old computer.

$$\text{EAC(capital costs)} = (\$300 - 0)(A/P, 15\%, 2) + \$0(0.15)$$
$$= \$300(0.61512) + \$0$$
$$= \$184.54$$

EAC(operating costs) = $800

EAC(defender, total over 2 years) = $984.53

Avril should hang on to her current computer because its EAC over two years is less than the EAC of the challenger over its five-year economic life.

SUMMARY

This chapter is concerned with replacement and retirement decisions. Replacement can be required because there may be a cheaper way to provide the same service, or the nature of the service may have changed. Retirement can be required if there is no longer a need for the asset.

Defenders that are still functioning well have a significant cost advantage over challengers or over obtaining the service performed by the defender from another source. This is because there are installation costs and because the capital cost per year of an asset diminishes over time.

If an asset is replaced by a stream of identical assets, it is useful to determine the economic life of the asset, which is the replacement interval that provides the minimum annual cost. The asset should then be replaced at the end of its economic life.

FIGURE 7.2   The Replacement Process

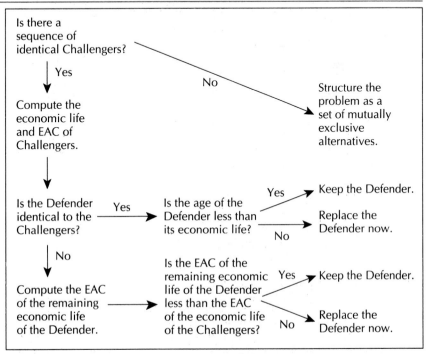

If there is a challenger which is different from the defender, and future changes in technology are not known, one can determine the minimum EAC of the challenger and compare this with the cost of keeping the defender. If keeping the defender for any period of time is cheaper than the minimum EAC of the challenger, the defender should be kept. Normally, it is sufficient to assess the cost of keeping the defender for one more year.

Where future changes in technology are expected, decisions about when and whether to replace defenders are more complex. In this case, possible replacement decisions must be enumerated as a set of mutually exclusive alternatives and subjected to any of the standard comparison methods.

Figure 7.2 provides a summary of the overall procedure for assessing a replacement decision.

Engineering Economics in Action, Part 7B: Decision Time

Naomi, Dave, and Clem were meeting in Clem's office. They had just finished a discussion of their steel-ordering policy. Clem turned to Naomi and said, "O.K. Let's look at the 10-stage progressive die. Where does that stand?"

Naomi said, "It looks possible. Did you get a chance to read Terry's report?"

"Yes, I did," Clem answered. "Was it his idea to use the five-stage die for small runs so that we don't have to take a big hit from scrapping it?"

"Actually, it was," Naomi said.

"The kid may be a little intense," Clem said, "but he does good work. So where does that leave us?"

"Well, as I said, it looks possible that the 10-stage die will pay off," Naomi responded. "We have to decide what the correct time horizon is for making the analysis. Then we need more precise estimates of the costs and salvage value for the 10-stage die."

Clem turned in his chair and asked, "What do you think, Dave?"

Dave straightened himself in his chair and said, "I really don't know. How much experience has Hamilton Tools had at making dies this complicated?"

Naomi answered. "Not much. If we took them up on their proposal, we'd be their second or third customer."

"What do you have in mind, Dave?" Clem asked.

Dave said, "Well, if it's only the second or third time they've done something like this, I think we can expect some improvements over the next couple of years. So maybe we ought to wait."

"That makes sense," Clem responded. "I'd like you two to work on this. Give Tan Wang at Hamilton Tools a call. He'll know if anything is in the works. Get him to give you an estimate of what to expect. Then I want you to consider some possibilities. You know: 'Replace now.' 'Wait one year.' 'Wait two years.' And so on. Don't make it too complicated. Then, evaluate the different possibilities. I want a recommendation for next week's meeting. It's getting to be decision time."

PROBLEMS

7.1 Determine the economic life for each of the items listed below. Salvage values can be estimated by a declining-balance rate of 20%. The MARR is 8%.

	Purchase	Installation	Operating
Item 1	$10 000	$2000	$300 first year, increasing by $300 per year
Item 2	$20 000	$2000	$200 first year, increasing by $200 per year
Item 3	$30 000	$3000	$2000 first year, increasing by $2000 per year

7.2 A new bottle-capping machine costs $45 000, including $5000 for installation. The machine is expected to have a useful life of eight years with no salvage value at that time (assume straight-line depreciation). Operating and maintenance costs are expected to be $3000 for the first year, increasing by $1000 each year thereafter. Interest is 12%.

(a) Construct a spreadsheet which has the following headings: Year, Salvage Value, Maintenance Costs, EAC(Capital Costs), EAC(Operating Costs), and EAC(Total Costs). Compute the EAC(Total Costs) if the bottle capper is kept for n years, $n = 1, \ldots, 8$.

(b) Construct a chart showing the EAC(Capital Costs), EAC(Operating Costs), and EAC(Total Costs) if the bottle capper were to be kept for n years, $n = 1, \ldots, 8$.

(c) What is the economic life of the bottle capper?

7.3 A roller conveyor system used to transport cardboard boxes along an order-filling line costs $100 000 plus $20 000 to install. It is estimated to depreciate at a declining-balance rate of 25% per year over its 15-year useful life. Annual maintenance costs are estimated to be $6000 for the first year, increasing by 20% each year thereafter. In addition, every third year, the rollers must be replaced at a cost of $7000. Interest is at 10%.

(a) Construct a spreadsheet which has the following headings: Year, Salvage Value, Maintenance Costs, EAC(Capital Costs), EAC(Maintenance Costs), and EAC(Total Costs). Compute the EAC(Total Costs) if the conveyor were to be kept for n years, $n = 1, \ldots, 15$.

(b) Construct a chart showing the EAC(Capital Costs), EAC(Maintenance Costs), and EAC(Total Costs) if the conveyor were to be kept for n years, $n = 1, \ldots, 15$.

(c) What is the economic life of the roller conveyor system?

7.4 Brockville Brackets (BB) has a three-year-old robot which welds small brackets onto car-frame assemblies. At the time the robot was purchased, it cost $300 000 and an additional $50 000 was spent on installation. BB acquired the robot as part of an eight-year contract to produce the car-frame assemblies. The useful life of the robot is 12 years, and its value is estimated to decline by 20% of current value per year, as shown in the table below. Operating and maintenance costs estimated when the robot was purchased are also in the table.

Defender, When New		
Life (Years)	Salvage Value ($)	Operating and Maintenance Costs ($)
0	300 000	
1	240 000	40 000
2	192 000	40 000
3	153 600	40 000
4	122 880	40 000
5	98 304	44 000
6	78 643	48 400
7	62 915	53 240
8	50 332	58 564
9	40 265	64 420
10	32 212	70 862
11	25 770	77 949
12	20 616	85 744

BB has found that the operating and maintenance costs for the robot have been higher than anticipated. At the end of the third year, new estimates of the operating and maintenance costs are as follows:

Costs for 3-Year-Old Defender		
Additional Life (Years)	Salvage Value ($)	Operating and Maintenance Costs ($)
0	153 600	
1	122 880	50 000
2	98 304	55 000
3	78 643	60 500
4	62 915	66 550
5	50 332	73 205

BB has determined that the reason their operating and maintenance costs were in error was that they positioned the robot too close to existing equipment so that the mechanics could not easily and quickly repair it. BB is considering moving the robot farther away from some adjacent equipment so that mechanics can get easier access for repairs. To move the robot will cause BB to lose valuable production time, which they estimate to have a cost of $25 000. However, once complete, the move will lower maintenance costs to what they originally had expected for the remainder of the contract (e.g., $40 000 for the fourth year, increasing by 10% per year thereafter). Moving the robot will not affect its salvage value.

If BB uses a MARR of 15%, should they move the robot? If so, when? Remember that the contract exists only for a further five years.

7.5 Consider Brockville Brackets from problem 7.4 but assume that they have a contract to produce the car assemblies for an indefinite period. If they do not move the robot, their operating and maintenance costs will be higher than expected. If they do move the robot (at a cost of $25 000), their operating and maintenance costs are expected to be what they originally expected for the robot. Furthermore, BB expects to be able to obtain new versions of the existing robot for an indefinite period in the future; each is expected to have an installation cost of $50 000.

(a) Construct a spreadsheet table showing the EAC(total costs) if BB keeps the current robot in its current position for n more years, $n = 1, \ldots, 9$.

(b) Construct a spreadsheet table showing the EAC(total costs) if BB moves the current robot and then keeps it for n more years, $n = 1, \ldots, 9$

(c) Construct a spreadsheet table showing the EAC(total costs) if BB is to buy a new robot and keep it for n years, $n = 1, \ldots, 12$.

(d) Based on your answers for parts (a) through (c), what do you advise BB to do?

7.6 Nico has a 20-year-old oil-fired hot air furnace in his house. He is considering replacing it with a new high-efficiency natural gas furnace. The oil-fired furnace has a scrap value of $500, which it will retain indefinitely. A maintenance contract costs $300 per year, plus parts. Nico estimates that parts will cost $200 this year, increasing by $100 per year in subsequent years. The new gas furnace will cost $4500 to buy and $500 to install. It will save $500 per year in energy costs. The maintenance costs for the gas furnace are covered under guarantee for the first five years. The market value of the gas furnace can be estimated from straight-line depreciation with a salvage value of $500 after 10 years. Using a MARR of 10%, should the oil furnace be replaced?

7.7 A certain machine cost $25 000 to purchase and install. It has salvage values and operating costs as shown in the table on page 266. The salvage value of $20 000 listed at the end of year 0 reflects the loss of the installation costs at the time of installation.

Costs and Salvage Values for Various Lives		
Life in Years (t)	Salvage value at end of year t	Operating cost in year t
0	$20 000.00	
1	16 000.00	$ 3 000.00
2	12 800.00	3 225.00
3	10 240.00	3 466.88
4	8 192.00	3 726.89
5	6 553.60	4 006.41
6	5 242.88	4 306.89
7	4 194.30	4 629.90
8	3 355.44	4 977.15
9	2 684.35	5 350.43
10	2 147.48	5 751.72
11	1 717.99	6 183.09
12	1 374.39	6 646.83
13	1 099.51	7 145.34
14	879.61	7 681.24
15	703.69	8 257.33
16	562.95	8 876.63
17	450.36	9 542.38
18	360.29	10 258.06

The MARR is 12%.

(a) What is the economic life of the machine?

(b) What is the equivalent annual cost over that life?

Now assume that the MARR is 5%.

(c) What is the economic life of the machine?

(d) What is the equivalent annual cost over that life?

(e) Explain the effect of decreasing the MARR.

7.8 Jack and Jill live on a hill in Deep Cove. Jack is a self-employed house painter who works out of their house. Jill works in Burnaby, to which she regularly commutes by car. The car is a four-year-old Japanese import.

Jill could commute by bus. They are considering selling the car and getting by with the van Jack uses for work.

The car cost $12 000 new. It dropped about 20% in value in the first year. After that it fell by about 15% per year. The car is now worth about $5900. They expect it to continue to decline in value by about 15% of current value each year. Operating and other costs are about $2670 per year. They expect this to rise by about 7.5% per year. A commuter pass costs $112 per month, and is not expected to increase in cost.

Jack and Jill have a MARR of 10%, which is what Jack earns on his business investment. Their time horizon is two years because Jill expects to quit work at that time.

(a) Will commuting by bus save money?

(b) Can you advise Jack and Jill about retiring the car?

Defender, When New		
Life (Years)	Salvage Value ($)	Operating and Maintenance Costs ($)
0	100 000	
1	85 000	15 000
2	72 250	20 000
3	61 413	25 000
4	52 201	30 000
5	44 371	45 000
6	37 715	20 000
7	32 058	25 000
8	27 249	30 000
9	23 162	35 000
10	19 687	50 000
11	16 734	25 000
12	14 224	30 000
13	12 091	35 000
14	10 277	40 000
15	8 735	45 000

7.9 Ener-G purchases new turbines at a cost of $100 000. Each has a 15-year useful life and must be overhauled periodically at a cost of $10 000. The salvage value of a turbine declines 15% of current value each year, and operating and maintenance costs (including the cost of the overhauls) of a typical turbine are as shown in the table on page 267 (the costs for the fifth and tenth years include a $10 000 overhaul, but an overhaul is not done in the fifteenth year since this is the end of the turbine's useful life):

(a) Construct a spreadsheet which gives, for each year, the *EAC*(Operating and Maintenance Costs), *EAC*(Capital Costs), and *EAC*(Total Costs) for the turbines. Interest is 15%. How long should Ener-G keep each turbine before replacing it, given a five-year overhaul schedule? What are the associated equivalent annual costs?

(b) If Ener-G were to overhaul its turbines every six years (at the same cost), the salvage value and operating and maintenance costs would be as follows:

Defender, When New		
Life (Years)	Salvage Value ($)	Maintenance Costs ($)
0	100 000	
1	85 000	15000
2	72 250	20 000
3	61 413	25 000
4	52 201	30 000
5	44 371	35 000
6	37 715	50 000
7	32 058	20 000
8	27 249	25 000
9	23 162	30 000
10	19 687	35 000
11	16 734	40 000
12	14 224	55 000
13	12 091	25 000
14	10 277	30 000
15	8 735	35 000

Should Ener-G switch to a six-year overhaul cycle?

7.10 The Burnaby Machine Company makes small parts under contract for manufacturers in the Vancouver area. The company makes a group of metal parts on a turret lathe for a local ski manufacturer. The current lathe is now six years old. It has a planned further life of three years. The contract with the ski manufacturer has three more years to run as well. A new, improved lathe has become available. The challenger will have lower operating costs than the defender.

The defender can now be sold for $1200 in the used-equipment market. The challenger will cost $25 000 including installation. Its salvage value after installation, but before use, will be $20 000. Further data for the defender and the challenger are shown below.

Defender		
Additional Life in Years (t)	Salvage with Additional Life of t Years ($)	Operating Cost in Year t ($)
0	1 200	
1	600	20 000
2	300	20 500
3	150	21 012.50

Challenger		
Life in Years (t)	Salvage with Life of t Years ($)	Operating Cost in Year t ($)
0	20 000	
1	14 000	13 875
2	9 800	14 360.63
3	6 860	14 863.25

Burnaby Machine is not sure if the contract it has with the ski company will be renewed. Therefore, Burnaby wants to make the decision about replacing the defender with the challenger using a three-year study period. Burnaby Machine uses a 12% MARR for this type of investment.

(a) What is the present worth of costs over the next three years for the defender?

(b) What is the present worth of costs over the next three years for the challenger?

(c) Now suppose that Burnaby did not have a good estimate of the salvage value of the challenger at the end of three years. What minimum salvage value for the challenger at the end of three years would make the present worth of costs for the challenger equal to that for the defender?

7.11 Suppose in the situation described in Problem 7.10, Burnaby Machine believed that the contract with the ski company would be renewed. Burnaby also believed that all challengers after the current challenger would be identical to the current challenger. Further data concerning these challengers are given below. Recall that a new challenger costs $25 000 installed.

Challenger		
Life in Years (t)	Salvage with Life of t Years ($)	Operating Cost in Year t ($)
0	20 000.00	
1	14 000.00	13 875.00
2	9 800.00	14 369.63
3	6 860.00	14 863.25
4	4 802.00	15 383.46
5	3 361.40	15 921.88
6	2 352.98	16 479.15
7	1 647.09	17 055.92
8	1 152.96	17 652.87
9	807.07	18 270.73
10	564.95	18 910.20
11	395.47	19 572.06
12	276.83	20 257.08

Burnaby were also advised that machines identical to the defender would be available indefinitely. New copies of the defender would cost $17 500, including installation. Further data concerning new defenders are shown in the table on page 271.

The MARR is 12%.

(a) Find the economic life of the challenger. What is the equivalent annual cost over that life?

(b) Should the defender be replaced with the challenger or with a new defender?

(c) When should this be done?

Defender When New		
Life in Years (t)	Salvage with Life of t Years ($)	Operating Cost in Year t ($)
0	15 000.00	
1	9 846.45	17 250.00
2	6 463.51	17 681.25
3	4 242.84	18 123.28
4	2 785.13	18 576.36
5	1 828.24	19 040.77
6	1 200.11	19 516.79
7	600.00	20 004.71
8	300.00	20 504.83
9	150.00	21 017.45
10	150.00	21 542.89
11	150.00	22 081.46
12	150.00	22 633.49
13	150.00	23 199.33

7.12 You own several copiers which are currently valued at $10 000. Operating and maintenance costs for next year are estimated at $9000 per year, increasing by 10% each year thereafter. Declining-balance depreciation on the existing equipment is about 20% per year.

You are considering replacing your existing copiers with new ones which have a suggested retail price of $25 000. Operating and maintenance costs for the new equipment will be $6000 per year, increasing by 10% each year. The salvage value of the new equipment is well approximated by a 20% drop from the suggested retail price per year. Furthermore, you can get a trade-in allowance of $12 000 for your equipment if you purchase the new equipment at its suggested retail price. Your MARR is 8%.

Should you replace your existing equipment now?

7.13 An existing piece of equipment has the following pattern of salvage values and operating and maintenance costs:

Defender					
Additional Life (Years)	Salvage Value ($)	Maintenance Costs ($)	EAC Capital Costs ($)	EAC Operating and Maintenance Costs ($)	EAC Total ($)
0	10 000				
1	8 000	2 000	3 500	2 000	5 500
2	6 400	2 500	3 174	2 233	5 407
3	5 120	3 000	2 905	2 454	5 359
4	4 096	3 500	2 682	2 663	5 345
5	3 277	4 000	2 497	2 861	5 359
6	2 621	4 500	2 343	3 049	5 391
7	2 097	5 000	2 214	3 225	5 439
8	1 678	5 500	2 106	3 391	5 497
9	1 342	6 000	2 016	3 546	5 562

A replacement asset is being considered. Its relevant costs over the next nine years are:

Challenger					
Additional Life (Years)	Salvage Value ($)	Maintenance Costs ($)	EAC Capital Costs ($)	EAC Operating and Maintenance Costs ($)	EAC Total ($)
0	12 000				
1	9 600	1 500	4 200	1 500	5 700
2	7 680	1 900	3 809	1 686	5 495
3	6 144	2 300	3 486	1 863	5 349
4	4 915	2 700	3 219	2 031	5 249
5	3 932	3 100	2 997	2 189	5 186
6	3 146	3 500	2 811	2 339	5 150
7	2 517	3 900	2 657	2 480	5 137
8	2 013	4 300	2 528	2 613	5 140
9	1 611	4 700	2 419	2 737	5 156

There is need for the asset (either the defender or the challenger) for the next nine years.

(a) What replacement alternatives are there?

(b) What replacement timing do you recommend?

7.14 The Brunswick Table Top Company makes tops for tables and desks. The company now owns a seven-year-old planer that is experiencing increasing operating costs. The defender has a maximum additional life of five years. They are considering replacing the defender with a new planer.

Defender		
Additional Life in Years (t)	**Salvage Value with Additional Life of t Years ($)**	**Operating Cost in t^{th} Added Year ($)**
0	4 000	
1	3 000	20 000
2	2 000	25 000
3	1 000	30 000
4	500	35 000
5	500	40 000

First Challenger		
Life in Years (t)	**Salvage Value with Life of t Years ($)**	**Operating Cost in t^{th} Year ($)**
0	25 000	
1	20 000	16 800
2	16 000	17 640
3	12 800	18 522
4	10 240	19 448
5	8 192	20 421
6	6 554	21 442
7	5 243	22 514
8	4 194	23 639
9	3 355	24 821
10	2 684	26 062

The new planer would cost $30 000 installed. Its value after installation, but before use, would be about $25 000. The company has been told that there will be a new model planer available in two years. The new model is expected to have the same first costs as the current challenger. However, it is expected to have lower operating costs. Data concerning the defender and the two challengers are shown in the tables on page 273 and above.

	Second Challenger	
Life in Years (t)	Salvage Value with Life of t Years ($)	Operating Cost in t^{th} Year ($)
0	25 000	
1	20 000	12 000
2	16 000	12 600
3	12 800	13 230
4	10 240	13 892
5	8 192	14 586
6	6 554	15 315
7	5 243	16 081
8	4 194	16 885
9	3 355	17 729
10	2 684	18 616

Brunswick Table has a 10-year planning period and uses a MARR of 10%.

(a) What are the combinations of planers that Brunswick can use to cover requirements for the next 10 years? For example, Brunswick may keep the defender one more year, then install the first challenger and keep it for nine years. Notice that the first challenger will not be installed after the second year when the second challenger becomes available. You may ignore combinations that involve installing the first challenger after the second becomes available. Recall also that the maximum additional life for the defender is five years.

(b) What is the best combination?

7.15 You estimate that your two-year-old car is now worth $12 000 and that it will decline in value by 25% of its current value each year of its eight-year remaining useful life. You also estimate that its operating and main-tenance costs will be $2100, increasing by 20% per year thereafter. Your MARR is 12%.

(a) Construct a spreadsheet showing (1) additional life, in years, (2) salvage value, (3) operating and maintenance costs, (4) EAC(operating and maintenance costs), (5) EAC(capital costs), and (6) EAC(total costs). What additional life minimizes the EAC(total costs)?

(b) Now you are considering the possibility of painting the car in three years' time for $2000. Painting the car will increase its salvage value. By how much will the salvage value have to increase before painting the car is economically justified? Modify the spreadsheet you developed for part (a) to show this salvage value and the EAC(total costs) for each additional year of life. Will painting the car extend its economic life?

7.16 A long-standing principle of computer innovations is that computers double in power for the same price, or, equivalently, halve in cost for the same power, every 18 months. Barrie Data Services (BDS) owns a single computer which is at the end of its third year of service. BDS will continue to buy computers of the same power as its current one. Its current computer would cost $80 000 to buy today, excluding installation. Given that a new model is released every 18 months, what replacement policy should BDS adopt for computers over the next three years?
   Other facts to be considered are:

1. Installation cost is 15% of purchase price.

2. Salvage values are computed at a declining-balance depreciation rate of 50%.

3. Maintenance is estimated as 10% of accumulated depreciation per year or as 15% of accumulated depreciation per 18-month period.

4. BDS uses a MARR of 12%.

7.17 A water pump to be used by the city's maintenance department costs $10 000 new. A running-in period, costing $1000 immediately, is required for a new pump. Operating and maintenance costs average $500 the first year, increasing by $300 per year thereafter. The salvage value of the pump at any time can be estimated by the declining-balance rate of 20%. Interest is at 10%. Using a spreadsheet, calculate the EAC for replacing the pump after one year, two years, etc. How often should the pump be replaced?

7.18 The water pump from the previous problem (7.17) is being considered to replace an existing one. The current one has a salvage value of $1000 and will retain this salvage value indefinitely.

(a) Operating costs are currently $2500 per year and are rising by $400 per year. Should the current pump be replaced? When?

(b) Operating costs are currently $3500 per year and are rising by $200 per year. Should the current pump be replaced? When?

7.19 Chatham Automotive purchased new electric forklifts to move steel automobile parts two years ago. These cost $75 000 each, including the charging stand. In practice, it was found that they do not hold a charge as long as claimed by the manufacturer, so operating costs are very high. This also results in their currently having a salvage value of about $10 000. Chatham Automotive is considering replacing them with propane models. The new ones cost $58 000. After one year, they have a salvage value of $40 000, and thereafter decline in value at a declining-balance depreciation rate of 20%, as does the electric model from this time on. The MARR is 8%. Operating costs for the electric model are currently $20 000 per year, rising by 12% per year. Operating costs for the propane model initially will be $10 000 per year, rising by 12% per year.

Should Chatham Automotive replace the forklifts now?

7.20 Suppose that Chatham Automotive (problem 7.19) can get a $14 000 trade-in value for their current electric model when they purchase a new propane model. Should they replace the electric forklifts now?

7.21 A joint former cost $60 000 to purchase and $10 000 to install seven years ago. The market value now is $33 000, and this will decline by 12% of current value each year for the next three years. Operating and maintenance costs are estimated to be $3400 this year, and are expected to increase by $500 per year.

(a) How much does the EAC of a new joint former have to be over its economic life to justify replacing the old one sometime in the next three years? The MARR is 10%.

(b) The EAC for a new joint former turns out to be $10 300 for a 10-year life. Should the old joint former be replaced within the next three years? If so, when?

(c) Is it necessary to consider replacing the old joint former more than three years from now, given that a new one has an EAC of $10 300?

7.22 Northwest Aerocomposite manufactures fibreglass and carbon fibre fairings. Their largest water-jet cutter will have to be replaced some time before the end of four years. The old cutter is currently worth $49 000. Other cost data for the current and replacement cutters can be found in the tables on page 277. The MARR is 15%. What is the economic life of the new cutter, and what is the equivalent annual cost for that life? When should the new cutter replace the old?

Data for the REPLACEMENT Water-Jet Cutter		
Life in Years	Salvage Value	Operating and Maintenance Costs
0	$90 000	
1	72 000	$12 000
2	57 600	14 400
3	46 080	17 280
4	36 864	20 736
5	29 491	24 883
6	23 593	29 860
7	18 874	35 832
8	15 099	42 998
9	12 080	51 598

Data for the Current Water-Jet Cutter		
Life in Years	Salvage Value	Operating and Maintenance Costs
0	$49 000	
1	36 500	$17 000
2	19 875	21 320
3	15 656	26 806
4	6 742	33 774

Problems 7.23 through 7.26 are concerned with the economic life of assets where there is a sequence of identical assets. The problems explore the sensitivity of the economic life to four parameters: the MARR, the level of operating cost, the rate of increase in operating cost, and the level of first cost. In each problem there is a pair of assets. The assets differ in only a single parameter. The problem asks you to determine the effect of this difference on the economic life and to explain the result.

All assets decline in value by 20% of current value each year. Installation costs are zero for all assets. Further data concerning the four pairs of assets are given in the table which follows.

Asset Number	First Cost	Initial Operating Cost	Rate of Operating Cost Increase	MARR
A1	$125 000	$30 000	12.5%/year	5%
B1	125 000	30 000	12.5%/year	25%
A2	100 000	30 000	2000/year	15%
B2	100 000	40 000	2000/year	15%
A3	100 000	30 000	5%/year	15%
B3	100 000	30 000	12.5%/year	15%
A4	75 000	30 000	5%/year	15%
B4	150 000	30 000	5%/year	15%

7.23 Consider Assets A1 and B1. They differ only in the MARR.

(a) Determine the economic lives for Assets A1 and B1.

(b) Create a diagram showing the equivalent annual capital cost, the equivalent annual operating cost, and the equivalent annual cost for Assets A1 and B1.

(c) Explain the difference in economic life between Asset A1 and Asset B1.

7.24 Consider Assets A2 and B2. They differ only in the level of operating cost.

(a) Determine the economic lives for Assets A2 and B2.

(b) Create a diagram showing the equivalent annual capital cost, the equivalent annual operating cost, and the equivalent annual cost for Assets A2 and B2.

(c) Explain the difference in economic life between Asset A2 and Asset B2.

7.25 Consider Assets A3 and B3. They differ only in the rate of increase of operating cost.

(a) Determine the economic lives for Assets A3 and B3.

(b) Create a diagram showing the equivalent annual capital cost, the equivalent annual operating cost, and the equivalent annual cost for Assets A3 and B3.

(c) Explain the difference in economic life between Asset A3 and Asset B3.

7.26 Consider Assets A4 and B4. They differ only in the level of first cost.

(a) Determine the economic lives for Assets A4 and B4.

(b) Create a diagram showing the equivalent annual capital cost, the equivalent annual operating cost, and the equivalent annual cost for Assets A4 and B4.

(c) Explain the difference in economic life between Asset A4 and Asset B4.

The following problem concerns the economic life of assets where there is a sequence of identical assets. In this case there is an opportunity to overhaul equipment. Two issues are explored. The first issue concerns the optimal life of equipment. The second issue concerns the decision as to whether or not to replace equipment that is past its economic life.

7.27 Consider a piece of equipment that costs $40 000 to buy and install. The equipment has a maximum life of 15 years. Overhaul is required in the fourth, eighth, and twelfth years.

The company uses a MARR of 20%. Further information is given in the table below:

Year	Salvage with Life of t Years ($)	Operating Cost in t^{th} Year ($)	Overhaul Cost ($)
0	15 000		
1	12 000	2 000	
2	9 600	2 200	
3	7 680	2 420	
4	7 500	2 662	2 500
5	6 000	2 000	
6	4 800	2 200	
7	3 840	2 420	
8	4 500	2 662	32 500
9	3 600	2 000	
10	2 880	2 800	
11	2 304	3 920	
12	2 000	5 488	17 500
13	1 200	4 000	
14	720	8 000	
15	432	16 000	

(a) Show that the economic life for this equipment is seven years.

(b) Suppose that, for whatever reason, the equipment is overhauled in the eighth year rather than replaced. Show that keeping the equipment for three more years (after the eighth year), until it next comes up for overhaul, has lower cost than replacing the equipment immediately.

Hint: The comparison must be done fairly and carefully. Assume that under either plan the replacement is kept for its optimal life of seven years. It is easier to compare the plans if they cover the same number of years. One way to do this is to consider an 11-year period as shown below.

Year	Plan A	Plan B
0		
1	Defender	Replacement #1
2	Defender	Replacement #1
3	Defender	Replacement #1
4	Replacement #1	Replacement #1
5	Replacement #1	Replacement #1
6	Replacement #1	Replacement #1
7	Replacement #1	Replacement #1
8	Replacement #1	Replacement #2
9	Replacement #1	Replacement #2
10	Replacement #1	Replacement #2
11	Replacement #2	Replacement #2

First, show that the present worth of costs over the 11 years is lower under Plan A than under Plan B. Second, point out that the equipment that is in place at the end of the eleventh year is newer under Plan A than under Plan B.

(c) Why is it necessary to take into account the age of the equipment at the end of the 11-year period?

7.28 Northfield Metal Works is a Manitoba household appliance parts manufacturer which has just won a contract with a major appliance company to supply replacement parts to service shops. The contract is for five years. Northfield is considering using three existing manual punch presses or a new automatic press for part of the work. The new press would cost $225 000 installed. Northfield is using a five-year time horizon for the project. The MARR is 25% for projects of this type. Further data concerning the two options are shown on page 281.

Automatic Punch Press		
Life in Years (t)	**Salvage Value with Life of t Years ($)**	**Operating Cost in tth Year ($)**
0	125 000	
1	100 000	25 000
2	80 000	23 750
3	64 000	22 563
4	51 200	21 434
5	40 960	20 363

Hand-Fed Press		
Additional Life in Years (t)	**Salvage Value with Additional Life of t Years ($)**	**Operating Cost in tth Added Year ($)**
0	10 000	
1	9 000	25 000
2	8 000	25 000
3	7000	25 000
4	6 000	25 000
5	5 000	25 000

Note that the hand-fed press values are for each of the three presses. Costs must be multiplied by three to get the costs for three presses.

Northfield is not sure of the salvage values for the new press. What salvage value at the end of five years would make the two options equal?

CHAPTER 8

Taxes

Engineering Economics in Action, Part 8A: It's in the Details

8.1 Introduction

8.2 The Capital Cost Allowance (CCA) System

8.3 Undepreciated Capital Cost

8.4 The Capital Cost Tax Factor

8.5 Components of a Complete Tax Calculation

8.6 Approximate After-Tax Rate of Return Calculations

Canadian Corporate Case 8.1: MT&T Tries to Reduce Its Taxes

Review Problems

Summary

Engineering Economics in Action, Part 8B: The Work Report

Problems

Appendix 8A: Deriving the Capital Cost Tax Factors

Engineering Economics in Action, Part 8A: It's in the Details

"Details, Terry. Sometimes it's all in the details." Naomi pursed her lips and nodded sagely. Terry and Naomi were sitting in the coffee room together. The main break periods for the line workers had passed, so they were alone except for a maintenance person on the other side of the room who was enjoying either a late breakfast or an early lunch.

"Uh, O.K., Naomi. What is?"

"Well," Naomi replied, "you know that rocker arm die deal? The one where we're upgrading to a 10-stage die? The rough replacement study you did seems to have worked out O.K. We're going to do something, sometime, but now we have to be a little more precise."

"O.K. What do we do?" Terry was interested now. Terry liked things precise and detailed.

"The main thing is to make sure we are working with the best numbers we can get. I'm getting good cost figures from Tan Wang at Hamilton Tools for this die and future possibilities, and we'll also work out our own costs for the changeover. Your cost calculations are going to have to be more accurate, too."

"You mean to more significant digits?" Naomi couldn't tell whether Terry was making a joke or the idea of more significant digits really did thrill him. She decided it was the former.

"Ha. Ha. No, I mean that we had better explicitly look at the tax implications of the purchase. Our rough calculations ignored taxes, and taxes can have a significant effect on the choice of best alternative. And when lots of money is at stake, the details matter."

8.1   Introduction

In Canada, the federal and provincial governments levy taxes on both individuals and corporations. These taxes can have a significant impact on the economic viability of a project. A vital component of a thorough economic analysis will therefore include the tax implications of an investment decision. This chapter provides an introduction to the tax environment in Canada and shows how this environment can affect engineering economics decisions.

When a firm makes an investment, the income from the project will affect the company's cash flows. If the investment yields a profit, the profits will be taxed. Since the taxes result as a direct consequence of the investment, they reduce the net profits associated with that investment. In this sense, taxes associated with a project are a disbursement. If the investment yields a loss, the company may be able to offset the loss from this project against the profits from another and end up paying less tax on an overall basis. As a result, when evaluating a loss-generating project, the net savings in tax can be viewed as a negative disbursement.

The most significant kind of tax for economic comparisons is *income tax*, which is charged on *net* income. In this context, net income is the difference between expenses and receipts for the company as a whole. Tax rates in Canada are generally between 35% and 60% of net income. The actual tax rate applied is fairly complicated and can depend on the size of the firm, whether or not it is a manufacturer, its location, and a variety of other factors. For example, to encourage the development of new technology, special rules were designed to reduce the tax burden on research and development projects. Our concern here is with the basic approach used in determining the impact of taxes on a project. For special tax rules, it is best to check with Revenue Canada or a tax specialist.

It is also worth noting that tax rules can change suddenly. As seen below, the current tax rules have applied only since 1981. Also, the Canadian tax rules are unique to Canada, so that the methods presented in this chapter may not apply elsewhere. For comparison, Close-Up 8.1 reviews the tax procedures used in the United States.

CLOSE-UP 8.1   UNITED STATES TAX RULES

In the U.S. tax system, all depreciable assets are designated as belonging to a "Modified Accelerated Cost Recovery System (MACRS) Class." The MACRS Class determines the declining-balance rate (usually double-declining-balance or 150% declining-balance) and the **recovery period**, which is the designated service life for depreciation calculation purposes.

The declining-balance method is not used for the entire recovery period. All assets are required to attain a book value of $0 at the end of the recovery period. Since, under a declining-balance depreciation method, a book value of $0 is never reached, at an appropriate point the depreciation method switches from declining-balance to straight-line.

8.2 The Capital Cost Allowance (CCA) System

When a firm buys a depreciable asset for use in its business, a **capital expense** is incurred. (Almost all tangible assets are depreciable. The primary exception to this is land.) Since the asset deteriorates through the passage of time, the firm must deduct the capital expense over a period of years. This is done by claiming a depreciation expense each year of the asset's useful life, as its value declines. The depreciation is recorded by accountants in the balance sheet as a reduction in the book value of the asset. It is also recorded as an expense on the income statement. Depreciation thus reduces the before-tax income even though, in reality, there has been no cash expense.

In general, a firm will want to "write off" (i.e., depreciate) an investment as fast as possible. This is because depreciation is considered an expense, and offsets revenue so as to reduce net income. Since net income is taxed, taxes can be deferred or reduced by depreciating assets quickly. The effect of deferring the taxes can be considerable. To counter this effect, the Canadian tax system defines a specific amount of depreciation that companies may claim in any year. This amount is called the *capital cost allowance (CCA)*. In this section, we examine how to apply CCA rules to investment decisions and compare the CCA to depreciation claimed for accounting records.

EXAMPLE 8.1

In the imaginary country of Monovia, companies can depreciate their capital asset purchases as fast as they want. Clive Cutler, owner of Monovia Manufacturing, has just bought $200 000 worth of equipment. He has made up two spreadsheets, shown in Tables 8.1 and 8.2, to illustrate the effect of different depreciation strategies over the next five years under the following assumptions:

1. Income is $300 000 per year.
2. Expenses excluding depreciation are $100 000 per year.
3. The tax rate is 50%.
4. Available cash is invested at 10% interest.
5. The salvage value of the equipment after five years is $0.

TABLE 8.1   Full Depreciation in One Year

Year	1	2	3	4	5
Income	$300 000	$300 000	$300 000	$300 000	$300 000
Expenses excluding depreciation	100 000	100 000	100 000	100 000	100 000
Depreciation expense	200 000	0	0	0	0
Net income	0	200 000	200 000	200 000	200 000
Taxes	0	100 000	100 000	100 000	100 000
Profit	0	100 000	100 000	100 000	100 000
Cash	200 000	100 000	100 000	100 000	100 000
Accumulated cash	200 000	320 000	452 000	597 200	756 920

TABLE 8.2   Straight-Line Depreciation over Five Years

Year	1	2	3	4	5
Income	$300 000	$300 000	$300 000	$300 000	$300 000
Expenses excluding depreciation	100 000	100 000	100 000	100 000	100 000
Depreciation expense	40 000	40 000	40 000	40 000	40 000
Net income	160 000	160 000	160 000	160 000	160 000
Taxes	80 000	80 000	80 000	80 000	80 000
Profit	80 000	80 000	80 000	80 000	80 000
Cash	120 000	120 000	120 000	120 000	120 000
Accumulated cash	120 000	252 000	397 200	556 920	732 612

Table 8.1 illustrates the case where the equipment is fully depreciated in the first year, although it generates revenue over its five-year life. In Table 8.2, straight-line depreciation is used over the five-year life.

When we look at the effects of depreciation on economic analyses, it is important to distinguish between expenses that represent a cash outflow and expenses that do not. Purchasing an asset, like a piece of equipment, will produce a cash outflow at the time the purchase is made. In particular, the balance sheet will reflect a transfer out of current assets (cash) and a transfer into fixed assets (equipment) and perhaps to current liabilities (bank loan).

Depreciation, on the other hand, does not actually represent a cash outflow, although it is recorded as an expense in the income statement. For example, in the first year of Table 8.1, writing off (depreciating) the entire cost of the equipment in its first year produced a depreciation expense of $200 000. There was no actual cash outflow due to the depreciation (although there was for the actual purchase of the asset), but depreciation caused the net income to be reduced to zero for that year, even though $200 000 in cash was actually available. Investing the $200 000 for the second year at 10% interest produces accumulated cash of $220 000. Adding this to the profit of $100 000 for the second year gives accumulated cash of $320 000 at the end of the second year. Continuing in this fashion produces accumulated cash of $756 920 at the end of the five-year period.

In contrast, if the equipment is depreciated on a straight-line basis over five years, only $732 612 in cash is accumulated. This can be seen by working through the expenses, net income, taxes, and profit for each year. For example, in year 1, a (straight-line) depreciation expense of $200 000/5 = $40 000 is claimed. This reduces net income by $40 000, to $160 000, and leaves after-tax profits of $80 000. Now, as before, the depreciation expense of $40 000 is not a cash outflow, so the cash actually available to invest at the end of the first year is the $80 000 profit *plus* $40 000. Since the depreciation expense is constant with the straight-line method, cash of $120 000 will be available to invest at the end of each of the five years. Thus, at the end of five years, the accumulated cash will be $732 612. This is $24 308 less than when the equipment was fully depreciated in the first year because taxes were delayed by depreciating more of the asset's value earlier. The extra income that was available for investment allowed more interest to accumulate over the five-year period. The $24 308 is significant, and illustrates why faster depreciation is preferred to slower depreciation.

As seen in Chapter 6, there are several generally accepted depreciation methods. The most prevalent methods in Canada are straight line and declining balance. For the purposes of preparing financial statements for investors, a firm may use any one (or all) of the generally accepted methods for calculating depreciation expenses, provided that the method used is the same from period to period. However, if companies had the freedom to depreciate as they wanted to for tax purposes, they would depreciate their assets immediately, since in that way they would get the largest benefit because of tax savings.

Governments have a different perspective, since they would prefer to receive the tax money as quickly as possible. They would want companies to depreciate assets as slowly as possible to keep taxable income as high as possible and produce the most taxes. In order to limit the depreciation amount which companies use for tax purposes, the Canadian government established a maximum level of capital cost expense (i.e., depreciation) which a company can claim each year. This maximum amount is referred to as the firm's **capital cost allowance (CCA)**. The system set up to allow firms to compute their capital cost allowance is called the **capital cost allowance (CCA) system**. According to the CCA system, the declining-balance method of depreciation must be used for claiming capital costs associated with most tangible assets. Straight-line depreciation is used for intangible assets. We are mainly concerned with tangible assets, so our discussion will focus on declining-balance depreciation.

The CCA system specifies the maximum rate a company can use to depreciate its assets for tax calculations; this is referred to as the **capital cost allowance (CCA) rate**. To implement the CCA system, a firm's assets are grouped by **capital cost allowance (CCA) asset class** and each class is managed individually. For example, all assets classified as office equipment (desks, chairs, filing cabinets, copiers, and the like) are grouped together, and depreciation expenses are based on the total remaining undepreciated cost of all assets in that class. Some examples of CCA rates and CCA asset classes are given in Table 8.3. Note that a 100% CCA rate means that the assets are **expensed**, that is, treated as an operating cost rather than a capital cost.

TABLE 8.3   Sample CCA Rates and Classes

CCA Rate (%)	Class	Description
5 to 10	1, 3, 6	Buildings and additions
20	8	Machinery and equipment which cost $200 or more
25	9	Aircraft, aircraft furniture, and equipment
30	10	Passenger vehicles, vans, trucks, computers
100	12	Dies, tools, instruments which cost less than $200

In addition to these standard rates, sometimes, as part of government policy, special rates are set to encourage certain kinds of investment. For example, in recent years the CCA rate for pollution-control equipment has been 100%.

Figure 8.1 illustrates how the remaining value of an asset subject to taxes diminishes within the standard range of CCA rates.

While capital cost allowance and depreciation are conceptually similar, it is important to distinguish between the two terms. Recall from Chapter 6 that, in determining net income, we deduct depreciation expenses from the revenues to arrive at net income. This is the net income for accounting purposes. For tax purposes, we need to determine taxable income. To

FIGURE 8.1   Effect of Different CCA Rates

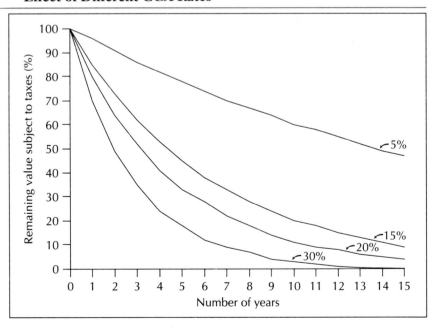

establish taxable net income, we start with the accounting net income, add back the depreciation expense for accounting purposes, and then deduct the CCA. Such accounting adjustments are common in determining the amount of tax that a company needs to pay. Given the complexities of the tax system, it is possible that net income for accounting purposes differs from net income for tax purposes by a large amount. For our purposes, we need only to distinguish between the depreciation for accounting purposes and capital cost allowance, which is depreciation for tax purposes.

8.3 Undepreciated Capital Cost

The basis for calculating capital cost allowance for assets in a particular asset class is the total undepreciated capital cost (UCC) of the assets included in that class. The capital cost of an asset when it is purchased is the total cost of acquiring the asset. This includes the purchase price, legal fees, accounting costs, and possibly other costs over and above the purchase price. As the asset is depreciated, companies keep track of the undepreciated portion of the original capital cost through an **undepreciated capital cost (UCC)** account. The UCC is like a remaining book value for the assets in a class, but instead of representing market or salvage value it represents the remaining amount subject to depreciation for taxation purposes.

The undepreciated capital cost for each asset is not recorded individually within a class; instead, assets in each class are pooled and only one account is maintained for each asset class. The capital cost allowance for a particular asset class is then calculated from the CCA rate for that class and its UCC.

Prior to November 13, 1981, a company was allowed to include in its base for the calculation of capital cost allowance the full purchase price of an asset purchased within the year, regardless of when during the taxation year the asset was purchased. Consequently, there was considerable motivation for companies to purchase assets at the end of their fiscal year. The Canadian government, recognizing the considerable tax losses brought about in this manner, changed the rules, effective Friday, November 13, 1981. Since that date, only half of the capital cost of acquiring an asset is considered in the CCA in the year of purchase of an item, while the other half is then included in the second year. This is commonly referred to as "the half-year rule" in the CCA system.

To see the effect of this change and to illustrate the UCC account, consider a company that has just purchased a $1 000 000 piece of equipment. For simplicity, we will assume that this equipment is the only equipment in its class. The CCA rate for the equipment is 20%, and the company's tax rate is 50%. Table 8.4 shows the company's UCC amounts for the first four years of the asset's life, assuming that the purchase occurred before the 1981 tax rule change. Table 8.5 shows equivalent figures, assuming that the purchase occurred after the 1981 tax change.

TABLE 8.4   UCC Amounts Using Pre-1981 CCA Rules

Year	Adjustments to UCC from Purchases and Dispositions	Base UCC Amount for Capital Cost Allowance	Capital Cost Allowance	Remaining UCC	Tax Savings Due to the CCA
1	$1 000 000	$1 000 000	$200 000	$800 000	$100 000
2	0	800 000	160 000	640 000	80 000
3	0	640 000	128 000	512 000	64 000
4	0	512 000	102 400	409 600	51 200

TABLE 8.5   UCC Amounts Using Post-1981 CCA Rules

Year	Adjustments to UCC from Purchases and Dispositions	Base UCC Amount for Capital Cost Allowance	Capital Cost Allowance	Remaining UCC	Tax Savings Due to the CCA
1	$1 000 000	$500 000	$100 000	$900 000	$50 000
2	0	900 000	180 000	720 000	90 000
3	0	720 000	144 000	576 000	72 000
4	0	576 000	115 200	460 800	57 600

To explain some of the amounts, we will start with Table 8.4. The UCC at the beginning of the year in which the asset was bought is the purchase cost of the asset. The CCA rate for the equipment is 20%. Thus the company can claim a capital cost allowance of 20% of the $1 000 000 for the first year, leaving a UCC of $800 000 at the end of the first year. In the second year, the CCA amount is 20% of the UCC from the end of the previous year: 20% of $800 000 = $160 000. The UCC of the asset thus declines by 20% of the *current* book value each year as the CCA rate is applied to the undepreciated capital cost from the previous year.

Table 8.5 shows what happens to the UCC account if it is assumed that the purchase occurred *after* the 1981 CCA tax regulation change. In the first year of the asset's life, the full first cost of $1 000 000 can be added to the UCC account, but only half of that amount is subject to a CCA claim. Thus the CCA amount in the first year is 20% of $500 000, leaving a balance of $900 000 of undepreciated capital cost. The CCA amount for the second year is then 20% of $900 000, or $180 000. The remainder of the CCA calculations are computed as usual.

Notice that the CCA expenses generate tax savings by reducing taxable income. At a 10% interest rate, the present worth of the tax savings using the pre-1981 rules is \$240 079, while that for the post-1981 rules is only \$213 271.

Since the change in the tax law pertaining to "the half-year rule" in 1981, there still remains an incentive to purchase equipment at the end of the (fiscal) year. However, the incentive has been reduced as the tax effects have been diminished.

The previous example illustrated a simple case where only one asset was purchased. In fact, a company typically purchases assets over time and disposes of them when they are no longer required. It is important to note that, if an asset is disposed of in the same year as another one in the same CCA class is purchased, the disposal amount (for the class) is subtracted from the purchase amount (for the class) before applying the half-year rule. For any given year, the UCC balance can be calculated as follows:

$$UCC_{\text{opening}} + \text{additions} - \text{disposals} - CCA = UCC_{\text{ending}}$$

To illustrate the use of UCC accounts when several assets of the same class are acquired and then disposed of, consider the following example.

EXAMPLE 8.2

Egonomical Corporation, an injection-moulding firm, is planning to set up business. It will purchase two used injection moulders for \$5000 each in 1998, a new, full-featured moulder for \$20 000 in 1999, and a computer controller for the new moulder for \$5000 in 2003. One used moulder will be salvaged for \$2000 in 2003, and the other for the same amount in 2004. If the CCA rate for all these assets is 20%, determine the balance of the UCC account for years 1998 to 2005.

Table 8.6 illustrates the calculations for the UCC balance for Example 8.2. It can be assumed that the original balance is zero, since the company is just starting up. In 1998, purchases totalling \$10 000 were made. However, only half of that amount, \$5000, is used for the CCA calculations because of the half-year rule. At 20%, the CCA amount is then \$1000. The UCC account for that class is increased by the full amount of the purchase, so subtracting the \$1000 from the UCC results in a balance of \$9000. In 1999, a purchase of \$20 000 increases the amount subject to the UCC to \$19 000 (since only half of the cost of the new purchase can be included in 1999), resulting in a CCA amount for that year of \$3 800. The UCC balance is calculated as \$9000 + \$20 000 − \$3800 = \$25 200. For the years 2000 to 2002, the CCA amount is simply 20% of the UCC balance for the previous year, since no acquisitions or disposals were made.

In 2003, two things happen at the same time. A computer controller is purchased for \$5000, and a moulder is salvaged for \$2000. This results in a net positive adjustment to the UCC of \$3000. It is this \$3000 which

**TABLE 8.6   UCC Computations with Several Changes
in Asset Holdings**

Year	Adjustments to UCC from Purchases and Dispositions	Base UCC Amount for Capital Cost Allowance	Capital Cost Allowance	Remaining UCC
1998	$10 000	$ 5 000	$1 000	$ 9 000
1999	20 000	19 000	3 800	25 200
2000	0	25 200	5 040	20 160
2001	0	20 160	4 032	16 128
2002	0	16 128	3 226	12 902
2003	3 000	14 402	2 880	13 022
2004	(2 000)	11 022	2 204	8 817
2005	0	8 817	1 763	7 054

is subject to the half-year rule. Thus the UCC amount for CCA calculations is half of this amount plus the UCC balance from the previous year:
$1500 + $12 902 = $14 402. The UCC balance at the end of 2003
includes the total $3000 amount: $12 902 + $3000 − $2880 = $13 022.
The negative adjustment in 2004 is not subject to the half-year rule since
the half-year rule only applies to net purchases over the year, so the UCC
amount for CCA calculations is $2000 less than the previous year's bal-
ance. In 2005, there are no adjustments to the UCC other than the CCA
amount, leaving a final balance in 2005 of $7054.

8.4   The Capital Cost Tax Factor

From the example illustrated in Tables 8.4 and 8.5, it is clear that the
CCA creates tax savings. For example, if an asset with a CCA rate
of 20% is purchased for $100 000, in the first year this provides a
CCA amount of $10 000. With a tax rate of 50%, this deduction from
income saves $5000 in taxes. This saving would not have occurred if the
$100 000 had not been spent for the asset in the first place. Therefore,
the present worth of the first cost of the asset is actually less than $100 000;
it is reduced by the present worth of all of the tax savings that result
from its depreciation in all future years. In this example, the tax saving
for each year of the asset's life is shown in Table 8.7.

TABLE 8.7   Tax Savings Due to the Capital Cost Allowance

Year	Base UCC Amount for Capital Cost Allowance	Capital Cost Allowance	Remaining UCC	Tax Savings Due to the CCA
1	$50 000	$10 000	$90 000	$5 000
2	90 000	18 000	72 000	9 000
3	72 000	14 400	57 600	7 200
4	57 600	11 520	46 080	5 760
5	46 080	9 216	36 864	4 608

The present worth of the savings is

$$\text{Present worth of tax savings} = \$5000(P/F, i, 1) + \$9000(P/F, i, 2) \\ + \$7200(P/F, i, 3) + \$5760(P/F, i, 4) \\ + \$4608(P/F, i, 5) + \cdots$$

The present worth of the tax savings essentially reduces the first cost of the investment because making the investment and depreciating it over time brings about tax benefits. The **capital cost tax factor (CCTF)** is a value that summarizes the effect of the future benefit of tax savings and allows analysts to take these benefits into account when calculating the present worth of an asset. The CCTF remains constant for a given CCA rate, interest rate, and tax rate, and allows the determination of the present worth independently of the actual first cost of the asset. This makes it a very useful number.

Because of the change in tax laws on November 13, 1981, there are two CCTFs: the old CCTF (CCTF_{old}) and the new CCTF (CCTF_{new}). The CCTF_{old} is valid for purchases made before November 13, 1981, and, as seen later in this chapter, is also used for the salvage of assets regardless of the time at which the salvage is made. The CCTF_{new} is used for capital purchases on or after November 13, 1981.

As shown in detail in Appendix 8A, the CCTF_{old} is given by

$$\text{CCTF}_{\text{old}} = 1 - \frac{td}{(i + d)}$$

where

t = taxation rate
d = CCA rate
i = after-tax interest rate

The CCTF$_{new}$ is also derived in Appendix 8A as

$$CCTF_{new} = 1 - \frac{td\left(1 + \dfrac{i}{2}\right)}{(i + d)(1 + i)}$$

For an asset purchased after 1981, the present worth of the first cost (at the time of purchase) is found by multiplying the first cost by the CCTF$_{new}$. This takes into account the tax benefits forever. When an asset is salvaged or scrapped, we need to terminate the remaining stream of tax savings. This is done by applying the CCTF$_{old}$. An example in Section 8.5 will clarify the process.

EXAMPLE 8.3

An automobile purchased this year by Lestev Corporation for $25 000 has a CCA rate of 30%. Lestev is subject to 43% corporate taxes and the corporate (after-tax) MARR is 12%. What is the present worth of the first cost of this automobile, taking into account the future tax benefits of depreciation?

The car is purchased this year, so the CCTF$_{new}$ applies. The CCTF$_{new}$ is calculated as:

$$CCTF_{new} = 1 - (0.43)(0.3)(1 + .06)/[(0.12 + 0.3)(1 + 0.12)]$$
$$= 0.709311$$

The present worth of the first cost of the car is then calculated as:

$$PW = 0.709311(\$25\ 000)$$
$$= \$17\ 732.78$$

The present worth of the first cost of the car, taking into account all future tax benefits due to depreciation, is about $17 733. The tax benefit due to claiming CCA has effectively reduced the cost of the car, in terms of present worth.

It may seem strange that the effective cost of purchasing an asset is less than its first cost. However, bear in mind that the first cost is not the only effect that the purchase of an asset has on cash flows. The purchase will also likely generate savings. These savings are income, which is also taxed. Taking taxes into account when determining the present worth or annual worth of an asset will affect the present or annual worth *positively* because of the tax benefits resulting from future CCA, but *negatively* because of the taxation of future savings.

8.5 Components of a Complete Tax Calculation

In evaluating projects with the explicit consideration of taxes, it is important to recognize that there is a difference between a before-tax MARR and an after-tax MARR. A before-tax MARR is chosen to reflect the fact that taxes are not explicitly taken into account in the economic calculations, and conversely the after-tax MARR is used where taxes are explicitly taken into account. The relationship between the two is clarified later in this chapter.

Evaluating the economic impact of purchasing a depreciable asset goes beyond the impact of taxes on the first cost. There are two other components to a complete economic analysis. First, we need to assess the tax implications of the savings or additional expenses brought about by the asset over its useful life. Second, when the asset is disposed of, we no longer can take advantage of its capital cost allowance and thus must terminate the stream of tax savings resulting from depreciating the asset.

Each of these components has a tax effect that has to be taken into account when doing a cash flow analysis such as determining present worth or annual worth. A summary of the procedure for a present worth computation is shown in Table 8.8.

TABLE 8.8 Components of a Complete Present-Worth Tax Calculation

Component	Treatment
First cost	Multiply by the $CCTF_{new}$.
Savings or expenses	Multiply by $(1 - t)$. Convert to present worth.
Salvage value	Multiply by the $CCTF_{old}$. Convert to present worth.

First cost: As presented in Section 8.4, the first cost of an asset purchased after 1981 is reduced by the tax savings due to CCA. Multiply the first cost by the $CCTF_{new}$ to find the after-tax first cost.

Savings or expenses: Reduce savings or expenses by the tax rate by multiplying by $(1 - t)$. There is an assumption that the company is making a profit, so that taxes are paid on all the savings at the rate t, and expenses will reduce taxes at the rate t.

Salvage value: Apply $CCTF_{old}$. When an asset is disposed of, the salvage value reduces the UCC for the *full* amount in the year of disposal (at least in the absence of a corresponding purchase in the same year). The effect of reducing the UCC is the same in magnitude but opposite in sign as increasing the UCC. The $CCTF_{new}$ has built into it a delay in depreciating half of the value of the asset, whereas when disposing of an asset, the full effect occurs immediately. Consequently, the $CCTF_{old}$ is the one to use at the time an asset is sold.

Note that technically, when assets are disposed of in a given year, they are netted against any additions for the year before the half-year rule is applied. However, in project analysis, we generally want to evaluate the project independently, at least in preliminary evaluation. Thus, when we determine the salvage value we do not consider the effects of other additions or disposals that the company may also be planning for the same year. Nevertheless, it is worth noting that significant tax advantages can be made by properly planning the timing of investment additions and disposals. Our goal is to decide on the merits of the project on a more basic level at this time.

EXAMPLE 8.4

The owner of a spring-water bottling company in Erbsville has just purchased an automated bottle capper. What is the after-tax present worth of the new automated bottle capper if it costs $10 000 and saves $4000 per year over its five-year life? Assume a $2000 salvage value and a 50% tax rate. The after-tax MARR is 12%.

A CCA rate is not given in this question. As production equipment, the new bottle capper can be assumed to be in CCA Class 8, with a rate of 20%.

The present worth of the first cost (assuming that the purchase took place after November 13, 1981) must take into account the tax benefits of CCA. The after-tax first cost is

$$PW1 = -\$10\ 000(CCTF_{new})$$

where the $CCTF_{new}$ is calculated as

$$CCTF_{new} = 1 - \frac{(0.5)(0.2)(1 + 0.06)}{(0.12 + 0.2)(1 + 0.12)}$$

$$= 0.70424$$

Therefore, the present worth of the first cost is

$$PW1 = -\$10\ 000(0.70424) = -\$7042.40$$

The annual savings are taxed at 50%, so the present worth of the savings is

$$PW2 = \$4000(P/A, 12\%, 5)\,(1 - t)$$

$$= \$4000(3.6047)(0.5)$$

$$= \$7\ 209.40$$

The salvage value is not simply $2000 five years from now. It reduces the UCC, and thus diminishes the tax benefits resulting from the CCA on the original purchase. The after-tax benefits can be determined by applying the pre-November 13, 1981, CCTF:

$$PW3 = \$2000(P/F, 12\%, 5)CCTF_{old}$$

$$CCTF_{old} = 1 - \frac{(0.5)(0.2)}{(0.12 + 0.2)}$$

$$= 0.6875$$

$$PW3 = \$2000(0.56743)(0.6875)$$

$$= \$780.22$$

Summing the present worths,

$$PW = PW1 + PW2 + PW3$$

$$= -\$7042.40 + \$7209.40 + \$780.22$$

$$= \$947.22$$

The present worth, after taxes, for the new bottle capper is $947. Had we not taken into account tax effects, this present worth would be

$$PW(\text{no taxes}) = -\$10\,000 + \$4000(P/A, 12\%, 5)$$
$$+ \$2000(P/F, 12\%, 5)$$

$$= -\$10\,000 + \$4000(3.6047) + \$2000(0.56743)$$

$$= \$5553.6$$

Indeed, there is a large difference between the two results. Though the first cost of purchasing the bottle capper was effectively reduced by the tax benefits, the savings from the capper are heavily taxed and the benefits over the five years of operation are therefore reduced.

Example 8.4 illustrated the complete effect of taxes for a present worth analysis. Similar adjustments are made to an annual worth computation, as illustrated in Table 8.9.

TABLE 8.9 Components of a Complete Annual-Worth Tax Calculation

Component	Treatment
First cost	Multiply by the $CCTF_{new}$. Convert to annual worth.
Savings or expenses	Multiply by $(1 - t)$.
Salvage value	Multiply by the $CCTF_{old}$. Convert to annual worth.

EXAMPLE 8.5

A small device used to test printed circuit boards has a first cost of $45 000. The tester is expected to reduce labour costs and improve the defect detection rate so as to bring about a saving of $23 000 per year. Additional operating costs are expected to be $7300 per year. The salvage value of the tester will be $5000 in five years. With an after-tax MARR of 12%, a CCA rate of 20%, and a tax rate of 42%, what is the annual worth of the tester, taking into account the effect of taxes?

The basic process for adjusting for tax effects is similar to a present worth analysis. First, we apply the $CCTF_{new}$ to the first cost, and convert it into an annual amount over five years. Next, the annual savings and expenses are multiplied by $(1 - t)$. Finally, the salvage value at the end of five years is multiplied by the old CCTF and then converted into an annual amount:

$$AW(\text{tester}) = -\$45\ 000(A/P, 12\%, 5)CCTF_{new}$$
$$+ (\$23\ 000 - \$7300)(1 - t)$$
$$+ \$5000(A/F, 12\%, 5)CCTF_{old}$$

Using $d = 0.20$, $t = 0.42$, and $i = 0.12$, we have

$$CCTF_{new} = 0.7516$$
$$CCTF_{old} = 0.7375$$

Therefore

$$AW(\text{tester}) = -\$45\ 000(0.27741)(0.7516)$$
$$+ (\$23\ 000 - \$7300)(0.58) + \$5000(0.15741)(0.7375)$$
$$= \$303.89$$

The annual worth, taking into account taxes, is $ 303.89.

As the previous two examples show, taking taxes into account for present worth and annual worth analyses is relatively straightforward. IRR computations are a bit more involved, however, as the next example illustrates.

EXAMPLE 8.6

Find the after-tax IRR for the testing equipment described in Example 8.5.

First, observe that, if we solve for i in AW(receipts) − AW(disbursements) = 0, or PW(receipts) − PW(disbursements) = 0, the resulting rate will be an after-tax IRR as the amounts will have been adjusted for taxes.

Since problem 8.5 was expressed in terms of annual amounts, we will find the after-tax IRR by solving for i in AW(receipts) − AW(disbursements) = 0, using the operations listed in Table 8.9:

$$(\$23\,000 - \$7300)(1 - t) + \$5000(A/F, i, 5)\text{CCTF}_{\text{old}}$$
$$- \$45\,000(A/P, i, 5)\text{CCTF}_{\text{new}} = 0$$

In order to solve the above equation, a trial and error approach is necessary because the interest rate i appears in the capital cost tax factors as well as in the compound interest factors. Table 8.10 shows the result of this process obtained through the use of a spreadsheet.

TABLE 8.10   Trial and Error Process for Finding the After-Tax IRR

i	AW(receipts) − AW(disbursements)
0.10	$997.5485
0.11	651.3784
0.12	304.3646
0.13	− 43.6201
0.14	− 392.682

From the spreadsheet computations, we can see that the after-tax IRR on the testing equipment is between 12% and 13%. Additional trial and error iterations with the spreadsheet program give an after-tax IRR of 12.87%.

8.6   Approximate After-Tax Rate of Return Calculations

The IRR is probably one of the most popular ways to assess the desirability of an investment. As we saw in Section 8.5, a detailed analysis can be somewhat involved. However, an approximate IRR analysis when taxes are explicitly considered can be very easy. The formula to use is

$$\text{IRR}_{\text{after-tax}} \approx \text{IRR}_{\text{before-tax}} \times (1 - t)$$

This formula is an approximation but is good enough for most purposes. It works because the IRR represents the percentage of the total investment that is net income. Since the tax rate is applied to net income, it correspondingly reduces the IRR by the same proportion. It is in error because it assumes that expenses offset receipts in the year in which they occur, rather than being spread over time (as CCA deductions are) as required by the Canadian tax laws. Consequently, this after-tax IRR will tend to be somewhat higher than it would be if calculated in a perfectly accurate manner.

This formula can also be used as a rough guide to the relationship between a before-tax MARR and an after-tax MARR:

$$\text{MARR}_{\text{after-tax}} \approx \text{MARR}_{\text{before-tax}} \times (1 - t)$$

EXAMPLE 8.7

What is the approximate IRR on the testing equipment described in Example 8.5?

First, we find the $\text{IRR}_{\text{before-tax}}$ by solving for i in

$$\text{AW(receipts)} - \text{AW(disbursements)} = 0$$

$$(\$23\,000 - \$7300) + \$5000(A/F, i, 5) - \$45\,000(A/P, i, 5) = 0$$

Through trial and error, we find that the $\text{IRR}_{\text{before-tax}}$ is 23.8%. The $\text{IRR}_{\text{after-tax}}$ is then approximately 13.8%:

$$\text{IRR}_{\text{after-tax}} \approx \text{IRR}_{\text{before-tax}}(1 - t)$$
$$\approx 0.238(1 - 0.42)$$
$$\approx 0.138$$

Notice that it is a little higher than the precise IRR of 12.87%.

When doing an after-tax IRR computation in practice, the approximate after-tax IRR can be used as a first pass on the IRR computation. If the approximate after-tax IRR turns out to be close to the after-tax MARR, a precise after-tax IRR computation may be required to make a fully informed decision about the project.

EXAMPLE 8.8

Waterloo Industries pays 40% corporate income taxes. Their after-tax MARR is 18%. A project has a before-tax IRR of 24%. Should the project be approved? What would your decision be if the after-tax MARR were 14%?

$$\text{IRR}_{\text{after-tax}} \approx \text{IRR}_{\text{before-tax}} \times (1 - t)$$
$$\approx 0.24 \times (1 - 0.040)$$
$$\approx 0.144$$

The after-tax IRR is approximately 14.4%. For an after-tax MARR of 18%, the project should not be approved. However, for an after-tax MARR of 14%, since the after-tax IRR is an approximation, a more detailed examination would be advisable.

In summary, we can simplify after-tax IRR computations by using an easy approximation. The approximate after-tax IRR may be adequate for decision making in many cases, but in others a detailed after-tax analysis may be necessary.

MT&T Tries to Reduce Its Taxes

Maritime Telephone and Telegraph Company Limited (MT&T) is the telephone utility that supplies telecommunications services to the province of Nova Scotia. It is headquartered in Halifax.

MT&T bills its customers on a monthly basis for local and long distance charges. Prior to 1984, MT&T reported its income using the *earned method*, for both taxation purposes and as part of its obligations to the Canadian Radio-Television and Telecommunications Commission (CRTC). In the earned method the billable income earned during a period is reported, even if it has not yet been billed. In the 1984 taxation year, MT&T changed the reporting method used for taxation purposes. Although it continued to use the earned method for the CRTC, it used the *billed method* for taxation purposes. In the billed method, income is recognized only when billed, not when earned. Using the billed method was an advantage for MT&T, since earned income that would normally be reported in one period could be delayed until the next. The delay provided a consequent temporary saving in taxes, or, more accurately, the use of the money for a period during which it would otherwise have been paid in taxes.

Unfortunately for MT&T, its use of the billed method was not permitted. Several court cases concluded that the earned method produced a truer picture of the company's income. In the case of telecommunications services, there was an exact record of the service performed, so there was no uncertainty about the income. MT&T had to return to the use of the earned method, and retroactively pay the extra taxes due for the time it had incorrectly used the billed method.

REVIEW PROBLEMS

Review Problem 8.1: UCC Computations

Angus and his sister Oona operate a small charter flight service that takes tourists on sightseeing tours over the beautiful Margaree River on Cape Breton Island. At the end of 1993, they had one four-seater plane in the aircraft asset class with a UCC of $30 000. In 1994, they purchased a second plane for $50 000. Business was going well in 1995, so they sold the old plane they had in 1993 for $15 000 and bought a newer version for $64 000. What was the UCC balance in the aircraft asset class at the end of 1996? The CCA rate for aircraft is 25%.

Answer

Table 8.10 shows the fluctuation in the UCC balance over time. At the end of 1993, the UCC for the aircraft asset class was $30 000. In 1994, half of the capital cost of the airplane purchased in 1994 ($25 000) contributed to the CCA calculation. The CCA rate of 25% gave a CCA amount of $13 750 and resulted in a UCC balance of $66 250 at the end of 1994. In 1995, the net positive adjustment to the UCC due to the capital cost of $64 000 for the new plane and $15 000 benefit from the sale of the old plane was $49 000. Half of this amount, $24 500, contributed to the CCA calculation. After subtracting the CCA amount of $22 688 for 1994, the remaining UCC was $92 563 ($66 250 + $49 000 − $22 688 = $92 563). Finally, in 1996, there were no further adjustments to the UCC, and after the CCA was deducted the closing UCC account balance was $69 422.

TABLE 8.11   Summary of UCC Computations for Review Problem 8.1

Year	Adjustments to UCC from Purchases or Dispositions	Base UCC Amount for Capital Cost Allowance	CCA Allowance	Remaining UCC
1993	$30 000			
1994	50 000	$55 000	$13 750	$66 250
1995	49 000	90 750	22 688	92 563
1996	0	92 563	23 141	69 422

▌ Review Problem 8.2: A Buy or Lease Decision and Taxes

David Cosgrove has just started a management consulting firm that he operates out of his home at Paradise Lake. As part of his new business, David is considering buying a new $30 000 van, which will be used 90% or more of the time for earning business income (if this were not the case, special limits on the allowable CCA would apply). He estimates that the expenses associated with operating the van will be $3000 per year in gas, $1200 per year for insurance, $600 annually for parking, and maintenance costs of $1000 for the first year, rising $400 per year thereafter. He expects to keep the van for five years. At the end of this time, he estimates a salvage value of $6000. The CCA rate for vans is 30%.

The alternative for David is to lease the van. With a lease arrangement, he will have to pay for parking, gas, and insurance, but the leasing company will pay for the repairs. The lease costs are $10 500 per year.

David estimates his after-tax cost of capital to be 12% per year and his tax rate is 40%. Based on an annual worth analysis over the five years, should David buy the van or lease it?

Answer

The approach will be to find the after-tax annual worth of each alternative. Since the parking, insurance, and gas costs are the same for both alternatives, we can exclude them from the analysis.

The after-tax annual costs of purchasing the van are

$$
\begin{aligned}
\text{AW(van)} = {}& \$30\,000(A/P, 12\%, 5)\,\text{CCTF}_{\text{new}} \\
& - \$6000(A/F, 12\%, 5)\text{CCTF}_{\text{old}} \\
& + [\$1000 + \$400(A/G, 12\%, 5)](1 - t)
\end{aligned}
$$

We can calculate that

$$
\begin{aligned}
\text{CCTF}_{\text{new}} &= 1 - \frac{td\left(1 + \dfrac{i}{2}\right)}{(i + d)(1 + i)} \\
&= 1 - \frac{0.4(0.3)(1 + 0.12/2)}{(0.12 + 0.30)(1 + 0.12)} \\
&= 0.7296
\end{aligned}
$$

$$
\begin{aligned}
\text{CCTF}_{\text{old}} &= 1 - \frac{td}{(i + d)} \\
&= 1 - \frac{0.4(0.3)}{(0.12 + 0.30)} \\
&= 0.71429
\end{aligned}
$$

Thus

$$
\begin{aligned}
\text{AW(van)} = {}& \$30\,000(0.27741)(0.7296) - \$6000(0.15741)(0.71429) \\
& + [\$1000 + \$400(1.7745)](1 - 0.4) \\
= {}& \$6423.21
\end{aligned}
$$

The annual cost of purchasing and operating the van over a five-year period is a little over $6400.

There is a large difference between buying and leasing. When we lease, we do not have a depreciable asset on which to claim depreciation expenses. We only have lease payment expenses. Therefore, the impact of taxes on the lease expense is simply to multiply the leasing costs by $(1 - t)$:

$$
\begin{aligned}
\text{AW(lease)} &= \$10\,500(1 - 0.4) \\
&= \$10\,500(0.6) \\
&= \$6300
\end{aligned}
$$

The after-tax annual cost of leasing is $6300. It is less expensive to lease the van than it is to buy it. Therefore, David should lease the van. It is, however, worth noting that this example has been simplified, since there are numerous tax rules relating to the eligibility of expenses for automobiles that have been ignored for illustration purposes.

Review Problem 8.3: An IRR Comparison and Taxes

Putco does subcontracting for an electronics firm that assembles printed circuit boards. Business has been good lately, and Putco is thinking of purchasing a new IC chip placement machine. It has a first cost of $450 000 and is expected to save them $125 000 per year in labour and operating costs compared with the manual system they have now. A similar system that also automates the circuit board loading and unloading process costs $550 000 and will save about $155 000 per year. The life of either system is expected to be four years. The salvage value of the $450 000 machine will be $180 000, and that of the $550 000 machine will be $200 000. Putco uses an after-tax MARR of 9% to make decisions about such projects. On the basis of an IRR comparison, which alternative (if either) should they choose? Putco pays taxes at a rate of 40%, and the CCA rate for the equipment is 20%.

Answer

Putco has three mutually exclusive alternatives:

(1) do nothing;

(2) buy the chip placement machine; or

(3) buy a similar chip placement machine with an automated loading and unloading process.

Following the procedure from Chapter 5, the projects are already ordered, based on first cost. We therefore begin with the first alternative: the before-tax (and thus the after-tax) IRR of the do-nothing alternative is 0%. We exclude it from further consideration. Next, the before-tax IRR on the second alternative can be found by solving for i in

$$- \$450\ 000 + \$125\ 000(P/A, i, 4) + \$180\ 000(P/F, i, 4) = 0$$

By trial and error, we obtain an $\text{IRR}_{\text{before-tax}}$ of 15.92%. This gives an approximate $\text{IRR}_{\text{after-tax}}$ of $0.1592(1 - 0.40) = 0.0944$ or 9.44%. With an after-tax MARR of 9%, it would appear that this alternative is acceptable, though a detailed after-tax computation may be in order. We need to solve for i in

$$(- \$450\ 000)\text{CCTF}_{\text{new}} + \$125\ 000(P/A, i, 4)\ (1 - t)$$
$$+ \$180\ 000(P/F, i, 4)\ \text{CCTF}_{\text{old}} = 0$$

Doing so gives an $\text{IRR}_{\text{after-tax}}$ of 9.5%. Since this exceeds the required after-tax MARR of 9%, this alternative becomes the current best. We next find the $\text{IRR}_{\text{after-tax}}$ on the incremental investment required for the third alternative. The $\text{IRR}_{\text{before-tax}}$ is first found by solving for i in

$$-(\$550\ 000 - \$450\ 000) + (\$155\ 000 - \$125\ 000)(P/A, i, 4)$$
$$+ (\$200\ 000 - \$180\ 000)(P/F, i, 4) = 0$$

This gives an $\text{IRR}_{\text{before-tax}}$ of 7.13%, or an approximate $\text{IRR}_{\text{after-tax}}$ of 4.28%. This is sufficiently below the required after-tax MARR of 9% to warrant rejection of the third alternative without a detailed incremental $\text{IRR}_{\text{after-tax}}$ computation. Putco should therefore select the second alternative.

Review Problem 8.4: Cyclic Replacement and Taxes

David Cosgrove (from Review Problem 8.2) is still thinking over whether or not to buy a van. Assuming he remains in business for the foreseeable future, he will need a vehicle for transportation indefinitely, whether he owns or leases it. In his original analysis, he assumed that the van would be replaced at the end of five years. Because appearances are important to David, he would not consider keeping a vehicle for longer than five years, but he now recognizes that the economic life of the van may be *shorter* than five years. Assuming that the van depreciates in value by a constant proportion each year, determine how frequently David should replace it. The CCA rate is 30% and his tax rate is 40%.

Answer

The first step in the solution is to recognize that David is facing a cyclic replacement problem, since it is reasonable to assume that he will replace each van with one similar to the previous, indefinitely. We now need to assess the annual cost of replacing a van each year, every two years, and so on, up to replacement every five years. Before proceeding, however, we need to determine the depreciation rate to use so that we can determine the approximate value of the van when it is n years old for $n = 1, 2, 3, 4,$ and 5. Referring back to Chapter 6, we have for the declining-balance method of depreciation

$$d = 1 - \sqrt[n]{\frac{S}{P}} = 1 - \sqrt[5]{\frac{\$6000}{\$30\,000}} = 0.27522$$

Using the formula $BV_{db}(n) = P(1 - d)^n$, we find that the book value of the van at the end of each year is:

End of Year	Book Value
0	$30 000
1	21 743
2	15 759
3	11 422
4	8 278
5	6 000

Note that these are book values, and not the UCC balances. The book values are estimates of the market value, which is needed to judge when the asset should be replaced. A UCC balance is similar to a book value, but is used for calculating the CCA only.

Now the annual worth computations can be done using the CCTF values calculated in Review Problem 8.2:

AW(replace every year) = AW(capital recovery) + AW(operating)

$$= \$30\,000(A/P, 12\%, 1)\text{CCTF}_{\text{new}} - \$21\,743(A/F, 12\%, 1)\text{CCTF}_{\text{old}}$$
$$+ (\$5800)(1 - t)$$
$$= \$12\,463$$

AW(replace every two years)

$$= \$30\,000(A/P, 12\%, 2)\text{CCTF}_{\text{new}} - \$15\,759(A/F, 12\%, 2)\text{CCTF}_{\text{old}}$$
$$+ \$5800(1 - t) + \$400(A/F, 12\%, 2)(1 - t)$$
$$= \$11\,235$$

AW(replace every three years)

$$= \$30\,000(A/P, 12\%, 3)\text{CCTF}_{\text{new}} - \$11\,422(A/F, 12\%, 3)\text{CCTF}_{\text{old}}$$
$$+ \$5800(1 - t) + [\$400(F/P, 12\%, 1) + \$800](A/F, 12\%, 3)(1 - t)$$
$$= \$10\,397$$

AW(replace every four years)

$$= \$30\,000(A/P, 12\%, 4)\text{CCTF}_{\text{new}} - \$8278(A/F, 12\%, 4)\text{CCTF}_{\text{old}}$$
$$+ \$5800(1 - t) + [\$400(F/P,12\%,2) + \$800(F/P, 12\%, 1)$$
$$+ \$1200](A/F, 12\%, 4)(1 - t)$$
$$= \$9775$$

AW(replace every five years)

$$= \$30\,000(A/P, 12\%, 5)\text{CCTF}_{\text{new}} - \$6000(A/F, 12\%, 5)\text{CCTF}_{\text{old}}$$
$$+ \$5800(1 - t) + [\$400(F/P, 12\%, 3) + \$800(F/P, 12\%, 2)$$
$$+ \$1200(F/P, 12\%, 1) + \$1600](A/F, 12\%, 5)(1 - t)$$
$$= \$9303$$

Based on these calculations, it is best for David to replace the van at the end of every five years. Its economic life may be longer than five years, but as far as David is concerned, a five-year-old van has reached the end of its useful life and must be replaced.

SUMMARY

Income taxes can have a significant effect on engineering economics decisions. In particular, taxes reduce the effective cost of an asset, the savings generated, and the value of the sale of an asset.

In this chapter, we provided a basic introduction to the Canadian capital cost allowance (CCA) system and the use of undepreciated capital cost (UCC) accounts. The CCA rate is a declining-balance rate that is mandated for use in calculating the depreciation expenses for capital assets. These depreciation expenses are then used in determining the amount of taxes owing for the year. Assets are designated as belonging to a particular CCA class. The book values for taxation purposes calculated for all the assets in each class are accumulated into a UCC account.

The future CCA claims that arise from the purchase of an asset are benefits that reduce the after-tax first cost. The $CCTF_{new}$ permits the quick calculation of the net effect of these benefits, while similarly the $CCTF_{old}$ permits the calculation of the net effect of future loss of CCA claims for assets that are sold or scrapped.

It was noted that, for after-tax calculations, an after-tax MARR must be used. After-tax calculations were illustrated for present worth, annual worth, and IRR evaluations. An approximate IRR comparison method was also given.

The review problems at the end of the chapter illustrated how taxes affect present worth and annual worth comparisons, replacement analysis, and internal rate of return computations.

Engineering Economics in Action, Part 8B: The Work Report

"So what is this, anyhow?" Clem was looking at the report that Naomi had handed him, "A consulting report?"

"Sorry, chief, it is a bit thick." Naomi looked a little embarrassed. "You see, Terry has to do a work report for his university. It's part of the co-op program that they have. He got interested in the 10-stage die problem and asked me if he could make that study his work report. I said O.K., subject to its perhaps being confidential. I didn't expect it to be so thick, either. But he's got a good executive summary at the front."

"Hmm..." The room was quiet for a few minutes while Clem read the summary. He then leafed through the remaining parts of the report. "Have you read this through? It looks really quite good."

"I have. He has done a very professional job, er, at least what seems to me to be very professional." Naomi suddenly remembered that she hadn't yet gained her professional engineer's designation. She also hadn't been working at Canadian Widgets much longer than Terry. "I gathered most of the data for him, but he did an excellent job of analyzing it. As you can see from the summary, he set up the replacement problem as a set of mutually exclusive alternatives, involving upgrading the die now or later and even more than once. He did a nice job on the taxes, too."

> *"How did he handle the taxes?"*
>
> *"Quite well. I had to hold his hand a bit to make sure he understood how the UCC accounts work, but once he had that everything else seemed to fall into place. He reduced the purchase price by the benefits of future CCA claims. The installation cost and future savings were reduced by the taxation rate, and the salvage values were reduced for loss of future CCA claims."*
>
> *"Did he understand about the old and new CCTFs?"*
>
> *"Yes, he did."*
>
> *"Not bad. I think we've got a winner there, Naomi. Let's make sure we get him back for his next work term."*
>
> *Naomi nodded. "What about his work report, Clem? Should we ask him to keep it confidential?"*
>
> *Clem laughed, "Well, I think we should, and not just because there are trade secrets in the report. I don't want anyone else knowing what a gem we have in Terry!"*

PROBLEMS

8.1 A company's first year's operations (in 1976) can be summarized as follows:

> Revenues: $110 000
>
> Expenses (except CCA): $65 000

Their capital asset purchases in the first year totalled $100 000. With a CCA rate of 20% and a tax rate of 55%, how much income tax did they pay?

8.2 A company's first year's operations (in 1996) can be summarized as follows:

> Revenues: $110 000
>
> Expenses (except CCA): $65 000

Their capital asset purchases in the first year totalled $100 000. With a CCA rate of 20% and a tax rate of 55%, how much income tax did they pay?

8.3 What is the after-tax present worth of a chip placer if it costs $55 000 and saves $17 000 per year? After-tax interest is at 10%. Assume the device will be sold for its $1000 salvage value at the end of its six-year life. The CCA rate is 20%, and the corporate income tax rate is 54%.

8.4 Canadian Widgets is looking at a $400 000 digital midget rigid widget gadget. It is expected to save $85 000 per year over its 10-year life, with no scrap value. Their tax rate is 45%, and their after-tax MARR is 15%. Should they invest in this gadget?

8.5 The UCC for a firm's automobile fleet at the end of 1993 was $10 000. There was one truck in service at this time. At the beginning of 1994, they purchased two trucks for a total of $50 000. At the beginning of 1996, they purchased another truck for $20 000. At the beginning of 1997, the truck owned in 1993 was sold for $3000. The CCA rate for automobiles is 30%. What was the firm's UCC at the end of 1997?

8.6 Churchill Metal Products opened for business in 1984. Over the following years, their transactions for CCA Class 8 assets consisted of the following:

Date	Item	Activity	Amount
March 11, 1984	Machine 1	Purchase	$ 50 000
April 24, 1984	Machine 2	Purchase	150 000
November 3, 1987	Machine 3	Purchase	250 000
November 22, 1987	Machine 1	Sale	10 000
May 20, 1991	Machine 4	Purchase	60 000
August 3, 1996	Machine 5	Purchase	345 000
September 12, 1997	Machine 3	Sale	45 000

What CCA amount can Churchill Metal Products claim for the 20% UCC account in 1998?

8.7 Calculate the $CCTF_{old}$ and $CCTF_{new}$ for each of the following:

(a) Tax rate of 50%, CCA of 20%, and an after-tax MARR of 9%

(b) Tax rate of 35%, CCA of 30%, and an after-tax MARR of 12%

(c) Tax rate of 55%, CCA of 5%, and an after-tax MARR of 6%

8.8 Use a spreadsheet program to create a chart showing how the values of the $CCTF_{old}$ and the $CCTF_{new}$ change for after-tax MARRs of 0% to 30%. Assume a fixed tax rate of 50% and a CCA rate of 20%.

8.9 What is the approximate after-tax IRR on a project for which the first cost is $12 000, savings are $5000 in the first year and $10 000 in the second year, and taxes are at 40%?

8.10 What is the total after-tax annual cost of a machine with a first cost of $45 000 and operating and maintenance costs of $0.22 per unit? It will be sold for $4500 at the end of five years. Production volumes are 750 units per day, 250 days per year. The CCA rate is 30%, the after-tax MARR is 20%, and the corporate income tax rate is 40%.

8.11 In 1965, the Sackville Furniture Company bought a new band saw for $360 000. Aside from depreciation expenses, their yearly expenses totalled

$1 300 000 versus $1 600 000 in income. How much tax (at 50%) would they have paid for 1965 if they had been permitted to use each of the following depreciation schemes?

(a) Straight line, with a life of 10 years and a 0 salvage value

(b) Straight line, with a life of five years and a 0 salvage value

(c) Declining balance, at 20%

(d) Declining balance, at 40%

(e) Fully expensed that year

8.12 Mulroney Brothers Salvage had several equipment purchases in the 70s. Their first asset was a tow truck bought in 1972 for $25 000. In 1974, a van was purchased for $14 000. A second tow truck was bought in 1977 for $28 000, and the first one was sold the following year for $5000. What was the value of their UCC at the end of 1979, with a 30% CCA rate (automobiles, trucks, and vans)?

8.13 Chrétien Brothers Salvage had several equipment purchases in the '80s. Their first asset was a tow truck bought in 1982 for $25 000. In 1984, a van was purchased for $14 000. A second tow truck was bought in 1987 for $28 000, and the first one was sold the following year for $5000. What was the value of their UCC at the end of 1989, with a 30% CCA rate (automobiles, trucks, and vans)?

8.14 Whitehorse Construction has just bought a crane for $380 000. At a CCA rate of 20%, what is the present worth of the crane, taking into account the future benefits of CCA? Whitehorse has a tax rate of 35% and an after-tax MARR of 6%.

8.15 Hull Hulls is considering the purchase of a 30-ton hoist. The first cost is expected to be $230 000. Net savings will be $35 000 per year over a 12-year life. It will be salvaged for $30 000. If their after-tax MARR is 8%, and they are taxed at 45%, what is the present worth of this project?

8.16 Kanata Konstruction is considering the purchase of a truck. Over its five-year life, it will provide net revenues of $15 000 per year, at an initial cost of $65 000 and a salvage value of $20 000. KK pays 35% in taxes, the CCA rate for trucks is 30%, and their after-tax MARR is 12%. What is the annual cost or worth of this purchase?

8.17 A new binder will cost Revelstoke Printing $17 000, incur net savings of $3000 per year over a seven-year life, and be salvaged for $1000. Revelstoke's before-tax MARR is 10%, they are taxed at 40%, and the binder has a 20% CCA rate. What is their IRR on this investment?

8.18 A slitter for sheet sandpaper owned by Abbotsford Abrasives (AA) requires regular maintenance costing $7500 per year. Every five years it is overhauled at a cost of $25 000. The original capital cost was $200 000, with an additional $25 000 in non-capital expenses that occurred at the time of installation. The machine has an expected life of 20 years and a $15 000 salvage value. The machine is not overhauled at the end of its life. AA pays taxes at a rate of 45%, and expects an after-tax rate of return of 10% on investments. Recalling that the CCA rate for production equipment is 20%, what is the after-tax annual cost of the slitter?

8.19 Rodney has discovered that, for the last three years, his company has been classifying as Class 8 items costing between $100 and $200 that should be in CCA Class 12. If an estimated $10 000 of assets per year were misclassified, what is the present worth today of the cost of this mistake? Assume that the mistake can only be corrected for assets bought in the future. Rodney's company pays taxes at 50%, and their after-tax MARR is 9%.

8.20 Identify each of the following according to their CCA class(es) and CCA rate(s):

(a) A soldering gun costing $75

(b) A garage used to store spare parts

(c) A new computer

(d) A 100-ton punch press

(e) A crop dusting attachment for a small airplane

(f) An oscilloscope worth exactly $200

8.21 Roch bought a $100 000 machine (Machine A) on November 12, 1981. As a CCA Class 8 asset, what was its book value, measured as its contribution to the UCC for that class, at the end of 1991? Roch purchased an identical $100 000 machine (Machine B) on November 14, 1981. What was its book value at the end of 1991?

8.22 A chemical recovery system costs $30 000 and saves $5280 each year of its seven-year life. The salvage value is estimated at $7500. The after-tax MARR is 9%, and taxes are at 45%. What is the net after-tax annual benefit or cost of purchasing the chemical recovery system?

8.23 PCB Electronix needs to expand its capacity. It has two feasible alternatives under consideration. Both alternatives will have essentially infinite lives.

Alternative 1: Construct a new building of 200 000 square feet now. The first cost will be $2 000 000. Annual maintenance costs will be $10 000.

In addition, the building will need to be painted every 15 years (starting in 15 years) at a cost of $15 000.

Alternative 2: Construct a new building of 125 000 square feet now and an addition of 75 000 square feet in 10 years. The first cost of the 125 000-square-foot building will be $1 250 000. The annual maintenance costs will be $5000 for the first 10 years (i.e., until the addition is built). The 75 000-square-foot addition will have a first cost of $1 000 000. Annual maintenance costs of the renovated building (the original building and the addition) will be $11 000. The renovated building will cost $15 000 to repaint every 15 years (starting 15 years after the addition is done).

Given a CCA rate of 5% for the buildings, a corporate tax rate of 45%, and an after-tax MARR of 15%, carry out an annual-worth comparison of the two alternatives. Which is preferred?

The following Ridgely Custom Metal Products case is used for problems 8.24 to 8.29.

Ridgely Custom Metal Products (RCMP) must purchase a new tube bender. There are three models:

Model	First Cost	Economic Life	Yearly Net Savings	Salvage Value
T	$100 000	5 years	$50 000	$20 000
A	150 000	5 years	60 000	30 000
X	200 000	3 years	75 000	100 000

RCMP's after-tax MARR is 11% and the corporate tax rate is 52%. A tube bender is a CCA Class 8 asset.

8.24 Using the present-worth method and the least-cost multiple of the service lives, which tube bender should they buy?

8.25 RCMP realizes that it can forecast demand for its products for only three years in advance. The salvage value for model T after three years is $40 000 and for model A, $80 000. Using the present-worth method and a three-year study period, which of the three alternatives is now best?

8.26 Using the annual-worth method, which tube bender should Ridgely buy?

8.27 What is the exact after-tax IRR for each of the tube benders?

8.28 What is the approximate after-tax IRR for each of the tube benders that Ridgely could buy?

8.29 Using the approximate after-tax IRR method, which of the tube benders should Ridgely buy? (*Reminder:* You must look at the increment of investment.)

8.30 Salim is considering the purchase of a backhoe for his pipeline contracting firm. The machine will cost $110 000, last six years with a salvage value of $20 000, and reduce annual maintenance, insurance, and labour costs by $30 000 per year. The after-tax MARR is 9%, and Salim's corporate tax rate is 55%. What is the accurate after-tax IRR for this investment? What is the approximate after-tax IRR for this investment? Should Salim buy the backhoe?

APPENDIX 8A: DERIVING THE CAPITAL COST TAX FACTORS

The change in tax laws of November 13, 1981, has made the formula for the CCTF a little complicated. To derive the CCTF formula, it is easiest to look at the situation before the laws were changed.

Before November 13, 1981, the tax *benefit* that could be obtained for a depreciable asset with a CCA rate d, a first cost P, when the company was paying tax at rate t is

Ptd for the first year

$Ptd(1-d)$ for the second year

$Ptd(1 - d)^{N-1}$ for the Nth year

Taking the present worth of each of these benefits and summing gives

$$\text{PW(benefits)} = Ptd\left(\frac{1}{(1+i)} + \frac{(1-d)}{(1+i)^2} + \ldots \frac{(1-d)^{N-1}}{(1+i)^N} + \ldots\right)$$

$$= \frac{Ptd}{(1+i)}\left(1 + \frac{(1-d)}{(1+i)} + \frac{(1-d)^2}{(1+i)^2} + \ldots + \frac{(1-d)^N}{(1+i)^N} + \ldots\right)$$

Noting that for $q < 1$

$$\lim_{n \to \infty} (1 + q + q^2 + \ldots + q^n) = \frac{1}{1-q}$$

and

$$\frac{1-d}{1+i} < 1$$

then

$$\text{PW(benefits)} = \frac{Ptd}{1+i}\left(\frac{1}{1 - \dfrac{(1-d)}{(1+i)}}\right)$$

$$= \frac{Ptd}{(1+i)}\left(\frac{1}{\dfrac{(1+i)}{(1+i)} - \dfrac{(1-d)}{(1+i)}}\right)$$

$$= \frac{Ptd}{(1+i)}\left(\frac{(1+i)}{(i+d)}\right)$$

$$= \frac{Ptd}{(i+d)}$$

If we subtract the present worth of the tax benefits from the first cost, it will give us the present worth of the asset, taking into account all tax benefits from depreciation forever.

$$PW(\text{asset}) = P - \frac{Ptd}{i + d}$$

$$= P\left(1 - \frac{td}{i + d}\right)$$

The factor $1 - \dfrac{td}{(i + d)}$ is called the *old* capital cost tax factor ($CCTF_{old}$), and was the formula in use before November 13, 1981.

The new tax rules mean that since November 13, 1981, only half of the first cost of an asset can be used in the calculations for the first year. By recognizing that the net effect of the new law is to delay the tax benefits of half of the first cost by one year. The present worth of the benefits is then

$$PW(\text{benefits}) = 0.5\,\frac{Ptd}{i + d} + 0.5\left[\frac{Ptd}{1 + d}\right]\left[\frac{1}{1 + i}\right]$$

$$= 0.5\,\frac{Ptd}{i + d}\left[1 + \frac{1}{1 + i}\right]$$

$$= 0.5\,\frac{Ptd}{i + d}\left[\frac{1+i}{1 + i} + \frac{1}{1 + i}\right]$$

$$= 0.5\,\frac{Ptd}{i + d}\left[\frac{2 + i}{1 + i}\right]$$

$$= P\,\frac{td\left(1 + \dfrac{i}{2}\right)}{(i + d)(1 + i)}$$

And the present worth of the asset itself is

$$PW(\textit{asset}) = P - P\,\frac{td\left(\dfrac{1 + i}{2}\right)}{(i + d)(1 + i)}$$

$$= P\left[1 - \frac{td\left(1 + \dfrac{i}{2}\right)}{(i + d)(1 + i)}\right]$$

Thus the $CCTF_{new}$ is

$$CCTF_{new} = 1 - \frac{td\left(1 + \dfrac{i}{2}\right)}{(i + d)(1 + i)}$$

Inflation

Engineering Economics in Action, Part 9A: The Inflated Expert

9.1   Introduction

9.2   Measuring the Inflation Rate

9.3   Real and Actual Dollars

    9.3.1   Converting between Real and Actual Dollars

9.4   The Effect of Correctly Anticipated Inflation

    9.4.1   The Effect of Inflation on the MARR

    9.4.2   The Effect of Inflation on the IRR

9.5   Economic Evaluation with Inflation

Canadian Corporate Case 9.1: Economic Comparison of High Pressure and Conventional Pipelines: Associated Engineering

Review Problems

Summary

Engineering Economics in Action, Part 9B: Exploiting Volatility

Problems

Appendix 9A: Computing a Price Index

Engineering Economics in Action, Part 9A: The Inflated Expert

Terry had left Canadian Widgets to go back for his last term of school. Naomi and Terry had cleaned up a lot of backed-up projects in the last few months, and Naomi had been increasingly taking part in projects involving sister companies of Canadian Widgets; all were owned by Canadian Conglomerate Inc., often referred to as "head office."

"There's a guy from head office to see you, Naomi." It was Carole announcing the expected visitor, Bill Astad. Bill was one of the company trouble shooters. His current interest concerned a sister company, Mexifab, a maquiladora on the Mexican border with Texas. (A maquiladora is an assembly plant that manufactures finished goods in Northern Mexico under special tariff and tax rules.) After a few minutes of socializing, Bill explained the concern.

"It's the variability in the Mexican inflation rate that causes the problems. Mexico gets a new president every six years, and usually, about the time the president changes, the economy goes out of whack. And we can't price everything to U.S. or Canadian dollars. We do some of that, but we are located in Mexico and so we have to use Mexican money for a lot of our transactions.

"I understand from Anna Kulkowski that you know something about how to treat problems like that," Bill continued.

Naomi smiled to herself. She had written a memo a few weeks earlier pointing out how Canadian Widgets had been missing some good projects by failing to take advantage of the current very low inflation rates, and suddenly she was the expert!

"Well," she said, "I might be able to help. What you can do is this."

9.1　Introduction

Prices of goods and services bought and sold by individuals and firms change over time. Some prices, like those of agricultural commodities, may change several times a day. Other prices, like those for electric power, change infrequently. While prices for consumer goods and services occasionally decrease, on average it is more typical for prices to increase over time. In fact, on a yearly basis, average prices of consumer goods and services in Canada have risen in every year but one since 1940.

Inflation is the increase, over time, in average prices. It can also be described as a decrease in the purchasing power of money over time. While Canada has experienced inflation in most years since World War II, there have been short periods when average prices in Canada have fallen. A decrease, over time, in average prices is called **deflation**. It can also be viewed as an increase in the purchasing power of money over time.

Prices are likely to change over the lives of most engineering projects because of inflation or deflation. These price changes will affect the cash flows associated with the projects, and it can be desirable for engineers to take these changes into account when evaluating projects.

In this chapter, we shall discuss how to incorporate an expectation of inflation into project evaluation. We focus on inflation because it has been the dominant pattern of price changes since the beginning of the twentieth century. The chapter begins with a discussion of how inflation is measured. We then show how to convert cash flows which occur at different points in time into dollars with the same purchasing power. We then consider how inflation affects the MARR, the internal rate of return, and the present worth of a project.

9.2 Measuring the Inflation Rate

The **inflation rate** is the rate of increase or decrease in average prices over a specified time period, usually a year. If all prices moved up and down together, determining the inflation rate would be trivial. If all prices increased by 2% over a year, it would be clear that the average inflation rate would also be 2%. But prices do not move in perfect synchronization. In any period, some prices will increase, others will fall, and some will remain about the same. For example, candy bars are about ten times as costly now as they were in the 1960's, but television sets are about the same price or cheaper.

Because prices do not move in perfect synchronization, a variety of methods have been developed to measure the inflation rate. Statistics Canada tracks movement of average prices for a number of different collections or "bundles" of goods and services and calculates inflation rates from the changes in prices in these collections over time.

One particular set of goods and services is representative of the consumption pattern of a typical urban Canadian family and forms the basis of the **consumer price index (CPI)**. The CPI relates the average price of this standard set of goods and services in a **base period** to the average price of the same set of goods and services in another period. The current CPI uses a base year of 1986. The base year index has been set at 100, and the index for all other years indicates the number of dollars needed to buy the standard set of goods and services in that year that was equivalent to $100 in 1986. This collection could have been bought for only $19 in 1950, and by 1995 its cost had increased to over $130. Figure 9.1 shows the CPI for the period from 1963 to 1994.

A national **inflation rate** can be estimated directly from the CPI by expressing the changes in the CPI as a year-by-year percentage change. This is probably the most commonly used estimate of a national inflation rate. Figure 9.2 shows the national inflation rate for the period from 1963 to 1994 as derived from the CPI quantities in Figure 9.1.

It is important to note that, although the CPI is a commonly accepted inflation index, many different indices are used to measure

FIGURE 9.1   **Canadian CPI 1963–1994**

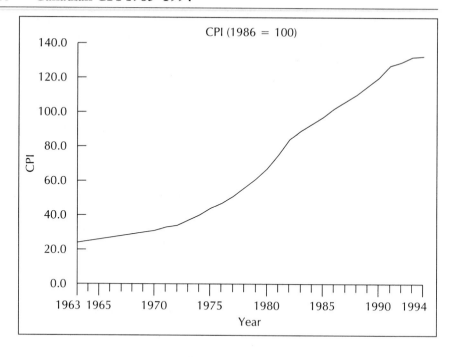

inflation. The value of an index will depend on the method used to compute the index and the set of goods and services for which the index measures price changes. To judge whether an index is appropriate for a particular purpose, the analyst should know how the goods and services for which he or she is estimating inflation compare with the set of goods and services used to compute the index. For this reason, we provide Appendix 9A, in which we illustrate the computation of one popularly used index.

As shown in Figures 9.1 and 9.2, inflation rates in Canada have varied considerably in the last 30 years, from a high of 12.4% in 1981 to a low of 0.2% in 1994. We shall see in this chapter how a small amount of predicted inflation may be safely ignored in economic calculations without concern, since it is implicit in our choice of the MARR. However, in periods when inflation is relatively high, it is necessary to include inflation in detailed calculations to avoid rejecting good projects. In some countries, inflation may be very high, up to several hundred per cent, in which case it is especially important to take inflation into account explicitly.

Throughout the rest of this chapter, we assume that an analyst is able to obtain estimates for expected inflation rates over the life of a project and that project cash flows will change at the same rate as average prices. In that case, the cash flows for a project can be assumed to increase at approximately the rate of inflation per year.

FIGURE 9.2   Canadian Inflation Rate 1963–1994

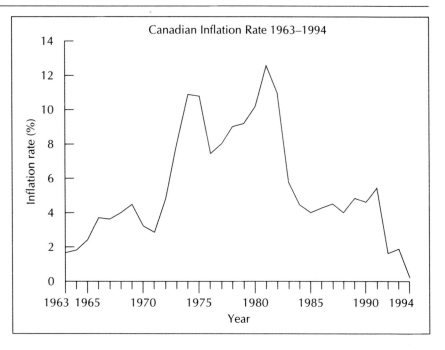

9.3 Real and Actual Dollars

When prices change, the amount of goods a dollar will buy changes too. If prices fall, more goods may be bought for a given number of dollars. The value of a dollar has risen. If prices rise, fewer goods may be bought for a given number of dollars. The value of a dollar has fallen.

In project evaluation, we cannot make comparisons of dollar values across time without taking the price changes into account. We want dollars, not for themselves, but for what we can get for them. Workers are not directly interested in the money wages they will earn in a job. They are interested in how many hours of work it will take to cover expenses for their families, or how long it will take them to accumulate enough to make down payments on houses. Similarly, investors want to know if making an investment now will enable them to buy more real goods in the future, and by how much the amount they can buy in the future will increase. To know if an investment will lead to an increase in the amount they can buy in the future, they must take into account expected price changes.

We can take price changes into account in an approximate way by measuring the cash flows associated with a project in monetary units of constant purchasing power called **real dollars** (sometimes called **constant dollars**). This is in contrast to the **actual dollars** (sometimes called **current** or **nominal dollars**), which are expressed in the monetary units at the time of the cash flows.

For example, if a photocopier will cost $2200 one year from now, the $2200 represents *actual* dollars since that is the amount that would be paid at that time. If inflation is expected to be 10% over the year, the $2200 is equivalent to $2000 real (today) dollars. Although the term "dollar" is used by convention when speaking of inflation, the principles apply to any monetary unit.

Real dollars always need to be associated with a particular date (usually a year), called the **base year**. The base year need not be the present; it could be any time. People will speak of "1990 dollars" or "1985 dollars" to indicate that real dollars are being used as well as indicating the base year associated with them. Provided that cash flows which occur at different times are converted into real dollars with the same base year, they can be compared fairly in terms of buying power.

9.3.1 Converting between Real and Actual Dollars

Converting actual dollars in year N into real dollars in year N relative to a base year 0 is straightforward, provided that the value of a global price index like the CPI at year N relative to the base year is available. Let

A_N = actual dollars in year N

$R_{0,N}$ = real dollars equivalent to A_N relative to year 0, the base year

$I_{0,N}$ = the value of a global price index (like the CPI) at year N, relative to year 0

Then the conversion from actual to real dollars is

$$R_{0,N} = \frac{A_N}{I_{0,N}/100} \qquad (9.1)$$

Note that in Equation (9.1), $I_{0,N}$ is divided by 100 to convert it into percentage terms; recall that the CPI for the base year is set at 100.

Transformation of actual dollar values into real dollars gives only an approximate offset to the effect of inflation. The reason is that there may be no readily available price index that accurately matches the spending patterns of those for whom the adjustment is made. Despite the fact that available price indices are approximate, they do provide a reasonable means of converting actual cash flows to real cash flows relative to a base year.

An alternative means of converting actual dollars to real dollars is available if we have an estimate for the average yearly inflation between now (year 0) and year N. Let

A_N = actual dollars in year N

$R_{0,N}$ = real dollars equivalent to A_N relative to year 0, the base year

f = the inflation rate per year, assumed to be constant from year 0 to year N

Inflation 323

Then the conversion from actual dollars in year N to real dollars in year N relative to the base year 0 is

$$R_{0,N} = \frac{A_N}{(1+f)^N}$$

When the base year is omitted from the notation for real dollars, it is understood that the current year (year 0) is the base year, as in

$$R_N = \frac{A_N}{(1+f)^N} \tag{9.2}$$

Equation (9.2) can also conveniently be written in terms of the present worth compound interest factor

$$R_N = A_N(P/F,f,N) \tag{9.3}$$

Note that here A_N is the actual dollar amount in year N, i.e., a future value. It should not be confused with an annuity A.

EXAMPLE 9.1

Elliot Weisgerber's income rose from $40 000 per year in 1990 to $42 000 per year in 1993. At the same time, the CPI rose from 119.5 in 1990 to 130.4 in 1993. Was Elliot worse off or better off in 1993 compared with 1990?

In order to find out whether Elliot's total purchasing power increased or decreased over the period from 1990 to 1993, we need to convert his actual income in 1990 and 1993 into real dollars in 1990 and 1993 with respect to a base year. Since the base year for the CPI is 1986, we will compare his 1990 and 1993 income in terms of real 1986 dollars.
His income in 1990 and 1993 in terms of 1986 dollars, using Equation (9.1), is

$$R_{86,90} = \frac{\$40\ 000}{1.195} = \$33\ 473$$

$$R_{86,93} = \frac{\$42\ 000}{1.304} = \$32\ 209$$

Even though Elliot's actual dollar income rose between 1990 and 1993, he was worse off, since the real dollar value of his income, based on the CPI, fell.

EXAMPLE 9.2

The cost of replacing a storage tank one year from now is expected to be $2 000 000. If inflation is assumed to be 5% per year, what is the cost of replacing the storage tank in real (today) dollars?

First, note that the $2 000 000 is expressed in actual dollars one year from today. The cost of replacing the tank in real (today) dollars can be found by letting

A_1 = $2 000 000 = the actual cost 1 year from the base year (today)

R_1 = the real dollar cost of the storage tank in 1 year

f = the inflation rate per year

Then, with Equation (9.2)

$$R_1 = \frac{A_1}{1 + f} = \frac{\$2\ 000\ 000}{1.05} = \$1\ 904\ 762$$

Alternatively, Equation (9.3) gives

$$R_1 = A_1(P/F, 5\%, 1) = \$2\ 000\ 000\ (0.9524) = \$1\ 904\ 762$$

The $2 000 000 actual cost is equivalent to $1 904 762 real (today) dollars at the end of one year.

EXAMPLE 9.3

The cost of replacing a storage tank in 15 years is expected to be $2 000 000. If inflation is assumed to be 5% per year, what is the cost of replacing the storage tank 15 years from now in real (today) dollars?

The cost of the tank 15 years from now in real dollars can be found by letting

A_{15} = $2 000 000 = the actual cost 15 years from the base year (today)

R_{15} = the real dollar cost of the storage tank in 15 years

f = the inflation rate per year

Then, with the use of Equation (9.2), we have

$$R_{15} = \frac{A_{15}}{(1 + f)^{15}} = \frac{\$2\ 000\ 000}{(1.05)^{15}} = \$962\ 040$$

Alternatively, Equation (9.3) gives

$$R_{15} = A_{15}(P/F, 5\%, 15) = \$2\ 000\ 000\ (0.48102) = \$962\ 040$$

In 15 years, the storage tank will cost $962 040 in real (today) dollars. Note that this $962 040 is money to be paid 15 years from now. What this means is that the new storage tank can be replaced at a cost that would have the same purchasing power as about $962 040 today.

Now that we have the ability to convert from actual to real dollars using an index or an inflation rate, we turn to the question of how inflation affects project evaluation.

9.4 The Effect of Correctly Anticipated Inflation

The main observation made in this section is that when prices associated with a project all move together with average prices, *correctly anticipated inflation has no real effect on project evaluation*. If all prices move together, correctly anticipated inflation increases both the *actual MARR* and the *actual internal rate of return* by the same proportion. The present worths of investment projects are unchanged by correctly anticipated inflation. This means that any project that would be acceptable without inflation remains acceptable with correctly anticipated inflation and that any project that would be unacceptable without inflation remains unacceptable with correctly anticipated inflation.

9.4.1 The Effect of Inflation on the MARR

If we expect inflation, the number of actual dollars that will be returned in the future does not tell us the value, in terms of purchasing power, of the future cash flow. The purchasing power of the earnings from an investment depends on the *real* dollar value of those earnings.

The **actual interest rate** is the stated or observed interest rate based on actual dollars. If we wish to earn interest at the actual interest rate, i, on a one-year investment, and we invest $\$M$, the investment will yield $\$M(1 + i)$ at the end of the year. If the inflation rate over the next year is f, the real value of our cash flow is $\$M \dfrac{1 + i}{1 + f}$. We can use this to define the *real interest rate*, i'. The **real interest rate**, i', is the interest rate that would yield the same number of real dollars in the absence of inflation as the actual interest rate yields in the presence of inflation.

$$M(1 + i') = M\left(\frac{1 + i}{1 + f}\right)$$

$$i' = \frac{1 + i}{1 + f} - 1 \tag{9.4}$$

We may see terms like "real rate of return" or "real discount rate." These are just special cases of the real interest rate.

The definition of the real interest rate can be turned around by asking the following question: If an investor wants a real rate of return, i', over the next year, and the inflation rate is expected to be f, what actual interest rate, i, must be realized to get a real rate of return of i'?

The answer can be obtained with some manipulation of the definition of the real interest rate in Equation (9.4):

$$i = (1 + i')(1 + f) - 1 \text{ or, equivalently, } i = i' + f + i'f \tag{9.5}$$

Therefore, an investor who desires a real rate of return i' and who expects inflation at a rate of f will require an actual interest rate $i = i' + f + i'f$. This has implications for the **actual MARR** used in economic analyses. The actual MARR is the minimum acceptable rate of return when cash flows are expressed in actual dollars. If investors expect inflation, they will require higher actual rates of return on their investments than if inflation were not expected. The actual MARR they will use will be the real MARR plus an upwards adjustment which reflects the effect of inflation. The **real MARR** is the minimum acceptable rate of return when cash flows are expressed in real, or constant, dollars.

If we denote the actual MARR by MARR_A and the real MARR by MARR_R, we have from Equation (9.5)

$$\text{MARR}_A = \text{MARR}_R + f + \text{MARR}_R \times f \qquad (9.6)$$

Note that if MARR_R and f are small, the term $\text{MARR}_R \times f$ may be ignored and $\text{MARR}_A = \text{MARR}_R + f$ can be used as a "back of the envelope" approximation.

The real MARR can also be expressed as a function of the actual MARR and the expected inflation rate:

$$\text{MARR}_R = \frac{1 + \text{MARR}_A}{1 + f} - 1 \qquad (9.7)$$

Figure 9.3 shows the Canadian experience with inflation, the actual interest rate and the real interest rate for the 1956-1993 period. From 1957 to 1971, when inflation was moderate and stable, the real interest rate was also stable, except for one blip in 1966-1967. In the 1970s, conditions were very different when inflation exploded. This was due partly to large jumps in energy prices. Real interest rates were negative for the period 1972 to 1975. In the 1980s and early 1990s, real interest rates were quite high.

The high inflation rates of the 1970s are very unusual. Inflation in the range of 2% to 4% per year is more typical of Canadian experience. Averages of real interest rates and inflation rates over sub-periods are shown in Table 9.1.

TABLE 9.1

| | Canadian Averages | |
Period	Real Interest Rate (%)	Inflation Rate (%)
1957–1971	1.56	2.77
1972–1981	−0.03	9.12
1982–1993	5.93	3.68

FIGURE 9.3   **Canadian Inflation Rates and Actual and Real Interest Rates 1956–1993**

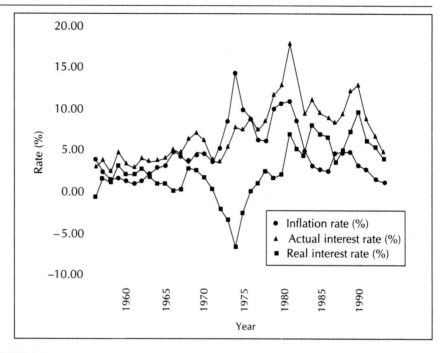

EXAMPLE 9.4

Security Trust is paying 12% on one-year guaranteed investment certificates (GICs). The inflation rate is expected to be 5% over the next year. What is the real rate of interest? For a $5000 GIC, what will be the real dollar value of the amount received at the end of the year?

The real interest rate is

$$i' = \frac{1 + i}{1 + f} - 1 = \frac{1.12}{1.05} - 1 = 0.067, \text{ or } 6.7\%$$

A $5000 GIC will return $5600 at the end of the year. The real value of the $5600 *in today's dollars* is $5600/1.05 = $5333. This is the same as if there were no inflation and the investment earned 6.7% interest.

EXAMPLE 9.5

Susan got a $1000 present from her aunt on her sixteenth birthday. She has noticed that Security Trust offers 6.5% on one-year guaranteed investment certificates (GICs). Her mother's *Financial Post* indicates that analysts are predicting an inflation rate of about 3.5% for the coming year. Susan's real MARR for such investments is 4%. If the analysts are correct, what is Susan's actual MARR? Should Susan invest

If the analysts are correct, Susan's actual MARR is

$$MARR_A = MARR_R + f + MARR_R \times f$$
$$= 0.04 + 0.035 + (0.04)(0.035)$$
$$= 0.0764$$

Susan's actual MARR is 7.64%. Since the actual interest rate on the GIC is only 6.5%, she should not invest in a GIC.

9.4.2 The Effect of Inflation on the IRR

The effect of expected inflation on the actual internal rate of return of a project is similar to the effect of inflation on the actual MARR. Suppose that we are considering an investment project with a first cost A_0 and actual cash flows for T years which we will denote by $A_1, A_2, \ldots, A_T$. (Note that this is not a series of equal payments, but a series of actual cash flows which may differ in size from period to period.) The **actual internal rate of return, IRR_A**, is the rate of return of a project based on actual dollar cash flows. It can be found by solving for i in

$$A_0 + \frac{A_1}{(1+i)} + \frac{A_2}{(1+i)^2} + \ldots + \frac{A_T}{(1+i)^T} = 0$$

Suppose, further, that a yearly inflation rate of f is expected over the T-year life of the project. In terms of *real* dollars (with a base year of the time of the first cost), the stream of actual cash flows can be written as $R_1(1+f), R_2(1+f)^2, \ldots, R_T(1+f)^T$ where $R_1, R_2, \ldots, R_T$ refers to the *real* dollar amounts equivalent to the cash flows $A_1, A_2, \ldots, A_T$. The expression which gives the actual internal rate of return can be rewritten as

$$A_0 + \frac{R_1(1+f)}{(1+i)} + \frac{R_2(1+f)^2}{(1+i)^2} + \ldots + \frac{R_T(1+f)^T}{(1+i)^T} = 0 \qquad (9.8)$$

In contrast, the **real internal rate of return** for the project, IRR_R, is the rate of return obtained on the real dollar cash flows associated with the project. It is the solution for i' in

$$A_0 + \frac{R_1}{(1+i')} + \frac{R_2}{(1+i')^2} + \ldots + \frac{R_T}{(1+i')^T} = 0 \qquad (9.9)$$

What is the relationship between IRR_R and IRR_A? We have from Equations (9.8) and (9.9)

$$\frac{1}{1+i'} = \frac{1+f}{1+i} \text{ or } i = i' + f + i'f$$

and thus, analogous to Equation (9.5)

$$IRR_A = IRR_R + f + IRR_R \times f \qquad (9.10)$$

Or, analogous to Equation (9.4), the real IRR can be expressed in terms of the actual IRR and the inflation rate:

$$\text{IRR}_R = \frac{1 + \text{IRR}_A}{1 + f} - 1 \tag{9.11}$$

In summary, the effect of inflation on the IRR is that the actual IRR will be the real IRR plus an upwards adjustment which reflects the effect of inflation.

EXAMPLE 9.6

Consider a two-year project which has a $10 000 first cost and which is expected to bring about a saving of $15 000 at the end of the two years. If inflation is expected to be 5% per year and the real MARR is 13%, should the project be undertaken? Base your answer on an IRR analysis.

From the information given, $A_0 = \$10\ 000$, $A_2 = \$15\ 000$, and $f = 0.05$. The actual IRR can be found by solving for i in

$$A_0 + \frac{A_2}{(1 + i)^2} = 0$$

$$\$10\ 000 = \$15\ 000/(1 + i)^2$$

which leads to an actual IRR of 22.475%.
The real IRR is then

$$\begin{aligned}
\text{IRR}_R &= \frac{1 + \text{IRR}_A}{1 + f} - 1 \\
&= \frac{1 + 0.22475}{1 + 0.05} - 1 \\
&= 0.1664 \text{ or } 16.64\%
\end{aligned}$$

Since the real IRR exceeds the real MARR, the project should be done.

In conclusion, the impact of inflation on the actual MARR and actual IRR is that both will have implicitly included in them an adjustment for expected inflation. The main implication of this observation is that, since both the actual MARR and the actual IRR increase by the same amount, any project that was acceptable without inflation remains acceptable when inflation is expected. Any project that was unacceptable remains unacceptable.

9.5 Economic Evaluation with Inflation

The engineer typically starts a project evaluation with an observed (actual) MARR and projections of cash flows. As we have seen, the actual MARR has two parts, the real rate of return on investment that investors require to put money into the company, plus an adjustment for the expected rate of inflation. The engineer usually observes only the sum and not the individual parts.

As for the projected cash flows, these are typically based on current prices. Because the projected cash flows are based on prices of the period in which evaluations are being carried out, they are in *real* dollars. They do not incorporate the effect of inflation. In this case, the challenge for the engineer is to correctly analyze the project when he or she has an *actual* MARR (which incorporates inflation implicitly) and *real* cash flows (which do not take into account inflation).

Though common, it is not always the case that the engineer or analyst starts out with an *actual* MARR and *real* cash flows. The cash flows may already have inflation implicitly factored in (in which case the cash flows are said to be actual amounts). To carry out a project evaluation properly, the analyst must know whether inflation has been accounted for already in the MARR and cash flows or whether it needs to be dealt with explicitly.

If the engineer has an estimate of inflation, there are two equivalent ways to carry out a project evaluation properly. The first is to work with actual values for cash flows and actual interest rates. The second is to work with real values for cash flows and real interest rates. *The two methods should not be mixed.*

These two methods of dealing with expected inflation, as well as two incorrect methods, are shown in Table 9.2.

TABLE 9.2   Methods of Incorporating Inflation into Project Evaluation

1. Real MARR and Real Cash Flows
The real MARR does not include the effect of expected inflation. Cash flows are determined by today's prices. **Correct**
2. Actual MARR and Actual Cash Flows
The actual MARR includes the effect of anticipated inflation. Cash flows include increases due to inflation. **Correct**
3. Actual MARR and Real Cash Flows
The actual MARR includes the effect of anticipated inflation. Cash flows are determined by today's prices. **Incorrect:** Biased against investments
4. Real MARR and Actual Cash Flows
The real MARR does not include the effect of expected inflation. Cash flows include increases due to inflation. **Incorrect:** Biased in favour of investments

The engineer must have a forecast of the inflation rate over the life of the project in order to adjust the MARR or cash flows for inflation. The best source of such forecasts may be the estimates of experts. Financial publications like the *Report on Business* of the *Globe and Mail* regularly report such predictions for relatively short periods of up to one year. Because there is evidence that even the short-term estimates are not totally reliable, and estimates for longer periods will necessarily be imprecise, it is good practice to determine a range of possible inflation values for both long- and short-term projects. The engineer should test for sensitivity of the decision to values in the range. The subject of sensitivity analysis is addressed more fully in the next chapter. Close-Up 9.1 discusses the problem of price changes that are specific to an industry.

CLOSE-UP 9.1   RELATIVE PRICE CHANGES

Engineers usually expect prices associated with a project to move together with the general inflation rate. However, there are situations where it makes sense to expect prices associated with a project to move differently from the average. This can happen when there are atypical forces affecting either the supply or the demand for the goods. Here are some examples:

1. Reductions in the availability of logs in North America have caused a decrease in the supply of wood for construction, furniture, and pulp and paper. This has caused the price of wood to rise relative to other prices.

2. Product development and increases in productivity have led to increases in the supply of computers. This, in turn, has led to reductions in the relative price of computing power.

3. Reductions in family size and in the proportion of the population in the 30- to 40-year-old age group have caused a drop in the demand for housing in Canada and the United States. This has made the relative price of housing fall in most cities.

Changes in the relative prices of the goods sold by a specific industry will generally not have a noticeable effect on a MARR because investors are concerned with the overall purchasing power of the dollars they receive from an investment. Changes in the relative prices of the goods of one industry will not have much effect on investors' abilities to buy what they want.

Because the relative price changes will not affect the MARR, the analyst must incorporate expected relative price changes directly into the expected cash flows associated with a project. If the rate of relative price change is expected to be constant over the life of the project, this can be done using a geometric gradient to present worth conversion factor.

EXAMPLE 9.7

Jagdeep can put his money into an investment that will pay him $1000 a year for the next four years and $10 000 at the end of the fifth year. Inflation is expected to be 5% over the next five years. Jagdeep's real MARR is 8%. What is the present worth of this investment?

The present worth may be obtained with real dollar cash flows and a real MARR or with actual dollar cash flows and an actual MARR.

The first solution approach will be to use real dollars and $MARR_R$. The real dollar cash flows *in terms of today's dollars* are

$$R_1, R_2, R_3, R_4, R_5 = \frac{A_1}{(1+f)}, \frac{A_2}{(1+f)^2}, \frac{A_3}{(1+f)^3}, \frac{A_4}{(1+f)^4}, \frac{A_5}{(1+f)^5}$$

$$= \frac{\$1000}{(1.05)}, \frac{\$1000}{(1.05)^2}, \frac{\$1000}{(1.05)^3}, \frac{\$1000}{(1.05)^4}, \frac{\$10\,000}{(1.05)^5}$$

The present worth of the real cash flows, discounted by $MARR_R = 8\%$, is

$$PW = \frac{\$1000}{(1.05)(1.08)} + \frac{\$1000}{(1.05)^2(1.08)^2} + \frac{\$1000}{(1.05)^3(1.08)^3}$$

$$+ \frac{\$1000}{(1.05)^4(1.08)^4} + \frac{\$10\,000}{(1.05)^5(1.08)^5}$$

$$= \$8282.47$$

The present worth of Jagdeep's investment is about $8282.

Alternatively, the present worth can be found in terms of actual dollars and $MARR_A$:

$$PW = \frac{\$1000}{(1 + MARR_A)} + \frac{\$1000}{(1 + MARR_A)^2} + \frac{\$1000}{(1 + MARR_A)^3}$$

$$+ \frac{\$1000}{(1 + MARR_A)^4} + \frac{\$10\,000}{(1 + MARR_A)^5}$$

where

$$MARR_A = MARR_R + f + MARR_R \times f$$

Note that this is the sum of a four-period annuity with equal payments of $1000 for four years and a single payment of $10 000 in period 5. With this observation, the present worth computation can be simplified by the use of compound interest formulas:

$$PW = \$1000(P/A, \text{MARR}_A, 4) + \$10\ 000(P/F, \text{MARR}_A, 5)$$

With a real MARR of 8% and an inflation rate of 5%, the actual MARR is then

$$\begin{aligned}
\text{MARR}_A &= \text{MARR}_R + f + \text{MARR}_R \times f \\
&= 0.08 + 0.05 + (0.08)(0.05) \\
&= 0.134
\end{aligned}$$

and the present worth of Jagdeep's investment is

$$\begin{aligned}
PW &= \$1000(P/A, 13.4\%, 4) + \$10\ 000(P/F, 13.4\%, 5) \\
&= \$8282.47
\end{aligned}$$

The present worth of Jagdeep's investment is about $8282, as was obtained through the use of the real MARR and a conversion from actual to real dollars.

Though there are two distinct means of correctly adjusting for inflation in project analysis, the norm for engineering analysis in Canada is to make comparisons with the actual MARR. One reason this is done has to do with how a MARR is chosen. As discussed in Chapter 3, the MARR is based on, among other things, the cost of capital. Since lenders and investors recognize the need to have a return on their investments higher than the expected inflation rate, they will lend to or invest in companies only at a rate that exceeds the inflation rate. In other words, the cost of capital already has inflation included. A MARR based on this cost of capital already includes, to some extent, inflation.

Consequently, if inflation is fairly static (even if it is high), an *actual* dollar MARR is sensible and will arise naturally. On the other hand, if changes in inflation are foreseen, or if sensitivity analysis specifically for inflation is desired, it may be wise to set a *real* dollar MARR and recognize an inflation rate explicitly in the analysis.

EXAMPLE 9.8

Lethbridge Communications is considering an investment in plastic moulding equipment for its product casings. The project involves $150 000 in first costs and is expected to generate net savings (in actual dollars) of $65 000 per year over its three-year life. They forecast an inflation rate of 15% over the next year, and then inflation of 10% thereafter. Their real dollar MARR is 5%. Should this project be accepted on the basis of an IRR analysis?

In this problem, the inflation rate is not constant over the life of the project, so it is easiest to consider the cash flows for each year separately and to work in real dollars. First, as shown in Table 9.3, the actual cash flows are converted into real cash flows.

TABLE 9.3   Converting from Actual to Real Dollars for Lethbridge Communications

Year	Actual Dollars	Real Dollars	
0	− $150 000	− $150 000	
1	65 000	56 522	[$65 000(P/F, 15%, 1) = $65 000(0.86957)]
2	65 000	51 384	[$65 000(P/F, 15%, 1)(P/F, 10%, 1) = $65 000(0.86957)(0.90909)]
3	65 000	46 713	[$65 000(P/F, 15%, 1)(P/F, 10%, 2) = $65 000(0.86957)(0.82645)]

Then, the real IRR can be found by solving for i' in

$$\$56\ 522(P/F, i', 1) + \$51\ 384(P/F, i', 2) + \$46\ 713(P/F, i', 3)$$
$$= \$150\ 000$$

At $i' = 1\%$, LHS (left-hand side) = $151 673

At $i' = 2\%$, LHS = $148 821

The real IRR is between 1% and 2%. This is less than the real dollar MARR of 5%, so the project should not be done.

EXAMPLE 9.9

New Glasgow Resources (NGR) has been offered a contract to sell land to the government at the end of 20 years. The contract states that NGR will get $500 000 20 years from today, with no costs or benefits in the intervening years. A financial analyst for the firm believes that the inflation rate will be 4% for the next two years, rise to 15% for the succeeding 10 years, and then go down to 10%, where it will stay forever. NGR's real dollar MARR is 10%. What is the present worth of the contract?

In this case, it is easiest to proceed by calculating the actual dollar MARR for each of the different inflation periods.

$$\text{MARR}_A, \text{years 13 to 20} = 0.10 + 0.10 + (0.10)(0.10)$$
$$= 0.21 \text{ or } 21\%$$

$$\text{MARR}_A, \text{years 3 to 12} = 0.10 + 0.15 + (0.10)(0.15)$$
$$= 0.265 \text{ or } 26.5\%$$

$$\text{MARR}_A, \text{years 0 to 2} = 0.10 + 0.04 + (0.10)(0.04)$$
$$= 0.144 \text{ or } 14.4\%$$

With the individual MARRs, the present worth of the $500 000 for each of years 12, 2, and 0 can be found.

$$PW(\text{year } 12) = \$500\ 000(P/F, 21\%, 8) = \$500\ 000 \times 1/(1.21)^8$$
$$= \$108\ 815$$

$$PW(\text{year } 2) = \$108\ 815\ (P/F, 26.5\%, 10) = \$108\ 815 \times 1/(1.265)^{10}$$
$$= \$10\ 370$$

$$PW(\text{year } 0) = \$10\ 370\ (P/F, 14.4\%, 2) = \$10\ 370 \times 1/(1.144)^2$$
$$= \$7924$$

The present worth of the contract is approximately $7924.

EXAMPLE 9.10

Bildmet is an extruder of aluminum shapes used in construction. They are experiencing a high scrap rate of 5%. The manager, Greta Kehl, estimates that reprocessing scrap costs about $0.30 per kilogram. The high scrap rate is due partly to operator error. Ms. Kehl believes that a short training course for the operator would reduce the scrap rate to about 4%. The course would cost about $1100. Bildmet is now working with a before tax MARR of 22%. Past experience implies that operators quit their jobs after about five years; the correct time horizon for the retraining project is, therefore, five years. The data pertaining to the training course are summarized in Table 9.4.

TABLE 9.4   Training Course Data

Output (kilograms/year)	125 000
Scrap (kilograms/year)	6 250
Reprocessing cost ($/kilogram)	0.30
Scrap cost ($/year)	1875
Savings due to training ($/year)	375
First cost of training ($)	1 100
Inflation rate (%/year)	5
Actual MARR (%/year)	22

Should Bildmet retrain its operator?

First, note that the actual MARR $i = 22\%$ incorporates an estimate by investors of inflation of $f = 5\%$ per year over the next five years. If this estimate of future inflation is correct, Ms. Kehl needs to make an adjustment to take inflation into account. Either the projected annual saving from reduced scrap needs to be increased by the 5% rate of inflation, or she needs to reduce the MARR to its real value. We shall illustrate the first approach with actual cash flows and the actual MARR.

Increasing savings to take inflation into account leads to projected (actual) savings as shown in the Table 9.5.

TABLE 9.5   Savings Due to the Training Course

Year	Actual Savings	Present Worth
1	$393.75	$322.75
2	$413.44	$277.77
3	$434.11	$239.07
4	$455.81	$205.75
5	$478.61	$177.08

For example, using Equation (9.2), the expected saving in year 3 is $375(1 + f)^3 = \$434.11$. The present worth of the savings in year 3 is $\$434.11/(1 + i)^3 = \$239.07$.

CANADIAN CORPORATE CASE 9.1

Economic Comparison of High Pressure and Conventional Pipelines: Associated Engineering

Associated Engineering of Toronto conducted an evaluation of sources of water supply for an Ontario municipality. One of the considerations was the choice of high-pressure or conventional pipelines for transmitting treated water from one of the Great Lakes to the municipality.

Conventional pipelines, most often made of concrete, have a limited maximum internal pressure, which for analysis purposes was taken to be 200 psi (pounds per square inch). High-pressure pipe, made of steel, can withstand up to 60,000 psi, although the pipe examined by Associated Engineering had a strength of 42,000 psi.

The major advantage of the steel pipe is that fewer pumping stations are needed than with the concrete pipe. The distance to be pumped is 85 kilometres; this requires either one pumping station for high-pressure pipe or six pumping stations for concrete pipe.

Each pipeline type was analyzed over a range of pipeline diameters ranging from 24″ to 72″. Construction costs included the pipe, pumping stations, and a reception reservoir, with the time of the cost taken to be the commissioning date of 2025. Operating and maintenance costs starting in 2026 were included, and administration, engineering fees, contingencies, and taxes were also accounted for.

Real 1993 dollars were used; an inflation rate of 2% was assumed for the period of study. The best alternative was chosen on the basis of a present worth comparison with a 4% discount rate. The result was that a 36″-diameter high-pressure pipeline was economically best, at a present cost $7.5 million lower than for the best conventional pipeline.

The present worth of the savings over the five-year time frame, when discounted at the actual MARR of 22%, is $1222.42. This makes the project viable, since its cost is $1100.

We note that the same result could have been reached by working with the real MARR and the constant cost savings of $375 per year. $MARR_R$ is given by

$$MARR_R = \frac{1 + MARR_A}{1 + f} - 1 = \frac{1.22}{1.05} - 1 = 0.1619$$

The present worth of the real stream of returns, when these are discounted by the real MARR, is given by

$$PW = \$375(P/A, 0.1619, 5) = \$1222.42$$

which is the same result obtained with the actual MARR and actual cash flows.

REVIEW PROBLEMS

Review Problem 9.1

Athabaska Engineering was paid $100 000 to manage a construction project in 1970. How much would the same job have cost in 1990 if the average annual inflation rate between 1970 and 1990 were 5%?

Answer

The compound amount factor can be used to calculate the value of 100 000 1970 dollars in 1990 dollars:

$$1990 \text{ dollars} = \$100\ 000(F/P, 5\%, 20)$$
$$= \$100\ 000\ (2.6533)$$
$$= \$265\ 330$$

The same job would have cost about $265 330 in 1990 dollars.

Review Problem 9.2

A computerized course drop-and-add program is being developed for a local community college. It will cost $300 000 to develop and is expected to save $50 000 per year in administrative costs over its 10 year life. If inflation is expected to be 4% per year for the next 10 years and a real MARR of 5% is required, should the project be done?

Answer

First, we can calculate the actual IRR for the project with the actual cash flows. The actual IRR is the solution for i in

$300\ 000 = \$50\ 000(P/A, i, 10)$

$(P/A, i, 10) = 6$

For $i = 11\%, (P/A, i, 10) = 5.8892$

For $i = 10\%, (P/A, i, 10) = 6.1445$

The actual IRR of 10.55% is found by interpolating between these two points. We then convert the actual IRR into a real IRR to determine if the project is viable:

$$IRR_R = \frac{1 + IRR_A}{1 + f} - 1 = \frac{1.1055}{1.04} - 1 = 0.06298 \text{ or } 6.3\%$$

Since the real IRR of 6.3% exceeds the MARR of 5%, the project should be done.

Review Problem 9.3

Robert is considering purchasing a bond with a face value of $5000 and a coupon rate of 8%, due in 10 years. Inflation is expected to be 5% over the next 10 years. Robert's real MARR is 10%, compounded semi-annually. What is the present worth of this bond to Robert?

Answer

This problem can be done with either real interest and real cash flows or actual interest and actual cash flows. It is somewhat easier to work with actual cash flows, so we must first convert the real interest rate given to an actual interest rate.

Robert's annual real MARR is $(1 + 0.10/2)^2 - 1 = 0.1025$. (Recall that the 10% is a nominal rate, compounded semi-annually.)

If annual inflation is 5%, Robert's actual *annual* MARR is

$$\begin{aligned}MARR_A &= MARR_R + f + MARR_R \times f \\ &= 0.1025 + 0.05 + (0.1025)(0.05) \\ &= 0.15763 \text{ or } 15.763\%\end{aligned}$$

The present worth of the $5000 Robert will get in 10 years is then

$$\begin{aligned}PW &= \$5000(P/F, MARR_A, 10) \\ &= \$5000(0.23138) = \$1156.89\end{aligned}$$

Next, the bond pays an annuity of $(\$5000 \times 0.08/2) = \$200$ every six months. To convert the annuity payments to their present worth, we need an actual six-month MARR. This can be obtained with a six-month inflation rate and Robert's six-month real MARR of $10\%/2 = 5\%$. With $f = 5\%$ per annum, the inflation rate per six-month period can be calculated with

$$f_{12} = (1 + f_6)^2 - 1$$
$$f_6 = (1 + f_{12})^{1/2} - 1$$
$$f_6 = (1 + 0.05)^{1/2} - 1 = 0.0247 = 2.47\%$$

The actual MARR per six-month period is then given by

$$MARR_A = MARR_R + f + MARR_R \times f$$
$$= 0.05 + 0.0247 + (0.05)(0.0247)$$
$$= 0.07593 \text{ or } 7.593\%$$

The present worth of the dividend payments is

$$PW(dividends) = \$200(P/A, 7.593, 20)$$
$$= \$200(10.125)$$
$$= \$2025$$

Finally,

$$PW(bond) = \$1156.89 + \$2025$$
$$= \$3182$$

The present worth of the bond is $3182.

■ Review Problem 9.4

Trimfit, a Southern Ontario manufacturer of automobile interior trim, is considering the addition of a new product to their line. Data concerning the project are given below.

New Product Line Information	
First cost ($)	11 500 000
Planned output (units/year)	275 000
Actual MARR	20%
Range of possible inflation rates	0% to 4%
Study period	10 years

Current 1996 Prices ($/unit)	
Raw materials	16.00
Labour	6.25
Product sales price	32.00

Should Trimfit accept the project?

Answer

First, we note that the expected net revenue per unit (not counting amortization of first costs) is $9.75 = $32 − $16 − $6.25. The project is potentially viable.

In doing the project evaluation, we can proceed with either actual dollars or real dollars. Since we do not know what the inflation rate will be, the easiest way to account for inflation is to keep all prices in real 1996 dollars and adjust the actual MARR to a real MARR by using values for the inflation rate within the potential range given. The project can then be evaluated with one of the standard methods. Since many of the figures are given in terms of annual amounts, an annual worth analysis will be carried out. Inflation rates of 0%, 1%, and 4% will be used. The results are shown below in Table 9.6.

TABLE 9.6   Annual Worth Computations for Trimfit

Annual Worth Comparisons for Various Inflation Rates					
Inflation Rate per Year	Real MARR	Fixed Cost per Year ($)	Variable Cost per Year ($)	Revenue per Year ($)	Annual Worth (Profit) per Year ($)
0.00%	20.00%	2 743 012	6 118 750	8 800 000	− 61 762
1.00%	18.81%	2 633 122	6 118 750	8 800 000	48 128
4.00%	15.38%	2 325 083	6 118 750	8 800 000	356 167

In Table 9.6, the annual worth of the project depends on the inflation rate assumed. Since the actual MARR of 20% implicitly includes anticipated inflation, different trial inflation rates imply different values for the real MARR. For example, at 1% inflation, the real MARR implied is

$$\text{MARR}_R = \frac{1 + \text{MARR}_A}{1 + f} - 1 = \frac{(1.20)}{(1.01)} - 1 = 0.1881 \text{ or } 18.81\%$$

The fixed cost per year is obtained by finding the annual amount over 10 years equivalent to the first cost when the appropriate real MARR is used. For example, with 1% inflation, the fixed cost per year is

$$A = P(A/P, \text{MARR}_R, 10) = \$11\ 500\ 000 \left(\frac{0.1881\ (1.1881)^{10}}{(1.1881)^{10}} - 1 \right)$$
$$= \$2\ 633\ 122$$

Next, the variable cost per year is the sum of the raw material cost and the labour cost per unit multiplied by the total expected output per year, i.e., $22.25 × 275 000 = $6 118 750. Revenue per year is the sales price multiplied by the expected output: $32 × 275 000 = $8 800 000. Notice that the variable cost and the revenue are the same for all three values of the inflation rate. This is because they are given in constant 1996 dollars.

Finally, the annual worth of the project is determined by the revenue per year less the fixed and variable costs per year. The annual worth is negative for zero inflation, but is positive for both 1% and 4% inflation rates. Since periods of at least 10 years in which there has been zero inflation have been rare in the twentieth century, it is probably safe to assume that there will be some inflation over the life of the project. Therefore, the project appears to be acceptable since its annual worth will be positive if inflation is at least 1%.

SUMMARY

In this chapter, the concept of inflation was introduced, and we considered the impact inflation has on project evaluation. We began by discussing methods of measuring inflation. The main result here was that there are many possible measures, all of which are only approximate.

The concept of actual cash flows and interest rates and real cash flows and interest rates was introduced. Actual dollars are in currency at the time of payment or receipt, while real dollars are constant over time and are expressed with respect to a base year. Compound amount factors can be used to convert single payments between real and actual dollars.

Most of the chapter was concerned with the effect of correctly anticipated inflation on project evaluation and on how to incorporate inflation into project evaluation correctly. We showed that, where engineers have no reason to believe project prices will behave differently from average prices, project decisions are the same with or without correctly anticipated inflation. Finally, we pointed out that predicting inflation is very difficult. This implies that engineers should work with ranges of values for possible future inflation rates. The engineer should test for sensitivity of decisions to possible inflation rates.

Engineering Economics in Action, Part 9B: Exploiting Volatility

Bill Astad of head office had been asking Naomi about how to deal with the variable inflation rates experienced by a sister company in Mexico. "O.K., Naomi, let's see if I have this straight. For long-term projects, of say six years or more, it makes sense to use a single inflation figure — the average rate. I can just add that to the real MARR to get an actual MARR. Boy, it's easy to get confused between the real and the actual. But I do understand the principle."

"And the short-term projects?" Naomi prompted.

"For the short-term ones, it makes more sense to break them up into time periods. For each period, select a "best guess" inflation rate, and do a stepwise

> *calculation from period to period. So the inflation rate in the middle of the pres-*
> *idential cycle would be relatively low, while near the changeover time it would*
> *be a higher estimate. Of course, the actual values used would depend on the*
> *political and economic situation at the time the decision is made. I understand*
> *that one, too, but it is complicated."*
>
> *"I agree," said Naomi. "I guess we're lucky things are more predictable here."*
>
> *"We are," Bill replied. "On the other hand, if we can make good decisions*
> *in spite of a volatile economy in Mexico, Mexifab may have an advantage over*
> *its competitors. Thanks for your help, Naomi."*

PROBLEMS

9.1 An investment pays $10 000 in five years.

(a) If inflation is 10% per year, what is the real value of the $10 000 in today's dollars?

(b) If inflation is 10% and the real MARR is 10%, what is the present worth?

(c) What actual dollar MARR is equivalent to a 10% real MARR when inflation is 10%?

(d) Compute the present worth using the actual dollar MARR from part (c).

9.2 An annuity pays $1000 per year for 10 years. Inflation is 6% per year.

(a) If the real MARR is 8%, what is the actual dollar MARR?

(b) Using the actual dollar MARR from part (a), calculate the present worth of the annuity.

9.3 An annuity pays $1000 per year for 12 years. Inflation is 6% per year. The annuity costs $7500 now.

(a) What is the actual dollar internal rate of return?

(b) What is the real internal rate of return?

9.4 A bond pays $10 000 per year for the next ten years. The bond costs $90 000 now. Inflation is expected to be 5% over the next 10 years.

(a) What is the actual dollar internal rate of return?

(b) What is the real internal rate of return?

9.5 The actual dollar MARR for Jungle Products Ltd. of Parador is 300%. The inflation rate in Parador is 250%. What is the company's real MARR?

9.6 Krystyna has a long-term consulting contract with an insurance company that guarantees her $25 000 per year for five years. Krystyna believes inflation will be 3% this year and 5% next year, and then will stay at 10% indefinitely. Krystyna's real dollar MARR is 12%. What is the present worth of this contract?

9.7 I have a bond that will pay me $2000 every year for the next 30 years. My first payment will be a year from today. I expect inflation to average 3% over the next 30 years. My real MARR is 10%. What is the present worth of this bond?

9.8 Ken will receive a $15 000 annual payment from a family trust. This will continue until Ken is 30; he is now 20. Inflation averages 4%, and Ken's real MARR is 8%. If the first payment is a year from now and a total of 10 payments are to be made, what is the present worth of his remaining income from the trust?

9.9 Inflation in Russistan currently averages 40% per month. It is expected to diminish to 20% per month following the presidential elections 12 months from now. The Russistan Oil Company (ROC) has just signed an agreement with the Canadian Petroleum Group for the sale of future shipments. The ROC will receive 500 million rubles per month over the next two years, and also 500 million rubles per month indexed to inflation (i.e., real rubles). If the ROC has a real MARR of 1.5% per month, what is the total present worth of this contract?

9.10 The widget industry maintains a price index for a standard collection of widgets. The base year was 1986 until 1995, when the index was recomputed with 1995 as the base year. The following data concerning prices for the years 1993 to 1996 are available:

Year	Price Index 1986 Base	Price Index 1995 Base
1993	125	n.a.
1994	127	n.a.
1995	130	100
1996	n.a.	110

What was the percentage increase in prices of widgets between 1993 and 1996?

9.11 Bosco Consulting of Calgary is considering a potential contract with the Upper Sobonian government to advise them on exploration for oil in Upper Sobonia. Bosco would make an investment of 1 500 000 Sobonian zerts to set up a Sobonian office in 1997. The Upper Sobonian government would pay Bosco 300 000 zerts in 1998. In the years 1999 to 2004, the actual zerts value of the payments would increase at the rate of inflation in Upper Sobonia. The following data are available concerning the project:

Investment in Upper Sobonia	
Expected Sobonian inflation rate (1997–2004)	15%/year
Expected Canadian inflation rate (1997–2004)	3%/year
Value of Sobonian zerts in 1997	$0.25
Expected decline in value of zerts (1997–2004)	10%/year
First cost in 1997 (zerts)	1 500 000
Cash flows in 1998–2004 (real 1998 zerts)	300 000
Bosco's actual dollar MARR	22%

(a) Construct a table with the following items:
Real (1997) zerts cash flows
Actual zerts cash flows
Actual dollar cash flows
Real dollar cash flows

(b) What is the present worth in 1997 dollars of this project?

9.12 Bildkit, an Alberta building products company, is considering an agreement with a distributor in Maloria to supply kits for constructing houses in Maloria. Sales would start next year. The expected receipts from the sale of the kits next year is 30 000 000 Malorian yen. The number of units sold is expected to grow by 10% per year over the life of the contract. The actual yen price is expected to grow at the rate of Malorian inflation.

There will be a first cost for Bildkit. As well, there will be operating costs over the life of the contract. Operating cost per unit will be constant in real dollars over the life of the contract. Since the number of units sold will rise by 10% per year, real operating costs will rise by 10% per year. Actual operating costs per unit will rise at the rate of inflation in Canada.

Bildkit in Maloria			
Receipts in first year (actual yen)	30 000 000	First cost now (actual $)	200 000
Growth of receipts (real yen)	10%/year	Operating cost in first year of operation (actual $)	350 000
Malorian inflation rate	1%/year	Canadian inflation rate	3%
Value of yen year 0 ($)	0.015	Actual dollar MARR	22%
Rate of interest in value of yen	2%	Study period	8 years

The value of the Malorian yen is expected to increase over the life of the contract. Data concerning the proposed contract are shown in the table on page 344.

(a) What is the present worth of receipts in dollars?

(b) What is the present worth of the cash outflows in dollars?

9.13 Leftway Information Systems of Saint John, New Brunswick, is considering a contract with the Ibernian government to supply consulting services over a five-year period. The following real Ibernian pounds cash flows are expected:

Cash Flows in 1997 Ibernian Pounds	
First cost (1997)	1 800 000
Net revenue 1998 to 2002 (real 1997 pounds)	550 000

Further information is in the table below:

Expected Ibernian inflation rate	10%
Value of Ibernian pound in 1997 ($)	1.25
Expected annual rate of decline in the value of the Ibernian pound	5%
Expected Canadian inflation rate	2.50%
Leftway's real MARR	15%

(a) What is the real Ibernian pound internal rate of return on this project? (*Hint:* Canada can be ignored in answering this question.)

(b) What is the actual pound internal rate of return? (*Hint:* Canada can be ignored in answering this question.)

(c) Use the internal rate of return in Canadian dollars to decide if Leftway should accept the proposed contract.

9.14 Sonar warning devices are being purchased by the St. James Bay department store chain to help trucks back up at store loading docks. The total cost of purchase and installation is $220 000. There are two types of saving from the system. Faster turn-around time at the congested loading docks will save $50 000 per year in today's dollars. Reduced damage to the loading docks will save $30 000 per year in today's dollars. St. James Bay has an observed actual dollar MARR of 18%. The sonar system has a life of four years. Its scrap value in today's dollars is $20 000. The inflation rate is expected to be 6% per year over the next four years.

(a) What is St. James Bay's real MARR?

(b) What is the real internal rate of return? (This is most easily done with a spreadsheet.)

(c) Use the theory developed in Section 9.4 to state the actual dollar internal rate of return.

(d) Compute the actual dollar internal rate of return. (This is most easily done with a spreadsheet.)

(e) What is the present worth of the system?

9.15 Johnson Products, a Wolfville, Nova Scotia, manufacturer, now buys a certain part for its chain saws. They are considering the production of the part in-house. They can install a production system that would have a life of five years with no salvage value. They believe that over the next five years the real price of purchased parts will remain fixed. They expect the real price of labour and other inputs to production in Wolfville to rise over the next five years. Further information about the situation is in the table below.

Annual cost of purchase ($/year)	750 000
Expected real change in cost of purchase	0%
Expected real change in labour cost	4%
Expected real change in other operating cost	2%
Labour cost/unit (first year of operation) ($)	10.5
Other operating cost/unit (first year of operation) ($)	9
In-house first cost ($)	200 000
Use rate (units/year)	25 000
Actual dollar MARR	20%
Study period (years)	5

(a) Assume inflation is 2% per year in the first year of operation. What will be the actual dollar cost of labour for in-house production in the second year?

(b) Assume inflation is 2% per year in the first two years of operation. What will be the actual dollar cost of other operating inputs for in-house production in the third year?

(c) Assume that inflation averages 2% per year over the five-year life of the project. What is the present worth of costs for purchase and for in-house production?

9.16 Lifewear, a Winnipeg manufacturer of women's sports clothes, is considering adding a line of skirts and jackets. The production would take place in a part of their factory that is now not being used. The first output would be available in time for the following year, for the 1998 fall season. The following information is available:

New Product Line Information	
First cost ($) (1997)	15 500 000
Planned output (units/year)	325 000
Observed, actual dollar MARR before tax	0.25
Study period	6 years

1997 Prices	
	($/ unit)
Materials	12
Labour	7.75
Output	35

(a) What is the real internal rate of return?

(b) What inflation rate will make the real MARR equal to the real internal rate of return?

(c) Calculate the present worths of the project under three possible future inflation rates. Assume that the inflation rate will be 1% per year, or 2% per year, or 3% per year.

(d) Decide if Lifewear should add this new line of skirts and jackets. Explain your answer.

9.17 Century Foods, a Saskatoon producer of frozen meat products, is considering a new plant near Calgary for its sausage rolls and frozen meat pies. The company has estimates of production cost and selling prices in the first year. It expects the real value of operating costs per unit to fall because of improved operating methods. It also expects competitive pressures to cause the real value of product prices to fall. The following data are available:

Century Food Plant Data	
Output price in 1997 ($/box)	22
Operating cost in 1997 ($/box)	15.5
Planned output rate (boxes/year)	275 000
Fall in real output price	1.5% per year
Fall in real operating cost per box	1.0% per year
First cost in 1996 ($)	7 500 000
Study period	10 years
Actual dollar MARR before tax	20%

(a) Assume that there is zero inflation. What is the present worth, in 1996, of the project?

(b) Assume that there is zero inflation. What is the internal rate of return? (This is most easily done with a spreadsheet.)

(c) At what inflation rate will the actual dollar internal rate of return equal 20%?

(d) Should Century Foods build the new plant? Explain your answer.

9.18 Metcan Ltd.'s Newfoundland smelter produces its own electric power. The plant's power capacity exceeds its current requirements. Metcan has been offered a contract to sell excess power to a nearby utility company. Metcan would supply the utility company with 17 500 MWh/year for 10 years. The contract would specify a price of $22.75/MWh for the first year of supply. The price would rise by 1% per year after this. This is independent of the actual rate of inflation over the 10 years.

Metcan would incur a first cost to connect its plant to the utility system. There would also be operating costs attributable to the contract. Metcan believes these costs would track the actual inflation rate.

The terms of the contract and Metcan's costs are shown in the tables below.

Metcan Sale of Power	
Output price in 1997 ($/MWh)	22.75
Price adjustment (1998–2006)	1% per year
Power to be supplied (MWh/year)	17 500
Contract length	10 years

Metcan's Costs	
First cost in 1996 ($)	175 000
Operating cost in 1997 ($)	332 500
Actual dollar MARR before tax	20%

(a) Find the present worth of the contract under the assumption that there is no inflation over the life of the contract.

(b) Find the present worths of the contract under four assumptions:
Inflation is 1% per year.
Inflation is 2% per year.
Inflation is 3% per year.
Inflation is 4% per year.

(c) Should Metcan accept the contract?

9.19 Clarkwood is a British Columbia wood products manufacturer. They are considering a modification to their production line that would enable an increase in their output. One of Clarkwood's concerns is that the price of wood is rising more rapidly than inflation. They expect that because of this their operating cost per unit will rise at a rate 4% higher than the rate of inflation. That is, if the rate of inflation is f, Clarkwood's operating cost will rise at the rate $f_c = 1.04(1 + f) - 1$. However, competitive pressures from plastics will prevent the prices of their products from rising more than 1% above the inflation rate. The particulars of the project are shown in the table below.

Clarkwood's Project	
Output price in 1997 ($/unit)	30
Price increase	2% above inflation
Operating cost in 1997 ($/unit)	24
Operating cost increase	4% above inflation
Expected output due to project (units/year)	50 000
First cost in 1996 ($)	900 000
Observed actual dollar MARR	0.25
Time horizon (years)	10

(a) Find the present worth of the project under the assumption of zero inflation.

(b) Find the present worth of the project under these assumptions:
   The expected inflation rate is 1%.
   The expected inflation rate is 2%.

(c) Should Clarkwood accept the project?

9.20 Smooth-Top is a British Columbia manufacturer of desktops. They are considering an increase of their capacity. Consulting engineers have submitted two routes to do this. (1) Install a new production line that would produce wood desktops finished with hardwood veneer. (2) Install a new production line that would produce wood desktops finished with simulated wood made from hard plastic.

Smooth-Top is concerned about the price of hardwood veneer. They believe that the price of veneer will rise over the next ten years. However, they believe the price of veneer finished desktops will rise by less than the rate at which the price of veneer rises. Information about the two potential projects is in the table on page 350.

Smooth-Top Desktop Project	
Plastic-finish real price and real cost change	0%
Veneer-finish expected real price change	1%
Veneer-finish expected real cost change	5%
Wood cost/unit ($)	12.5
Plastic cost/unit ($)	9
Wood price/unit ($)	32
Plastic price/unit ($)	26
Wood first cost ($)	2 050 000
Plastic first cost ($)	2 700 000
Wood output rate (units/year)	30 000
Plastic output rate (units/year)	45 000
Study period	10 years
Actual dollar MARR	25%

(a) Compute the present worth of each option under the assumption that the real price of hardwood-finished desktops and real cost of hardwood veneer do not change (rather than as stated in the table). Assume zero inflation.

(b) Compute the present worth of each option under the assumption that the real price of hardwood-finished desktops and the real value of hardwood veneer desktop operating costs increase as indicated in the table. Assume that inflation is expected to be 2% over the study period.

9.21 Belmont Grocers has a distribution centre in Calgary. The manual materials-handling system at the centre has deteriorated to the point at which it must be either replaced or substantially refurbished. Replacement with an automated system would cost about $240 000. Refurbishing the manual system would cost about $50 000. In either case, capital expenditures would take place this year. Operating either the new system or the refurbished system would begin next year. It is expected that either the new system or the refurbished system will operate for ten years with no further capital expenditures. Belmont is concerned that labour costs in Calgary may rise in real terms over the next ten years. The range of increases in real terms that appears possible is from 4% to 7% per year. Inflation rates between 2% and 4% are expected over the next ten years. Complete data on the two alternatives are in the table below.

Materials Handling Data	
Automated expected real operating cost change	0%
Manual expected real operating cost change	4% to 7%
Manual operating cost/unit (first year of operation) ($)	10.5
Automated operating cost/unit (first year of operation) ($)	9
Manual first cost ($)	50 000
Automated first cost ($)	240 000
Output rate (units/year)	15 000
Actual dollar MARR	20%
Study period	10 years
Possible inflation rates	2% to 4%

(a) Find the total costs per unit for each of the two alternatives under the assumption of zero inflation and no increase in costs for the manual system.

(b) Make a recommendation as to which alternative to adopt. Base the recommendation on the present worth of costs for the two systems under various assumptions concerning inflation and the rate of change in the real operating cost of the manual system. Explain your recommendation.

9.22 The United Gum Workers have a cost of living clause in their contract with Mont-Gum-Ery Foods. The contract is for two years. The contract states that, if the inflation rate in the first year exceeds 1%, wages in the second year will increase by the inflation rate of the first year. Does this clause increase or decrease risk? Explain.

9.23 Free Wheels Manitoba has a plant that assembles bicycles in Louisbourg, Manitoba. The plant now has a small cafeteria for the workers. The kitchen equipment is in need of substantial overhaul. Free Wheels has been offered a contract by Besteats to supply food to their workers. The particulars of the situation are shown in the table on page 352.

Food Service In-House Versus Contract	
Food service labour (hours/year)	6 000
Wage rate (real, time 1, $/hour)	7.5
Overhead cost (real, time 1, $/year)	18 000
Kitchen equipment first cost (actual, time 0, $)	25 000
Contract cost, years 1 to 3 (actual $)	55 000
Contract cost, years 4 to 6 (actual $)	63 700
Actual dollar MARR	22%
Expected annual inflation rate	5%
Study period (years)	6

Which alternative has the lower cost?

APPENDIX 9A: Computing a Price Index

We can represent changes in average prices over time with a **price index**. A price index relates the average price of a given set of goods in some period, t_1, to the average price of the same set of goods in another period. Commonly used price indexes work with weighted averages, because simple averages do not reflect the differences in importance of the various goods and services in which we are interested.

Many different ways of weighting changes in prices may be used, and each method leads to a different price index. We shall discuss only the most commonly used index, the **Laspeyres price index**. It can be explained as follows:

Suppose there are n goods in which we are interested. We want to represent their prices at a time, t_1, relative to a **base period**, t_0, the period from which the expenditure shares are calculated.

The prices of the n goods at times t_0 and t_1 are denoted by $p_{01}, p_{02}, \ldots, p_{0n}$ and $p_{11}, p_{12}, \ldots, p_{1n}$. The quantities of the n goods purchased at t_0 are denoted by $q_{01}, q_{02}, \ldots, q_{0n}$. The share, s_{0i}, of good i in the total expenditure for the period, t_0, is defined as

$$s_{0i} = \frac{p_{0i}q_{0i}}{p_{01}q_{01} + p_{02}q_{02} + \ldots + p_{0n}q_{0n}}$$

Note that

$$\sum_{j=1}^{n} s_{0j} = 1$$

A Laspeyres price index, π_{01}, is defined as a weighted average of relative prices.

$$\pi_{01} = \left(\frac{p_{11}}{p_{01}} s_{01} + \frac{p_{12}}{p_{02}} s_{02} + \ldots + \frac{p_{1n}}{p_{0n}} s_{0n} \right) 100$$

The term in the brackets is a weighted average because the weights (the expenditure shares in the base period) sum to one. The relative prices are the prices of the individual goods in period t_1 relative to the base period, t_0. The weighted average is multiplied by 100 to put the index in percentage terms.

EXAMPLE 9A.1

A student uses four foods for hamburgers: (1) ground beef, (2) hamburger buns, (3) onions, and (4) breath mints. Suppose that, in one year, the price of ground beef fell by 10%, the price of buns fell by 1%, the price of onions increased by 5%, and breath mints rose in price by 50%.

The price and quantity data for the student's hamburger are shown in Table 9A.1.

TABLE 9A.1

	Quantity at t_0	Price at t_0 ($)	Price at t_1 ($)
Ground beef (kg)	0.25	3.5	3.15
Buns	1	0.4	0.396
Onions	1	0.2	0.21
Breath mints	1	0.1	0.15

The Laspeyres price index is calculated in four steps:

1. Compute the base period expenditure for each ingredient.
2. Compute the share of each ingredient in the total base period expenditure.
3. Then compute the relative price for each ingredient.
4. Use the shares to form a weighted average of the relative prices.

These computations are shown in Table 9A.2.

TABLE 9A.2

	Price at t_0 ($)	Share at t_0	Relative Price	Weighted Relative Price
Ground beef (kg)	0.875	0.556	0.900	0.500
Buns	0.400	0.254	0.990	0.251
Onions	0.200	0.127	1.050	0.133
Breath mints	0.100	0.063	1.500	0.095
Sums	1.575	1.000		0.980

As an example of the computations, the price of the ground beef per hamburger at t_0 is found by multiplying the price per kilogram by the weight of the hamburger used: $3.50/kg × 0.25 kg = $0.87. Similar computations for each of the other ingredients lead to a total cost of $1.575 per hamburger. The ground beef then represents a share of 0.875/1.575 = 0.556 of the total cost. The relative price for the hamburger is 3.15/3.5 = 0.9 and thus the weighted relative price is 0.556 × 0.9 = 0.50. Similar computations for the other ingredients lead to a total weighted average of 0.98. After multiplying by 100, the Laspeyres price index is 98 (it is understood that this is a percentage). Therefore, the cost of the hamburger ingredients at t_1 was 2% lower than in the base period.

Statistics Canada compiles many Laspeyres price indexes. The consumer price index (CPI) is a Laspeyres price index in which the weights are the shares of urban consumers' budgets in the base year, currently

1986. Another well-known Laspeyres price index is the GNP deflator. For the GNP deflator, the weights are the shares of total output in the base year (also 1986).

The CPI and the GNP deflator are global indexes in that they represent an economy-wide set of prices. As well, Statistics Canada produces sector Laspeyres price indexes. For example, there are price indexes for durable consumer goods, for exports, and for investment by businesses. It is up to the analyst to know the composition of the different indexes and to decide which is best for his or her purpose.

EXAMPLE 9A.2

We can classify consumer goods and services into four classes: durable goods, semi-durable goods, non-durable goods, and services. Groups of these goods and services were formed. They had the following prices in 1986 and 1993:

Category	1986	1993
Durable	2.421	2.818
Semi-durable	2.849	3.715
Non-durable	4.926	6.404
Services	4.608	6.263

Quantities in 1986 were:

Quantity in 1986 (units)	
Durable	21.304
Semi-durable	11.315
Non-durable	19.159
Services	31.422

Find the Laspeyres price index for 1993 with 1986 as a base.

We first calculate the relative prices.

	Price		
Category	1986	1993	Relative Price
Durable	2.421	2.818	1.164
Semi-durable	2.849	3.715	1.304
Non-durable	4.926	6.404	1.300
Services	4.608	6.263	1.359

We next determine expenditure shares in 1986.

Category	Expenditure	Share
Durable	51.583	0.1597
Semi-durable	32.235	0.0998
Non-durable	94.381	0.2922
Services	144.801	0.4483
Total	323.000	

We then multiply the relative prices by the shares and sum. We get the index by multiplying the sum by 100.

The term for durable goods is given by $1.164(0.1597) = 0.186$

Index	
Durable	0.186
Semi-durable	0.130
Non-durable	0.380
Services	0.609
Total	1.305

This gives a Laspeyres price index of 130.5.

10

Sensitivity Analysis

Engineering Economics in Action, Part 10A: Filling a Vacuum

10.1   Introduction

10.2   Sensitivity Graphs

10.3   Break-Even Analysis

    10.3.1   Break-Even Analysis for a Single Project

    10.3.2   Break-Even Analysis for Multiple Projects

10.4   Scenario Analysis

Canadian Corporate Case 10.1: Metro Toronto's Main Treatment Plant

Review Problems

Summary

Engineering Economics in Action, Part 10B: Where the Risks Lie

Problems

Appendix 10A: Other Methods of Dealing with Uncertain Outcomes

Engineering Economics in Action, Part 10A: Filling a Vacuum

"I have something new for you, Naomi. It's going to require some imagination and disciplined thinking at the same time." Anna's tone indicated to Naomi that something interesting was coming.

"As you may know, Canadian Widgets has been working toward getting into consumer products for some time." Anna continued, "An opportunity has come up to co-operate on a new vacuum cleaner with Powerluxe. They have some potential designs for a vacuum with electronic sensing capabilities. It will sense carpet height and density. It will then adjust the power and the angle of the head to optimize cleaning on a continuous basis. Our role in this would be to design the manufacturing system and to do the actual manufacturing for North America. Sound interesting so far?"

"Yes, Ms. Kulkowsi," Naomi answered. Naomi couldn't help being respectful in front of Anna, who was Canadian Widget's president, among other things. "What would my role be?"

"For one thing, you will be working with Bill Astad from head office. I think you know him." Naomi did; she had given Bill some advice on handling variable rates of inflation a few weeks earlier. "First, we want to establish some idea of the demand for the product. We have to see how this might affect our manufacturing capacity and capital costs to determine if the whole idea is even feasible. Later on, we will have to make some design decisions, but the general feasibility comes first."

"Do we have any market studies from Powerluxe?" Naomi asked.

"Yes, but they seem to be guesswork and magic, not hard figures. After all, no one has sold a product like this before."

Naomi looked pensive. "Sounds as though we'll need to do some sensitivity analysis on this one." She muttered more to herself than Anna. Then to Anna, "Right. We'll do what we can. Thanks for the nice opportunity, Anna. This is interesting!"

10.1 Introduction

To this point in our coverage of engineering economics, we have assumed that the cash flows used in an economic analysis are known with certainty, both in timing and size. In fact, the timing and size of the cash flows are only estimates, and are subject to error. This chapter is concerned with a variety of basic methods for assessing the potential impact of these and other errors on the economic viability of a project and on the choice among alternative projects.

There are several reasons why estimates of cash flows may not match the actual outcome. Technological change can unexpectedly shorten the life of a product or piece of equipment. A change in the number of competing firms may affect sales volume or market share or the life of a product. In addition, the general economic environment may affect inflation and interest rates and general activity levels within an industry.

All of these factors may result in cash flows different from what was expected in both timing and size.

Economic analyses are not complete unless we try to assess the potential effects of these uncertainties on the outcomes of the analyses. Because cash flows can be so hard to estimate, analysts will usually consider a range of possible values for uncertain components of a project. There will then naturally be a range of values for present worth, annual worth, or whatever the relevant performance measure is. In this way, the analyst gets a better feel for the range of possible outcomes and can make better decisions.

In this chapter, we will consider three basic methods used by analysts in order to understand better the effect that errors in parameters such as estimated cash flows have on economic decisions. The first is the use of sensitivity graphs. Sensitivity graphs illustrate the sensitivity of a particular measure (e.g., present worth or annual worth) to changes in one or more of the parameters of a project. Sensitivity graphs will reveal key parameters that have a significant impact on the performance measure, and hence we may be particularly careful to get good estimates for these key parameters. The second method is the use of break-even analysis. Break-even analysis can answer such questions as: "What production level is necessary in order for the present worth of the project to be greater than zero?" or "Below what interest rate will the project have a positive annual worth?" Break-even analysis can also give insights into comparisons between projects. With break-even analysis, we can answer questions like, "What scrap value for the proposed forklift will cause us to be indifferent between replacing the old forklift and not replacing it?" The third method we will introduce is called scenario analysis. Both sensitivity graphs and break-even analysis have the drawback that we can look at parameter changes only one at a time. Scenario analysis allows us to look at the overall impact of a variety of outcomes, usually "optimistic," "expected," and "pessimistic." In this way, the analyst comes to understand the range of possible economic outcomes.

Each of these three methods—sensitivity graphs, break-even analysis, and scenario analysis—is an example of sensitivity analysis. Each method tries to assess the sensitivity of an economic measure to errors in estimates in the various parameters of the problem. A thorough economic evaluation should include aspects of all three types of analysis.

Appendix 10A provides a brief look at additional ways in which an analyst can incorporate information about the probability distribution of project parameters into economic evaluation.

10.2 Sensitivity Graphs

The first sensitivity analysis tool we will look at is the sensitivity graph. Sensitivity graphs are used to assess the effect of changes in key parameters of a project on an economic performance measure. We begin with a "base case" where all the estimated parameters are used to evaluate the present worth, annual worth, or IRR of a project, whatever the appropriate measure is. We then vary parameters above and below the base case one at a time, holding all other variables fixed. A graph of the changes in a performance measure brought about by these one-at-a-time parameter changes is called a **sensitivity graph**. From the graph, the analyst can see which parameters have a significant impact on the performance measure and which do not.

EXAMPLE 10.1

Cogenesis Corporation is replacing their current steam plant with a 6MW cogeneration plant that will also produce steam and electric power for their operations. The new plant will use wood as a source of fuel, and it will eliminate the need for Cogenesis to purchase a large amount of electric power from a public utility. To move to the new system, Cogenesis will have to integrate a new turbogenerator and cooling tower with their current system. The estimated first cost of the equipment and installation is $3 000 000, though there is some uncertainty surrounding this estimate. The plant is expected to have a 20-year life and no scrap value at the end of this life. In addition to the first cost, the turbogenerator will require an overhaul with an estimated cost of $35 000 at the end of years 4, 8, 12, and 16. The cooling tower will need an overhaul at the end of 10 years. This is expected to cost $17 000. The cogeneration system is expected to have higher annual operating and maintenance costs than the current system, and will require the use of chemicals to treat the water used in the new plant. These incremental costs are estimated to be $65 000 per year. The incremental annual costs of wood fuel are estimated to be $375 000. The cogeneration plant will save Cogenesis from having to purchase 40 000 000 kWh of electricity per year at $0.025 /kWh, an annual savings of $1 000 000. Cogenesis uses a MARR of 12%. What is the present worth of the incremental investment in the cogeneration plant? What is the impact of a 5% and 10% increase and decrease in each of the parameters of the problem?

PW(cogeneration plant)
$$= - \$3\,000\,000 - (\$65\,000 + \$375\,000 - \$1\,000\,000)$$
$$\times (P/A, 12\%, 20) - \$17\,000(P/F, 12\%, 10)$$
$$- \$35\,000[(P/F, 12\%, 4) + (P/F, 12\%, 8) + (P/F, 12\%, 12)$$
$$+ (P/F, 12\%, 16)]$$
$$= \$1\,126\,343$$

The present worth of the incremental investment is $1 126 343. Based on this assessment, the project appears to be economically viable.

In order to better understand the situation, analysts for Cogenesis have also completed some sensitivity graphs which indicate how sensitive the present worth is to changes in some of the parameters. In particular, they feel that some of the cash flows may turn out to be different from their estimates, and they would like to get a feel for what impact these errors may have on the evaluation of the cogeneration plant. To investigate, they have labelled their current estimates the "base case" and have generated other cash flow estimates that are 5% and 10% above and below the base case for each major cash flow category. These are summarized in Table 10.1.

TABLE 10.1: Summary Data for Example 10.1

Cost Category	−10%	−5%	Base Case	5%	10%
Initial investment	$2 700 000	$2 850 000	$3 000 000	$3 150 000	$3 300 000
Annual chemical, operations, and maintenance costs	58 500	61 750	65 000	68 250	71 500
Cooling tower overhaul (after 10 years)	15 300	16 150	17 000	17 850	18 700
Turbogenerator overhauls (after 4, 8, 12, and 16 years)	31 500	33 250	35 000	36 750	38 500
Annual wood costs	337 500	356 250	375 000	393 750	412 500
Annual savings in electricity costs	900 000	950 000	1 000 000	1 050 000	1 100 000
MARR	0.108	0.114	0.12	0.126	0.132

For example, the initial investment may be more than the estimate of $3 000 000 if they run into unforeseen difficulties in the installation. Or the savings in electricity costs may be overestimated if the cost per kW drops in the future. The analysts would like to get a better understanding of which of these changes would have the greatest impact on the evaluation of the plant.

To keep the illustration simple, we will consider changes to the initial investment, annual chemical, operations, and maintenance costs, the MARR, and the savings in electrical costs. Each of these is varied one at a time, leaving all other cash flow estimates at the base case values. For example, if the initial investment is 10% below the initial estimate of $3 000 000, and all other estimates are as in the base case, the present worth of the project will be $1 426 343 (see the first row of Table 10.2, under −10%). Similarly, if the first cost is 10% more than the original estimate, the present worth drops to $826 343.

Interest rate uncertainty will almost always be present in an economic analysis. If Cogenesis' MARR increases by 10% (with all other parameters at their base case values), the present worth of the project drops to $835 115, about the same impact as if the first cost ended up being 10% more than expected. Other variations are shown in Table 10.2. A sensitivity graph, shown in Figure 10.1, illustrates the impact of one-at-a-time parameter variations on the present worth.

Small changes in the annual chemical, operations, and maintenance costs do not have much of an impact on the present worth of the project, as can be seen from Table 10.2 and Figure 10.1. What appears to have the greatest impact on the viability of the project is the savings in electricity costs. A 10% drop in the savings causes the present worth of the project to drop to about one-third of the base case estimate. This change could occur because of a drop in electricity rates or a drop in demand. Alternatively, the present worth of the project increases to almost $1 900 000 if the savings are higher than anticipated. This could, once again, occur because of a change in either rates or demand for power. Clearly, if Cogenesis is to expend effort in getting better forecasts, it should be for energy consumption and power rates.

One final point about this example should be noted. If management feels that, individually, the cash flow estimates will fall within the +/−10% range, the investment looks economically viable and they should go ahead with it.

TABLE 10.2 Present Worth of Variations from Base Case in Example 10.1

Cost Category	−10%	−5%	Base Case	5%	10%
Initial investment	$1 426 343	$1 276 343	$1 126 343	$ 976 343	$ 826 343
Annual chemical, operations, and maintenance costs	1 174 894	1 150 619	1 126 343	1 102 067	1 077 792
Cooling tower overhaul (after 10 years)	1 126 890	1 126 617	1 126 343	1 126 069	1 125 796
Turbogenerator overhauls (after 4, 8, 12, and 16 years)	1 131 450	1 128 897	1 126 343	1 123 789	1 121 236
Annual wood costs	1 406 447	1 266 395	1 126 343	986 291	846 239
Savings in electricity costs	379 399	752 871	1 126 343	1 499 815	1 873 287
MARR	1 456 693	1 286 224	1 126 343	976 224	835 115

As we can see from Example 10.1, the benefit of a sensitivity graph is that it can be used to select key parameters in an economic analysis. It is easy to understand, and communicates a lot of information in a single diagram. There are, however, several shortcomings of sensitivity graphs.

FIGURE 10.1   Sensitivity Graph for Example 10.1

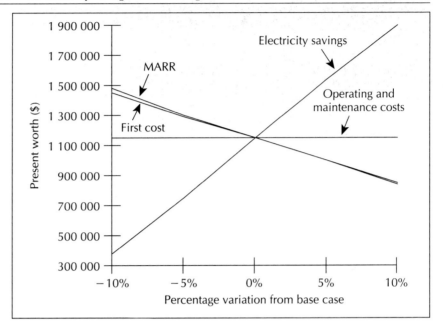

First, they are valid only over the range of parameter values in the graph. The impact of parameter variations outside the range considered may not be simply a linear extrapolation of the lines in the graph. If you need to assess the impact of greater variations, the computations should be redone. Second, and probably the greatest drawback of sensitivity graphs, is that they do not consider the interaction between two or more parameters that may be in error. You cannot simply "add up" the impact of individual changes when several parameters are varied. We will come back to this issue in the section on scenario analysis, where we do consider entire "packages" of changes from the base case.

10.3 Break-Even Analysis

In this section, we cover a second type of sensitivity analysis called break-even analysis. Once again, we are trying to answer the question of what impact changes (or errors) in parameter estimates will have on the economic performance measures we use in our analyses, or on a decision made on the basis of an economic performance measure. In general, **break-even analysis** is the process of varying a parameter of a problem and determining what parameter value causes the performance measure to reach some threshold or "break-even" value. In Example 10.1, we saw that an increase in the MARR caused the present worth of the cogeneration plant to decrease. If the MARR were to increase sufficiently, the project might have a zero present worth. A break-even analysis could answer the question, "What MARR will result in a zero present worth?" This analysis would be particularly useful if Cogenesis were uncertain about the MARR and wanted to find a threshold MARR above which the project would not be viable. Other such break-even questions could be posed for the cogeneration problem, to try to get a better understanding of the impact of changes in parameter values on the economic analysis.

Break-even analysis can also be used in the comparison of two or more projects. We have already seen in Chapter 4 (Comparison Methods, Part 1) that the best choice among mutually exclusive alternatives may depend on the interest rate, production level, or a variety of other problem parameters. Break-even analysis applied to multiple projects can answer questions like, "Over what range of interest rates is project A the best choice?" or "For what output level are we indifferent between two projects?" Notice that we are varying a single parameter in two or more projects and asking when the performance measure for the projects meets some threshold or break-even point. The point of doing this analysis is to try to get a better understanding of how sensitive a decision is to changes in the parameters of the problem.

10.3.1 Break-Even Analysis for a Single Project

In this section, we show how break-even analysis can be applied to a single project to illustrate how sensitive a project evaluation is to changes in project parameters. We will continue with Example 10.1 to expand upon the information provided by the sensitivity graphs.

EXAMPLE 10.2

Having completed the sensitivity graph in Example 10.1, management recognizes that the present worth of the cogeneration plant is quite sensitive to the savings in electricity costs, the MARR, and the initial costs. Since there is some uncertainty about these estimates, they want to explore further the impact of changes in these parameters on the viability of the project. You are to carry out a break-even analysis for each of these parameters to find out what range of values results in a viable project (i.e., PW > 0) and to determine the "break-even" parameter values which make the present worth of the project zero. You are also to construct a graph to illustrate the present worth of the project as a function of each parameter.

First, Figure 10.2 shows the present worth of the project as a function of the MARR. It shows that the break-even MARR is 17.73%. In other words, the project will have a positive present worth for any MARR less than 17.73% (all other parameters fixed) and a negative present worth for a MARR more than 17.73%. Notice that the break-even interest rate is, in fact, the IRR for the project.

FIGURE 10.2   Break-even Chart for the MARR

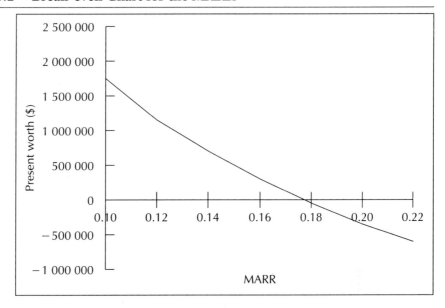

A similar break-even chart for the first cost, Figure 10.3, shows that the first cost can be as high as $4 126 350 before the present worth declines to zero. Assuming that all other cost estimates are accurate, the project will be viable as long as the first cost is below this break-even amount. One issue management should assess is the likelihood that the first cost will exceed $4 126 350.

FIGURE 10.3   Break-even Chart for First Cost

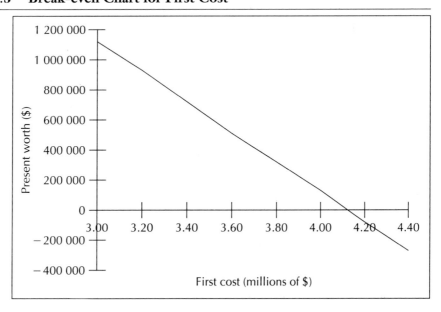

FIGURE 10.4   Break-even Chart for Electricity Savings

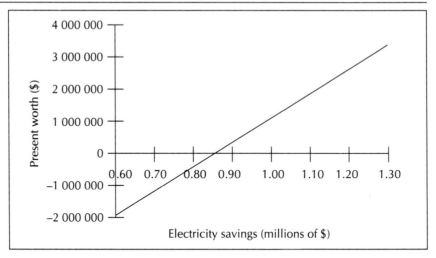

Finally, a break-even chart for the savings in electrical power costs is shown in Figure 10.4. We have already seen from the sensitivity graph that the viability of the project is very sensitive to the savings in electricity produced by the cogeneration plant. Provided that the annual savings are above $849 207, the project is viable. Below this break-even level, the present worth of the project is negative. If the actual saving in electrical power costs is likely to be much below the estimate, this will put the project's viability at risk. Given the particular sensitivity of the present worth to the savings, it may be worthwhile to spend additional time looking into the two factors that make up these savings: the cost per kilowatt-hour and the total kilowatt-hours of demand provided for by the new plant.

Break-even analysis done for a single project expands upon the information sensitivity graphs provide. It has the advantage that it is easy to apply and allows us to determine the range of values for a parameter within which the project is viable or some other criteria are met. It can provide us with break-even parameter values that give an indication of how much a parameter can change from its original estimate before the project's viability becomes a concern. Graphical presentation of the break-even analysis, as in Figures 10.2, 10.3, and 10.4, summarizes the information in an easily understood way.

10.3.2 Break-Even Analysis for Multiple Projects

In the previous section, we saw how break-even analysis can be applied to a single project in order to understand more clearly the impact of changes in parameter values on the evaluation of the project. This break-even analysis may influence a decision as to whether the project should be done or not. When there is a choice among several projects, be they independent or mutually exclusive, the basic question remains the same. We are concerned with the impact that changes in problem parameters have on the relevant economic performance measure, and, ultimately, on the decision made with respect to the projects. With one project, we are concerned with whether the project should be done and how changes in parameter values affect this decision. With multiple projects, we are concerned about how changes in parameter values affect which project or projects are chosen.

For multiple independent projects, assuming that there are sufficient funds to finance all projects, break-even analysis can be carried out on each project independently, as was done for a single project in the previous section. This will lead to insights into how robust a decision is under changes in the parameters.

For mutually exclusive projects, the best choice will seldom stand out as clearly superior from all points of view. Even if we have narrowed down the choices, it is still likely that the best choice is a function of the interest rate, level of output, or first cost. A break-even comparison can reveal the range over which each alternative is preferred and can show the break-even points where we are indifferent between two projects. Break-even analysis will provide a decision maker with further information about each of the projects and how they relate to one another when parameters change.

EXAMPLE 10.3

Westmount Waxworks (see Problem 4.10) is considering buying a new wax melter for their line of replicas of statues of government leaders. They have two choices of suppliers, Finedetail and Simplicity. The proposals are as follows:

	Finedetail	Simplicity
Expected life	7 years	10 years
First cost	$200 000	$350 000
Maintenance	$10 000/year + $0.05/unit	$20 000/year + $0.01/unit
Labour	$1.25/unit	$0.50/unit
Other costs	$6 500/year + $0.95/unit	$15 500/year + $0.55/unit
Salvage value	$5 000	$20 000

The marketing manager has indicated that sales have averaged 50 000 units per year over the past five years. In addition to this information, management thinks that they will sell about 30 000 replicas per year if there is stability in world governments. If the world becomes very unsettled so that there are frequent overturns of governments, sales may be as high as 200 000 units per year. There is also some uncertainty about the variable other costs of the Simplicity wax melter. These include energy costs and an allowance for scrap. Though the costs are estimated to be \$0.55 per unit, the Simplicity model is a new technology, and the variable costs may be as low as \$0.45 per unit or as high as \$0.75 per unit. Westmount Waxworks would like to carry out a break-even analysis on the sales volume and on the variable other costs of the Simplicity wax melter. They want to know what the preferred supplier would be as sales vary from 30 000 per year to 200 000 per year. They also wish to know what the preferred supplier is if the variable other costs per unit for the Simplicity model are as low as \$0.45 per unit or as high as \$0.75 per unit. Westmount Waxworks uses a MARR of 15% for equipment projects. Their tax rate is 40% and the CCA rate for such equipment is 30%.

Assuming that the variable other costs of the Simplicity wax melter are \$0.55 per unit, a break-even chart which shows the present worth of the projects as a function of sales levels can give much insight into the supplier selection. Table 10.3 gives the annual cost of each of the two alternatives, and Figure 10.5 shows the break-even chart for sales level. A sample computation for the Finedetail wax melter at the 60 000 sales level is

$$AW(\text{Finedetail}) = CCTF_{new}(\$200\ 000)(A/P,\ 15\%,\ 7)$$
$$- CCTF_{old}(\$5000)(A/F,\ 15\%,\ 7) + (1 - t)[\$10\ 000$$
$$+ \$6500 + (\$0.05 + \$1.25 + \$0.95)(\text{sales level})]$$
$$= 0.750725(\$200\ 000)(0.24036) - 0.7333(\$5000)(0.09036)$$
$$+ (1 - 0.4)[\$16\ 500 + \$2.25(60\ 000)]$$
$$= \$125\ 814$$

where

$$CCTF_{old} = 1 - \frac{td}{i+d} = 1 - \frac{0.4(0.3)}{0.15 + 0.30} = 0.73333$$

$$CCTF_{new} = 1 - \frac{td\left(1 + \dfrac{i}{2}\right)}{(i+d)(1+i)} = 1 - \frac{(0.4)(0.3)(1+0.075)}{(0.15+0.30)(1+0.15)}$$
$$= 0.750725$$

TABLE 10.3: Annual Cost as a Function of Sales

Sales	Annual Costs (\$)	
(Units)	Finedetail	Simplicity
20 000	71 814	84 421
60 000	125 814	109 861
100 000	179 814	135 301
140 000	233 814	160 741
180 000	287 814	186 181
220 000	341 814	211 621

FIGURE 10.5   Break-even Chart for Sales Level

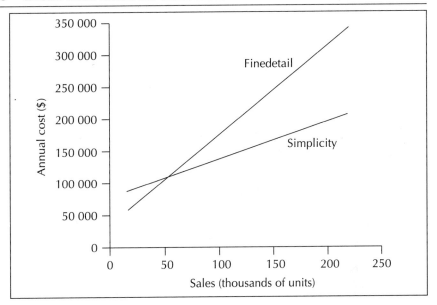

If sales are 30 000 units per year, the Finedetail wax melter is slightly preferred to the Simplicity melter. At a sales level of 200 000 units per year, the preference is for the Simplicity wax melter. Interpolation of the amounts in Table 10.3 indicates that the break-even sales level is 37 658 units. That is to say, for sales below 37 658 per year, Finedetail is preferred, and Simplicity is preferred for sales levels of 37 658 units and above.

Since 30 000 units per year is the lowest sales will likely be, and sales have averaged 50 000 units per year over the past five years, it appears that the Simplicity wax melter would be the preferred choice, assuming that its variable other costs total per unit is $0.55. The robustness of this decision may be affected by the other costs per unit of the Simplicity melter.

To assess the sensitivity of the choice of wax melter to the variable other costs of Simplicity, a break-even analysis similar to that for sales level can be carried out. We can vary the variable other costs from the estimate of $0.45 per unit to $0.75 per unit and observe the effect on the preferred wax melter. Table 10.4 gives the annual costs for the two wax melters as a function of the variable other costs of the Simplicity model for sales levels of 30 000, 50 000, and 200 000 units per year. In each case, we see that the best choice is not sensitive to the variable other costs of the Simplicity wax melter. In fact, for a sales level of 30 000 units per year, the break-even variable other cost is only $0.25, as shown in Figure 10.6. This means that the other cost per unit would have to be lower than $0.25 for the best choice to change from Finedetail to Simplicity. For a sales level of 200 000 per year, the break-even variable other cost is much higher, at $1.52 per unit, and for a sales level of 50 000 units per year the break-even cost per unit is $0.85. For both of the latter sales levels, however, the Simplicity model is preferred.

TABLE 10.4:   Annual Cost as a Function of Simplicity's Other Costs Per Unit

Other Cost per Unit ($)	Sales = 30 000 units/year Annual Costs ($)		Sales = 50 000 units/year Annual Costs ($)		Sales = 200 000 units/year Annual Costs ($)	
	Finedetail	Simplicity	Finedetail	Simplicity	Finedetail	Simplicity
0.45	85 314	88 981	112 314	100 501	314 814	186 901
0.55	85 314	90 781	112 314	103 501	314 814	198 901
0.65	85 314	92 581	112 314	106 501	314 814	210 901
0.75	85 314	94 381	112 314	109 501	314 814	222 901

FIGURE 10.6   Break-even Chart for Simplicity's Other Costs Per Unit (Sales = 30,000 Units)

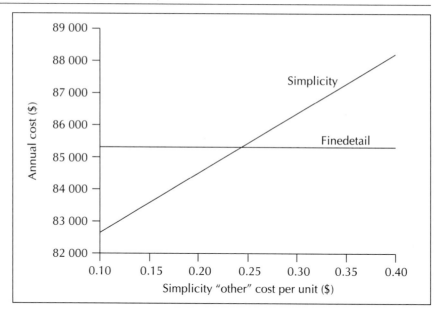

Having done the break-even analysis for both sales level and other costs per unit for the Simplicity wax melter, it would appear that the Simplicity model is the better choice if sales are at all likely to exceed the break-even sales level of 37 658. Historically, sales have exceeded this amount. Even if sales in a particular year fall below the break-even level, the Simplicity wax melter does not have annual costs far in excess of those of the Finedetail model, so the decision would appear to be robust with respect to possible sales levels. Similarly, the decision is not sensitive to the other cost per unit of the Simplicity wax melter.

We have seen in this section that break-even analysis for either a single project or for multiple projects is a simple tool and that it can be used to extract insights from a modest amount of data. It communicates threshold (break-even) parameter values where preference changes from one alternative to another or where a project changes from being uneconomic to economic. Break-even analysis is a popular means of assessing the impact of errors or changes in parameter values on an economic performance measure or a decision.

The main disadvantage of break-even analysis is that it cannot easily capture interdependencies among variables. Although we can vary one or two parameters at a time and graph the results, more complicated analyses are not often feasible. This disadvantage can be overcome to some degree by what is referred to as scenario analysis, the subject of the next section.

10.4 Scenario Analysis

The third type of sensitivity analysis tool that we will look at is **scenario analysis**. Scenario analysis is the process of examining the consequences of several possible sets of variables associated with a project. Scenario analysis recognizes that many estimates of cash flows or other project parameters may vary from what is projected. It is useful to look at several "what if" scenarios in order to understand the effect of changes in values of whole sets of parameters. Commonly used scenarios are the "optimistic" (or "best case") outcome, the "pessimistic" (or "worst case") outcome, and the "expected" (or "most likely") outcome. The best case and worst case outcomes can, in some sense, capture the entire range of possible outcomes for a project or a comparison among projects and provide an enriched view of the decision.

EXAMPLE 10.4

Cogenesis (refer to Example 10.1) wishes to do a scenario analysis of their cogeneration decision problem. They have come up with optimistic, pessimistic, and expected estimates of each of the parameters for their decision problem in order to get a better understanding of the possible range of present worth outcomes for the cogeneration plant. The three scenarios and the associated estimates are summarized in Table 10.5.

The scenarios capture combinations of parameter estimates which reflect, respectively, the worst, best, and expected outcomes for the project. In contrast with sensitivity graphs and break-even analysis, the scenario analysis allows entire groups of parameters to be changed at one time.

Evaluation of each scenario reveals that the present worth of the cogeneration plant will be negative if all parameters take on their worst case values. The major problem is that the savings in electricity costs are insufficient to make up for the high first cost of the project. In contrast, both the expected case and best case scenarios lead to positive present worths. (To put the present worths into context, the expected case and best case sce-

TABLE 10.5: Present Worth of Cogeneration Plant Scenarios

Cost Category	Pessimistic Scenario	Expected Scenario	Optimistic Scenario
Initial investment ($)	3 300 000	3 000 000	2 700 000
Annual chemical, operations, and maintenance costs ($)	75 000	65 000	60 000
Cooling tower overhaul (after 10 years) ($)	21 000	17 000	13 000
Turbogenerator overhauls (after 4, 8, 12, and 16 years) ($)	40 000	35 000	30 000
Additional annual wood costs ($)	400 000	375 000	350 000
Savings in annual electricity costs ($)	920 000	1 000 000	1 080 000
MARR	0.13	0.12	0.11
Present worth of Cogeneration plant ($)	–234 639	1 126 343	2 583 848

narios have IRRs of 17.73% and 24.29%, respectively.) Though there is some risk that the cogeneration project will have a negative present worth, this will occur only if the worst case scenario does occur. Even if the worst case outcome does occur, the loss is not huge. What Cogenesis needs to do if they wish to look further into the project's viability is assess the risk (or likelihood) that the worst outcome will occur. This is beyond the scope of this text, but is discussed briefly in Appendix 10A.

As we can see from Example 10.4, scenario analysis allows us to look at the effect of multiple changes in parameter values on an individual project's viability. It can also be used to evaluate the effect of scenarios in the case where there are several alternatives.

EXAMPLE 10.5

Westmount Waxworks has carried out a scenario analysis for three possible outcomes they feel represent pessimistic, optimistic, and expected outcomes for sales levels and the Simplicity wax melter's other costs per unit. The scenarios and the annual costs of the two wax melters are summarized in Table 10.6.

From the scenario analysis, we see that the Simplicity wax melter is the preferred choice for the expected and optimistic scenarios. The Finedetail wax melter is preferred only if the pessimistic scenario occurs. In terms of the opportunity cost of making the wrong choice, it is far larger if the optimistic outcome occurs ($314 814 − $186 901 = $127 913) than if the pessimistic outcome occurs ($94 381 − $85 314 = $9067).

As was seen in Examples 10.4 and 10.5, scenario analysis allows us to take into account the interrelationships among parameters when making a choice, by examining likely groupings of parameter values in scenarios.

TABLE 10.6: Scenario Analysis for Westmount Waxworks

	Pessimistic Scenario	Expected Scenario	Optimistic Scenario
Sales level (units)	30 000	50 000	200 000
Other costs per unit (Simplicity)	$0.75	$0.55	$0.45
Annual Cost: Finedetail	$85 314	$112 314	$314 814
Annual Cost: Simplicity	$94 381	$103 501	$186 901

The most commonly used scenarios are the pessimistic, optimistic, and expected outcomes. The use of scenarios allows an analyst to capture the range of possible outcomes for a project or group of projects. Done in combination with sensitivity graphs and break-even analysis, a great deal of information about the decision can be obtained.

The one drawback common to each of the three sensitivity analysis methods covered in this chapter is that they do not capture the likelihood that a parameter will take on a certain value or the likelihood that a certain scenario will occur. This information can further guide a decision maker and is often crucial to assessing the risk of the worst case outcome. For students with a background in probability, Appendix 10A describes briefly how these concerns are addressed.

CANADIAN CORPORATE CASE 10.1

Metro Toronto's Main Treatment Plant

Metro Toronto's Main Treatment Plant is the largest activated-sludge plant in Canada, with a rated treatment capacity of 818 million litres per day. It serves a population of 1.25 million people. Treatment effluent is discharged into Lake Ontario.

A remedial action plan for this area of the lake was developed by the Ontario Ministry of Environment and Energy that would require nitrification of the effluent. A preliminary estimate of cost to achieve nitrification was about $220 million. In 1992, the municipality hired a consultant to assess the ability of the existing plant to meet the expected requirements, and to propose modifications which might be required.

A year-long assessment of the process was undertaken which included extensive data collection from over 50 on-line instruments. From this assessment, it was surmised that future requirements could be met by modifying existing procedures and facilities.

Based on the data collected during the assessment, a simulation model was developed. The simulation was used to confirm the prediction made in the initial assessment and to test the response of the modified plant to different operating scenarios.

The estimated capital cost of the necessary improvements to the existing facilities was less than $32 million.

Source: Canadian Consulting Engineer, September/October, 1994.

REVIEW PROBLEMS

The following case is the basis of Review Problems 10.1 through 10.3, and Review Problem 10A.1 in Appendix 10A.

Burnaby Insurance Inc. is considering two independent energy efficiency improvement projects. Each has a lifetime of 10 years and will have a scrap value of zero at the end of this time. Burnaby can afford to do both if both are economically justified. The first project involves installing high efficiency motors in their air conditioning system. High efficiency units use about 7% less electricity than the current motors, which represents annual savings of 70 000 kWh. They cost $28 000 to purchase and install and will require maintenance costs of $700 annually.

The second project involves installing a heat exchange unit in the current ventilation system. During the winter, the heat exchange unit transfers heat from warm room air to the cold ventilation air before the air is sent back into the building. This will save about 2 250 000 cubic feet of natural gas per year. In the summer, the heat exchange unit removes heat from the hot ventilation air before it is added to the cooler room air for recirculation. This saves about 29 000 kilowatt-hours of electricity annually. Each heat exchange unit costs $40 000 to purchase and install and annual maintenance costs are $3200.

Burnaby Insurance would like to evaluate the two projects, but there is some uncertainty surrounding what electricity and natural gas prices will be over the life of the project. Current prices are $0.07 per kilowatt-hour for electricity and $3.50 per thousand cubic feet of natural gas, but some changes are anticipated. They use a MARR of 10%.

▌ Review Problem 10.1

Construct a sensitivity graph to determine the effect that a 5% and 10% drop or increase in the cost of electricity and the cost of natural gas would have upon the present worth of each project.

Answer

Table 10.7 gives the costs of electricity and natural gas with 5% and 10% increases and decreases from the base case of $0.07 per kWh for electricity and $3.50 per 1000 cubic feet of natural gas. The table also shows the present worths of the two energy efficiency projects as the costs vary.

A sample calculation for the heat exchange unit with base case costs is

$$PW(\text{Heat exchanger}) = -\$40,000 + (P/A, 10\%, 10)$$
$$\times [\$29,000(0.07) + \$2250(3.50) - \$3200]$$
$$= \$1199$$

TABLE 10.7: Costs Used as the Basis of the Sensitivity Graph for Review Problem 10.1

	-10%	**-5%**	**0%**	**5%**	**10%**
Cost of electricity ($/kWh)	0.063	0.0665	0.07	0.0735	0.077
Cost of natural gas ($/1000 cubic feet)	3.15	3.325	3.5	3.675	3.85
PW of high efficiency motor ($)					
With changes to electricity costs	-5204	-3698	-2193	-687	818
With changes to natural gas cost	-2193	-2193	-2193	-2193	-2193
PW of heat exchanger ($)					
With changes to electricity costs	-48	576	1199	1823	2447
With changes to natural gas cost	-3640	-1220	1199	3619	6038

The high efficiency motor is not economically viable at the current prices for electricity and gas. Only if there is an increase of almost 10% in electricity costs for the life of the project will the motor produce sufficient savings for the project to have a positive present worth. Figure 10.7 is a sensitivity graph for the high efficiency motor. It graphically illustrates the effect of changes in the costs of electricity and natural gas on the present worth of a motor.

FIGURE 10.7   Sensitivity Graph for the High Efficiency Motor

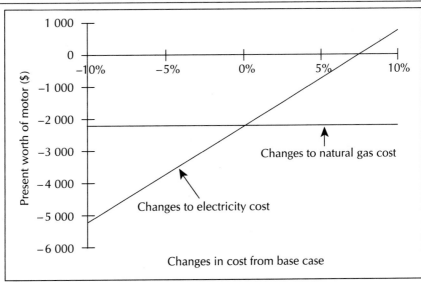

Figure 10.8 is the sensitivity graph for the heat exchange unit. The heat exchange unit has a positive present worth for the current prices, but the present worth is quite sensitive to the price of natural gas. A drop in the price of natural gas in the range of only 1% to 2% (reading from the graph) will cause the project to have a negative present worth.

FIGURE 10.8   Sensitivity Graph for the Heat Exchanger

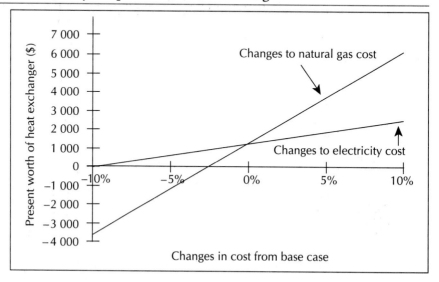

Review Problem 10.2

Refer to Review Problem 10.1. How much of a drop in the cost of natural gas will result in the heat exchange unit's having a present worth of zero? Construct a break-even graph to illustrate this break-even cost.

> ### Answer
>
> By varying the cost of natural gas from the base case, the break-even graph shown in Figure 10.9 can be constructed. The break-even cost of natural gas is $3.413 per 1000 cubic feet, which is not much below the current price for gas. Burnaby Insurance should probably look more seriously into forecasts of natural gas prices for the life of the heat exchange unit.

Review Problem 10.3

Analysts at Burnaby Insurance have established what they think are three scenarios for the prices of electricity and natural gas over the lives of the two projects under consideration in Review Problem 10.1. The scenarios along with the appropriate present worth computations are summarized in Table 10.8. What insight does this add to the investment decision for Burnaby Insurance?

FIGURE 10.9   Break-Even Chart of the Cost of Natural Gas

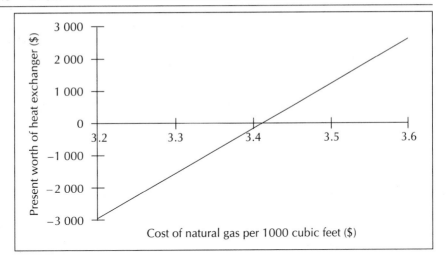

Cost of natural gas per 1000 cubic feet ($)

TABLE 10.8: Scenario Analysis for Burnaby Insurance

	Pessimistic Scenario	Expected Scenario	Optimistic Scenario
Cost of electricity ($/kWh)	0.063	0.070	0.077
Cost of natural gas ($/1000 cubit feet)	3.35	3.50	3.65
PW of high efficiency motor ($)	−5204	−2193	818
PW of heat exchange unit ($)	−2122	1199	4520

Answer

The additional insight that the scenario analysis brings to Burnaby insurance is the effect of changes in both electricity and natural gas costs on the two proposed projects. Sensitivity graphs and the break-even analysis can look only at the effect of one-at-a-time parameter changes on the present worth computations. It appears that the high efficiency motor is a bad investment, as its present worth is not much above zero even if the optimistic scenario occurs. The heat exchange unit appears to be a better investment, but even that has a chance of having a negative present worth if the pessimistic outcome occurs. What Burnaby really needs to know is the likelihood of each of these scenarios occurring, or some other means of assessing the likelihood of what energy prices will be in the future.

SUMMARY

In this chapter, we considered three basic methods used by analysts in order to better understand the effect that errors in estimated cash flows have on economic decisions. The first was the use of sensitivity graphs. Sensitivity graphs illustrate the sensitivity of a particular measure (e.g., present worth or annual worth) to changes in one or more of the parameters of a project. The second method was the use of break-even analysis for both evaluating individual projects and comparisons among projects. Finally, scenario analysis allowed us to look at the overall impact of a variety of outcomes, usually optimistic, expected, and pessimistic.

Engineering Economics in Action, Part 10B: Where the Risks Lie

Bill Astad and Naomi were working through the market demand figures provided by Powerluxe for the new self-adjusting vacuum.

"These figures are pretty ambiguous," Bill said. "We have three approaches: a set of opinions taken from focus groups and surveys of customers, the same thing from dealers and distributors, and an analysis of trends in a set of parallel products such as fuzzy-logic appliances. Like Anna said, nothing hard."

"What we really want to know," said Naomi, "is whether we have the capacity to handle the manufacturing for the product. Based on the surveys and the trend information, let's come up with three scenarios: low demand, expected demand, and high demand. If we behave according to expected demand, and the true demand is low, we will lose money because our capital investments won't be recouped as fast, and we may have passed up other opportunities. Similarly, if the demand is high, we will lose by having to pay overtime, paying for contracting out, or losing customers. But if we make money in all three cases, there really isn't much of a problem.

"And if it turns out we don't make money in all three cases?" Bill asked. "What then?"

"I know it's a lot of work, Bill, but let's do it and find out," Naomi replied. "At minimum, we will know where our risks lie."

PROBLEMS

10.1 The Inuvik Go-Kart Club has decided to build a clubhouse and track several years from now. The club needs to accumulate $50 000 by setting aside a uniform amount at the end of each year. They believe it possible to set aside $7000 each year at 10% interest. They wish to know how many years it will take to save $50 000 and how sensitive this result is to a 5% and a 10% increase or decrease in the amount saved per year and in the interest rate. Construct a sensitivity graph to illustrate the situation.

10.2 A new software package is expected to improve productivity at Saskatoon Insurance. However, because of training and implementation costs, savings are not expected to occur until the third year of operation. Annual savings of approximately $10 000 are expected, increasing by about $1000 per year for the following five years. After this time (eight years from implementation), the software will be abandoned with no scrap value. Construct a sensitivity graph showing what would happen to the present worth of the software with 7.5% and 15% increases and decreases in the interest rate, the $10 000 base savings, and the $1000 savings gradient.

10.3 The Regional Municipality of Kitchener is studying a water supply plan for the tri-city and surrounding area to the end of the year 2040. To satisfy the water demand, one suggestion is to construct a pipeline from one of the Great Lakes. It is now the end of 1995. Construction would start in the year 2000 (five years from now) and take five years to complete at a cost of $20 million per year. Annual maintenance and repair costs are expected to be $2 million dollars and will start the year following project completion (all costs are based on current estimates). From a predicted inflation rate of 3% per year, and the real MARR, city engineers have determined that a MARR of 7% per year is appropriate. Assume that all cash flows take place at the end of the year and that there is no salvage value at the end of 2040.

(a) Find the present worth of the project.

(b) Construct a sensitivity graph showing the effect of 5% and 10% increases and decreases in the construction costs, maintenance costs, and inflation rate. To which is the present worth most sensitive?

10.4 The city of Surrey is installing a new swimming pool in the downtown recreation centre. One design being considered is a reinforced concrete pool which will cost $6 000 000 to install. Thereafter, the inner surface of the pool will need to be refinished and painted every 10 years at a cost of $40 000 per refinishing. Assuming that the pool will have essentially an infinite life, what is the present worth of the costs associated with the pool design? The city uses a MARR of 5%. If the installation costs, refinishing costs, and MARR are subject to 5% or 10% increases or decreases, how is the present worth affected? To which parameter is the present worth most sensitive?

10.5 You and two friends are thinking about setting up a grocery delivery service for local residents to finance your last two years at university. In order to start up the business, you will need to purchase a car. You have found a used car which will cost $6000 and you expect to be able to sell it for $3000 at the end of two years. Insurance costs are $600 for each six months of operation, starting now. Advertising costs (e.g., flyers, newspaper advertisements) are estimated to be $100 per month, but these could vary as much as 20% above or below the $100, depending on the intensity of your advertising. The big questions you have now are how many customers you will have and how much of a service fee to charge per delivery. You estimate that you will have 300 deliveries each month, and are thinking of setting a $2 per delivery fee, payable at the end of each month. The interest rate over the two-year period is expected to be 8% per year, compounded monthly, but may be 20% above or below this figure.

Using equivalent monthly worth, construct a sensitivity graph showing how sensitive the monthly worth of this project will be to the interest rate, advertising costs, and the number of deliveries you make each month. To which parameter is the equivalent monthly worth most sensitive?

10.6 Timmons Testing (TT) does subcontracting work for printed circuit board manufacturers. They perform a variety of specialized functional tests on the assembled circuit boards. TT is considering buying a new probing device which will assist the technicians in diagnosing functional defects in the printed circuit boards. Two vendors have given them quotes on first costs and expected operating costs over the life of their equipment.

	Vendor A	Vendor B
Expected life	7 years	10 years
First cost	$200 000	$350 000
Maintenance costs	$10 000/year + $0.05/unit	$20 000/year + $0.01/unit
Labour costs	$1.25/unit	$0.50/unit
Other costs	$6 500/year + $0.95/unit	$15 000/year + $0.55/unit
Salvage value	$5 000	$20 000

Production levels vary for TT. They may be as low as 20 000 boards per year or could be as high as 200 000 units per year if a contract currently under negotiation comes through. They expect, however, that production quantities will be about 50 000 boards. Timmons Testing uses a MARR of 15% for equipment projects, and will be using an annual worth comparison for the two devices.

Timmons Testing is aware that the equipment vendors have given them estimates only for costs. In particular, TT would like to know how sensitive the annual worth of each device is to the first cost, annual fixed costs (maintenance + other), variable costs (maintenance + labour + other), and the salvage value.

(a) Construct a sensitivity graph for Vendor A's device, showing the effects of 5% and 10% decreases and increases in the first cost, annual fixed costs, variable costs, and the salvage value. Assume an annual production level of 50 000 units.

(b) Construct a sensitivity graph for Vendor B's device, showing the effects of 5% and 10% decreases and increases in the first cost, annual fixed costs, variable costs, and the salvage value. Assume an annual production level of 50 000 units.

10.7 Manitoba Metalworks would like to implement a local area network (LAN) for file transfer, E-mail, and database access throughout its facility. Two feasible network topologies have been identified, which they have labelled Alternative A and Alternative B. The three main components of costs for the network are (1) initial hardware and installation costs, (2) initial software development costs, and (3) software and hardware maintenance costs. The installation and hardware costs for both systems are somewhat uncertain as prices for the components are changing and Manitoba Metalworks are not sure of the installation costs for the LAN hardware. The costs for each alternative are summarized below.

Benefits from the LAN are increased productivity because of faster file transfer times, reduced data redundancy, and improved data accuracy because of the database access. The benefits were difficult to quantify and are stated below as only a range of possible values and an average.

	Alternative A	Alternative B
Initial hardware and installation costs ($)		
Optimistic estimate	70 000	86 000
Average estimate	92 500	105 500
Pessimistic estimate	115 000	125 000
Initial software cost ($)	138 750	158 250
Annual maintenance costs ($)	9 250	10 550
Annual benefits ($)		
Optimistic estimate	80 000	94 000
Average estimate	65 000	74 000
Pessimistic estimate	50 000	54 000

Manitoba Metalworks uses a 15% MARR and has established a 10-year study period for this decision. They wish to compare the projects based on annual worth.

(a) Construct a sensitivity graph for Alternative A. For the base case, use the average values for the initial hardware cost and the annual benefits. Each graph should indicate the effect of a 5% and a 10% drop or increase in the initial hardware cost and the annual benefits. Which of the two factors most affects the annual worth of Alternative A?

(b) Construct a sensitivity graph for Alternative B. For the base case, use the average values for the initial hardware cost and the annual benefits. Each graph should indicate the effect of a 5% and a 10% drop or increase in the initial hardware cost and the annual benefits. Which of the two factors most affects the annual worth of Alternative B?

10.8 **(a)** Refer back to problem 10.5. Assuming base case figures for advertising costs and interest rates, what is the break-even number of deliveries per month? Construct a graph showing the break-even number.

(b) Assuming base case figures for advertising costs and number of deliveries per month, what is the break-even interest rate? Construct a graph illustrating the break-even interest rate.

10.9 Refer back to Problem 10.1. Members of the Go-Kart Club do not wish to wait for more than five years to build their clubhouse. They have decided to start a fund-raising campaign to increase their ability to save each year between $7000 and whatever is necessary to have $50 000 saved in five years. Construct a table and a graph which illustrate how the number of years they must wait depends on the amount they save each year. What additional funds per year will allow them to save $50,000 in five years? Use a 10% interest rate.

10.10 Refer back to Problem 10.7 in which Manitoba Metalworks is considering two LAN alternatives.

(a) For Alternative A, by how much will the installation cost have to rise before the annual worth becomes zero? In other words, what is the break-even installation cost? Is the break-even level within or above the range of likely values Manitoba Metalworks has specified?

(b) What is the break-even annual benefit for Alternative A? Use the average installation costs. Is the break-even level within or above the range of likely values Manitoba Metalworks has specified?

10.11 Repeat problem 10.10 for Alternative B.

10.12 (a) Refer back to Timmons Testing, problem 10.6. TT charges $3.25 per board tested. Assuming that costs are as in Vendor A's estimates, what production level per year will allow TT to break even if they select Vendor A's equipment? That is, for what production level will annual revenues equal annual costs? Construct a graph showing total revenues and total costs for various production levels, and indicate on it the break-even production level.

(b) Repeat (a) for Vendor B's equipment.

10.13 The Bountiful Bread Company produces home bread-making machines. Currently, they pay a custom moulder $0.19 per piece (not including material costs) for the clear plastic face on the control panel. Demand for the bread-makers is forecast to be 200 000 machines per year, but there is some uncertainty surrounding this estimate. Bountiful is considering installing a plastic moulding system to produce the parts themselves. The moulder costs $20 000 plus $7000 to install, and has an expected life of six years. Operating and maintenance costs are expected to be $30 000 in the first year and to rise at the rate of 5% per year. Bountiful estimates its capital costs using a declining-balance depreciation model with a rate of 40%, and uses a MARR of 15% for such investments.

Determine what the total equivalent annual cost of the new moulder is. What is the cost per unit, assuming that production is 200 000 units per year? Determine what the break-even production quantity is. That is, what is the production quantity below which it is better to continue to purchase parts and above which it is better to purchase the moulder and make the parts in-house?

10.14 Trenton Trucking is considering the purchase of a new $65 000 truck. The truck is expected to generate revenues between $12 000 and $22 000 each year, and will have a salvage value of $20 000 at the end of its five-year life. TT pays taxes at the rate of 35%. The CCA rate for trucks is 30%, and their after-tax MARR is 12%. Find the annual worth of the truck if the annual revenues are $12 000, and for each $1000 revenue increment up to $22 000. What is the break-even annual revenue? Provide a graph to illustrate the break-even annual revenue.

10.15 Antigonish Footwear can invest in one of two different automated clicker cutters. The first, A, has a $10 000 first cost. A similar one, B, with many extra features, has a first cost of $40 000. A will save $5000 per year over the cutter now in use. B will save between $12 000 and $15 000 per year. Each clicker cutter will last five years and have a zero scrap value.

(a) If the MARR is 10%, and B will save $15 000 per year, which alternative is better?

(b) B will save between $12 000 and $15 000 per year. Determine the IRR for the incremental investment from A to B for this range, in increments of $500. Plot savings of B versus the IRR of the incremental investment. Over what range of savings per year is your answer from part (a) valid? What is the break-even savings for alternative B such that, below this amount, A is preferred and above this amount B is preferred?

10.16 Sam is considering buying a new lawn mower. He has a choice between a "Lawn Guy" mower or a Bargain Joe's "Clip Job" mower. Sam has a MARR of 5%. The mowers' salvage values at the end of their respective service lives is zero. Sam has collected the following information about the two mowers:

	Lawn Guy	Clip Job
First cost	$350	$120
Life	10 years	4 years
Annual gas	$60	$40
Annual maintenance	$30	$60

Although Sam has estimated the maintenance costs of the Clip Job at $60, he has heard that the machines have had highly variable maintenance costs. One friend claimed that her Clip Job had maintenance costs comparable to those of the Lawn Guy, but another said the maintenance costs could be as high as $80 per year. Construct a table which shows the annual worth of the Clip Job for annual maintenance costs varying from $30 per year to $80 per year. What Clip Job maintenance costs would make Sam indifferent between the two mowers, based on annual worth? Construct a graph showing the break-even maintenance costs. What mower would you recommend to Sam?

10.17 Ganesh is considering buying a $24 000 car. After five years, he thinks he will be able to sell the car for $8000, but this is just an estimate that he is not certain about. He is confident that gas will cost $2000 per year, insurance $800 per year, and parking $600 per year, and that maintenance costs for the first year will be $1000, rising by $400 per year thereafter.

The alternative is for Ganesh to take taxis everywhere. This will cost an estimated $7000 per year. If he has no car, Ganesh will rent a car for the family vacation each year at a total (year-end) cost of $1000. Ganesh values money at 11% annual interest. If the salvage value of the car is $8000, should he buy the car? Base your answer on annual worth. Determine the annual worth of the car for a variety of salvage values so that you can help Ganesh decide whether this uncertainty will affect his decision. For what break-even salvage value will he be indifferent between taking taxis and buying a car? Construct a break-even graph showing the annual worth of both alternatives as a function of the salvage value of the car. What advice would you give Ganesh?

10.18 Ridgely Custom Metal Products (RCMP) must purchase a new tube bender. They are considering two alternatives which have the following characteristics:

	Model T	Model A
First cost	$100 000	$150 000
Economic life	5 years	5 years
Yearly savings	$50 000	$62 000
Salvage value	$20 000	$30 000

Construct a break-even graph showing the present worth of each alternative as a function of interest rates between 6% and 20%. Which is the preferred choice at 8% interest? Which is the preferred choice at 16% interest? What is the break-even interest rate?

10.19 Julia must choose between two different designs for a safety enclosure. Model A has a life of three years, has a first cost of $8000, and requires maintenance of $1000 per year. She believes that a salvage value can be estimated for Model A using a depreciation rate of between 30% and 40% and declining-balance depreciation. Model B will last four years, has a first cost of $10 000, and has maintenance costs of $700 per year. A salvage value for Model B can be estimated using straight-line depreciation and the knowledge that after one year the salvage value will be $7500. Interest is at 11%. Which of the two models would you suggest Julia choose? What break-even depreciation rate for Model A will make her indifferent between the two models? Construct a sensitivity graph showing the break-even depreciation rate.

10.20 Your neighbour, Kelly Strome, is trying to make a decision about his growing home-based copying business. He needs to acquire colour copiers able to handle maps and other large documents. He is looking at one set of copiers that will cost $15 000 to purchase. If he purchases the equipment, he will need to buy a maintenance contract that will cost $1000 for the first year, rising by $400 per year afterwards. He intends to keep the copiers for five years, and expects to salvage them for $2500. The CCA rate for office equipment is 20%.

Rather than buy the copiers, Kelly could lease them for $5500 per year with no maintenance fee. His business volume has varied over the past few years, and his tax rate has varied from a low of 20% to a high of 40%. Kelly's current cost of capital is 8%. Kelly has asked you for some help in deciding what to do. He wants to know whether he should lease or buy the copiers, and, moreover, he wants to know the impact of his tax rate on the decision. Evaluate both alternatives for him for a variety of tax rates between 20% and 40% so that you can advise him confidently. What do you advise?

10.21 Refer back to problem 10.7 in which Manitoba Metalworks is looking at several LAN alternatives. Conduct a scenario analysis for each alternative, using the pessimistic, expected (average), and optimistic outcomes for both installation costs and annual benefits. Which of the two alternatives would you choose? Why?

10.22 Refer back to problem 10.1 in which the Inuvik Go-Kart Club is trying to save $50 000 in order to build a clubhouse and track. They have established optimistic, expected, and pessimistic estimates for both the interest rate they will earn on their savings and the amount they will be able to save per year. Conduct a scenario analysis which shows the number of years required to save $50 000 for the three scenarios, using the data below.

Parameter	Pessimistic Scenario	Expected Scenario	Optimistic Scenario
Savings per year ($)	6000	7000	8000
Interest rate	8.00%	10.00%	12.00%
Number of years to save $50 000	6.64	5.66	4.94

10.23 Timmons Testing (refer back to problem 10.6) has established pessimistic, expected, and optimistic figures for the first cost and other costs of the two testing devices offered by Vendors A and B. They would like you to carry out a scenario analysis to determine which of the two alternatives to choose. They charge $3.25 per board tested. What recommendations would you give Timmons Testing?

	Alternative A		
Parameter	Pessimistic Scenario	Expected Scenario	Optimistic Scenario
First cost ($)	220 000	200 000	190 000
Annual fixed costs ($)	18 000	16 500	13 000
Annual variable costs ($ per board)	2.35	2.25	2.20
Salvage value ($)	2 000	5 000	7 000
Annual production volume (boards)	40 000	50 000	80 000

	Alternative B		
Parameter	Pessimistic Scenario	Expected Scenario	Optimistic Scenario
First cost ($)	365 000	350 000	320 000
Annual fixed costs ($)	45 000	35 500	25 000
Annual variable costs ($ per board)	1.100	1.060	1.010
Salvage value ($)	17 000	20 000	23 000
Annual production volume (boards)	40 000	50 000	80 000

10.24 The Bountiful Bread Company (problem 10.13) currently pays a custom moulder $0.19 per piece (not including material costs) for the clear plastic face on the control panel of bread-maker machines they manufacture. Demand for the bread-makers is estimated at 200 000 machines per year, but there is some uncertainty surrounding this estimate. Bountiful is considering installing a plastic moulding system to produce the parts themselves. Installation costs are $7000, and the moulder has an expected life of six years. Operating and maintenance costs are somewhat uncertain, but are expected to be $30 000 in the first year and to rise at the rate of 5% per year. Bountiful estimates its capital costs with a declining-balance depreciation model with a rate of 40%, and uses a MARR of 15% for such investments.

Parameter	Pessimistic Scenario	Expected Scenario	Optimistic Scenario
First cost ($)	25 000	20 000	18 000
Base annual operating and maintenance costs ($)	35 000	30 000	27 000
Production volume (units)	170 000	200 000	240 000

The project engineers have come up with pessimistic, expected, and optimistic figures for the first cost, operating and maintenance costs, and production levels. Determine the total equivalent annual cost of the new moulder for each scenario and then the cost per unit. What advice would you give to Bountiful regarding the purchase of the moulder?

APPENDIX 10A: Other Methods of Dealing with Uncertain Outcomes

When there is some uncertainty about the value of one or more parameters of a decision, be it the size and timing of a cash flow or some other aspect of an engineering decision, sensitivity analysis is an excellent means of assessing how sensitive a performance measure is to changes in the parameter values. However, sensitivity analysis is only part of a full treatment of this uncertainty. As was pointed out earlier in this chapter, sensitivity graphs, break-even analysis, and scenario analysis can provide information regarding the range of possible performance measure values. These methods do not, however, give any insights into how likely it is that a parameter will take on a specific value, or the likelihood that a particular scenario will occur. This section is intended to touch on two methods used to incorporate probability into the decision-making process. The first method is based on expected value and the second is referred to as Monte Carlo simulation.

If a decision maker is able to assess the probability that a parameter will take on each of its possible values or the probability that each particular scenario will occur, then an expected value of the performance measure can be calculated. In this way, the sensitivity analysis can be augmented by additional information about the outcomes.

EXAMPLE 10A.1

Management of Westmount Waxworks (refer to Example 10.5) has been able to assess, based on expert opinion, the probability of the pessimistic, expected, and optimistic scenarios. They think that the likelihood that sales will be 50 000 per year for the next few years is roughly 50%, and that the pessimistic and optimistic scenarios have likelihoods of 20% and 30%, respectively. Based on expected annual costs, which is the best choice?

The expected annual cost of the Finedetail wax melter is

EAC(Finedetail)

$$= Pr(pessimistic)(\$85\ 314) + Pr(expected)(\$112\ 314)$$
$$+ Pr(optimistic)(\$314\ 814)$$
$$= 0.2(\$85\ 314) + 0.5(\$112\ 314) + 0.3(\$314\ 814)$$
$$= \$167\ 664$$

The expected annual cost of the Simplicity wax melter is

EAC(Simplicity)

$$= Pr(pessimistic)(\$94\ 381) + Pr(expected)(\$103\ 501)$$
$$+ Pr(optimistic)(\$186\ 901)$$
$$= 0.2(\$94\ 381) + 0.5(\$103\ 501) + 0.3(\$186\ 901)$$
$$= \$126\ 697$$

The expected annual cost of the Simplicity model is lower than that of the Finedetail one. Hence, the Simplicity wax melter is preferred on the basis of expected annual costs.

Expected value computations can incorporate into decision making information as to how likely each of several scenarios is or the likelihood that a parameter will take on a particular value. Expected value is, by its nature, a single measure and does not capture the likelihood of the entire range of possible performance measure values.

Monte Carlo simulation, the second approach we will touch upon in this section, can be used to determine the probability distribution for various performance measures for a project. Thus, the probability that a project will have a positive present or annual worth can be determined. The method is best described through a simple example.

EXAMPLE 10A.2

While considering the cogeneration plant project outlined in Example 10.1, Cogenesis Corporation wishes to determine the probability distribution of the project's present worth so that the risk of having a negative present worth on the project can be better assessed. The three variables they wish to investigate are the initial investment, the savings in electricity costs, and the extra wood costs. Previously, management determined that the range of possible values for the initial costs was between $2 800 000 and $3 300 000, that the range for savings in electricity costs was $920 000 to $1 080 000 per year, and that the additional wood costs was $350 000 to $400 000 per year. To the best of their knowledge, management thinks that any outcome for first cost, electricity savings, and additional wood costs between the lower and upper bound is equally likely (that is to say, uniformly distributed).

By randomly sampling repeatedly from each of these distributions, we can construct a probability distribution of the present worth of the project. A portion of the Monte Carlo simulation results derived, assuming that all other parameters are fixed at their expected scenario values, is shown in Table 10A.1.

TABLE 10A.1: Partial Results for the Monte Carlo Simulation

Initial Cost	Electricity Savings	Additional Wood Costs	Present Worth
3 266 308	1 042 318	358 032	1 302 867
3 259 569	991 150	399 991	613 999
2 953 792	945 040	398 196	588 765
2 897 632	958 986	389 622	813 137
.	.	.	.
.	.	.	.

FIGURE 10A.1 Histogram of Present Worths for Cogenesis

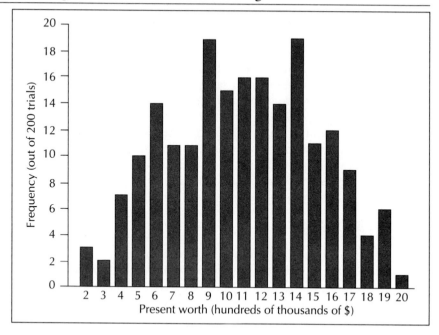

By sampling a total of 200 times, and for each sample computing a present worth, management arrived at the histogram shown in Figure 10A.1.

After analyzing 200 randomly chosen samples for initial cost, savings in electricity costs, and additional wood costs, the average present worth was calculated as $1 144 929 with a minimum of $271 004 and a maximum of $2 009 104. In the sample, there were no instances where the present worth turned out to be zero or less. The risk of this project's yielding a negative present worth appears to be negligible (of course, assuming that the probability distributions for the input parameters have been specified correctly).

The benefit of Monte Carlo simulation is that it allows an analyst to determine the range of possible performance measure values for a project as well as the likelihood that each will occur. The drawback of the method is that the probability distributions of each of the input parameters must be specified. This may be a difficult task. However, in conjunction with sensitivity analysis methods, Monte Carlo simulation is a powerful tool in assessing project viability and the economic risks of investment.

■ Review Problem 10A.1

Burnaby Insurance (see Review Problems 10.1 to 10.3) has consulted several energy experts in order to further understand the implications of electricity and natural gas price changes on their two energy efficiency projects. They have estimated that the cost of electricity has a uniform probability distribution with a minimum of $0.63 per kWh and a maximum of $0.077 per kWh. Similarly, the price of natural gas has a uniform probability distribution with a minimum of $3.35 and a maximum of $3.65 per

1000 cubic feet. Carry out a Monte Carlo simulation to determine the probability distribution of the present worth of the two energy efficiency projects.

Answer

To conduct the Monte Carlo simulation, 300 samples were drawn from the electricity cost and natural gas cost distributions. The present worth of each project was then computed for each of the 300 simulated outcomes, and a histogram of the results was constructed. Figure 10A.2 is a histogram for the present worth of the high efficiency motor, and Figure 10A.3 is a histogram for the present worth of the heat exchange unit.

FIGURE 10A.2 Monte Carlo Simulation Results for the High Efficiency Motor

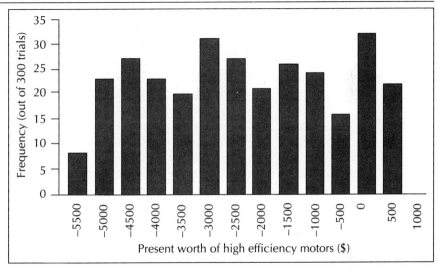

FIGURE 10A.3 Monte Carlo Simulation Results for the Heat Exchange Unit

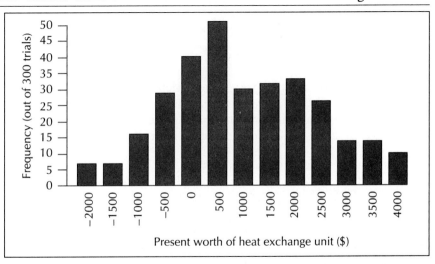

It is clear from the simulations that the high efficiency motor has only a small chance of having a positive present worth and hence is not a good investment. The heat exchange unit, on the other hand, has only a small chance of having a negative present worth, and hence looks like a better choice for Burnaby Insurance.

PROBLEMS

10A.1 An oil company owns a tract of land that has good potential for containing oil. The size of the oil deposit is unknown, but, from previous experience with land of similar characteristics, the geological engineers predict that an oil well drilled on this land will yield an annual number of barrels which is uniformly distributed between 0 barrels (a dry well) and 100 000 barrels per year, over a five-year period. The cost of drilling a well is $100 000, and the profit per barrel (after deducting production costs) is $1.50 per barrel. Interest is at 10% per year. Carry out a Monte Carlo simulation of 100 wells. Construct a histogram of the present worth of drilling a well. Comment on your observations. Do you recommend drilling?

10A.2 A fabric manufacturer has been asked to extend a line of credit to a new customer, a dress manufacturer. The mill has, in the past, extended credit to customers, and, although most pay back the debt, some have defaulted on the payments and the fabric manufacturer has lost money. Previous experience with similar new customers indicates that 20% of customers are bad risks, 50% are average risks, and 30% are good risks.

	Bad Risk	Average Risk	Good Risk
Minimum annual profit ($)	−50 000	10 000	20 000
Maximum annual profit ($)	15 000	30 000	50 000
Average length of business affiliation (years)	2	5	10
Probability	0.2	0.5	0.3

Construct a spreadsheet which has the headings used in the table on page 393. Generate 100 random customers. From those 100, construct a frequency distribution for the present worth of extending a line of credit to a random customer. Use an interest rate of 10% per year.

Sample	Risk Random Number	Risk Rating	Profit Random Number	Annual Profit ($)	Number of Years	Present Worth ($)
1	0.003	1	0.837	4 423	2	7 677
2	0.458	2	0.170	13 407	5	50 824
3	0.417	2	0.306	16 128	5	61 138
4	0.032	1	0.361	−26 559	2	−46 095
5	0.743	3	0.914	47 430	10	291 437
6	.	.	.	.	.	.
.	.	.	.	.	.	.
.	.	.	.	.	.	.

Public Sector Decision Making

Engineering Economics in Action, Part 11A: Trouble in Lotus Land

11.1 Introduction

11.2 Market Failure

    11.2.1 Market Failure Defined

    11.2.2 Remedies for Market Failure

11.3 Decision Making in the Public Sector

    11.3.1 Measuring the Costs and Benefits of Government Services

    11.3.2 Benefit-Cost Ratios

    11.3.3 The MARR in the Public Sector

Canadian Corporate Case 11.1: Wood Pulp Mill Effluent Treatment in Alberta

Review Problems

Summary

Engineering Economics in Action, Part 11B: Look at It from Their Side

Problems

Engineering Economics in Action, Part 11A: Trouble in Lotus Land

"*H*i, *Naomi. How's it going in Lotus Land?*" *Naomi could easily imagine Bill's feet up on his desk, leaning back in his chair, telephone wedged against his ear. Naomi was in Vancouver, checking out how British Columbia's regulations on absorbable organic halides (AOX) in effluent will affect the Edgemont Pulp Mill, a sister company of Canadian Widgets.*

Naomi answered. "Lotus Land is great. I can look out my window and see green grass and rhododendrons with new buds. Not bad for late February. But the situation at the Edgemont Pulp Mill is not so bright. Basically, what I found is that the regulations are really tough. It's not clear that Edgemont can meet them and still be competitive in the bleached pulp export market."

"What's going on?" Bill asked. "We've spent over 40 million in the last few years making sure that mill is up-to-date. You're not telling me that all that's going down the drain, are you?"

"Well," Naomi began, "by the end of 2002 pulp mills must have AOX down to zero. That's the tough part. They will have to go to ozone and hydrogen peroxide bleaching rather than the chlorine bleaching method they use now. You can get the AOX level very low, say a half kilogram per ton, by improving conventional chlorine bleaching. But you can't get it to zero without going to ozone and hydrogen peroxide. The cost of converting will be very high for Edgemont. Worse still, most of their competitors in other countries will not have such stringent regulations. Only Sweden is moving as fast as B.C. Of course, that could change because of pressure from environmental groups. But I don't think we should hold our collective breaths."

"Can we get the government to soften up on the regulations?" asked Bill.

"Maybe if we did a broadly focussed benefit-cost analysis. Can we do that?" asked Naomi.

"I'm not sure," Bill responded. "Let's explore the idea. Talk to the people at the mill today. I'll try to get some ideas from the people here. See if you can get a flight back to town for this afternoon. I'll try to set up a meeting for us with Anna Kulkowski in the next couple of days. I suspect she won't want to quit on the Edgemont mill just yet."

11.1 Introduction

All companies, and the engineers who work for them, must take into account the effects of what they do on society as a whole. Consider these two examples.

1. MacMillan Bloedel (MB) is a British Columbia-based forest products company. In the spring of 1995, MB was faced with a campaign that included boycotts of their customers, demonstrations, and even a bomb threat against MB's headquarters. The

campaign was a protest against MB's timber cutting practices in the Clayoquot area of Vancouver Island. The protesters were concerned about the impact of MB's clear-cutting on the ecological balance in Clayoquot. The object of the boycott was to pressure MB into changing its cutting practices. By the spring of 1995, the boycott had already cost MB a $5 million contract to supply a British subsidiary of the Scott Paper Company, and other customers were being pressured to stop buying from MB. In May 1995, MB announced, in hopes of reducing this pressure, that it would adhere to the recommendations of a panel set up by the British Columbia government.

2. In August 1982, the Manville Corporation had over 25 000 employees in the United States and Canada. It had over $2 billion in assets and stood 181st on the Fortune 500 list. Nevertheless, on August 26, 1982, the Manville Corporation filed for reorganization under the United States Bankruptcy Code. They did this to enable the company to continue operating in the face of claims that far exceeded the value of their assets. Manville was the defendant in over 16 000 lawsuits related to the health effects of asbestos, and they expected over 50 000 more lawsuits. Most of these suits came from men, or families of men, who had worked as installers of asbestos insulation made by Manville. These men had contracted asbestosis and other lung diseases as a result of long-term exposure to asbestos dust.

The MB and Manville examples illustrate a recent phenomenon that has important implications for engineers. It is not enough to produce goods and services at a cost that customers are willing to pay. Engineers must also pay attention to broader social values. This is because the market prices that guide most production decisions may not reflect all the social benefits and costs of engineering decisions adequately. Where markets fail to reflect all social benefits and costs, society uses other means of attaining social values.

In this chapter, we shall look at the social aspects of engineering decision making. First, we shall consider the reasons markets may fail in such areas as the environment and health. We shall also consider different methods that society may use to correct these failures. Second, we shall consider decision making in the public sector. Here we shall be concerned mainly with government projects or government supported projects.

11.2 Market Failure

The prices that guide most production decisions may not reflect all the social benefits and costs of engineering decisions adequately. In these situations, we say that there has been a market failure.

Somehow, society will find a means of correcting for the failure, be it litigation or boycotts, as seen in the two examples above, or some other remedy. In this section, we define market failure and give examples of the effects of market failure. Then we discuss a number of ways in which society seeks remedies for market failure.

11.2.1 Market Failure Defined

Most decisions that lead to behaviour in markets have desirable outcomes. This is because these decisions affect mainly those people who are party to those decisions. Since people can generally freely choose to participate in markets, it is reasonable to assume that the individuals who participate must somehow benefit by their actions. In most cases, this is the end of the story.

In some cases, however, decisions have important effects on others who are not party to the decisions. In these cases, it is possible that the gains to the decision makers, and any others who might benefit from the decisions, are less than the losses imposed on outsiders. Such situations are clearly undesirable. These decisions are instances of market failure. **Market failure** occurs where decisions are made in which aggregate benefits to all persons who benefit from the decision are less than aggregate costs imposed on persons who incur costs which result from the decision. Market failure can occur if the decision maker does not correctly take into account the gains and losses imposed on others by the consequences of a decision.

There are several reasons for market failure. First, there may be no market through which those affected by the decision can induce the decision maker to take into account their situations. Or losses may exceed gains, even where there is a market, if the market gives the wrong signals about the gains and losses resulting from decisions. Market failure can even occur where someone decides *not* to do something that would create benefits to others. The market would fail if the cost of creating the benefits were less than the value of the benefits.

Acid rain is an example of the effects of market failure. The burning of high-sulphur coal by thermal electric power plants is believed to be one of the causes of acid rain. These plants can burn low-sulphur fuels, but they do not use low-sulphur fuels partly because low-sulphur fuels are more expensive than high-sulphur fuels. If there were a market through which those affected by acid rain could buy a reduction in power plant sulphur emissions, they could try to make a deal with the power plants. They would be able to offer the power plants enough to offset the higher costs of low-sulphur fuel and still come out ahead. But there is no such market. The reason for this is that there is no single private individual or group whose loss from acid rain is large enough to make it worthwhile to offer the power plants payment to reduce sulphur emissions. It would require a large number of those affected by acid rain to form a coalition to make the offer. There are markets for electric power and for coal. However, they do not lead to socially desirable decisions about the use of power or coal. This is because the market prices for power and coal do not reflect the costs related to acid rain. If the prices for power and high-sulphur coal reflected these costs, less power would be used, and less of it would be made with high-sulphur coal. Both would reduce acid rain.

The health damage to Manville's asbestos-insulation workers is another example of the effects of market failure. There was market failure in this case in that the health costs to the installers probably far outweighed all the benefits of asbestos insulation to all parties. The problem was not that the work was dangerous. There are jobs that are inherently dangerous, but whose objectively estimated expected benefits are greater than their expected costs. The market failed in this case because the installers of asbestos insulation whose health was damaged did not have the information necessary to evaluate the risks of this type of work. The insulation producers did not actually have the relevant information either. They could have obtained the information at moderate cost. The main gap in knowledge was the actual level of exposure of installers to asbestos dust under various conditions. The companies made no effort to get the information. Had they done so, they would have found that installers' exposure exceeded industry standards. If the insulation producers had warned the workers of the dangers involved, the market would not have failed. The workers probably would not have agreed to work as installers without higher pay and better protection against exposure to dust. In this case, if the companies provided higher wages and better protection against dust, and if the workers agreed to work, we can assume that objectively estimated expected benefits of the deal would have been greater than expected costs for both sides.

We can see how market failure has caused socially undesirable outcomes such as acid rain and health problems for asbestos workers. When markets fail, as in cases such as these, society will seek to remedy these problems through a variety of mechanisms. These remedies are the subject of the next section.

11.2.2 Remedies for Market Failure

There are four main formal methods of eliminating or reducing the impact of market failure. They are:

1. Economic regulation by government
2. Monetary incentives or monetary deterrents
3. Permitting persons or companies who are adversely affected by the actions of others to seek compensation in courts
4. Government provision of goods and services

We shall discuss the first three methods in this section. Government provision of goods and services is discussed in the next section under decision making in the public sector.

The first and most common means of trying to deter or reduce the effects of market failure is *economic regulation*. **Economic regulation** is the imposition of rules by government that are intended to modify behaviour. The rules are backed by the use of penalties for failure to obey the rules. We have regulations concerning such widely differing areas as product labelling, automobile emissions, and the use of bodies of water to dispose of waste.

One efficient form of economic regulation is *monetary incentives or deterrents*. This is particularly true where the market failure leads to excessive dumping of undesirable products into the environment. Monetary incentives can be in terms of subsidies or special tax treatment. Deterrents could be in terms of charges. For example, there could be subsidies for the installation of equipment that would reduce dumping, or there could be charges for dumping noxious materials. As another example, suppose that we wish to improve the quality of a lake. One step in doing that may be to have regulations related to the biological oxygen demand (BOD) of effluents from industrial and municipal sources on the lake. Any uniform regulation will, however, impose different costs on different sources. To attain any given reduction in BOD in their effluent, some sources will have to make expensive changes to their procedures, while others can respond at low cost. The most efficient way to obtain a given reduction in BOD in the lake is to have those for whom the cost of cleaning effluent is low do most of the cleaning. One way to do this would be to set a fee for BOD levels. Those sources that can reduce their BOD cheaply will do so, since for them this will be cheaper than paying the fees. Those for whom the cost of reducing dumping is greater than the fees will continue to dump. By setting the appropriate fee, the desired reduction can be attained.

A third means of reducing the effects of market failure is *litigation*. The use of courts as a means of reducing the health and safety effects of market failure has grown in both Canada and the United States. Since the 1970s in Canada (the exact year depending on the province), courts have held that regular sellers of a product implicitly guarantee that the product is fit for reasonable use. Where the cost of reducing a risk in the use of their product is less than the objectively estimated expected loss, sellers are supposed to reduce the risk. Moreover, these sellers are held legally responsible for having expertise in the production and use of the products. It is not enough for sellers to say they did not know that use of the product was risky. Sellers are supposed to make reasonable efforts to determine potential risks in the use of products they sell. This is the basis of Manville's loss in the suits against them.

The fourth formal method of reducing the effects of market failure is *government provision of goods and services*. Market failure is remedied when public sector analysts take into account all parties affected by a decision through a comprehensive assessment of total costs and benefits of a decision. Health care provision, transportation, municipal services, and electric and gas utilities are some examples of goods and services provided by the public sector — all of which require numerous economic decisions to be made in the best interests of the public. Public sector decision making is of sufficient importance for us to devote a separate section to the topic.

Before we leave the topic of methods of reducing the impact of market failure and turn to public sector decision making, note that, in addition to formal methods, *informal methods* of control like boycotts are also used. They may have been effective in changing MB's behaviour, as mentioned in the introduction to this chapter. The story of MB appears to have been heard elsewhere in the forest products industry. *The Globe and Mail* for June 2, 1995, carried an advertisement for a "Forest Ecology Co-ordinator" by Weyerhauser Canada, a large forest products company. The person hired would be expected to "support the integration of non-fibre (i.e., non-wood) forest values into company business plans." The person would also manage "contract specialists in soils, wildlife, hydrology, and ecology." Such advertisements point out the increasing importance being placed on avoiding market failure.

11.3 Decision Making in the Public Sector

This section is devoted to the decision-making process in the public sector. Public (or government) production in Canada has occurred mainly in two classes of goods and services. The first class includes those services for which there is no market because it is not practical to require people to pay for the service. Police and fire protection, defence, and the maintenance of city streets are examples of government services where it is not practical for users to pay for use.

The second class includes those services for which scale economies make it inefficient to have more than one provider. Where there is only a single provider of a service, there is no market competition to enforce efficiency and low prices. There is a danger that the single provider, called a monopolist, will charge excessive prices and/or be inefficient. To ameliorate this potential problem, governments often are the provider. It is also possible for the government to monitor and regulate the performance of a private monopolist.

For example, local telephone service is a case where scale economies are important enough that having more than one provider is not efficient. Local telephone service is provided by both government-owned and privately-owned government-regulated monopolies. In all three Prairie Provinces, there is government-owned telephone service. In the other provinces, there are private companies.

In this section, we shall consider three major issues concerning engineering projects where there is government provision of services. These issues are

(1) the valuation of costs and benefits where government provides services,

(2) the use of benefit-cost ratios to evaluate government projects, and

(3) the choice of the MARR for government projects.

We will examine these issues in the next three sections.

11.3.1 Measuring the Costs and Benefits of Government Services

The most important and frequently the most difficult part of evaluating government projects is measuring costs and benefits in the government sector. There are two reasons measuring costs and benefits of government services may be difficult. First, it may be difficult to identify all the costs and benefits. Second, actual measurement of the costs and benefits that have been identified is frequently difficult.

Identifying all the costs and benefits associated with a project may be difficult because some of the costs and benefits of public projects may not be reflected in the monetary flows of the project. We are concerned with the real effects of a project, but the cash flows may or may not reflect all these real effects. For example, in building a road, there are cash flows for the wages of the workers who construct the road. This is a real cost, and the wages reflect these costs well. In contrast, consider the cost of disruption of traffic during road construction. These costs are not reflected in the cash flows of a project, but are, nonetheless, an important cost of putting the road in place.

There may be cash flows associated with a project that reflect neither costs nor benefits. Suppose that a toll were charged to users of a new road. The cash flows that come from the toll are neither a cost nor a benefit. There is a revenue from the tolls that goes to the government. This can be counted as a benefit to taxpayers, but there is an exactly off-setting cost to those who pay the tolls. From a social point of view, the tolls represent neither a gain nor a loss.

The second reason that measuring costs and benefits may be difficult is that there may be no prices to reflect their values. With goods and services that are distributed through markets, we have prices to measure values. If someone is willing to pay $500 for a suit, we can assume that the suit is worth at least $500 to that person. We may not be able to make similar inferences about publicly produced services because they are not sold to users.

Consider the following three examples of the difficulty of identifying and measuring costs and benefits of government services.

EXAMPLE 11.1

A major improvement in a highway near an urban area, like Highway 401 which goes through Toronto, is being considered. What are the costs and benefits? How are they measured?

Obvious costs are the labour, materials, and equipment used for the project. But one major cost is not explicitly measured. This is the cost of traffic disruption during the work. Measuring this cost requires an evaluation of the time delays incurred by car passengers and trucks. There are approximations to these delay costs based on earnings per hour of passengers and the hourly cost of running trucks. The approximation for the value of travellers' time is based on the idea that a person who can earn, for example, $35 an hour working should be willing to pay $35 an hour for time saved travelling to work. The disruption costs may be large enough that they make it more efficient to have the work done at night, despite the fact that this will raise the explicit construction cost.

There is a long list of benefits from a highway improvement. These include reduced travel time, lower vehicle costs, and improved safety. The value of reduced travel time can be determined by the earnings of travellers. Lower vehicle costs are based on crude approximations to the average cost under different road conditions. The value of improved safety may be difficult to estimate and is often qualitatively valued as an extra benefit in such projects.

EXAMPLE 11.2

What are the costs and benefits of a university education? There are obvious costs for such items as salaries and materials. The major benefit is the increased productivity of students. Are there other costs and benefits? How are costs and benefits measured?

A major cost that is not explicitly measured is the value of students' time. This is usually measured by foregone earnings. That is, study is viewed as a form of work. This work could have earned a certain amount that is foregone when the time is spent at university. When student time is measured by foregone earnings, it accounts for over half of the costs of university education in Canada. Measuring foregone earnings requires estimating what the students could have earned during the time they were in university had they not gone to university.

Increased productivity of university graduates is difficult to measure. The measurement is based on the idea that students would have worked with or without education. If they have a university education, their productivity is, presumably, greater and this will result in greater output, which, in turn, will yield higher incomes for students and their employers. The actual measurement of increased productivity is usually based on the assumption that students capture the entire benefit of increased productivity in higher incomes. Benefit measurement then consists of estimating what students could have earned over their whole lifetimes without the education versus what they are expected to earn over their lifetimes with a university education. The benefit stream is then estimated as the difference between these two earnings streams.

Another benefit of publicly supported university education is the social benefit of having a society in which there are opportunities for self advancement for large parts of the population. It is not possible to put a reasonable monetary value on this benefit, but it may be the main justification for subsidizing university education in Canada. There is no obvious reason for public subsidy to increase the productivity of students. The students, and the companies for which they will work, should be willing to pay for the increased productivity.

EXAMPLE 11.3

Consider the construction of a bridge across a narrow part of a lake that gives access to a provincial park. The major benefit of the bridge will be reduced travel time to get to the park from a nearby urban centre. This will lower the cost of camping trips at the park. As well, more people are expected to use the park because of the lower cost per visit. How can these benefits be measured?

Data concerning the number of week-long visits and their costs are shown in Table 11.1.

TABLE 11.1: Average Cost per Visit and Number of Visits per Year

	Without Bridge	With Bridge
Travel cost per visit ($)	140.00	87.50
Use of equipment ($)	50.00	50.00
Food cost per visit ($)	100.00	100.00
Total cost per visit ($)	290.00	237.50
Number of visits/year	8000	11 000

First, the reduction in cost for the 8000 visits that would have been made even without the bridge creates a straightforward benefit:

Travel cost saving on 8000 visits = ($140 − $87.50)8000 = $420 000

There is a benefit of $420 000 per year from reduced travel cost on the 8000 visits that would have been taken even without the bridge.

Next, we see that the number of visits to the park is expected to rise from 8000 per year to 11 000 per year. But how much is this worth? We do not have prices for park visits, but we do have data that enable estimates of actual costs to campers. These costs may be used to infer the value of visits to campers.

We see that before the bridge the cost of a week-long park visit, including travel and other costs, averaged $290. It is reasonable to assume that a week spent camping was worth at least $290 to anyone who incurred that cost. The average cost of a week-long visit to a park has fallen from $290 per visit to $237.50 per visit. We are concerned with the value of the incremental 3000 visits per year. Clearly, none of these visits would be made if the cost were $290 per trip. And each of them is worth at least $237.50 or else the trip would not have been taken. The standard approximation in cases like this is halfway between the highest and lowest possible values. This gives an aggregate benefit of the increased use of the park of

$$\frac{(\$290.00 + \$237.50)}{2} (3000) = \$791\ 250$$

Therefore, the value of the incremental 3000 visits per year is estimated as approximately $791 000 per year. However, there is also a cost of $237.50 per visit. The net benefit of the incremental 3000 visits is therefore

$$\$791\ 250 - \$237.5(3000) = \$78\ 750$$

The total value of benefits of the bridge is the sum of the reduced travel cost plus increased use:

$$\$420\ 000 + \$78\ 750 = \$498\ 750$$

The total value of the benefits yielded by the bridge is almost $500 000 per year. These benefits are the shaded area shown in Figure 11.1. These benefits need to be weighed against the costs of the bridge.

FIGURE 11.1   Benefits from Bridge

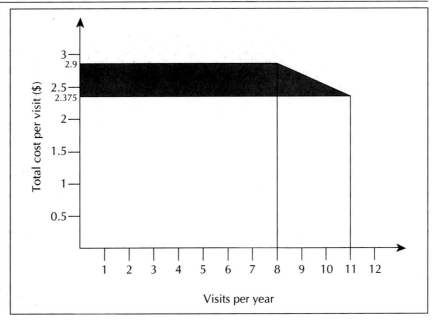

11.3.2 Benefit-Cost Ratios

The same comparison methods that are used for private sector projects are appropriate for government sector projects. That is, we can use the present worth, annual worth, and internal rate of return performance measures in the same ways in both the private and government sectors. It is important to emphasize this, because other methods based on ratios of benefits to costs have been used frequently in government project evaluations, almost to the exclusion of present worth, annual worth, and internal rate of return methods. Because of the prevalent use of these ratios, this section is devoted to a discussion of several benefit-cost ratios that are commonly used in public sector decision making. We then point out several problems associated with the use of benefit-cost ratios so that the reader is aware of them and understands the correct and incorrect ways of using them.

Benefit-cost ratios can be based on either the present worths or the annual worths of benefits and costs of projects. The resulting ratios are equivalent in that they lead to the same decisions. We shall discuss the ratios in terms of present worths, but the reader should be aware that everything we say about ratios based on present worths applies to ratios based on annual worths.

The conventional **benefit-cost ratio**, denoted BCR, is given by the ratio of the present worth of benefits to the present worth of costs for a project, that is,

$$BCR = \frac{PW(\text{benefits})}{PW(\text{costs})}$$

A **modified benefit-cost ratio**, also in common use, denoted BCRM, is given by the ratio of the present worth of benefits minus the present worth of operating costs to the present worth of capital costs, that is,

$$BCRM = \frac{PW(\text{benefits}) - PW(\text{operating costs})}{PW(\text{capital costs})}$$

In general, a project is considered desirable if its benefit-cost ratio exceeds one, which is to say, its benefits exceed its costs. If we hope to go a step further and compare two projects with the use of benefit-cost ratios, the comparison becomes tricky because the ratios are not unique. This is a significant problem with the use of benefit-cost ratios. Benefit-cost ratios (either conventional or modified) are not unique because it is not clear whether certain positive effects of projects are benefits or reductions in cost, or whether certain negative effects are reductions in benefits or increases in costs. For this reason the Treasury Board of Canada's *Benefit-Cost Analysis Guide*, which was written for internal federal government use, recommends that benefit-cost ratios not be used for project comparisons. Despite this recommendation, benefit-cost ratios are still used for many public projects. Since they are still in use, we present readers with enough material in this section so that they may understand the problems associated with the use of benefit-cost ratios and so that they may properly construct and interpret such a ratio.

To illustrate the ambiguity associated with the use of a benefit-cost ratio, consider this example adapted from the Treasury Board's *Guide*. The example is concerned with a *negative effect* of a project that may be classified as a reduction in benefit or increase in cost.

EXAMPLE 11.4

We want to evaluate a project to construct a small local airport with a benefit-cost ratio. One of the effects of the airport is to create noise which will lower the value of nearby residential property by $500 000. Otherwise, the present worths of benefits and costs are $2 000 000 and $500 000, respectively. What is the benefit-cost ratio?

The answer depends on how the $500 000 in reduced property values is treated. If we consider this to be a *reduction in benefits*, the benefit-cost ratio is

$$BCR_1 = \frac{\$2\ 000\ 000 - \$500\ 000}{\$500\ 000} = 3$$

On the other hand, if we consider the $500 000 in reduced property values to be a *cost*, the benefit-cost ratio is

$$BCR_2 = \frac{\$2\ 000\ 000}{(\$500\ 000 + \$500\ 000)} = 2$$

We see from this example that some ambiguity arises in the use of benefit-cost ratios when a negative effect exists. The ambiguity can give rise to different values for the benefit-cost ratios, depending on how the negative effect is classified.

A similar problem arises with the classification of *positive effects* of a project. Example 11.5 concerns a positive effect that may be classified as a benefit or a reduction in capital cost.

EXAMPLE 11.5

A department of a provincial government is considering the installation of four new microcomputers for their statistical analysts. They have decided to get computers with model 486 microprocessors rather than Pentium microprocessors. They will offset the use of the slower computers (the 486s) by switching to a higher-speed operating system. A side benefit of changing to the new operating system is that it will be installed on three other existing computers that are used for statistical analysis in the department. This will make possible a delay in replacing the three other computers. Not counting the effect of installing the new operating system on the delay in replacing the three other computers, the present worths of benefits and costs are

PW(benefits) = $25 000

PW(operating costs) = $2500

PW(capital cost) = $9000

The present worth of the delay in replacing the three other computers is $1500. What is the modified benefit-cost ratio?

The answer depends on how the delay in replacing the three other computers is treated. If this is seen as a benefit, we get a modified benefit-cost ratio of 2.67.

$$BCRM_1 = \frac{(\$25\ 000 + \$1500 - \$2500)}{\$9000} = 2.67$$

If the effect on the three other computers is treated as a reduction in capital cost, we get a benefit-cost ratio of 3.

$$BCRM_2 = \frac{\$25\ 000 - \$2500}{\$9000 - \$1500} = 3.00$$

This lack of uniqueness of benefit-cost ratios means that *a comparison of the benefit-cost ratios of two projects is meaningless*. That is, if we compare the benefit-cost ratios of two projects, A and B, we may find that project A has a higher benefit-cost ratio. However, there may be another way of classifying some of the negative effects of the two projects as costs or reductions in benefits. As well, there may be another way of classifying the positive effects as benefits or as reductions in costs. The different classifications can give project B a higher benefit-cost ratio.

The lack of uniqueness of benefit-cost ratios does not mean that the ratios cannot be used. It is possible to state comparison methods based on benefit-cost ratios that remain valid even though the benefit-cost ratios are not unique. The reason is that the comparison methods depend only on whether the benefit-cost ratio is less than or greater than one. Whether the benefit-cost ratio is greater than one or less than one does not depend upon how positive and negative effects are classified. This may be seen in the following example.

A certain project has present worth of benefits, B, and present worth of costs, C. As well, there is a positive effect with a present worth of d; the analyst is unsure of whether this positive effect is a benefit or a reduction in cost. There are two possible benefit-cost ratios,

$$BCR_1 = \frac{B + d}{C}$$

and

$$BCR_2 = \frac{B}{C - d}$$

For a ratio to exceed one, the numerator must be greater than the denominator. This means that, for BCR_1,

$$BCR_1 = \frac{B + d}{C} > 1 \Leftrightarrow B + d > C \Leftrightarrow B > C - d$$

But this is the same as

$$\frac{B}{C - d} = BCR_2 > 1$$

Consequently, any BCR that is greater than one or less than one will be so regardless of whether any positive effects are treated as positive benefits or as negative costs. A similar analysis would show that the choice of classification of a negative effect as a cost or as a reduction in benefits does not affect whether the benefit-cost ratio is greater or less than one.

Notice also that if the conventional benefit-cost ratio is greater than one, it follows that the modified benefit-cost ratio will be greater than one. And if the conventional benefit-cost ratio is less than one, the modified benefit-cost ratio will also be less than one. This means that the conventional benefit-cost ratio and the modified benefit-cost ratio will lead to the same decision. We present both because the reader may encounter either ratio.

For *independent* projects the following decision rule may be used: *Accept all projects with a benefit-cost ratio greater than one.* In other words, accept a project if

$$BCR = \frac{PW(\text{benefits})}{PW(\text{costs})} > 1, \text{ or}$$

$$BCRM = \frac{PW(\text{benefits}) - PW(\text{operating costs})}{PW(\text{capital costs})} > 1$$

This rule, using either the benefit-cost ratio or the modified benefit-cost ratio, is equivalent to the rule that all projects with a present worth of benefits greater than the present worth of costs should be accepted. A present worth of benefits greater than the present worth of costs is the same as having a positive present worth for the project itself. This is then the same rule that used present worth for evaluating investments that was presented in Chapter 4.

$$\text{BCR(alternative A)} = \frac{\$337.95}{(\$150 + \$50 + \$92.169)} = 1.156$$

and the BCR of alternative A counting the increased travel time as a benefit reduction is

$$\text{BCR(alternative A)} = \frac{(\$337.95 - \$92.169)}{(\$150 + \$50)} = 1.228$$

First, in Table 11.3, note that all benefit-cost ratios exceed one. Both alternatives are viable. We must, therefore, choose between the two alternatives. If we try to choose by ranking the alternatives by benefit-cost ratios, we are unable to choose. If we count the two effects as costs, the current airport has a slightly higher benefit-cost ratio. If we count the effects as reductions in benefits, the new airport has a slightly higher benefit-cost ratio. Neither of these comparisons tells us anything.

To decide which alternative is better, we must compute the benefit-cost ratio of the difference between the alternatives.

$$\text{BCR(difference)} = \frac{B_A - B_B}{C_A - C_B}$$

$$= \frac{\$337.95 - \$175.10}{(\$92.17 + \$50 + \$150) - (\$10 + \$115 + \$25)} = 1.145$$

The ratio of the benefits of the new airport minus the benefits of the current airport modification over the difference in their costs is greater than one. We interpret this to mean that the benefit-cost ratio ranks the new airport ahead of the current airport.

We also note that the same ranking would result if we were to compare the present worths of the two alternatives. The present worth of the new airport is $45.78 = $337.95 - $92.17 - $150 - $50 (in millions of $). The present worth of modifying the current airport is $25.10 = $175.10 - $10 - $115 - $25 (in millions of $).

In addition to the quantifiable aspects of each of the two airports, recall that the new airport is preferred in terms of the unmeasured value of room for further growth. Together with the benefit-cost ratios (or, equivalently, the present worths), this means that the city should build the new airport.

In summary of this section, we can say several things about the evaluation of public sector projects. First, the comparison methods developed in Chapters 4 and 5 are fully applicable to public sector projects. Second, the reader may encounter the use of benefit-cost ratios for public projects, despite the fact that benefit-cost ratios can be ambiguous. Next, the reader should be wary of decisions based on the relative sizes of benefit-cost ratios, as these ratios may be changed by reclassification of some of the positive effects of projects as benefits or as reductions in cost, or by reclassification of some of the negative effects as reductions in benefits or increases in costs. However, since the classifications do not affect whether a ratio is greater or less than one, it is possible to use benefit-cost ratios to give the same results that would come from use of the methods of Chapter 4.

11.3.3 The MARR in the Public Sector

The correct MARR for government projects, as in the private sector, is the opportunity cost of the funds that are used in the project. Implementing this idea in the public sector is difficult, because the opportunity cost of funds used in the public sector is not easy to determine. We assume that, if funds were not to be used in a particular public sector project, the funds would not be collected by the government and used elsewhere in the public sector. They would remain in and be invested by the private sector. Assuming that the funds would not be used elsewhere in the public sector implies that the government can always raise more funds if required and that there is no constraint on government spending. If there were a constraint on the availability of funds for the government, there might be a use of the funds by the government that would have a higher value than the funds would have in the private sector.

What, then, is the opportunity cost of funds used for a government project? It will be the return that the funds could earn if invested by the private sector. However, the return that funds could earn in the private sector is ambiguous. For example, assume that the income tax rate is 40%, and investing in shirt-making equipment provides a before-tax return of 20%. The after-tax return to investors is only 12%. Consequently, investors are willing to invest for a return of 12% rather than consume. The actual return on the investment, however, is 20%. Which, then, is the correct measure of return on funds in the private sector? Should the government invest under the same conditions as private sector investors do, in this example at 12%, or to achieve the same return on investment that private sector projects achieve, in this example 20%.

What, then, is the opportunity cost of funds used for a government project? The answer is that the opportunity cost depends on whether a reduction in government use of funds will lead to an increase in private investment or an increase in private consumption. The typical situation is that the funds that are released will go partly to investment and partly to consumption. We will not know what the split is. The bottom line is that we can only state a range for the opportunity cost of funds used by government. The upper end of the range is the marginal before-tax rate of return on private sector investments. This assumes that all funds that might be released by the government are used in private sector investment. The bottom end of the range is the after-tax return to investors in low risk investments. This assumes that all funds that might be released are used in consumption.

The inability to specify a unique, correct MARR for government projects means that it is good practice for the analyst to work with the upper and lower ends of the range of possible rates to see if this makes a difference in decisions. This is the recommendation of the Treasury Board's *Guide*.

CANADIAN   CORPORATE   CASE   11.1

Wood Pulp Mill Effluent Treatment in Alberta

The Alberta government's policy concerning wood pulp mills has two major objectives: to encourage the development of pulp mills to provide income for Albertans, and to avoid harm to humans, plants, or wildlife that could result from the release of liquid effluent into nearby bodies of fresh water.

The most common way for a government to limit damage to the environment by industrial effluents is to establish regulations that limit the release of the effluents. The regulations usually apply uniformly to all companies and plants that fall in certain classes defined by the regulations. Uniform regulation usually is inefficient for two reasons. First, different companies will have different costs of reducing effluent. This means that efficiency could be increased by having plants that have low costs of reducing effluent reduce more than plants with high costs. Second, the same amounts of effluent released will have different impacts in different locations. This means that efficiency could be increased by requiring higher standards where the impact of effluent release is greatest.

Alberta has adopted an unusual approach to promoting development while preventing damage from pulp mill effluent release. The Alberta government has negotiated individual licences with the six pulp mills that were started in the province between 1957 and 1993. Infrastructure grants and effluent limitations depend on each mill's particular situation.

This approach has the potential of being more efficient than uniform regulation. There are two drawbacks, however. First, individual licensing is feasible only where the number of sites being controlled is relatively small. Second, the cost of the subsidies to the government may be high. This is because there is always some uncertainty about the cost of attaining a given level of effluent control. Engineers representing the companies will want to avoid underestimating these costs. In the process, they may overestimate them. Since their knowledge of the situation is likely to be better than the knowledge of engineers representing the government, the company engineers' overestimates are likely to prevail.

Source: K. M. Lindsay and D. W. Smith, "Factors Influencing Pulp Mill Effluent Treatment in Alberta," *Journal of Environmental Management*, Vol. 44 (1995), pp. 11-27.

REVIEW PROBLEMS

Review Problem 11.1

This review problem is adapted from an example in the Treasury Board's *Benefit-Cost Analysis Guide*.

There are periodic floods in the spring and drought conditions in the summer that cause losses in a 15 000 square kilometre Prairie river basin which has a population of 50 000 people. The area is mostly farmland, but there are several towns. Several flood control and irrigation alternatives are being considered:

1. Dam the river to provide flood control, irrigation, and recreation.
2. Dam the river to provide flood control and irrigation without recreation.
3. Control flooding with a joint Canada-United States water control project on the river.
4. Develop alternative land uses that would not be affected by flooding.

The constraints faced by the government are the following:

1. The project must not reduce arable land.
2. Joint Canada-United States projects are subject to delays caused by legal and political obstacles.
3. Damming of the river in the United States will cause damage to wildlife refuges.
4. The target date for completion is three years.

Taking into account the constraints, alternatives 3 and 4 above were eliminated, leaving two:

1. Construct a dam for flood control, irrigation, and recreation.
2. Construct a dam for flood control and irrigation only.

A number of assumptions were made with respect to the dam and the recreational facilities:

1. An earthen dam will have a 50-year useful life.
2. Population and demand for recreational facilities will grow by 3.25% per year.
3. A three-year planning and construction period is reasonable for the dam.
4. Operating and maintenance costs for the dam will be constant in real dollars.
5. Recreational facilities will be constructed in year 2.
6. It will be necessary to replace the recreational facilities every 10 years. This will occur in years 12, 22, 32, and 42. Replacement costs will be constant in real dollars.
7. Operating and maintenance costs for the recreational facilities will be constant in real dollars.
8. The real dollar opportunity cost of funds used for this project is estimated to be in the range of 5% to 15%.

The benefits and costs of the two projects are shown in Tables 11.4 and 11.5.

Notice that the benefits and costs are estimated averages. For example, the value of reduced flood damages will vary from year to year, depending on such factors as rainfall and snowmelt. It is not possible to predict actual values for a 50-year period.

(a) What is the present worth of building the dam only? What is the benefit-cost ratio? What is the modified benefit-cost ratio? Use 10% as the MARR.

(b) What is the present worth of building the dam plus the recreational facilities? Use 10% as the MARR.

(c) What is the benefit-cost ratio for building the dam and recreation facilities together? What is the modified benefit-cost ratio?

(d) Which project, 1 or 2, is preferred, based on your benefit-cost analysis? Use 10% as the MARR.

TABLE 11.4: Estimated Average Benefits of the Two Projects

Year	Flood Damage Reduction (real $)	Irrigation Benefits (real $)	Recreation Benefits (real $)
0	0	0	0
1	0	0	0
2	0	0	0
3	182 510	200 000	27 600
4	182 510	200 000	28 497
:	:	:	:
52	182 510	200 000	132 288

TABLE 11.5: Estimated Average Costs of the Two Projects

Year	Dam Construction ($)	Operating and Maintenance Dam ($)	Recreation Construction ($)	Operating and Maintenance Recreation ($)
0	300 000	0	0	0
1	750 000	0	0	0
2	1 500 000	0	50 000	0
3	0	30 000	0	15 000
4	0	30 000	0	15 000
:	:	:	:	:
11	0	30 000	0	15 000
12	0	30 000	20 000	15 000
13	0	30 000	0	15 000
:	:	:	:	:
21	0	30 000	0	15 000
22	0	30 000	20 000	15 000
23	0	30 000	0	15 000
:	:	:	:	:
31	0	30 000	0	15 000
32	0	30 000	20 000	15 000
33	0	30 000	0	15 000
:	:	:	:	:
41	0	30 000	0	15 000
42	0	30 000	20 000	15 000
43	0	30 000	0	15 000
:	:	:	:	:
52	0	30 000	0	15 000

Answer

(a) We need to get the present worth of benefits and costs of the dam alone. There are two benefits from the dam alone. They are reduced flood damage and the benefits of irrigation. Both are approximated as annuities that start in year 3. We get the present worths of these benefits by multiplying the annual benefits by the series present worth factor and the present worth factor.

$$\text{PW(flood control)} = \$182\ 510(P/A, 10\%, 50)(P/F, 10\%, 2)$$

$$= \frac{\$182\ 510(9.99148)}{(1.1)^2}$$

$$= \$1\ 495\ 498$$

Similar computations give the present worth of irrigation as

$$\text{PW(irrigation)} = \$1\ 638\ 812$$

There are two costs for the dam. There are capital costs that are incurred at the ends of years 0, 1, and 2. Then there are operating and maintenance costs that are approximated as an annuity that begins in year 3. Capital costs are given by

$$\begin{aligned}\text{PW(dam, capital cost)} &= \$300\ 000 + \$750\ 000(P/F, 10\%, 1) \\ &\quad + \$1\ 500\ 000(P/F, 10\%, 2)\end{aligned}$$

$$= \$2\ 221\ 487$$

The present worth of operating and maintenance costs is obtained in the same way as the present worths of flood control and irrigation benefits. The result is

$$\text{PW(operating and maintenance)} = \$245\ 822$$

We get the present worth of the dam alone as

$$\begin{aligned}\text{PW(dam)} &= \$1\ 495\ 498 + \$1\ 638\ 812 \\ &\quad - (\$2\ 221\ 488 + \$245\ 822) = \$667\ 001\end{aligned}$$

The benefit-cost ratio for the dam is

$$\text{BCR(dam)} = \frac{\$1\ 495\ 498 + \$1\ 638\ 812}{\$2\ 221\ 488 + \$245\ 822} = 1.270$$

The modified benefit-cost ratio is given by

$$\text{BCRM(dam)} = \frac{\$1\ 495\ 498 + \$1\ 638\ 812 - \$245\ 822}{\$2\ 221\ 488} = 1.300$$

The present worth of the dam alone is positive, and both benefit-cost ratios are greater than 1. The dam alone appears to be economically viable.

(b) We already have the present worths of benefits and costs for the dam alone. Therefore, we need only compute the present worths of benefits and costs for the recreation facilities. The capital costs for the recreation facilities consists of five outlays, in years 2, 12, 22, 32, and 42. The present worth of capital costs for the recreational facilities is given by

$$PW(\text{recreation facilities capital cost}) = \$50\,000(P/F, 10\%, 2)$$
$$+ \$20\,000[(P/F, 10\%, 12) + (P/F, 10\%, 22)$$
$$+ (P/F, 10\%, 32) + (P/F, 10\%, 42)]$$
$$= \$51\,464$$

Operating and maintenance costs are approximated by an annuity that starts in year 3. The computation is the same as the computation of similar annuities that were shown for the benefits and operating and maintenance costs of the dam. We get them as the present worth of recreation operating and maintenance costs.

$$PW(\text{recreation facilities operating and maintenance}) = \$122\,911$$

To obtain the present worth of the benefits from recreation, we need to define a growth adjusted interest rate with $i = 10\%$ and $g = 3.25\%$ per year.

$$i° = \frac{1 + i}{1 + g} - 1 = \frac{1 + 0.10}{1 + 0.0325} - 1 = 0.0653$$

We then use this to get the present worth geometric gradient series factor,

$$(P/A, g, i, N) = \left(\frac{(1 + i°)^N - 1}{i°(1 + i°)^N} \right) \frac{1}{1 + g}$$

$$= \left(\frac{(1.0653)^{50} - 1}{0.0653(1.0653)^{50}} \right) \frac{1}{1.0325} = 14.190$$

To bring this to the end of year 0, we multiply by $(P/F, i, 2)$. We then multiply by the initial value to get the present worth of recreation benefits.

$$PW(\text{recreation benefits}) = (P/A, 3.25\%, 10\%, N)(\$27\,600)$$
$$(P/F, i, 2)$$
$$= 14.19(\$27\,600)(1.1)^{-2}$$
$$= \$323\,679$$

Another way to get this result is to use a spreadsheet. First, a column that contains the benefits in each year is obtained. The benefits start at $27 600 in the third year and grow at 3.25% each year. These benefits are then multiplied by the appropriate present worth factor in another column to obtain the present worth of the benefits. The individual present worths are then summed to obtain the overall total of $323 679. Some of the spreadsheet computations are shown in Table 11.6.

TABLE 11.6: Spreadsheet Computations

Year	Recreation Benefits ($)	PW of Recreation Benefits ($)
0	0.00	0.00
1	0.00	0.00
2	0.00	0.00
3	28 600.00	20 736.29
4	28 497.00	19463.83
5	29 423.15	18 269.46
6	30 379.40	17 148.38
:	:	:
52	132 288.48	323 678.84
Total PW		323 678 .84

The total present worth of the recreation facilities is

$$PW(\text{total recreation facilities}) = \$323\ 679 - \$51\ 464 \\ - \$122\ 911 \\ = \$149\ 304$$

We get the present worth of the dam plus recreation facilities simply by adding the present worth of the dam alone to the present worth of the recreation facility. The final result is given by

$$PW(\text{dam and recreation facility}) = \$667\ 001 + \$149\ 304 \\ = \$816\ 305$$

In present worth terms, the present worth of the dam *and* recreation facility exceeds that of the dam alone, so the dam and the recreation facility should be chosen.

(c) The benefit-cost ratio for the dam and recreation facilities together is

$$BCR(\text{dam and recreation}) \\ = \frac{(\$1\ 495\ 498 + \$1\ 638\ 812 + \$323\ 679)}{(\$2\ 221\ 488 + \$245\ 822 + \$51\ 464 + \$122\ 911)} = 1.3090$$

The modified benefit-cost ratio is

BCRM(dam and recreation)

$$= \frac{(\$1\,495\,498 + \$1\,638\,812 + \$323\,679 - \$245\,822 - \$122\,911)}{(\$2\,221\,488 + \$51\,464)}$$

$$= 1.359$$

The dam and recreation facilities project appears to be viable, since the benefit-cost ratios are greater than one.

(d) Based on benefit-cost ratios, which of the two projects, project 1 or project 2, should be chosen? The dam and recreation facility is more costly, so the correct benefit-cost ratio for comparing the two is

$$\text{BCRD} = \frac{\text{Benefits(dam and recreation facility)} - \text{Benefits(dam)}}{\text{Costs(dam and recreation facility)} - \text{Costs(dam)}}$$

$$= \frac{\$323\,679}{(\$51\,464 + \$122\,911)} = 1.8561$$

The ratio exceeds one, and hence the dam and recreation facilities project should be chosen. This is consistent with the original present worth computations.

SUMMARY

Chapter 11 concerns decision making in the public sector. We started by considering why markets may fail to lead to efficient decisions. We presented four formal methods by which society seeks to remedy market failure. One of these methods is to have production by government. Next, we laid out three issues in decision making about government production. First, we saw that identification and measurement of costs and benefits in the public sector are more difficult than in the private sector. Identification may be difficult because there may not be cash flows that reflect the costs or benefits. Measurement may be difficult because there are no prices to indicate values. Second, we discussed the use of benefit-cost ratios in public sector project evaluation. While it is possible to use benefit-cost ratios so as to give the same results as using the standard methods with either present worth or annual worth, the ratios may also be misused. Therefore, the use of benefit-cost ratios is not recommended by the Treasury Board of the Canadian federal government. Third and last, we considered the MARR for government sector investments. The result of this discussion is that we can only state a range in which the opportunity cost of funds used in the public sector may lie. Therefore, the analyst should test to see if the choice of the MARR from within this range will affect the decision choice.

Engineering Economics in Action, Part 11B: Look at It from Their Side

"How was your trip, Naomi?" Anna Kulkowski asked as she walked into the conference room. Bill and Naomi were already there waiting.

"Well, I'm here," responded Naomi, "but my jets are still lagging."

"Get used to it." Anna looked at Bill. "So, what's it going to cost to upgrade the mill?"

"Naomi got some back-of-the-envelope figures from the people at Edgemont," Bill answered. "They're talking over a hundred million between now and 2002. If we amortize that over twenty years it's going to add about 20% to total costs per ton of pulp. It looks as though the only way we can keep pulp bleaching viable long-term is to get the B.C. government to change the regulation."

"Well," Naomi continued, "I did talk to the people at the mill yesterday before coming home. Things may not be quite as bleak as I first told Bill. First, even if costs do go up by 20%, we may still be able to compete by finding niches that demand 'environmentally friendly' pulp. Unfortunately, if 'environmentally friendly' means only very low AOX, there will be offshore mills that will be able to underprice us, even in the niche markets."

"That doesn't sound like a big help," Anna said. "What's the other reason for hope?"

"The other reason is that we may be able to make a reasonable argument for modifying the regulation," Naomi said. "The form of the regulation, in terms of AOX per ton of output, doesn't make sense from an environmental point of view."

"Why not?" Anna asked.

"Well," said Naomi, "we're really interested in water quality, not AOX measured at the end of the pipe. Water quality around the mill can vary greatly for a given effluent concentration. It will depend on the degree of dilution, and water flow patterns which vary over time and across mills, depending on season and location. The main implication is that it is possible that a reasonable rule in terms of water quality would not require zero AOX. There is background AOX, in any case. This is stuff that would be there even if the mills shut down."

"Where does this leave us, Naomi?" Anna asked.

"Well, I'm not sure," Naomi said. "But it certainly makes more sense, from an environmental point of view, to state the regulations in terms of water quality at some distance from mills. This would mean different effluent concentration limits for different mills, depending on location. Administratively, it would be more difficult for the government. But we're talking about fewer than twenty bleached pulp mills in the province. If a revised form of regulation enabled some of the mills to avoid zero AOX, it would save everybody a lot of money."

"That sounds interesting, Naomi," Anna said. "Why don't you write this up. I'm going to B.C. in a few weeks. I'll see if I can get a meeting with some people in the environment ministry. I'll try the idea out on them. It's worth a shot."

"By the way, Naomi," Anna continued, "good work!"

PROBLEMS

11.1 The following data are available for a project:

Present worth of benefits: $17 000 000
Present worth of operating and maintenance costs: $5 000 000
Present worth of capital costs: $6 000 000

(a) Find the benefit-cost ratio.

(b) Find the modified benefit-cost ratio.

11.2 The following data are available for two mutually exclusive projects:

	Project A ($)	Project B ($)
PW (benefits)	19 000 000	15 000 000
PW (operating and maintenance costs)	5 000 000	8 000 000
PW (capital cost)	5 000 000	1 000 000

(a) Compute the benefit-cost ratios for both projects.

(b) Compute the modified benefit-cost ratios for both projects.

(c) Compute the benefit-cost ratio for the difference between the projects.

(d) Compute the present worths of the two projects.

(e) Which is the preferred project? Explain.

11.3 The following data are available for two mutually exclusive projects:

	Project A ($)	Project B ($)
PW (benefits)	17 000 000	17 000 000
PW (operating and maintenance costs)	5 000 000	11 000 000
PW (capital cost)	6 000 000	1 000 000

(a) Compute the benefit-cost ratios for both projects.

(b) Compute the modified benefit-cost ratios for both projects.

(c) Compute the benefit-cost ratio for the difference between the projects.

(d) Compute the present worths of the two projects.

(e) Which is the preferred project? Explain.

11.4 The following data are available for two mutually exclusive projects:

	Project A ($)	Project B ($)
PW (benefits)	17 000 000	15 000 000
PW (operating and maintenance costs)	5 000 000	8 000 000
PW (capital cost)	6 000 000	3 000 000

(a) Compute the benefit-cost ratios for both projects.

(b) Compute the modified benefit-cost ratios for both projects.

(c) Compute the benefit-cost ratio for the difference between the projects.

(d) Compute the present worths of the two projects.

(e) Which is the preferred project? Explain.

11.5 There are two beef packing plants, Plant A and Plant B, in the town of Reybourne, Saskatchewan. Both plants dump partially treated liquid waste into Lake Jeannette. The two plants together dump over 33 000 kilograms of BOD5 per day. (BOD5 is the amount of oxygen used by micro-organisms over five days to decompose the waste.) This is more than half the total BOD5 dumped into Lake Jeannette. Reybourne town council wants to reduce the BOD5 dumped by the two plants by 10 000 kilograms per day.

The following data are available concerning the two plants:

Outputs of the Two Plants		
	Steers/day	BOD5/steer (kg)
Plant A	20 000	1.0
Plant B	9 000	1.5

The costs of making reductions in BOD5 per steer are shown below:

Incremental Cost of Reducing BOD ($/kg/steer)							
Reduction (kg/steer)	0.1	0.2	0.3	0.4	0.5	0.6	0.7
Plant A	0.05	0.08	0.12	0.25	0.45	0.65	0.95
Plant B	0.15	0.15	0.15	0.15	0.15	0.35	0.45

For example, to reduce the BOD5 of plant A by 0.25 kg/steer, the cost is calculated as

$$(0.1 \times 0.05) + (0.1 \times 0.08) + (0.05 \times 0.12) = 0.019/steer$$

The council is considering three methods of inducing the plants to reduce their BOD5 dumping: (1) a regulation that limits BOD5 dumping to 0.81 kilograms/steer, (2) a tax of $0.16 per kilogram of BOD5 dumped, and (3) a subsidy paid by the town to the plants of $0.16 per kilogram reduction from their current levels in BOD5 dumped.

(a) Verify that, if both plants reduce their BOD5 dumping to 0.81 kilograms/steer, there will be a 10 000 kilograms/day reduction in BOD5 dumped. What will this cost?

(b) Under a tax of $0.16 per kilogram, how much BOD5 will Plant A dump? How much will Plant B dump? (Assume that outputs of steers would not be affected by the tax.) Verify that this will lead to more than a 10 000 kilograms/day reduction in BOD5. What will this cost?

(c) Under a subsidy of $0.16 per kilogram reduction in BOD5, how much will Plant A dump? How much will Plant B dump? Verify that this will lead to more than a 10 000 kilograms/day reduction in BOD5. What will this cost?

(d) Explain why the tax and subsidy schemes lead to the same behaviour by the meat packing plants.

(e) Explain why the tax and subsidy schemes have lower costs for the company than the regulation.

11.6 There are three petrochemical plants, Plant A, Plant B, and Plant C, in Port Jayne, Ontario. The three plants produce Good Stuff. Unfortunately, they also dump Bad Stuff into the air. Data concerning their outputs of Stuff are shown below:

	Outputs	
	Good (kg/day)	**Bad/Good (cl/kg)**
Plant A	17 000	10
Plant B	11 000	15
Plant C	8 000	18

The town council wants to reduce the dumping of Bad Stuff by 150 000 cl/day. Costs for reducing the concentration of Bad Stuff in output are shown below:

Cost of Reducing Bad Stuff/Good Stuff ($/cl/kg)								
Reduction (cl/kg)	**1**	**2**	**3**	**4**	**5**	**6**	**7**	**8**
Plant A	0.02	0.032	0.048	0.1	0.18	0.26	0.38	0.57
Plant B	0.06	0.06	0.063	0.068	0.075	0.193	0.27	0.405
Plant C	0.25	0.25	0.25	0.25	0.25	0.25	0.25	0.375

The council is considering two methods: (1) Require all plants to meet the performance level of the best-practice plant, Plant A, which is 10 centilitres of Bad Stuff per kilogram of Good Stuff. (2) Impose a tax of $0.20 per centilitre of Bad Stuff dumped.

(a) What will be the reduction in dumping of Bad Stuff under the best-practice regulation? What will be the cost of this reduction?

(b) Under the tax, what will be the dumping of Bad Stuff of the three plants combined? What will be each plant's reduction in dumping per kilogram of Good Stuff?

(c) What will be the cost of the reduction of dumping for each company under the tax?

11.7 An electric utility company is considering a re-engineering of a major hydro-electric facility. The project would yield greater capacity and lower cost per kilowatt-hour of power. As a result of the project, the price of power would be dropped. This is expected to increase the quantity of power demanded. The following data are available:

Effect of Reduced Price of Power	
Current price ($/kWh)	0.07
Current consumption (kWh/year)	9 000 000
New price ($/kWh)	0.05
Expected consumption (kWh/year)	12 250 000

What is the annual benefit to consumers of power from this project?

11.8 Brisbane and Johnsonburg are two Prairie towns. They are separated by the Wind River. Traffic between the two towns crosses the river by ferry. The ferry is run by the Johnsonburg Ferry Company. They charge a toll for crossing. The province is considering building a bridge somewhat upstream from the ferry crossing. There would be no toll on the bridge. Travel time between the towns would be about the same with the bridge as with the ferry because of the bridge's upstream location. The following information is available concerning the crossing:

Ferry/Bridge Information	
Ferry crossings (number/year)	60 000
Average cost of ferry trip ($/crossing)	1
Ferry fare ($/crossing)	1.5
Bridge toll ($/crossing)	0
Expected bridge crossings (number/year)	90 000
EAC of bridge ($/year)	85 000

(Note that all data are on an annual basis. The cost of the bridge is given as the equivalent annual cost of capital and operating costs. We assume that all bridge costs are independent of use, that is, there are no costs which are due to use of the bridge. The average cost per crossing of the ferry includes capital cost and operating cost.)

(a) If the bridge were built, what would be the annual benefits to travellers?

(b) How much would the owners of the Johnsonburg Ferry Company lose if the bridge were built?

(c) What would be the effect on taxpayers if the bridge were built? (Assume that Johnsonburg Ferry pays no taxes.)

(d) What would be the net social gain or loss if the bridge were built? Take into account the effects on travellers, Johnsonburg Ferry owners, and taxpayers.

(e) Would the net social gains or losses be improved if there were a toll for crossing the bridge?

11.9 There is an example concerning the effect of a flood control project in the benefit-cost analysis chapter of an imaginary engineering economics text. The benefits of the project are stated as:

Prevented losses due to floods in the Conestogo River Basin	$480 000/year
Annual worth of increased land value in the Conestogo River Basin	$48 000/year

Comment on these two items.

11.10 A province is considering the construction of a bridge. The bridge would cross a narrow part of a lake near a provincial park. The major benefit of the bridge would be reduced travel time to go to a camp site from a nearby urban centre. This lowers the cost of camping trips at the park. As well, they expect an increase in the number of visits resulting from the lower cost per visit.

Data concerning the number of week-long visits and their costs are shown below:

Number of Visits and Average Cost per Visit to Park		
Inputs	**Without Bridge**	**With Bridge**
Travel cost ($)	140	87.5
Use of equipment ($)	50	50
Food ($)	100	100
Total ($)	290	237.5
Number of visits/year	8000	11 000

The following data are available as well:

1. The bridge will take one year to build.
2. The bridge will have a 25-year life once it is completed. This means that the time horizon for computations is 26 years.
3. Construction cost for the bridge is $3 750 000. Assume that this cost is incurred at the beginning of year 1.
4. Annual operating and maintenance costs for the bridge are given by

    Operating and Maintenance Cost per year = 7500 + 0.25q

    where

    q is the number of crossings.

5. Operating and maintenance costs are incurred at the end of each year the bridge is in operation. This is at the ends of years 2, 3, . . ., 26.

    MARR is 10%.

(Notice that you need not compute annual benefits for this project. The annual benefits were computed as part of the discussion of Example 11.3.)

(a) Compute the net present worth of the project.

(b) Compute the benefit-cost ratio.

(c) Compute the modified benefit-cost ratio.

11.11 Continue with the bridge project of problem 11.10. In that problem, we assumed that there would be no toll for crossing the bridge. Now suppose the province is considering a toll of $7 per round trip over the bridge. They estimate that, if the toll is charged, the number of park visits will rise to only 10 600 per year instead of 11 000 visits per year.

(a) Compute the net present worth of the project if the toll is charged.

(b) Why is the net present worth of the project reduced by the toll?

11.12 The town of Migli Lake, Manitoba, has a new subdivision, Paradise Mountain, at the outskirts of the town. The town wants to encourage the growth of Paradise Mountain by improving transportation between Paradise Mountain and the centre of Migli Lake. Two alternatives are being considered: (1) new buses on the route between Paradise Mountain and Migli Lake centre; and (2) improvement of the road between Paradise Mountain and Migli Lake centre.

Both projects will have as their main benefit improved transportation between Paradise Mountain and Migli Lake centre. Rather than measure the value of this directly to the city, engineers have estimated the benefit in terms of an increase in the value of land in Paradise Mountain. That is, potential residents are expected to show their evaluations of the present worth of improved access to the town centre by their willingness to pay for homes in Paradise Mountain.

The road improvement will entail construction cost and increased operating and maintenance costs. As well, the improved road will require construction of a parking garage in the centre of Migli Lake. The new buses will have a first cost as well as operating and maintenance costs. Information about the two alternatives is shown below.

	Road Improvement	New Buses
First cost	$15 000 000	$ 4 500 000
PW (operating and maintenance cost)	5 000 000	12 000 000
Parking garage cost	4 000 000	
Estimated increased land value	26 000 000	18 000 000

(a) Compute the benefit-cost ratio of the road improvement under two assumptions: (1) that the parking garage is a cost, and (2) that the parking garage is a reduction in benefits.

(b) Compute the benefit-cost ratio of the new buses project.

(c) Compute the present worths of the two alternatives. Which is preferred?

11.13 A provincial government is considering a new two-lane road through a mountainous area. The new road would improve access to a city from farms on the other side of the mountains. The improved access would permit farmers to switch from grains to perishable soft fruits that would be either frozen at an existing plant near the city or sold in the city. Two routes are being considered. Route A is more roundabout. Even though the speed on route B would be less than on Route A, the trip on Route B would take less time. Almost all vehicles using either road would go over the full length of the road. A Department of Transport engineer has produced the following table.

The province uses a 10% MARR for road projects. The road will take one year to build. The province is using a 21-year time horizon for this project, since it is not known what the market for perishable crops will be in the distant future.

Comment on the engineer's list of benefits; he may have made a couple of errors.

11.14 Continue with the road project in problem of 11.13. (*Note:* Correct for the errors mentioned.)

(a) Compute a benefit-cost ratio for Route A with road use costs counted as a cost.

(b) Compute a benefit-cost ratio for Route A with road use costs counted as a reduction in benefits.

Costs and Benefits of the New Road		
	Route A	**Route B**
Properties		
Distance (km)	24	16
Construction cost ($)	53 400	75 000
Operating and maintenance cost per year ($)	60	45
Resurfacing after 10 years of use ($)	3 100	2 350
Road Use		
Number of vehicles per year (000)	1 000	1 200
Vehicle cost per km ($)	0.3	0.3
Speed (kph)	100	80
Value of time per vehicle hour ($)	15	15
Benefits		
Increased crop value per year ($)	13 500	18 000
Increased land value ($)	104 484.6	139 312.8
Increased tax collections per year ($)	811.21	1 081.61

(c) In what way are the two benefit-cost ratios consistent, even though the numerical values differ?

(d) Make a recommendation as to what the province should do regarding these two roads. Explain your answer briefly.

11.15 Find the net present worths for the dam and the dam plus recreation facilities considered in Review Problem 11.1. Use a MARR = 15%. Make a recommendation as to which option should be adopted.

11.16 What determines the MARR that is used on government funded projects?

11.17 How will a decrease in the tax rate on investment income affect the MARR that is used for evaluating government funded projects?

11.18 How does an expectation of inflation affect the MARR for public sector projects?

11.19 A provincial department of transportation has $16 500 000 that it can commit to highway safety projects. The goal is to reduce loss of life due to highway accidents. The potential projects are: (1) flashing lights at 10 railroad crossings; (2) flashing lights and gates at the same 10 railroad crossings; (3) widening the roadway on an existing rural bridge from 3 meters to 3.5 meters; (4) widening the roadway on a second rural bridge from 3 meters to 3.5 meters; (5) reduction of the density of utility poles on rural roads from 30 poles to 15 poles per kilometre; and (6) building runaway lanes for trucks on steep downhills.

The data for the flashing-lights and the flashing-lights-with-gates projects reflect the costs and benefits for the entire set of 10 crossings. Portions of the projects may also be completed for individual crossings at proportional reductions in costs and savings. At any single site, the lights and lights-with-gates projects are mutually exclusive. Any fraction of the reduction of utility pole density project can be carried out. Data concerning costs and safety effects of the projects are shown below. (A life-year saved is one year of additional life for one person.)

Highway Safety Projects			
		Total Cost ($)	Life-Years Saved per Year
1	Flashing lights	450 000	14
2	Flashing lights and gates	750 000	20
3	Widening bridge #1	1 200 000	14
4	Widening bridge #2	700 000	10
5	Widening bridge #3	1 100 000	18
6	Pole density reduction	3 000 000	96
7	Runaway lane #1	6 000 000	206
8	Runaway lane #2	6 000 000	156

Advise the department of transportation how best to commit the $16 500 000. Assume that the money must be used to increase highway safety.

11.20 A provincial department of transportation is considering widening lanes on major highways from 6 meters to 7.5 meters. The objective is to reduce the accident rate. Accidents have both material and human costs. The following data are available for highway section XYZ:

Lane Widening on Section XYZ	
Accidents per 100 000 000 vehicle km in 6-meter lanes	150
Accidents per 100 000 000 vehicle km in 7.5-meter lanes	90
Serious personal injuries per accident	10%
Average non-human cost per accident ($)	2500
Annual road use (vehicles)	7 500 000
First cost per kilometre ($)	175 000
Operating and maintenance costs per km/year ($)	7500
Project life (years)	25
MARR	10%

(a) Compute the present worth of costs of lane widening.

(b) Compute the present worth of savings of non-human accident costs.

(c) What is the minimum value for a serious personal injury that would justify the project?

Qualitative Considerations and Multiple Criteria

Engineering Economics in Action, Part 12A: Don't Box Them In

12.1   Introduction

12.2   Efficiency

12.3   Decision Matrices

12.4   The Analytic Hierarchy Process

12.5   The Consistency Ratio for AHP

Canadian Corporate Case 12.1: Northwind Stoneware

Review Problems

Summary

Engineering Economics in Action, Part 12B: Moving On

Problems

Appendix 12A: Calculating the Consistency Ratio for AHP

Engineering Economics in Action, Part 12A: Don't Box Them In

N aomi and Bill Astad were seated in Naomi's office. "O.K.," said Naomi. "Now that we know we can handle the demand, it's time to work on the design, right? What is the best design?" She was referring to the self-adjusting vacuum cleaner project for Powerluxe that she and Bill had been working on for several months.

"Probably the best way to find out," Bill answered, "will be to get the information from interviews with small groups of consumers."

"All right," said Naomi. "We have to know what to ask them. I guess the most important step for us is to define the relevant characteristics of vacuums."

"I agree," Bill responded. "We couldn't get meaningful responses about choices if we left out some important aspect of vacuums like suction power. One way to get the relevant characteristics will be to talk to people who have designed vacuums before, and probably to vacuum cleaner sales people, too." They both smiled at the humorous prospect of seeking out vacuum cleaner sales people, instead of trying to avoid them.

"We're going to need some technical people on the team," Naomi said. "We will have to develop a set of technically feasible possibilities."

"Exactly," Bill replied. "Moreover, we need to have working models of the feasible types. That is, we can't just ask questions about attributes in the abstract. Most people would have a hard time inferring actual performance from numbers about weight or suction power, for example. Also, consumers are not directly interested in these measurements. They don't care what the vacuum weighs. They care about what it takes to move it around and go up and down stairs. This depends on several aspects of the cleaner. It includes weight, but also the way the cleaner is balanced, and the size of the wheels."

"That makes sense," Naomi said. "I assume that we would want to structure the interviews to make use of some form of MCDM approach."

"Huh?" Bill said.

12.1 Introduction

M ost of this book has been concerned with making decisions based on a single economic measure such as present worth, annual worth, or internal rate of return. This is natural, since many of the decisions that are made by an individual, and most that are made by businesses, have the financial impact of a project as a primary consideration. However, rarely are costs and benefits the only consideration in evaluating a project. Sometimes other considerations are paramount.

For decisions made by and for an individual, cost may be relatively unimportant. One individual may buy vegetables based on their freshness, regardless of the cost. A dress or suit may be purchased because it is fashionable or attractive. A car may be chosen for its comfort and not its cost.

Traditionally, firms were different from individuals in this way. It was felt that all decisions for a firm *should* be made on the basis of the costs and benefits as measured in money (even if they sometimes were not, in practice), since the firm's survival depended solely on being financially competitive.

Society has changed, however. Companies now can be seen to make decisions that apparently involve factors that are very difficult to measure in monetary terms. Money spent by firms on charities and good causes provides a benefit in image that is very hard to quantify. Resource companies that demonstrate a concern for the environment incur costs with no clear financial benefit. Companies that provide benefits for employees beyond statute or collective agreement norms gain something that is hard to measure.

The fact that firms are making decisions on the basis of criteria other than only money most individuals would hail as a good thing. It seems to be a good thing for the companies, too, since those that do so tend to be successful. However, it can make the process of decision making more difficult because there is no longer a single measure of value.

Money has the convenient feature that, in general, more is better. For example, of several mutually exclusive projects (of identical service lives), the one with the highest present worth is the best choice. People prefer a higher salary to a lower one. If there are reasons to make a choice other than just the cost, things get somewhat more difficult. For example, which is better: the project with the higher present worth but which involves clear-cutting a forest, or the one with lower present worth but which preserves the forest? Does a high salary compensate for working for a company that does business with a totalitarian government?

Although such considerations have been having particular influence in recent years, the problem of having both qualitative *and* quantitative criteria in engineering decisions has always been present. This leads to the question of how a decision maker deals with multiple objectives, be they quantitative or qualitative. There are three basic approaches to the problem:

1. Model and analyze the costs alone. Leave out the other considerations to be dealt with on the basis of experience and managerial judgment. In other words, consider the problem in two stages. First, treat it as if cost were the only important criterion. Subsequently, make a decision based on the refined cost information — the economic analysis — and all other considerations. The benefit of this approach is its simplicity; the methods for analyzing costs are well established and defensible. The liability is that, for complicated problems, errors can be made, since humans have only a limited ability to process information. A bad decision can be made, and, moreover, it can be hard to explain why a particular decision was made.

2. Convert other criteria to money, and then treat the problem as a cost-minimization or profit-maximization problem. Before environmental issues were recognized as being so important, the major criterion that was not easily converted to money was human health and safety. Elaborate schemes were developed to measure the cost of a lost life or injury so that good economic decisions were made. For example, one method was to estimate the money that would have been made by a worker if he had lived the rest of his life. With an estimate like this, the cost, in lives and injuries, of a project could be compared with the profits obtained. A benefit of this approach is that it does take non-monetary criteria into account. A drawback is the difficult and politically sensitive task of determining the cost of a human life or the cost of cutting down a 300-year-old tree.

3. Use a **multi-criterion decision making (MCDM)** approach. There are several MCDM methods that explicitly take into account multiple criteria and guide a decision maker to superior or optimal choices. The benefit of MCDM is that all important criteria can be explicitly taken into account in an appropriate manner. The main drawback is that MCDM methods take time and effort to use.

In recent years it has become particularly widely recognized that in many circumstances looking at only the monetary costs and benefits of projects is inappropriate. Consequently, considerable attention has been focussed on how best to make a choice under competing criteria. The first two approaches listed above still have validity in some circumstances; in particular, when non-monetary criteria are relatively unimportant, it makes sense to look at costs alone. However, it is necessary to use an MCDM method of some sort in much of engineering decision making today.

In this chapter, we focus on three useful MCDM approaches. The first, *efficiency*, permits the identification of a subset of superior alternatives when there are multiple criteria. The second approach, *decision matrices*, is a version of multi-attribute utility theory (MAUT) which is widely practiced. The third, the *analytic hierarchy method*, is a relatively new but popular MAUT approach. It should be noted that all of these methods make assumptions about the trade-offs among criteria that may not be suitable in particular cases. They should not be applied blindly, but critically and with a strong dose of common sense.

12.2 Efficiency

When dealing with a single criterion like cost, it is usually clear which alternatives are better. The rule for a present worth analysis of mutually exclusive alternatives (with identical service lives) is, for example, that the highest present worth alternative is best.

All criteria can be measured in some way. The scale might be continuous, such as "weight in kilograms" or "distance from home," or discrete, such as "number of doors" or "operators needed." The measurement might be subjective, such as a rating of "excellent," "very good," "good," "fair," and "poor," or conform to an objective physical property like voltage or luminescence.

Once measured, the value of the alternative can be established with respect to that criterion. It may be that the smaller or lower measurement is better, as is often the case with cost, or the higher is better, as is the case with a criterion like "lives saved." Sometimes a target is desired, for example, a target weight. In this case, the criterion could be adjusted to be the distance from the target, with a shorter distance being better.

Consequently, given one criterion, we can recognize which of several alternatives is best. However, once there are more than one criterion, the problem is more difficult. This is because an alternative can be highly valued with respect to one criterion and lowly valued with respect to another.

EXAMPLE 12.1

Simcoe Meats will be replacing its effluent treatment system. It has evaluated several alternatives, shown in Figure 12.1. Two criteria were considered, present worth and discharge purity. Which alternatives can be eliminated from further consideration?

Consider alternatives A and E in Figure 12.1. Alternative E dominates alternative A because it is less costly and it provides purer discharge. If these are the only criteria to consider in making a choice, one would always choose E over A. Similarly, one can eliminate F, B, and H, all of which are dominated by D and other alternatives.

Now consider alternative G, which has the same cost as E but has poor discharge purity. One would still always choose E over G since, for the purity criterion, E is better at the same price.

There now remain only three alternatives, E, D, and C. E is cheapest, but provides the least purity output. C is the most expensive, but provides the greatest purity, while D is in the middle. Certainly none of these dominates the others. There is a natural tendency to focus on D, since it seems to balance the two criteria, but it really depends on the relative importance of the criteria to the decision maker. For example, if cost were very important, E could be the best choice, since the difference in purity between E and C may be considered to be relatively small.

Decisions that involve only two criteria can be simplified graphically as done for Example 12.1, but when there are more than two criteria graphical methods become more difficult.

An alternative is **efficient** if there is no alternative which is valued as at least equal to it for all criteria and preferred to it for at least one. If an alternative is not efficient it is **inefficient**; this is the same as a **dominated** alternative.

FIGURE 12.1   Selecting an Effluent Treatment

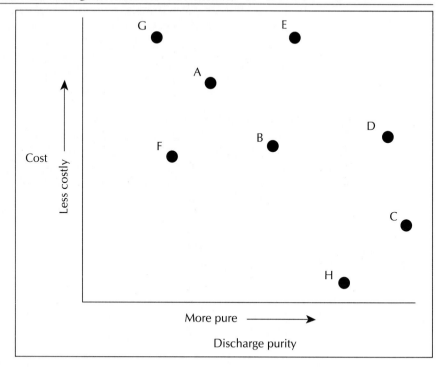

EXAMPLE 12.2

Skiven is evaluating surveillance cameras for a security system. The criteria he is taking into account are price, weight, picture clarity, and low-light performance. The details for the ten models are shown in Table 12.1. Skiven wants a camera with low cost, low weight, a high score for picture clarity, and a high score for low-light performance. Which models can be eliminated from further consideration?

To determine the efficient alternatives, the following algorithm can be used:

1. Order the alternatives according to one criterion, the *index criterion*. The cameras for Example 12.2 are already ordered by cost, so cost can be the index criterion.

2. Start with the second most preferred alternative for the index criterion. Call this the *candidate alternative*.

3. Compare the candidate alternative with each of the alternatives that are more preferred for the index criterion. (For the first candidate alternative, there is only one.)

4. If any alternative equals or exceeds the candidate for all criteria, and exceeds it for at least one, the candidate is dominated, and

can be eliminated from further consideration. If no alternative equals or exceeds the candidate for all criteria and exceeds it for at least one, the candidate is efficient.

5. The next most preferred alternative for the index criterion becomes the new candidate; go to step 3. Stop if there are no more alternatives to consider.

TABLE 12.1 Surveillance Camera Characteristics

Camera	Price ($)	Weight (grams)	Picture Clarity (10-point scale)	Low-Light Performance (10-point scale)
1	230	900	3	6
2	243	640	5	4
3	274	910	3	5
4	313	433	5	7
5	365	450	2	4
6	415	330	6	6
7	418	552	7	5
8	565	440	3	6
9	590	630	7	4
10	765	255	9	5

The algorithm for Example 12.2 starts by comparing camera 2 against camera 1. It can be seen that camera 2 is better for weight and picture clarity, although worse for low-light and cost, so it is not dominated. Looking at camera 3, it is equal to camera 1 for picture clarity, and worse than camera 1 for all other characteristics. It is dominated, since to avoid domination it would have to be better than 1 for at least one criterion. Moreover, we need not consider it for the remainder of the algorithm. We then compare camera 4 with only cameras 1 and 2. Since it is better in weight than the other two, it is not dominated, and we continue to camera 5. Camera 5 is dominated in comparison with camera 4, since it is worse in all respects.

Carrying through in this manner shows that camera 3 is dominated by camera 1, camera 5 is dominated by camera 4, camera 8 is dominated by camera 6, and camera 9 is dominated by camera 7. The set of efficient alternatives consists of cameras 1, 2, 4, 6, 7, 10.

The set of efficient alternatives clearly includes the best choice, since there is no reason to choose a dominated alternative. However, usually there will still be more that one alternative in the efficient set. Sometimes reducing the number of alternatives to be considered makes the problem easier to solve through intuition or judgment, but usually it is desirable to have some clear method for selecting a single alternative. One popular method is to use decision matrices.

12.3 Decision Matrices

Usually not all of the criteria that can be identified for a decision problem are equally important. Often cost is the most important criterion, but in some cases another criterion, safety, for example, might be most important. As suggested with Example 12.1, the choice of what is the most important criterion will have a direct effect on which alternative is best.

One approach to choosing the best alternative is to put numerical weights on the criteria. For example, if cost were most important, it would have a high weight, while a less important criterion could be given a low weight. If criteria are evaluated according to a scale that can be used directly as a measure of preference, then the weights and preference measures can be combined mathematically to determine a best alternative. This approach is called **multi-attribute utility theory (MAUT)**.

There are many different specific techniques for making decisions that are based on MAUT. This section deals with decision matrices, which are commonly used in engineering studies. The subsequent section reviews the analytic hierarchy method, a MAUT method of increasing popularity.

In a **decision matrix**, the rows of the matrix represent the criteria, and the columns the alternatives. There is an extra column for the weights of the criteria. The cells of the matrix (other than the criteria weights) contain an evaluation of the alternatives on a scale from 0 to 10, where 0 is worst and 10 is best. The weights are chosen so that they sum to 10.

The following algorithm can be used:

1. Give a weight to each criterion to express its relative importance: the higher the weight, the more important the criterion. Choose the weight values so that they sum to 10.

2. For each alternative, give a rating from 0 to 10 of how well it meets the corresponding criterion. A rating of 0 is given to the worst possible fulfilment of the criterion, and 10 to the best possible.

3. For each alternative, multiply each rating by the corresponding criterion weight, and sum to give an overall score.

4. The alternative with the highest score is best. The value of the score can be interpreted as the percentage of an ideal solution achieved by the alternative being evaluated.

5. Vary weights or rating estimates to verify the indicated decision or to determine under which conditions different choices are made.

EXAMPLE 12.3

Skiven is evaluating surveillance cameras for a security system. The criteria he is taking into account, in order of importance for him, are low-light performance, picture clarity, weight, and price. The details for the six efficient models are shown in Table 12.2. Which model is best?

TABLE 12.2 Efficient Set of Surveillance Camera Alternatives

Camera	Price ($)	Weight (grams)	Picture Clarity (10-point scale)	Low-Light Performance (10-point scale)
1	230	900	3	6
2	243	640	5	4
4	313	433	5	7
6	415	330	6	6
7	418	552	7	5
10	765	255	9	5

Following the steps given above, we need to determine the weightings of the criteria. It is usually fairly easy for a decision maker to determine which criteria are more important than others, but generally more difficult to specify particular weights. There exist many formal methods for establishing such weights in a rigorous way, but in practice estimating weights based on careful consideration or a discussion with the decision maker is sufficient. Recall that a sensitivity analysis forms part of the overall decision process, and this compensates somewhat for the imprecision of the weights.

A discussion with Skiven suggests that weights of 1, 1.5, 3.5, and 4 for price, weight, picture clarity, and low-light performance, respectively, are appropriate weights for this problem. These weights can be seen listed as the second column of Table 12.3.

TABLE 12.3 Decision Matrix for Example 12.3

Criteria	Weights	Alternatives					
		1	2	4	6	7	10
Price	1.0	10.0	9.8	8.4	6.5	6.5	0.0
Weight	1.5	0.0	4.0	7.2	8.8	5.4	10.0
Clarity	3.5	3.0	5.0	5.0	6.0	7.0	9.0
Low-light performance	4.0	6.0	4.0	7.0	6.0	5.0	5.0
Score		10.0	44.5	49.3	64.8	64.8	59.1	66.5

The ratings for each alternative for picture clarity and low-light performance are already on a scale from 0 to 10, so those ratings can be used directly. To select ratings for the price and weight, two different measures could be used:

1. *Normalization.* The rating r for the least preferred alternative (α) is 0 and the most preferred (β) is 10. For each remaining measure (γ) the rating r can be determined as:

$$r = 10 \times \frac{\gamma - \alpha}{\beta - \alpha}$$

For example, for this problem, the rating of alternative 6 for price would be

$$r_{6,price} = 10 \times \frac{415 - 765}{230 - 765} = 6.54$$

The advantage of normalization is that it provides a mathematical basis for the rating evaluations. One disadvantage is that the rating may not reflect the value as perceived by the decision maker. A second disadvantage is that it may overrate the best alternative and underrate the worst, since these are set to the extreme values. A third disadvantage is that the addition or deletion of a single alternative (the one with the highest or lowest evaluation for a criterion) will change the entire set of ratings.

2. *Subjective evaluation.* Ask the decision maker to rate the alternative on the 0 to 10 scale. For example, asked to rate alternative 6 for cost, Skiven might say it should rate a 7. The advantages of subjective evaluation include that it is relatively immune to changes in the alternative set, and that it may be more accurate since it includes perceptions of worth that cannot be directly calculated from the criteria measures. Its main disadvantage is that people often make mistakes.

For the ratings shown in Table 12.3, the normalization process was used.

The overall score is calculated by summing for each alternative the rating for a criterion multiplied by the weighting for that criterion. From Table 12.3, the total score for alternative 1 is calculated as

$$1 \times 10 + 1.5 \times 0 + 3.5 \times 3 + 4 \times 6 = 44.5$$

It can be seen in Table 12.3 that the highest score is for alternative 10. This means essentially that the greatest total benefit is achieved if alternative 10 is taken.

Also note that a "perfect" alternative, that is, one that rated 10 on every criterion, would have a total score of 100. Thus the 66.5 score for alternative 10 means that it is only about 66.5% of the score of a perfect alternative. The practice of making weights sum to 10 and rating the alternatives on a scale from 0 to 10 is done specifically so that the resulting score can be interpreted as a percentage of the ideal; if this is not desired, any relative weights or rating scale can be used.

Alternative 10 is the best choice for the particular weights and ratings given, but there should be some sensitivity analysis done to verify its robustness. There are several ways to do this sensitivity analysis, but the most sensible is to vary the weights of the criteria to see how the results change. This is easy to do when a spreadsheet is being used to calculate the scores.

Table 12.4 shows a range of criteria weights and the corresponding alternative scores. It can be seen that cameras 4 and 6 also can be identified as best in some of the criteria weight possibilities. In order to decide, it may be necessary to review these results with Skiven to let him determine which of the weight possibilities are most appropriate.

TABLE 12.4 Sensitivity Analysis for the Surveillance Camera

Criteria Weights							
Price	1	1	1	1	2	2.5	1
Weight	1.5	2	1	2	2	2.5	1
Picture clarity	3.5	3	3	2	2	2.5	4
Low-light performance	4	4	5	5	4	2.5	4
Alternative Scores							
Camera 1	44.5	43.0	49.0	46.0	50.0	47.5	46.0
Camera 2	49.3	48.8	48.8	47.8	53.6	57.0	49.8
Camera 4	64.8	65.9	65.7	67.9	69.4	67.2	63.7
Camera 6	64.8	66.2	63.4	66.2	66.8	68.4	63.4
Camera 7	59.1	58.3	57.9	56.3	57.8	59.7	59.9
Camera 10	66.5	67.7	62.0	63.6	58.0	60.0	66.0

As has been seen in Example 12.3, the decision matrix approach structures information about the problem. An additive utility model permits the calculation of an overall score for each alternative. A comparison of the scores permits the best one to be selected. Doing a sensitivity analysis may reveal alternatives that offer promise which arises from relatively small changes in the alternative weight assumptions.

12.4 The Analytic Hierarchy Process

The **analytic hierarchy process (AHP)** is also a MAUT approach. It offers two things beyond what is done in decision matrices. First, it provides a mechanism for structuring the problem that is particularly useful for large, complex decisions. Second, it provides a better method for establishing the criteria weights.

AHP is somewhat more complicated to carry out than decision matrices. In order to describe the procedure, we first list the basic steps. The example which follows the list of steps below explains in more detail the operations at each step. The basic steps of AHP are as follows:

1. Identify the decision to be made, called the **goal**. Structure the goal, criteria, and alternatives into a hierarchy, as illustrated in Figure 12.2. The criteria could be more than one level (not illustrated in Figure 12.2) to provide additional structure to very complex problems.

FIGURE 12.2   AHP Heirarchy

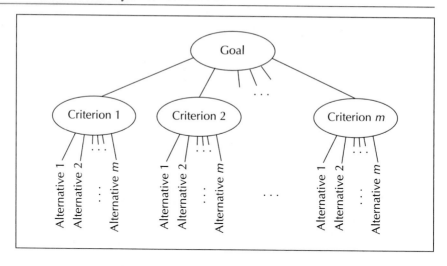

2. **Pairwise comparisions** are made for all possible pairs of alternatives with respect to each criterion. This is done by giving each pair of alternatives a value according to Table 12.5 for their relationship for that criterion. These values are placed in a **pairwise comparison matrix** (PCM).

3. **Priority weights** for the alternatives are calculated by normalizing the elements of the PCM and averaging the row entries.

4. As in steps 2 and 3, all pairs of criteria are compared. A PCM is determined, and priority weights are calculated for the criteria.

5. Alternative priority weights are multiplied by the corresponding criteria priority weights and summed to give an overall alternative ranking.

TABLE 12.5 The AHP Value Scale on Alternatives or Criteria A and B

Value	Verbal interpretation
1/9 = 0.111	Extreme preference/importance of B over A
1/7 = 0.1429	Very strong preference/importance of B over A
1/5 = 0.2	Strong preference/importance of B over A
1/3 = 0.333	Moderate preference/importance of B over A
1	Equal preference/importance of A and B
3	Moderate preference/importance of A over B
5	Strong preference/importance of A over B
7	Very strong preference/importance of A over B
9	Extreme preference/importance of A over B
Intermediate values	For more detail between above values

The following example illustrates this process.

EXAMPLE 12.4

Oksana is examining the cooling of a laboratory at Beaconsfield Pharmaceuticals. She has determined that a 12 000 BTU/hour cooling unit is suitable, but there are several models available with different features. The available quantitative data concerning the choices are shown in Table 12.6. The energy efficiency rating is a standard measure of power consumption efficiency.

TABLE 12.6 Cooling Unit Features

Model	Price	Energy Efficiency Rating
1	$640	9.5
2	$600	9.1
3	$959	10.0
4	$480	9.0
5	$460	9.0

Oksana also has several subjective criteria to take into account. She will use AHP to help her make this decision.

The first step for this problem is to structure the hierarchy. The goal is clear: to choose a cooling unit. The alternatives are also known, and are listed in Table 12.6. After some consideration, Oksana concludes that the following are critical to her consideration:

(1) Cost

(2) Energy consumption

(3) Loudness

(4) Perceived comfort

The resulting hierarchy is illustrated in Figure 12.3.

The second step is to construct a PCM for the alternatives of each criterion. For illustration purposes, we will do this step for the criterion "perceived comfort" only.

Oksana considers two of the alternatives only, say 1 and 2, with respect to "perceived comfort." She gives the preferred one (which is alternative 1) a rating from the scale shown in Table 12.5. In this case, Oksana judges that alternative 1 is moderately better than 2; the rating is a 3. This appears in the PCM shown in Figure 12.4 in row 1, column 2, corresponding to alternative 1 and alternative 2. Correspondingly, the reciprocal, 1/3, is put in row 2, column 1. This can be interpreted loosely as indicating that alternative 1 is three times as desirable as alternative 2 for perceived comfort, and correspondingly criterion 2 is 1/3 as desirable as alternative 1.

FIGURE 12.3   The AHP Hierarchy for Example 12.4

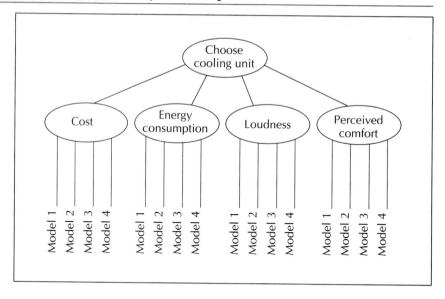

FIGURE 12.4 PCM for Perceived Comfort

$$\begin{bmatrix} 1 & 3 & 5 & 1 & 3 \\ \frac{1}{3} & 1 & 3 & \frac{1}{3} & 1 \\ \frac{1}{5} & \frac{1}{3} & 1 & \frac{1}{5} & \frac{1}{3} \\ 1 & 3 & 5 & 1 & 3 \\ \frac{1}{3} & 1 & 3 & \frac{1}{3} & 1 \end{bmatrix}$$

As another example, consider the comparison of alternatives 3 and 4. Alternative 4 is strongly preferred to 3 in "perceived comfort," so a 5 appears in row 4, column 3, and 1/5 appears in row 3 column 4. Similar comparisons of all pairs complete the PCM in Figure 12.4 for "perceived comfort." In summary, row 1 of Figure 12.4 shows the results of comparing alternative 1 with alternatives 1, 2, 3, 4, and 5. Row 2 shows the results of comparing alternative 2 with alternatives 1, 2, 3, 4, and 5, and so on. Note that an alternative is equally preferred to itself, so all main diagonal entries are 1. PCM for the other three criteria are developed in exactly the same manner.

The next step is to determine priority weights for the alternatives. This is done by first normalizing the columns of the PCM, and then averaging the rows. To normalize the columns, sum the column entries, and divide each entry by this sum. To average the rows, sum the rows (after normalizing) and divide by the number of entries per row.

For example, the sum of column 1 of the PCM in Figure 12.4 is 2.866. Then the normalized entries for the column will be 1/2.866, 0.333/2.866, etc. The complete normalized PCM for "perceived comfort" is shown in Figure 12.5. The priority weights are then calculated as the average of each row of the normalized PCM, and are also illustrated in Figure 12.5.

FIGURE 12.5 Normalized PCM for Perceived Comfort

Normalized PCM					Average
0.349	0.360	0.294	0.349	0.360	0.342
0.116	0.120	0.176	0.116	0.120	0.130
0.070	0.040	0.059	0.070	0.040	0.056
0.349	0.360	0.294	0.349	0.360	0.342
0.116	0.120	0.176	0.116	0.120	0.130

A similar process can be carried out for the other three criteria. The four columns (one for each criterion) of priority weights form a priority matrix, shown in Figure 12.6. The first column of this matrix consists of the priority weights for cost, the second for energy efficiency, the third for noise, and the fourth for perceived comfort.

FIGURE 12.6 Priority Matrix for Example 12.4

0.90	0.256	0.033	0.342
0.114	0.230	0.468	0.130
0.031	0.338	0.282	0.056
0.383	0.088	0.086	0.342
0.383	0.088	0.131	0.130

The next step is to construct a PCM for the criteria. This is done in the same manner as is done for the alternatives for each criterion, except that now one rates the criteria in pairwise comparisons with each other. The PCM Oksana creates is illustrated as Figure 12.7, with the rows and columns in the order: cost, energy consumption, loudness, and perceived comfort. For example, energy consumption is moderately more important than energy cost. Thus, there is a 1/3 in row 1, column 2, and a 3 in row 2, column 1. The normalized PCM and row averages are shown in Figure 12.8.

FIGURE 12.7 PCM for Goal

$$\begin{bmatrix} 1 & \frac{1}{3} & 5 & 1 \\ 3 & 1 & 7 & 3 \\ \frac{1}{5} & \frac{1}{7} & 1 & \frac{1}{5} \\ 1 & \frac{1}{3} & 5 & 1 \end{bmatrix}$$

FIGURE 12.8 Normalized PCM and Average Values for Goal

Average

$$\begin{bmatrix} 0.192 & 0.184 & 0.278 & 0.192 \\ 0.577 & 0.553 & 0.389 & 0.577 \\ 0.038 & 0.079 & 0.056 & 0.038 \\ 0.192 & 0.184 & 0.278 & 0.192 \end{bmatrix} \qquad \begin{bmatrix} 0.212 \\ 0.524 \\ 0.053 \\ 0.212 \end{bmatrix}$$

The order of the rows and columns of Figures 12.7 and 12.8 are: cost, noise, energy efficiency, and perceived comfort. Thus, the criterion with the highest priority rating is noise, at 0.524, then cost and perceived comfort identical at 0.212, and finally energy efficiency last at 0.053.

The final stage of the process consists of determining an overall score for each of the alternatives. Note that the entire process of AHP has essentially led to the development of a decision matrix: the priority ratings for the criteria are the weights, while the priority ratings for the alternatives are the ratings of the alternatives for the criteria. Consequently, the final score is determined by multiplying each alternative priority rating by the appropriate criterion rating and then summing.

This can also be viewed as matrix multiplication of the priority matrices for the alternatives by the vector of priority weights of the criteria, as shown in Figure 12.9. The interpretation of the column vector on the right in Figure 12.9 is a ranking of the alternatives. The best alternative is number 1, followed by number 3, then 4; 2 and 5 are the worst.

FIGURE 12.9 Final Alternative Scores for Example 12.4

$$\begin{bmatrix} 0.090 & 0.256 & 0.033 & 0.342 \\ 0.114 & 0.230 & 0.468 & 0.130 \\ 0.031 & 0.338 & 0.282 & 0.056 \\ 0.383 & 0.088 & 0.086 & 0.342 \\ 0.383 & 0.088 & 0.131 & 0.130 \end{bmatrix} \times \begin{bmatrix} 0.212 \\ 0.524 \\ 0.053 \\ 0.212 \end{bmatrix} = \begin{bmatrix} 0.227 \\ 0.197 \\ 0.211 \\ 0.204 \\ 0.162 \end{bmatrix}$$

In conclusion, the best cooling unit is model 1. Oksana should buy this one for the laboratory.

12.5 The Consistency Ratio for AHP

The subjective evaluation of the PCMs can be inconsistent. For example, Joe can say that alternative 1 is five times as important as alternative 2, and alternative 2 is five times as important as alternative 3, but then claim that alternative 1 is only twice as important as alternative 3. Or he might even say alternative 1 is less important than alternative 3.

The fact that the construction of PCMs includes redundant information is useful because it helps get a good estimate of the best rating for the alternative. However, there has to be a check made that the decision maker is being consistent.

A measure called the **consistency ratio** (to measure the consistency of the reported comparisons) can be calculated for any PCM. The consistency ratio ranges from 0 (perfect consistency) to 1 (no consistency). A consistency ratio of 0.1 or less is considered acceptable. The calculation of the consistency ratio is outside the scope of this textbook; a summary of the procedure is reviewed in the appendix to this chapter.

CANADIAN CORPORATE CASE 12.1

Northwind Stoneware

Northwind Stoneware of Kitchener, Ontario, makes consumer stoneware products. Stoneware is fired in a kiln, which is an enclosure made of a porous brick having heating elements designed to raise the internal temperature to over 1200°C. Clay items such as stoneware can be hardened by firing them, following a particular temperature pattern called a firing curve.

Quality and cost problems led Northwind to examine better ways to control the firing curve. Alternatives available to them included:

1. Direct human control. The temperature sensitivity of the human eye cannot be matched by any automatic control.

2. Use of a "Kilnsitter," which is a mechanical switch that shuts off the kiln at a preset temperature

3. Use of a pyrometer, which is an electrical instrument for measuring heat, with a programmable controller

4. Use of a pyrometer and a computer

The criteria used to determine the best choice included installation cost, effectiveness, reliability, energy savings, maintenance costs, and other applications.

A decision matrix evaluation method was used. Under a variety of criteria weights, the use of a pyrometer and a computer was the recommended choice. The exception was when installation cost was given overwhelming weight; in this case the use of a Kilnsitter was recommended.

REVIEW PROBLEMS

Review Problem 12.1

Contrex makes thermostat controls for baseboard heaters. As part of the control manufacturing process, a 2-cm. steel diaphragm is fitted to a steel cup. The diaphragm is used to open a safety switch rapidly to avoid arcing across the contacts. Currently the cup is seam welded, which is both expensive and a source of quality problems. The company wants to explore the use of adhesives to replace the welding process. Table 12.7 lists the ones examined, along with various properties for each.

TABLE 12.7 Possible Adhesives for Thermostat Control

Adhesive	Maximum Temperature (°F)	Tensile Bond Strength (psi)	Pressure Resistance (psi)	Curing Speed	Cost
Acrylic	212	3 000	534	Medium	Cheap
Silicone	400	450	80	Slow	Medium
Cyanoacrylate	500	500	90	Fast	Cheap
Methacrylate A	450	4 000	712	Slow	Expensive
Methacrylate B	450	1 000	178	Medium	Expensive

High-temperature resistance is desirable, as are tensile bond strength and pressure resistance. Fast curing speeds are desirable to reduce work-in-progress inventory storage costs, and, of course, cheaper material costs are important.

Contrex wants to select a single adhesive type for comparison experiments against the current seam-welding method.

(a) Are any of the listed adhesives in Table 12.7 inefficient?

(b) Discussions with management indicate that the criteria can be weighted as follows:

Temperature resistance	1.5
Bond strength	1.5
Pressure resistance	2.5
Curing speed	3.5
Cost	1.0
Total	10.0

Create a decision matrix for this problem using the above weights. Normalize the data in Table 12.7 to estimate the ratings of each alternative for each criterion. Use only the efficient alternatives. Use the maximum temperature figures to measure temperature resistance. For curing speed, set fast as 8, medium as 5, and slow as 2, while for cost, set expensive as 10, medium as 5, and cheap as 2. Under these conditions, which is the recommended adhesive?

(c) The analytic hierarchy process (AHP) was performed for this problem. The hierarchy is shown in Figure 12.10. The priority matrix in Figure 12.11 represents the results from PCMs calculated for the different criteria. The rows of Figure 12.11 correspond to the alternatives acrylic, cyanoacrylate, methacrylate A, and methacrylate B, respectively, while the columns correspond to temperature resistance, bond strength, pressure resistance, curing speed, and cost, respectively.

FIGURE 12.10 The AHP Hierarchy for Review Problem 12.1(c)

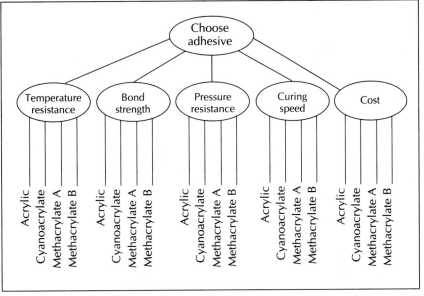

FIGURE 12.11 Priority Matrix for Review Problem 12.1 (c)

$$
\begin{bmatrix}
0.095 & 0.368 & 0.392 & 0.213 & 0.341 \\
0.331 & 0.077 & 0.067 & 0.502 & 0.278 \\
0.287 & 0.445 & 0.438 & 0.061 & 0.188 \\
0.287 & 0.110 & 0.103 & 0.224 & 0.193
\end{bmatrix}
$$

A PCM for the goal is shown in Figure 12.12, with the criteria in the same order as for Figure 12.11.

FIGURE 12.12 PCM for Goal for Review Problem 12.1 (c)

$$
\begin{bmatrix}
1 & 1 & \frac{1}{2} & \frac{1}{3} & 2 \\
1 & 1 & \frac{1}{2} & \frac{1}{3} & 2 \\
2 & 2 & 1 & \frac{1}{2} & 3 \\
3 & 3 & 2 & 1 & 4 \\
\frac{1}{2} & \frac{1}{2} & \frac{1}{3} & \frac{1}{4} & 1
\end{bmatrix}
$$

With this information, what is the best adhesive to recommend for the experiment?

Answer

(a) It can be observed that silicone is dominated by cyanoacrylate in all criteria, and therefore is inefficient.

(b) **TABLE 12.8 Decision Matrix of Adhesives**

Criteria	Weights	Acrylic	Cyanoacrylate	Methacrylate A	Methacrylate B
			Alternatives		
Temperature resistance	1.5	0.0	10.0	8.3	8.3
Bond strength	1.5	7.1	0.0	10.0	1.4
Pressure resistance	2.5	7.1	0.0	10.0	1.4
Curing speed	3.5	5.0	8.0	2.0	5.0
Cost	1	2.0	2.0	10.0	10.0
Score	10	48.1	45.0	69.4	45.6

As shown in Table 12.8, under the weighting and rating conditions specified, the methacrylate A adhesive is clearly best.

(c) First we have to normalize the PCM for the goal, and then average to get the criteria weights, as shown in Figure 12.13.

FIGURE 12.13 Normalized PCM for Goal for Review Problem 12.1 (c)

Normalized PCM   **Average**

$$
\begin{bmatrix}
0.133 & 0.133 & 0.115 & 0.138 & 0.167 \\
0.133 & 0.133 & 0.115 & 0.138 & 0.167 \\
0.267 & 0.267 & 0.231 & 0.207 & 0.250 \\
0.4 & 0.4 & 0.462 & 0.414 & 0.333 \\
0.067 & 0.067 & 0.077 & 0.130 & 0.083
\end{bmatrix}
\begin{bmatrix}
0.137 \\
0.137 \\
0.244 \\
0.402 \\
0.079
\end{bmatrix}
$$

Then we multiply the priority matrix by the average criteria weights, as illustrated in Figure 12.14.

FIGURE 12.14 Calculating Alternative Weights for Review Problem 12.1 (c)

$$
\begin{bmatrix}
0.095 & 0.368 & 0.392 & 0.213 & 0.341 \\
0.331 & 0.077 & 0.067 & 0.502 & 0.278 \\
0.287 & 0.445 & 0.438 & 0.061 & 0.188 \\
0.287 & 0.110 & 0.103 & 0.224 & 0.193
\end{bmatrix}
\times
\begin{bmatrix}
0.137 \\
0.137 \\
0.244 \\
0.402 \\
0.079
\end{bmatrix}
=
\begin{bmatrix}
0.272 \\
0.296 \\
0.247 \\
0.185
\end{bmatrix}
$$

Since the second alternative in Figure 12.14 has the highest net weight, it is preferred. The recommended adhesive using AHP is the cyanoacrylate. This disagrees with the result obtained using decision matrices.

SUMMARY

In this chapter, three approaches for dealing explicitly with multiple criteria were presented. The first, *efficiency*, allows the identification of alternatives that are not dominated by others. An alternative is dominated if there is another alternative at least as good with respect to all criteria, and better in at least one.

The second approach, *decision matrices*, is in wide usage. Decision matrices are a multi-attribute utility theory (MAUT) method in which criteria are subjectively weighted, and then multiplied by subjectively evaluated criteria ratings to give an overall score. The weights sum to 10.0, and the criteria ratings are on a scale from 0 to 10, resulting in an overall score that could range from 0 to 100. The alternative with the highest score is best, and the value of the score can be consider a percentage of an "ideal" alternative.

The third approach presented in this chapter is the *analytic hierarchy process*. AHP is also a MAUT method. Pairwise comparisons are used to extract criterion weights in a more rigorous manner than for decision matrices. Pairwise comparisons similarly are used to rate alternatives. Multiplying criterion weights and alternative ratings gives an overall evaluation for each alternative.

Engineering Economics in Action, Part 12B: Moving On

Three months later Naomi was seated in Anna Kulkowski's office. The Powerluxe project report had been submitted two days before.

"Naomi, the work you and Bill did and your report are first rate," Anna said. "We're going to start negotiations with Powerluxe to bring the Adaptamatic line of vacuum cleaners to market. I had no idea anybody could make such clear recommendations on such a complex problem. Congratulations on a good job."

Naomi thought back on all the people that had helped her in her almost two years at Canadian Widgets: how Clem had taught her practical problem solving; how Dave had shown her the ropes; how Terry had helped her realize the benefits of attention to detail. Bill had shown her how the real world mixed engineering with marketing, business, and government. Anna, too, had shown her how to manage people. "Thank you very much, Ms. Kulkowski," Naomi responded, a small break in her voice betraying her emotions.

"Do you enjoy this kind of work?" Anna asked.

"Yes, I do," Naomi replied. "It's exciting to see how the engineering relates to everything else."

"I think we have a new long-term assignment for you," Anna said. "This is just the first step for Canadian Widgets in developing new products. We have a first-rate team of engineers. We want to make better use of them. Ed Burns is going to head up a product development group. He read your report on the Adaptamatic line of vacuum cleaners. He was quite impressed. He and I would

like you in that development group. We need someone who understands the engineering and can relate it to markets. What do you say?"

"I'm in!" Naomi had a big grin on her face.

A few days later, Naomi answered the phone.

"Hey, Naomi, it's Terry. I hear you got promoted!"

"Hi, Terry. Nice to hear from you. Well, the money's about the same, but it sure will be interesting. How are things with you?" Naomi had fond memories of working with Terry.

"Well, I graduate next month, and I have a job. Guess where?"

Naomi knew exactly where. Clem had told her about the interviews. He wasn't really fair to the other candidates—Clem had decided to hire Terry as soon as he had applied. "Not here? Really?"

PROBLEMS

12.1 The table below shows information about alternative choices. Criteria C and E are to be minimized, while all the rest are to be maximized. Which of the alternatives can be eliminated from further consideration?

Criterion Alternative	A	B	C	D	E
1	340	5	11	1.2	1
2	570	8	22	3.3	1
3	410	9	22	3.2	2
4	120	4	36	0.9	3
5	122	1	46	1.3	2
6	345	8	47	0.6	3
7	119	4	57	1.1	2
8	554	2	89	2.1	3
9	317	9	117	0.9	1
10	129	5	165	1.5	3

12.2 The following is a partially completed pairwise comparison matrix. Complete it. What are the corresponding priority weights?

$$\begin{bmatrix} - & \frac{1}{2} & - & \frac{1}{9} \\ - & - & - & - \\ 4 & 2 & - & \frac{1}{2} \\ - & 4 & - & - \end{bmatrix}$$

12.3 The Toronto Transit Commission is considering building a new subway line. All the alternatives are shown in the Alternative Subway Lines table, with their criteria values. The relevant criteria are:

C1 Population and jobs served per kilometre

C2 Projected daily traffic per kilometre

C3 Capital cost per kilometre (in millions of dollars)

C4 IRR

C5 Structural effect on urbanization

It is desirable to have high population served, high traffic, low capital cost per kilometre, and a high IRR. Criterion C5 concerns the benefits for urban growth caused by the subway location, and is measured on a scale from 0 to 10, with the higher values being preferred.

Alternative Subway Lines (Data for problem 12.3)						
Criterion	Project					
	P1	P2	P3	P4	P5	P6
C1	81 900	31 800	11 500	31 100	23 000	16 100
C2	25 500	11 600	7 100	10 500	10 200	3 500
C3	65	45	29	35	40	10
C4	8.6	6.3	4.5	14.1	12.	11.8
C5	3	7	4	6	5	4
Criterion	Project					
	P7	P8	P9	P10	P11	P12
C1	13200	28 200	36 500	24 400	18 400	13 900
C2	3 700	7 400	10 300	7 100	4 700	3 100
C3	32	30	12.2	40	43	25
C4	3.9	6	3	3.7	3.7	5.8
C5	9	10	6	9	5	4

(a) Which of these alternatives are efficient?

(b) Establish ratings for each of the efficient alternatives from part (a) for a decision matrix through normalization. The weights of the five criteria are: C1: 1.5, C2: 2, C3: 2.5, C4: 3, C5: 1. Construct a decision matrix and determine the best subway route.

(c) If the criteria weights were C1: 2, C2: 2, C3: 2, C4: 2, C5: 2, would the recommended alternative be different?

12.4 Sudbury Steel is considering buying a new CNC punch press. They place high value on the reliability of this equipment, since it will be central to their production process. Speed and quality are also important to them, but not as important as reliability. As well as examining these factors, the company will make sure that the equipment will be easily adaptable to changes in production.

Construct a decision matrix for the alternatives listed and appropriate criteria. Select appropriate weightings for the criteria (state any assumptions), and determine the preferred alternative. Do a reasonable sensitivity analysis to determine the conditions under which the choice of alternative may change. A spreadsheet program should be used. Hand in enough spreadsheet printouts to demonstrate your results.

The alternatives are:

1. Name: Accumate Plasmapress
   Cost: $428 600
   Service: Average
   Reliability: Average
   Speed: High
   Quality: Good
   Flexibility: Excellent
   Size: Average
   Other: None

2. Name: Weissman Model 4560
   Cost: $383 765
   Service: Below average
   Reliability: Average
   Speed: High
   Quality: Fair
   Flexibility: Not good
   Size: Average
   Other: Many tool stations (desirable), but small tools (not desirable)

3. Name: A.D. Hockley Model 661-84
   Cost: $533 725
   Service: Untested
   Reliability: Average
   Speed: Slow
   Quality: Very good
   Flexibility: Very good
   Size: Very compact
   Other: Small turret (not desirable)

4. Name: Frammit Manu-Centre 1500/45
   Cost: $393 000
   Service: Average
   Reliability: Below average
   Speed: Average
   Quality: Average
   Flexibility: Average
   Size: Average
   Other: Has perforating and coining feature (very desirable)
                Poor torch design causes too rapid wear (undesirable)

5. Name: Frammit Manu-Centre Lasertool 1250/30/1500
   Cost: $340 056
   Service: Average
   Reliability: Average
   Speed: Exceptionally fast
   Quality: Exceptionally good
   Flexibility: Average
   Size: Undesirably small
   Other: Cannot handle heavy gauge metal (not desirable)

6. Name: Boxcab 3025/12P CNC
   Cost: $405 232
   Service: Untested
   Reliability: Excellent
   Speed: Average
   Quality: Very good
   Flexibility: Average
   Size: Average
   Other: None

12.5 Complete each of the following pairwise comparison matrices:

(a)
$$
\begin{bmatrix}
- & 1 & - & - \\
- & - & - & 2 \\
\frac{1}{5} & 3 & - & - \\
3 & - & \frac{1}{2} & -
\end{bmatrix}
$$

(b)
$$
\begin{bmatrix}
- & 9 & - & 1 & 3 \\
- & - & 3 & - & - \\
\frac{1}{7} & - & - & \frac{1}{4} & 2 \\
- & 6 & - & - & - \\
- & 1 & - & 2 & -
\end{bmatrix}
$$

12.6 For each of the pairwise comparison matrices in problem 12.5, compute priority weights for the alternatives.

12.7 (a) Francis has several job opportunities for his co-op work term. He would like a job with good pay, that is close to home, that contributes to his engineering studies, and is with a smaller company. Which of the opportunities listed below should be removed from further consideration?

Criteria Job	Pay	Home	Studies	Size
1. Spinoff Consulting	1700	2	3	5
2. Nub Automotive	1600	5	3	500
3. Soutel	2200	80	4	150
4. Provincial Hydro	1800	100	3	3000
5. Fitzsimon Associates	1700	100	1	20
6. General Auto	2000	150	2	2500
7. Ring Canada	2200	250	5	300
8. Jones Mines	2700	500	3	20
9. Resources, Inc.	2700	2000	2	40

Pay: Monthly salary in dollars
Home: Distance from home in kilometres
Studies: Contribution to engineering studies, 0 = none, 5 = a lot
Size: Number of employees at that location

(b) Francis feels that the following weights can represent the importance of his four criteria:

Pay:	4.0
Home:	2.5
Studies:	2.0
Size:	1.5

Using normalization to establish the ratings, which job is best?

Problems 12.8 to 12.23 are based on the following situation.

John is considering the selection of a consultant to provide ongoing support for a computer system. John wishes to contract with one consultant only, based on the criteria of cost, reliability, familiarity with equipment, location, and quality. Cost is measured by the quoted daily rate. Reliability and quality are measured on a qualitative scale based on discussions with references and interviews with the consultants. Familiarity with equipment has three possibilities: none, some, or much. Location is measured by distance from the consultant's office to the plant site, in kilometres.

The specific data for the consultants are as follows:

	Consultant				
Criterion	A	B	C	D	E
Cost	$500	$500	$450	$600	$400
Reliability	Good	Good	Excellent	Good	Fair
Familiarity	None	Some	Some	Much	Some
Location	3	1	5	2	1
Quality	Excellent	Good	Fair	Excellent	Good

12.8 Is any choice of consultant inefficient?

12.9 John can assign weights to the criteria as follows:

Criterion	Weight
Cost	2
Reliability	3
Familiarity	1
Location	1
Quality	3

Using the following tables to convert qualitative evaluations to numbers, and using the formula for determining ratings by normalization, construct a decision matrix for choosing a consultant. Which consultant is best?

For Reliability and Quantity	
Description	Value
Excellent	5
Very Good	4
Good	3
Fair	2
Poor	1

For Familiarity	
Description	Value
None	1
Some	2
Much	3

12.10 Draw an AHP hierarchy for this problem.

12.11 John considers a cost difference of $100 or more to be of strong importance, and a difference of $50 to be of moderate importance. Construct a PCM for the criterion *cost*.

12.12 John considers the difference between good reliability and fair reliability to be of moderate importance, and the difference between good and excellent to be of strong importance. He considers the difference between fair and excellent to be of very strong importance. Construct a PCM for the criterion *reliability*.

12.13 John considers the difference between no familiarity with the computing equipment and some familiarity to be of strong importance, and the difference between none and much familiarity to be of extreme importance. He considers the difference between some and much to be of strong importance. Construct a PCM for the criterion *familiarity*.

12.14 John considers each kilometre of distance worth two units on the AHP value scale. For example, the value of the location of consultant D over consultant C is $(5 - 2) \times 2 = 6$, and a 6 would be placed in the fourth row, third column, of the PCM for the criterion *location*. Construct the complete PCM for the criterion *location*.

12.15 John considers the difference between fair quality and good quality to be of strong importance, and the difference between good and excellent to be of very strong importance. He considers the difference between fair and excellent to be of extreme importance. Construct a PCM for the criterion *quality*.

12.16 Calculate the priority weights for the criterion *cost* from the PCM constructed in problem 12.11.

12.17 Calculate the priority weights for the criterion *reliability* from the PCM constructed in problem 12.12.

12.18 Calculate the priority weights for the criterion *familiarity* from the PCM constructed in problem 12.13.

12.19 Calculate the priority weights for the criterion *location* from the PCM constructed in problem 12.14.

12.20 Calculate the priority weights for the criterion *quality* from the PCM constructed in problem 12.15.

12.21 Construct the priority matrix from the answers to problems 12.16 to 12.20.

12.22 A partially completed PCM for the criteria is shown below. Complete the PCM and calculate the priority weights for the criteria.

$$
\begin{bmatrix}
- & \frac{1}{3} & - & 3 & - \\
- & - & - & - & 1 \\
\frac{1}{3} & \frac{1}{7} & - & 1 & - \\
- & \frac{1}{6} & - & - & - \\
1 & - & 7 & 7 & -
\end{bmatrix}
$$

12.23 Determine the overall score for each alternative. Which consultant is best?

Problems 12.24 to 12.31 are based on the following case.

Fabian has several job opportunities for his co-op work term. The pay is in dollars per month. The distance from home is in kilometres. Relevance to studies is on a five-point scale, with a 5 meaning very relevant to studies and a 0 meaning not relevant at all. The company size refers to the number of employees at the job location.

In general, Fabian wants a job with good pay, that is close to home, contributes to his engineering studies, and is with a smaller company.

Criteria / Job	Pay	Distance from Home	Relevance to Studies	Company Size
1. Spinoff Consulting	1700	2	3	5
2. Soutel	2200	80	4	150
3. Ring Canada	2200	250	5	300
4. Jones Mines	2700	500	3	20

12.24 Draw an AHP hierarchy for this problem.

12.25 (a) Complete the PCM below for *Pay*.

$$\begin{bmatrix} - & \frac{1}{5} & \frac{1}{5} & \frac{1}{7} \\ - & - & 1 & \frac{1}{5} \\ - & - & - & \frac{1}{5} \\ - & - & - & - \end{bmatrix}$$

(b) What are the priority weights for *Pay*?

12.26 (a) Complete the PCM below for *Distance from Home*.

$$\begin{bmatrix} - & - & - & - \\ \frac{1}{5} & - & - & - \\ \frac{1}{7} & \frac{1}{5} & - & - \\ \frac{1}{9} & \frac{1}{7} & \frac{1}{2} & - \end{bmatrix}$$

(b) What are the priority weights for *Distance from Home*?

12.27 (a) Complete the PCM below for *Studies*.

$$\begin{bmatrix} - & - & \frac{1}{3} & - \\ 2 & - & - & 2 \\ - & 2 & - & - \\ 1 & - & \frac{1}{3} & - \end{bmatrix}$$

(b) What are the priority weights for *Studies?*

12.28 **(a)** Complete the PCM below for *Size.*

$$
\begin{bmatrix}
- & - & - & 1 \\
\frac{1}{7} & - & - & \frac{1}{7} \\
\frac{1}{9} & \frac{1}{2} & - & \frac{1}{9} \\
- & - & - & -
\end{bmatrix}
$$

(b) What are the priority weights for *Size?*

12.29 Form a priority matrix for the PCMs in problems 12.25 to 12.28.

12.30 Given the following PCM for the criteria, calculate the priority weights for the criteria.

PCM for Criteria

$$
\begin{bmatrix}
1 & 3 & 5 & 5 \\
\frac{1}{3} & 1 & 3 & 3 \\
\frac{1}{5} & \frac{1}{3} & 1 & 2 \\
\frac{1}{5} & \frac{1}{3} & \frac{1}{2} & 1
\end{bmatrix}
$$

12.31 Using the results of problems 12.29 and 12.30, calculate the priority weights for the goal. Which job is Fabian's best choice? His second best choice?

APPENDIX 12A: Calculating the Consistency Ratio for AHP

The consistency ratio (*CR*) for AHP provides a measure of the ability of a decision maker to report preferences over alternatives or criteria. Calculating the *CR* can be done without understanding the concepts underlying it, but some background can be helpful. In this appendix, a brief overview of the basis for the *CR* is given, but the main purpose is to present an algorithm for calculating the *CR*. For the background information, some understanding of linear algebra is desirable, but the algorithm for calculating the *CR* can be easily followed without this background information.

Recall that in AHP a pairwise comparison matrix (PCM) is developed by comparing, for example, the alternatives with respect to one criterion. If alternative *x* is compared with *y*, and found to be twice as preferred, and *y* is compared with *z*, and is three times as preferred, then it is easy to deduce that x should be six times as preferred as z. However, in AHP every pairwise comparison is made, giving several judgments about the same relationship. Humans will not necessarily be perfectly consistent in reporting preferences; one of the strengths of AHP is that by getting redundant preference information the quality of the information is improved.

Observe that if a decision maker were perfectly consistent, the columns of a PCM would be multiples of each other. They would differ in scale because for each column n the nth row is fixed as 1, but the relative values would be constant.

Recall that an eigenvalue λ is one of n solutions to the equation

$$\mathbf{Aw} = \lambda\mathbf{w}$$

where $\mathbf{A}$ is a square $n \times n$ matrix and $\mathbf{w}$ is an $n \times 1$ eigenvector.

There is one eigenvector corresponding to each eigenvalue λ. A PCM is unusual in that, in addition to being a square matrix, all of the entries are positive, the corresponding entries across the main diagonal are reciprocals, and there are 1s along the main diagonal. It can be shown that, in this case, if the decision maker is perfectly consistent, there will be a single non-zero eigenvalue, and $n - 1$ eigenvectors of value 0.

In practice, a PCM $\mathbf{A}$ will not be perfectly consistent. However, assuming that the error is relatively small, there should be one large eigenvalue $\lambda_{\max}$ and $n - 1$ small ones. Further, it can be shown that, with small inconsistencies, $\lambda_{\max} > n$.

The *CR* is developed from the difference between $\lambda_{\max}$ and n. First, this difference is divided by $n - 1$, effectively distributing it over the other, supposedly zero, eigenvalues. This gives the *consistency index (CI)*.

$$CI = \frac{\lambda_{\max} - n}{n - 1}$$

Second, the *CI* is divided by the *CI* of a random matrix of the same size, called a *random index (RI)*, to form the *consistency ratio (CR)*. The *RI* for matrices of up to 10 rows and columns is shown in Table 12A.1; these were developed by averaging the *CI*s for hundreds of randomly generated matrices.

$$CR = \frac{CI}{RI}$$

The idea is that, if the PCM were completely random, we would expect the *CI* to be equal to the *RI*. Thus, a random PCM would have a *CR* of 1. However, a consistent PCM, having a *CI* of 0, would also have a *CR* of 0. *CR*s of between 0 and 1 indicate how consistent or random the PCM is, in a manner that is independent of the size of the matrix.

TABLE 12A.1 Random Indexes for Various Sizes of Matrices

Size (n − n)	Random Index
2	0
3	0.58
4	0.90
5	1.12
6	1.24
7	1.32
8	1.41
9	1.45
10	1.49

The *CR* is actually a well-designed statistical measure of the deviation of a particular PCM from perfect consistency. As a rule of thumb, an upper limit of 0.1 is usually used. Thus, if $CR \leq 0.1$, the PCM is *acceptably* consistent. If the $CR > 0.1$, the PCM should be re-evaluated by the decision maker.

This background can be used to construct an algorithm for calculating the CR for any PCM. Essentially, one determines λ_{max} and its associated eigenvector, called the **principal eigenvector**. The general algorithm for a PCM **A** of size $n \times n$ is as follows:

1. Find **w**, the eigenvector associated with λ_{max}, from normalizing the following:

$$\mathbf{w} = \lim_{k \to \infty} \frac{\mathbf{A}^k \mathbf{e}}{n}$$

where **e** is a column vector $[111...111]^{T}$

In other words, form a sequence of powers of the matrix **A**. Normalize each of the resulting matrices by dividing each element of **A** by the sum of the elements from the corresponding column. Form **w** by summing each row of normalized **A** and dividing this by n. Eventually, **w** will not noticeably change from one power of **A** to the next higher power. This value of **w** is the desired principal eigenvector.

In the main part of this chapter, we calculated the priority weights for a PCM. That procedure was an approximate method of determining **w**; the priority weights and the eigenvector associated with λ_{max} are the same thing. The procedure mentioned here is more accurate, but more difficult to compute.

2. Since **w** is a vector, λ_{max} can be found by solving $\mathbf{A}\mathbf{w} = \lambda_{max}\mathbf{w}$ or any element of **w**, or equivalently, any row of **A**. Thus, for any i, solve:

$$\lambda_{max} = \frac{\sum_j (a_{ij} \times w_j)}{w_i}$$

3. Calculate the *CI* from

$$CI = \frac{\lambda_{max} - n}{n - 1}$$

4. With reference to Table 12A.1, calculate the CR from

$$CR = \frac{CI}{RI}$$

If $CR \leq 0.1$, the PCM is acceptably consistent.

EXAMPLE 12A.1

Does the PCM of Figure 12.4 meet the requirement for a consistency ratio of less than or equal to 0.1?

The PCM of Figure 12.4 is reproduced as Figure 12A.1, with successive powers of the original matrix, normalized versions of the powers, and the calculated **w**. The calculations were done using a spreadsheet program; most popular spreadsheet programs can automatically find powers of matrices.

It can be seen that **w** converges very quickly to a stable set of values. Normally, the less consistent is a PCM, the longer it will take to converge. Also, note that the elements of **w** are very close to the priority weights that were calculated for this PCM in Section 12.4.

To determine λ_{max}, we must now solve $\mathbf{Aw} = \lambda_{max}\mathbf{w}$ for one row of **A**. Selecting the first row of **A** results in the following expression:

$$[1\ 3\ 5\ 1\ 3] \begin{bmatrix} 0.343 \\ 0.129 \\ 0.055 \\ 0.343 \\ 0.129 \end{bmatrix} = \lambda_{max} \times 0.343$$

Or, equivalently:

$$\lambda_{max} = \frac{(1 \times 0.343) + (3 \times 0.129) + 5 \times 0.055) + (1 \times 0.343) + (3 \times 0.129)}{0.343}$$

$$= 5.0583$$

FIGURE 12A.1 Calculating the Principal Eigenvector w

	A					Normalized					w
	1	3	5	1	3	0.349	0.36	0.29	0.349	0.36	0.342
A¹	0.2	0.333	1	0.2	0.333	0.07	0.04	0.06	0.07	0.04	0.056
	1	3	5	1	3	0.349	0.36	0.29	0.349	0.36	0.342
	0.333	1	3	0.33	1	0.116	0.12	0.18	0.116	0.12	0.130
	5	13.67	33	5	13.667	0.34	0.346	0.35	0.34	0.346	0.343
	1.933	5	12.3	1.93	5	0.132	0.126	0.13	0.132	0.126	0.129
A²	0.822	2.2	5	0.82	2.2	0.056	0.056	0.05	0.056	0.056	0.055
	5	13.67	33	5	13.667	0.34	0.346	0.35	0.34	0.346	0.343
	1.933	5	12.3	1.93	5	0.132	0.126	0.13	0.132	0.126	0.129
	25.711	68.33	165	25.7	68.333	0.343	0.343	0.34	0.343	0.343	0.343
	9.667	25.71	61.7	9.67	25.711	0.129	0.129	0.13	0.129	0.129	01.29
A³	4.111	1	26.4	4.11	11	0.055	0.055	0.06	0.055	0.055	0.055
	25.711	68.33	165	25.7	68.333	0.343	0.343	0.34	0.343	0.343	0.343
	9.667	25.71	61.7	9.67	25.711	0.129	0.129	0.13	0.129	0.129	01.29
	129.98	345.9	832	130	345.93	0.343	0.343	0.34	0.343	0.343	0.349
	48.807	130	313	48.8	129.98	0.129	0.129	0.13	0.129	0.129	0.129
A⁴	20.84	55.47	134	20.8	55.474	0.055	0.055	0.06	0.055	0.055	0.055
	129.98	345.9	832	130	345.93	0.343	0.343	0.34	0.343	0.343	0.349
	48.807	130	313	48.8	129.98	0.129	0.129	0.13	0.129	0.129	0.129
	657	1749	4207	657	1749.1	0.343	0.343	0.34	0.343	0.343	0.343
	246.79	657	1581	247	657	0.129	0.129	0.13	0.129	0.129	0.129
A⁵	105.37	280.5	675	105	280.5	0.055	0.055	0.06	0.055	0.055	0.055
	657	1749	4207	657	1749.1	0.343	0.343	0.34	0.343	0.343	0.343
	246.79	657	1581	247	657	0.129	0.129	0.13	0.129	0.129	0.129

The consistency index can then be calculated from

$$CI = \frac{\lambda_{max} - n}{n - 1}$$
$$= \frac{5.0583 - 5}{5 - 1}$$
$$= 0.0146$$

As seen in Table 12A.1, the *RI* for a matrix of five rows and columns is 1.12. We can then calculate the consistency ratio as

$$CR = \frac{CI}{RI} = \frac{0.0146}{1.12} = 0.013$$

Clearly, the *CR* is very much less than 0.1. It can thus be concluded that the original PCM is acceptably consistent.

PROBLEMS FOR APPENDIX 12A

12A.1 Does the following PCM meet the requirement for a consistency ratio of less than or equal to 0.1? What are the values of the consistency index and the consistency ratio?

$$\begin{bmatrix} 1 & \frac{1}{2} & \frac{1}{4} & \frac{1}{9} \\ 2 & 1 & \frac{1}{2} & \frac{1}{4} \\ 4 & 3 & 1 & 1 \\ 9 & 7 & 1 & 1 \end{bmatrix}$$

12A.2 Does the following PCM meet the requirement for a consistency ratio of less than or equal to 0.1? What are the values of the consistency index and the consistency ratio?

$$\begin{bmatrix} 1 & \frac{1}{2} & \frac{1}{4} & \frac{1}{9} \\ 2 & 1 & \frac{1}{2} & \frac{1}{4} \\ 4 & 3 & 1 & 1 \\ 9 & 7 & 1 & 1 \end{bmatrix}$$

12A.3 Does the following PCM meet the requirement for a consistency ratio of less than or equal to 0.1? What are the values of the consistency index and the consistency ratio? How does an accurate evaluation of the principal eigenvector for this PCM compare with the priority weights calculated in problem 12.30?

$$\begin{bmatrix} 1 & 3 & 5 & 5 \\ \frac{1}{3} & 1 & 3 & 3 \\ \frac{1}{5} & \frac{1}{3} & 1 & 2 \\ \frac{1}{5} & \frac{1}{3} & \frac{1}{2} & 1 \end{bmatrix}$$

Compound Interest Factors for Discrete Compounding, Discrete Cash Flows

i = 0.5%   Discrete Compounding, Discrete Cash Flows

	SINGLE PAYMENT		UNIFORM SERIES				Arithmetic Gradient Series Factor
	Compound Amount Factor	Present Worth Factor	Sinking Fund Factor	Uniform Series Factor	Capital Recovery Factor	Series Present Worth Factor	
N	(F/P,i,N)	(P/F,i,N)	(A/F,i,N)	(F/A,i,N)	(A/P,i,N)	(P/A,i,N)	(A/G,i,N)
1	1.0050	0.99502	1.0000	1.0000	1.0050	0.99502	0.00000
2	1.0100	0.99007	0.49875	2.0050	0.50375	1.9851	0.49875
3	1.0151	0.98515	0.33167	3.0150	0.33667	2.9702	0.99667
4	1.0202	0.98025	0.24813	4.0301	0.25313	3.9505	1.4938
5	1.0253	0.97537	0.19801	5.0503	0.20301	4.9259	1.9900
6	1.0304	0.97052	0.16460	6.0755	0.16960	5.8964	2.4855
7	1.0355	0.96569	0.14073	7.1059	0.14573	6.8621	2.9801
8	1.0407	0.96089	0.12283	8.1414	0.12783	7.8230	3.4738
9	1.0459	0.95610	0.10891	9.1821	0.11391	8.7791	3.9668
10	1.0511	0.95135	0.09777	10.228	0.10277	9.7304	4.4589
11	1.0564	0.94661	0.08866	11.279	0.09366	10.677	4.9501
12	1.0617	0.94191	0.08107	12.336	0.08607	11.619	5.4406
13	1.0670	0.93722	0.07464	13.397	0.07964	12.556	5.9302
14	1.0723	0.93256	0.06914	14.464	0.07414	13.489	6.4190
15	1.0777	0.92792	0.06436	15.537	0.06936	14.417	6.9069
16	1.0831	0.92330	0.06019	16.614	0.06519	15.340	7.3940
17	1.0885	0.91871	0.05651	17.697	0.06151	16.259	7.8803
18	1.0939	0.91414	0.05323	18.786	0.05823	17.173	8.3658
19	1.0994	0.90959	0.05030	19.880	0.05530	18.082	8.8504
20	1.1049	0.90506	0.04767	20.979	0.05267	18.987	9.3342
21	1.1104	0.90056	0.04528	22.084	0.05028	19.888	9.8172
22	1.1160	0.89608	0.04311	23.194	0.04811	20.784	10.299
23	1.1216	0.89162	0.04113	24.310	0.04613	21.676	10.781
24	1.1272	0.88719	0.03932	25.432	0.04432	22.563	11.261
25	1.1328	0.88277	0.03765	26.559	0.04265	23.446	11.741
26	1.1385	0.87838	0.03611	27.692	0.04111	24.324	12.220
27	1.1442	0.87401	0.03469	28.830	0.03969	25.198	12.698
28	1.1499	0.86966	0.03336	29.975	0.03836	26.068	13.175
29	1.1556	0.86533	0.03213	31.124	0.03713	26.933	13.651
30	1.1614	0.86103	0.03098	32.280	0.03598	27.794	14.126
31	1.1672	0.85675	0.02990	33.441	0.03490	28.651	14.601
32	1.1730	0.85248	0.02889	34.609	0.03389	29.503	15.075
33	1.1789	0.84824	0.02795	35.782	0.03295	30.352	15.548
34	1.1848	0.84402	0.02706	36.961	0.03206	31.196	16.020
35	1.1907	0.83982	0.02622	38.145	0.03122	32.035	16.492
40	1.2208	0.81914	0.02265	44.159	0.02765	36.172	18.836
45	1.2516	0.79896	0.01987	50.324	0.02487	40.207	21.159
50	1.2832	0.77929	0.01765	56.645	0.02265	44.143	23.462
55	1.3156	0.76009	0.01584	63.126	0.02084	47.981	25.745
60	1.3489	0.74137	0.01433	69.770	0.01933	51.726	28.006
65	1.3829	0.72311	0.01306	76.582	0.01806	55.377	30.247
70	1.4178	0.70530	0.01197	83.566	0.01697	58.939	32.468
75	1.4536	0.68793	0.01102	90.727	0.01602	62.414	34.668
80	1.4903	0.67099	0.01020	98.068	0.01520	65.802	36.847
85	1.5280	0.65446	0.00947	105.59	0.01447	69.108	39.006
90	1.5666	0.63834	0.00883	113.31	0.01383	72.331	41.145
95	1.6061	0.62262	0.00825	121.22	0.01325	75.476	43.263
100	1.6467	0.60729	0.00773	129.33	0.01273	78.543	45.361

i = 1%   **Discrete Compounding, Discrete Cash Flows**

	SINGLE PAYMENT		UNIFORM SERIES				Arithmetic Gradient Series Factor
	Compound Amount Factor	Present Worth Factor	Sinking Fund Factor	Uniform Series Factor	Capital Recovery Factor	Series Present Worth Factor	
N	(*F/P,i,N*)	(*P/F,i,N*)	(*A/F,i,N*)	(*F/A,i,N*)	(*A/P,i,N*)	(*P/A,i,N*)	(*A/G,i,N*)
1	1.0100	0.99010	1.0000	1.0000	1.0100	0.99010	0.00000
2	1.0201	0.98030	0.49751	2.0100	0.50751	1.9704	0.49751
3	1.0303	0.97059	0.33002	3.0301	0.34002	2.9410	0.99337
4	1.0406	0.96098	0.24628	4.0604	0.25628	3.9020	1.4876
5	1.0510	0.95147	0.19604	5.1010	0.20604	4.8534	1.9801
6	1.0615	0.94205	0.16255	6.1520	0.17255	5.7955	2.4710
7	1.0721	0.93272	0.13863	7.2135	0.14863	6.7282	2.9602
8	1.0829	0.92348	0.12069	8.2857	0.13069	7.6517	3.4478
9	1.0937	0.91434	0.10674	9.3685	0.11674	8.5660	3.9337
10	1.1046	0.90529	0.09558	10.462	0.10558	9.4713	4.4179
11	1.1157	0.89632	0.08645	11.567	0.09645	10.368	4.9005
12	1.1268	0.88745	0.07885	12.683	0.08885	11.255	5.3815
13	1.1381	0.87866	0.07241	13.809	0.08241	12.134	5.8607
14	1.1495	0.86996	0.06690	14.947	0.07690	13.004	6.3384
15	1.1610	0.86135	0.06212	16.097	0.07212	13.865	6.8143
16	1.1726	0.85282	0.05794	17.258	0.06794	14.718	7.2886
17	1.1843	0.84438	0.05426	18.430	0.06426	15.562	7.7613
18	1.1961	0.83602	0.05098	19.615	0.06098	16.398	8.2323
19	1.2081	0.82774	0.04805	20.811	0.05805	17.226	8.7017
20	1.2202	0.81954	0.04542	22.019	0.05542	18.046	9.1694
21	1.2324	0.81143	0.04303	23.239	0.05303	18.857	9.6354
22	1.2447	0.80340	0.04086	24.472	0.05086	19.660	10.100
23	1.2572	0.79544	0.03889	25.716	0.04889	20.456	10.563
24	1.2697	0.78757	0.03707	26.973	0.04707	21.243	11.024
25	1.2824	0.77977	0.03541	28.243	0.04541	22.023	11.483
26	1.2953	0.77205	0.03387	29.526	0.04387	22.795	11.941
27	1.3082	0.76440	0.03245	30.821	0.04245	23.560	12.397
28	1.3213	0.75684	0.03112	32.129	0.04112	24.316	12.852
29	1.3345	0.74934	0.02990	33.450	0.03990	25.066	13.304
30	1.3478	0.74192	0.02875	34.785	0.03875	25.808	13.756
31	1.3613	0.73458	0.02768	36.133	0.03768	26.542	14.205
32	1.3749	0.72730	0.02667	37.494	0.03667	27.270	14.653
33	1.3887	0.72010	0.02573	38.869	0.03573	27.990	15.099
34	1.4026	0.71297	0.02484	40.258	0.03484	28.703	15.544
35	1.4166	0.70591	0.02400	41.660	0.03400	29.409	15.987
40	1.4889	0.67165	0.02046	48.886	0.03046	32.835	18.178
45	1.5648	0.63905	0.01771	56.481	0.02771	36.095	20.327
50	1.6446	0.60804	0.01551	64.463	0.02551	39.196	22.436
55	1.7285	0.57853	0.01373	72.852	0.02373	42.147	24.505
60	1.8167	0.55045	0.01224	81.670	0.02224	44.955	26.533
65	1.9094	0.52373	0.01100	90.937	0.02100	47.627	28.522
70	2.0068	0.49831	0.00993	100.68	0.01993	50.169	30.470
75	2.1091	0.47413	0.00902	110.91	0.01902	52.587	32.379
80	2.2167	0.45112	0.00822	121.67	0.01822	54.888	34.249
85	2.3298	0.42922	0.00752	132.98	0.01752	57.078	36.080
90	2.4486	0.40839	0.00690	144.86	0.01690	59.161	37.872
95	2.5735	0.38857	0.00636	157.35	0.01636	61.143	39.626
100	2.7048	0.36971	0.00587	170.48	0.01587	63.029	41.343

$i = 1.5\%$ Discrete Compounding, Discrete Cash Flows

	SINGLE PAYMENT		UNIFORM SERIES				Arithmetic Gradient Series Factor
	Compound Amount Factor	Present Worth Factor	Sinking Fund Factor	Uniform Series Factor	Capital Recovery Factor	Series Present Worth Factor	
N	(F/P,i,N)	(P/F,i,N)	(A/F,i,N)	(F/A,i,N)	(A/P,i,N)	(P/A,i,N)	(A/G,i,N)
1	1.0150	0.98522	1.0000	1.0000	1.0150	0.98522	0.00000
2	1.0302	0.97066	0.49628	2.0150	0.51128	1.9559	0.49628
3	1.0457	0.95632	0.32838	3.0452	0.34338	2.9122	0.99007
4	1.0614	0.94218	0.24444	4.0909	0.25944	3.8544	1.4814
5	1.0773	0.92826	0.19409	5.1523	0.20909	4.7826	1.9702
6	1.0934	0.91454	0.16053	6.2296	0.17553	5.6972	2.4566
7	1.1098	0.90103	0.13656	7.3230	0.15156	6.5982	2.9405
8	1.1265	0.88771	0.11858	8.4328	0.13358	7.4859	3.4219
9	1.1434	0.87459	0.10461	9.5593	0.11961	8.3605	3.9008
10	1.1605	0.86167	0.09343	10.703	0.10843	9.2222	4.3772
11	1.1779	0.84893	0.08429	11.863	0.09929	10.071	4.8512
12	1.1956	0.83639	0.07668	13.041	0.09168	10.908	5.3227
13	1.2136	0.82403	0.07024	14.237	0.08524	11.732	5.7917
14	1.2318	0.81185	0.06472	15.450	0.07972	12.543	6.2582
15	1.2502	0.79985	0.05994	16.682	0.07494	13.343	6.7223
16	1.2690	0.78803	0.05577	17.932	0.07077	14.131	7.1839
17	1.2880	0.77639	0.05208	19.201	0.06708	14.908	7.6431
18	1.3073	0.76491	0.04881	20.489	0.06381	15.673	8.0997
19	1.3270	0.75361	0.04588	21.797	0.06088	16.426	8.5539
20	1.3469	0.74247	0.04325	23.124	0.05825	17.169	9.0057
21	1.3671	0.73150	0.04087	24.471	0.05587	17.900	9.4550
22	1.3876	0.72069	0.03870	25.838	0.05370	18.621	9.9018
23	1.4084	0.71004	0.03673	27.225	0.05173	19.331	10.346
24	1.4295	0.69954	0.03492	28.634	0.04992	20.030	10.788
25	1.4509	0.68921	0.03326	30.063	0.04826	20.720	11.228
26	1.4727	0.67902	0.03173	31.514	0.04673	21.399	11.665
27	1.4948	0.66899	0.03032	32.987	0.04532	22.068	12.099
28	1.5172	0.65910	0.02900	34.481	0.04400	22.727	12.531
29	1.5400	0.64936	0.02778	35.999	0.04278	23.376	12.961
30	1.5631	0.63976	0.02664	37.539	0.04164	24.016	13.388
31	1.5865	0.63031	0.02557	39.102	0.04057	24.646	13.813
32	1.6103	0.62099	0.02458	40.688	0.03958	25.267	14.236
33	1.6345	0.61182	0.02364	42.299	0.03864	25.879	14.656
34	1.6590	0.60277	0.02276	43.933	0.03776	26.482	15.073
35	1.6839	0.59387	0.02193	45.592	0.03693	27.076	15.488
40	1.8140	0.55126	0.01843	54.268	0.03343	29.916	17.528
45	1.9542	0.51171	0.01572	63.614	0.03072	32.552	19.507
50	2.1052	0.47500	0.01357	73.683	0.02857	35.000	21.428
55	2.2679	0.44093	0.01183	84.530	0.02683	37.271	23.289
60	2.4432	0.40930	0.01039	96.215	0.02539	39.380	25.093
65	2.6320	0.37993	0.00919	108.80	0.02419	41.338	26.839
70	2.8355	0.35268	0.00817	122.36	0.02317	43.155	28.529
75	3.0546	0.32738	0.00730	136.97	0.02230	44.842	30.163
80	3.2907	0.30389	0.00655	152.71	0.02155	46.407	31.742
85	3.5450	0.28209	0.00589	169.67	0.02089	47.861	33.268
90	3.8189	0.26185	0.00532	187.93	0.02032	49.210	34.740
95	4.1141	0.24307	0.00482	207.61	0.01982	50.462	36.160
100	4.4320	0.22563	0.00437	228.80	0.01937	51.625	37.530

i = 2%   Discrete Compounding, Discrete Cash Flows

	SINGLE PAYMENT		UNIFORM SERIES				Arithmetic Gradient Series Factor
	Compound Amount Factor	Present Worth Factor	Sinking Fund Factor	Uniform Series Factor	Capital Recovery Factor	Series Present Worth Factor	
N	(F/P,i,N)	(P/F,i,N)	(A/F,i,N)	(F/A,i,N)	(A/P,i,N)	(P/A,i,N)	(A/G,i,N)
1	1.0200	0.98039	1.0000	1.0000	1.0200	0.98039	0.00000
2	1.0404	0.96117	0.49505	2.0200	0.51505	1.9416	0.49505
3	1.0612	0.94232	0.32675	3.0604	0.34675	2.8839	0.98680
4	1.0824	0.92385	0.24262	4.1216	0.26262	3.8077	1.4752
5	1.1041	0.90573	0.19216	5.2040	0.21216	4.7135	1.9604
6	1.1262	0.88797	0.15853	6.3081	0.17853	5.6014	2.4423
7	1.1487	0.87056	0.13451	7.4343	0.15451	6.4720	2.9208
8	1.1717	0.85349	0.11651	8.5830	0.13651	7.3255	3.3961
9	1.1951	0.83676	0.10252	9.7546	0.12252	8.1622	3.8681
10	1.2190	0.82035	0.09133	10.950	0.11133	8.9826	4.3367
11	1.2434	0.80426	0.08218	12.169	0.10218	9.787	4.8021
12	1.2682	0.78849	0.07456	13.412	0.09456	10.575	5.2642
13	1.2936	0.77303	0.06812	14.680	0.08812	11.348	5.7231
14	1.3195	0.75788	0.06260	15.974	0.08260	12.106	6.1786
15	1.3459	0.74301	0.05783	17.293	0.07783	12.849	6.6309
16	1.3728	0.72845	0.05365	18.639	0.07365	13.578	7.0799
17	1.4002	0.71416	0.04997	20.012	0.06997	14.292	7.5256
18	1.4282	0.70016	0.04670	21.412	0.06670	14.992	7.9681
19	1.4568	0.68643	0.04378	22.841	0.06378	15.678	8.4073
20	1.4859	0.67297	0.04116	24.297	0.06116	16.351	8.8433
21	1.5157	0.65978	0.03878	25.783	0.05878	17.011	9.2760
22	1.5460	0.64684	0.03663	27.299	0.05663	17.658	9.7050
23	1.5769	0.63416	0.03467	28.845	0.05467	18.292	10.1320
24	1.6084	0.62172	0.03287	30.422	0.05287	18.914	10.5550
25	1.6406	0.60953	0.03122	32.030	0.05122	19.523	10.9740
26	1.6734	0.59758	0.02970	33.671	0.04970	20.121	11.391
27	1.7069	0.58586	0.02829	35.344	0.04829	20.707	11.804
28	1.7410	0.57437	0.02699	37.051	0.04699	21.281	12.214
29	1.7758	0.56311	0.02578	38.792	0.04578	21.844	12.621
30	1.8114	0.55207	0.02465	40.568	0.04465	22.396	13.025
31	1.8476	0.54125	0.02360	42.379	0.04360	22.938	13.426
32	1.8845	0.53063	0.02261	44.227	0.04261	23.468	13.823
33	1.9222	0.52023	0.02169	46.112	0.04169	23.989	14.217
34	1.9607	0.51003	0.02082	48.034	0.04082	24.499	14.608
35	1.9999	0.50003	0.02000	49.994	0.04000	24.999	14.996
40	2.2080	0.45289	0.01656	60.402	0.03656	27.355	16.889
45	2.4379	0.41020	0.01391	71.893	0.03391	29.490	18.703
50	2.6916	0.37153	0.01182	84.579	0.03182	31.424	20.442
55	2.9717	0.33650	0.01014	98.587	0.03014	33.175	22.106
60	3.2810	0.30478	0.00877	114.05	0.02877	34.761	23.696
65	3.6225	0.27605	0.00763	131.13	0.02763	36.197	25.215
70	3.9996	0.25003	0.00667	149.98	0.02667	37.499	26.663
75	4.4158	0.22646	0.00586	170.79	0.02586	38.677	28.043
80	4.8754	0.20511	0.00516	193.77	0.02516	39.745	29.357
85	5.3829	0.18577	0.00456	219.14	0.02456	40.711	30.606
90	5.9431	0.16826	0.00405	247.16	0.02405	41.587	31.793
95	6.5617	0.15240	0.00360	278.08	0.02360	42.380	32.919
100	7.2446	0.13803	0.00320	312.23	0.02320	43.098	33.986

$i = 3\%$ Discrete Compounding, Discrete Cash Flows

	SINGLE PAYMENT		UNIFORM SERIES				Arithmetic Gradient Series Factor
	Compound Amount Factor	Present Worth Factor	Sinking Fund Factor	Uniform Series Factor	Capital Recovery Factor	Series Present Worth Factor	
N	(F/P,i,N)	(P/F,i,N)	(A/F,i,N)	(F/A,i,N)	(A/P,i,N)	(P/A,i,N)	(A/G,i,N)
1	1.0300	0.97087	1.0000	1.0000	1.0300	0.97087	0.00000
2	1.0609	0.94260	0.49261	2.0300	0.52261	1.9135	0.49261
3	1.0927	0.91514	0.32353	3.0909	0.35353	2.8286	0.98030
4	1.1255	0.88849	0.23903	4.1836	0.26903	3.7171	1.4631
5	1.1593	0.86261	0.18835	5.3091	0.21835	4.5797	1.9409
6	1.1941	0.83748	0.15460	6.4684	0.18460	5.4172	2.4138
7	1.2299	0.81309	0.13051	7.6625	0.16051	6.2303	2.8819
8	1.2668	0.78941	0.11246	8.8923	0.14246	7.0197	3.3450
9	1.3048	0.76642	0.09843	10.159	0.12843	7.7861	3.8032
10	1.3439	0.74409	0.08723	11.464	0.11723	8.5302	4.2565
11	1.3842	0.72242	0.07808	12.808	0.10808	9.2526	4.7049
12	1.4258	0.70138	0.07046	14.192	0.10046	9.9540	5.1485
13	1.4685	0.68095	0.06403	15.618	0.09403	10.635	5.5872
14	1.5126	0.66112	0.05853	17.086	0.08853	11.296	6.0210
15	1.5580	0.64186	0.05377	18.599	0.08377	11.938	6.4500
16	1.6047	0.62317	0.04961	20.157	0.07961	12.561	6.8742
17	1.6528	0.60502	0.04595	21.762	0.07595	13.166	7.2936
18	1.7024	0.58739	0.04271	23.414	0.07271	13.754	7.7081
19	1.7535	0.57029	0.03981	25.117	0.06981	14.324	8.1179
20	1.8061	0.55368	0.03722	26.870	0.06722	14.877	8.5229
21	1.8603	0.53755	0.03487	28.676	0.06487	15.415	8.9231
22	1.9161	0.52189	0.03275	30.537	0.06275	15.937	9.3186
23	1.9736	0.50669	0.03081	32.453	0.06081	16.444	9.7093
24	2.0328	0.49193	0.02905	34.426	0.05905	16.936	10.095
25	2.0938	0.47761	0.02743	36.459	0.05743	17.413	10.477
26	2.1566	0.46369	0.02594	38.553	0.05594	17.877	10.853
27	2.2213	0.45019	0.02456	40.710	0.05456	18.327	11.226
28	2.2879	0.43708	0.02329	42.931	0.05329	18.764	11.593
29	2.3566	0.42435	0.02211	45.219	0.05211	19.188	11.956
30	2.4273	0.41199	0.02102	47.575	0.05102	19.600	12.314
31	2.5001	0.39999	0.02000	50.003	0.05000	20.000	12.668
32	2.5751	0.38834	0.01905	52.503	0.04905	20.389	13.017
33	2.6523	0.37703	0.01816	55.078	0.04816	20.766	13.362
34	2.7319	0.36604	0.01732	57.730	0.04732	21.132	13.702
35	2.8139	0.35538	0.01654	60.462	0.04654	21.487	14.037
40	3.2620	0.30656	0.01326	75.401	0.04326	23.115	15.650
45	3.7816	0.26444	0.01079	92.720	0.04079	24.519	17.156
50	4.3839	0.22811	0.00887	112.80	0.03887	25.730	18.558
55	5.0821	0.19677	0.00735	136.07	0.03735	26.774	19.860
60	5.8916	0.16973	0.00613	163.05	0.03613	27.676	21.067
65	6.8300	0.14641	0.00515	194.33	0.03515	28.453	22.184
70	7.9178	0.12630	0.00434	230.59	0.03434	29.123	23.215
75	9.1789	0.10895	0.00367	272.63	0.03367	29.702	24.163
80	10.641	0.09398	0.00311	321.36	0.03311	30.201	25.035
85	12.336	0.08107	0.00265	377.86	0.03265	30.631	25.835
90	14.300	0.06993	0.00226	443.35	0.03226	31.002	26.567
95	16.578	0.06032	0.00193	519.27	0.03193	31.323	27.235
100	19.219	0.05203	0.00165	607.29	0.03165	31.599	27.844

i = 4%   **Discrete Compounding, Discrete Cash Flows**

	SINGLE PAYMENT		UNIFORM SERIES				Arithmetic Gradient Series Factor
	Compound Amount Factor	Present Worth Factor	Sinking Fund Factor	Uniform Series Factor	Capital Recovery Factor	Series Present Worth Factor	
N	(F/P,i,N)	(P/F,i,N)	(A/F,i,N)	(F/A,i,N)	(A/P,i,N)	(P/A,i,N)	(A/G,i,N)
1	1.0400	0.96154	1.0000	1.0000	1.0400	0.96154	0.00000
2	1.0816	0.92456	0.49020	2.0400	0.53020	1.8861	0.49020
3	1.1249	0.88900	0.32035	3.1216	0.36035	2.7751	0.97386
4	1.1699	0.85480	0.23549	4.2465	0.27549	3.6299	1.4510
5	1.2167	0.82193	0.18463	5.4163	0.22463	4.4518	1.9216
6	1.2653	0.79031	0.15076	6.6330	0.19076	5.2421	2.3857
7	1.3159	0.75992	0.12661	7.8983	0.16661	6.0021	2.8433
8	1.3686	0.73069	0.10853	9.2142	0.14853	6.7327	3.2944
9	1.4233	0.70259	0.09449	10.583	0.13449	7.4353	3.7391
10	1.4802	0.67556	0.08329	12.006	0.12329	8.1109	4.1773
11	1.5395	0.64958	0.07415	13.486	0.11415	8.7605	4.6090
12	1.6010	0.62460	0.06655	15.026	0.10655	9.3851	5.0343
13	1.6651	0.60057	0.06014	16.627	0.10014	9.9856	5.4533
14	1.7317	0.57748	0.05467	18.292	0.09467	10.563	5.8659
15	1.8009	0.55526	0.04994	20.024	0.08994	11.118	6.2721
16	1.8730	0.53391	0.04582	21.825	0.08582	11.652	6.6720
17	1.9479	0.51337	0.04220	23.698	0.08220	12.166	7.0656
18	2.0258	0.49363	0.03899	25.645	0.07899	12.659	7.4530
19	2.1068	0.47464	0.03614	27.671	0.07614	13.134	7.8342
20	2.1911	0.45639	0.03358	29.778	0.07358	13.590	8.2091
21	2.2788	0.43883	0.03128	31.969	0.07128	14.029	8.5779
22	2.3699	0.42196	0.02920	34.248	0.06920	14.451	8.9407
23	2.4647	0.40573	0.02731	36.618	0.06731	14.857	9.2973
24	2.5633	0.39012	0.02559	39.083	0.06559	15.247	9.6479
25	2.6658	0.37512	0.02401	41.646	0.06401	15.622	9.9925
26	2.7725	0.36069	0.02257	44.312	0.06257	15.983	10.331
27	2.8834	0.34682	0.02124	47.084	0.06124	16.330	10.664
28	2.9987	0.33348	0.02001	49.968	0.06001	16.663	10.991
29	3.1187	0.32065	0.01888	52.966	0.05888	16.984	11.312
30	3.2434	0.30832	0.01783	56.085	0.05783	17.292	11.627
31	3.3731	0.29646	0.01686	59.328	0.05686	17.588	11.937
32	3.5081	0.28506	0.01595	62.701	0.05595	17.874	12.241
33	3.6484	0.27409	0.01510	66.210	0.05510	18.148	12.540
34	3.7943	0.26355	0.01431	69.858	0.05431	18.411	12.832
35	3.9461	0.25342	0.01358	73.652	0.05358	18.665	13.120
40	4.8010	0.20829	0.01052	95.026	0.05052	19.793	14.477
45	5.8412	0.17120	0.00826	121.03	0.04826	20.720	15.705
50	7.1067	0.14071	0.00655	152.67	0.04655	21.482	16.812
55	8.6464	0.11566	0.00523	191.16	0.04523	22.109	17.807
60	10.520	0.09506	0.00420	237.99	0.04420	22.623	18.697
65	12.799	0.07813	0.00339	294.97	0.04339	23.047	19.491
70	15.572	0.06422	0.00275	364.29	0.04275	23.395	20.196
75	18.945	0.05278	0.00223	448.63	0.04223	23.680	20.821
80	23.050	0.04338	0.00181	551.24	0.04181	23.915	21.372
85	28.044	0.03566	0.00148	676.09	0.04148	24.109	21.857
90	34.119	0.02931	0.00121	827.98	0.04121	24.267	22.283
95	41.511	0.02409	0.00099	1012.8	0.04099	24.398	22.655
100	50.505	0.01980	0.00081	1237.6	0.04081	24.505	22.980

i = 5%   Discrete Compounding, Discrete Cash Flows

	SINGLE PAYMENT		UNIFORM SERIES				Arithmetic Gradient Series Factor
	Compound Amount Factor	Present Worth Factor	Sinking Fund Factor	Uniform Series Factor	Capital Recovery Factor	Series Present Worth Factor	
N	(F/P,i,N)	(P/F,i,N)	(A/F,i,N)	(F/A,i,N)	(A/P,i,N)	(P/A,i,N)	(A/G,i,N)
1	1.0500	0.95238	1.0000	1.0000	1.0500	0.95238	0.00000
2	1.1025	0.90703	0.48780	2.0500	0.53780	1.8594	0.48780
3	1.1576	0.86384	0.31721	3.1525	0.36721	2.7232	0.96749
4	1.2155	0.82270	0.23201	4.3101	0.28201	3.5460	1.4391
5	1.2763	0.78353	0.18097	5.5256	0.23097	4.3295	1.9025
6	1.3401	0.74622	0.14702	6.8019	0.19702	5.0757	2.3579
7	1.4071	0.71068	0.12282	8.1420	0.17282	5.7864	2.8052
8	1.4775	0.67684	0.10472	9.5491	0.15472	6.4632	3.2445
9	1.5513	0.64461	0.09069	11.027	0.14069	7.1078	3.6758
10	1.6289	0.61391	0.07950	12.578	0.12950	7.7217	4.0991
11	1.7103	0.58468	0.07039	14.207	0.12039	8.3064	4.5144
12	1.7959	0.55684	0.06283	15.917	0.11283	8.8633	4.9219
13	1.8856	0.53032	0.05646	17.713	0.10646	9.3936	5.3215
14	1.9799	0.50507	0.05102	19.599	0.10102	9.8986	5.7133
15	2.0789	0.48102	0.04634	21.579	0.09634	10.380	6.0973
16	2.1829	0.45811	0.04227	23.657	0.09227	10.838	6.4736
17	2.2920	0.43630	0.03870	25.840	0.08870	11.274	6.8423
18	2.4066	0.41552	0.03555	28.132	0.08555	11.690	7.2034
19	2.5270	0.39573	0.03275	30.539	0.08275	12.085	7.5569
20	2.6533	0.37689	0.03024	33.066	0.08024	12.462	7.9030
21	2.7860	0.35894	0.02800	35.719	0.07800	12.821	8.2416
22	2.9253	0.34185	0.02597	38.505	0.07597	13.163	8.5730
23	3.0715	0.32557	0.02414	41.430	0.07414	13.489	8.8971
24	3.2251	0.31007	0.02247	44.502	0.07247	13.799	9.2140
25	3.3864	0.29530	0.02095	47.727	0.07095	14.094	9.5238
26	3.5557	0.28124	0.01956	51.113	0.06956	14.375	9.8266
27	3.7335	0.26785	0.01829	54.669	0.06829	14.643	10.122
28	3.9201	0.25509	0.01712	58.403	0.06712	14.898	10.411
29	4.1161	0.24295	0.01605	62.323	0.06605	15.141	10.694
30	4.3219	0.23138	0.01505	66.439	0.06505	15.372	10.969
31	4.5380	0.22036	0.01413	70.761	0.06413	15.593	11.238
32	4.7649	0.20987	0.01328	75.299	0.06328	15.803	11.501
33	5.0032	0.19987	0.01249	80.064	0.06249	16.003	11.757
34	5.2533	0.19035	0.01176	85.067	0.06176	16.193	12.006
35	5.5160	0.18129	0.01107	90.320	0.06107	16.374	12.250
40	7.0400	0.14205	0.00828	120.80	0.05828	17.159	13.377
45	8.9850	0.11130	0.00626	159.70	0.05626	17.774	14.364
50	11.467	0.08720	0.00478	209.35	0.05478	18.256	15.223
55	14.636	0.06833	0.00367	272.71	0.05367	18.633	15.966
60	18.679	0.05354	0.00283	353.58	0.05283	18.929	16.606
65	23.840	0.04195	0.00219	456.80	0.05219	19.161	17.154
70	30.426	0.03287	0.00170	588.53	0.05170	19.343	17.621
75	38.833	0.02575	0.00132	756.65	0.05132	19.485	18.018
80	49.561	0.02018	0.00103	971.23	0.05103	19.596	18.353
85	63.254	0.01581	0.00080	1245.1	0.05080	19.684	18.635
90	80.730	0.01239	0.00063	1594.6	0.05063	19.752	18.871
95	103.03	0.00971	0.00049	2040.7	0.05049	19.806	19.069
100	131.50	0.00760	0.00038	2610.0	0.05038	19.848	19.234

$i = 6\%$ **Discrete Compounding, Discrete Cash Flows**

	SINGLE PAYMENT		UNIFORM SERIES				Arithmetic Gradient Series Factor
	Compound Amount Factor	Present Worth Factor	Sinking Fund Factor	Uniform Series Factor	Capital Recovery Factor	Series Present Worth Factor	
N	(F/P,i,N)	(P/F,i,N)	(A/F,i,N)	(F/A,i,N)	(A/P,i,N)	(P/A,i,N)	(A/G,i,N)
1	1.0600	0.94340	1.0000	1.0000	1.0600	0.94340	0.00000
2	1.1236	0.89000	0.48544	2.0600	0.54544	1.8334	0.48544
3	1.1910	0.83962	0.31411	3.1836	0.37411	2.6730	0.96118
4	1.2625	0.79209	0.22859	4.3746	0.28859	3.4651	1.4272
5	1.3382	0.74726	0.17740	5.6371	0.23740	4.2124	1.8836
6	1.4185	0.70496	0.14336	6.9753	0.20336	4.9173	2.3304
7	1.5036	0.66506	0.11914	8.3938	0.17914	5.5824	2.7676
8	1.5938	0.62741	0.10104	9.8975	0.16104	6.2098	3.1952
9	1.6895	0.59190	0.08702	11.491	0.14702	6.8017	3.6133
10	1.7908	0.55839	0.07587	13.181	0.13587	7.3601	4.0220
11	1.8983	0.52679	0.06679	14.972	0.12679	7.8869	4.4213
12	2.0122	0.49697	0.05928	16.870	0.11928	8.3838	4.8113
13	2.1329	0.46884	0.05296	18.882	0.11296	8.8527	5.1920
14	2.2609	0.44230	0.04758	21.015	0.10758	9.2950	5.5635
15	2.3966	0.41727	0.04296	23.276	0.10296	9.7122	5.9260
16	2.5404	0.39365	0.03895	25.673	0.09895	10.106	6.2794
17	2.6928	0.37136	0.03544	28.213	0.09544	10.477	6.6240
18	2.8543	0.35034	0.03236	30.906	0.09236	10.828	6.9597
19	3.0256	0.33051	0.02962	33.760	0.08962	11.158	7.2867
20	3.2071	0.31180	0.02718	36.786	0.08718	11.470	7.6051
21	3.3996	0.29416	0.02500	39.993	0.08500	11.764	7.9151
22	3.6035	0.27751	0.02305	43.392	0.08305	12.042	8.2166
23	3.8197	0.26180	0.02128	46.996	0.08128	12.303	8.5099
24	4.0489	0.24698	0.01968	50.816	0.07968	12.550	8.7951
25	4.2919	0.23300	0.01823	54.865	0.07823	12.783	9.0722
26	4.5494	0.21981	0.01690	59.156	0.07690	13.003	9.3414
27	4.8223	0.20737	0.01570	63.706	0.07570	13.211	9.6029
28	5.1117	0.19563	0.01459	68.528	0.07459	13.406	9.8568
29	5.4184	0.18456	0.01358	73.640	0.07358	13.591	10.103
30	5.7435	0.17411	0.01265	79.058	0.07265	13.765	10.342
31	6.0881	0.16425	0.01179	84.802	0.07179	13.929	10.574
32	6.4534	0.15496	0.01100	90.890	0.07100	14.084	10.799
33	6.8406	0.14619	0.01027	97.343	0.07027	14.230	11.017
34	7.2510	0.13791	0.00960	104.18	0.06960	14.368	11.228
35	7.6861	0.13011	0.00897	111.43	0.06897	14.498	11.432
40	10.286	0.09722	0.00646	154.76	0.06646	15.046	12.359
45	13.765	0.07265	0.00470	212.74	0.06470	15.456	13.141
50	18.420	0.05429	0.00344	290.34	0.06344	15.762	13.796
55	24.650	0.04057	0.00254	394.17	0.06254	15.991	14.341
60	32.988	0.03031	0.00188	533.13	0.06188	16.161	14.791
65	44.145	0.02265	0.00139	719.08	0.06139	16.289	15.160
70	59.076	0.01693	0.00103	967.93	0.06103	16.385	15.461
75	79.057	0.01265	0.00077	1300.9	0.06077	16.456	15.706
80	105.80	0.00945	0.00057	1746.6	0.06057	16.509	15.903
85	141.58	0.00706	0.00043	2343.0	0.06043	16.549	16.062
90	189.46	0.00528	0.00032	3141.1	0.06032	16.579	16.189
95	253.55	0.00394	0.00024	4209.1	0.06024	16.601	16.290
100	339.30	0.00295	0.00018	5638.4	0.06018	16.618	16.371

i = 7%   Discrete Compounding, Discrete Cash Flows

	SINGLE PAYMENT		UNIFORM SERIES				Arithmetic Gradient Series Factor
	Compound Amount Factor	Present Worth Factor	Sinking Fund Factor	Uniform Series Factor	Capital Recovery Factor	Series Present Worth Factor	
N	(F/P,i,N)	(P/F,i,N)	(A/F,i,N)	(F/A,i,N)	(A/P,i,N)	(P/A,i,N)	(A/G,i,N)
1	1.0700	0.93458	1.0000	1.0000	1.0700	0.93458	0.00000
2	1.1449	0.87344	0.48309	2.0700	0.55309	1.8080	0.48309
3	1.2250	0.81630	0.31105	3.2149	0.38105	2.6243	0.95493
4	1.3108	0.76290	0.22523	4.4399	0.29523	3.3872	1.4155
5	1.4026	0.71299	0.17389	5.7507	0.24389	4.1002	1.8650
6	1.5007	0.66634	0.13980	7.1533	0.20980	4.7665	2.3032
7	1.6058	0.62275	0.11555	8.6540	0.18555	5.3893	2.7304
8	1.7182	0.58201	0.09747	10.260	0.16747	5.9713	3.1465
9	1.8385	0.54393	0.08349	11.978	0.15349	6.5152	3.5517
10	1.9672	0.50835	0.07238	13.816	0.14238	7.0236	3.9461
11	2.1049	0.47509	0.06336	15.784	0.13336	7.4987	4.3296
12	2.2522	0.44401	0.05590	17.888	0.12590	7.9427	4.7025
13	2.4098	0.41496	0.04965	20.141	0.11965	8.3577	5.0648
14	2.5785	0.38782	0.04434	22.550	0.11434	8.7455	5.4167
15	2.7590	0.36245	0.03979	25.129	0.10979	9.1079	5.7583
16	2.9522	0.33873	0.03586	27.888	0.10586	9.4466	6.0897
17	3.1588	0.31657	0.03243	30.840	0.10243	9.7632	6.4110
18	3.3799	0.29586	0.02941	33.999	0.09941	10.059	6.7225
19	3.6165	0.27651	0.02675	37.379	0.09675	10.336	7.0242
20	3.8697	0.25842	0.02439	40.995	0.09439	10.594	7.3163
21	4.1406	0.24151	0.02229	44.865	0.09229	10.836	7.5990
22	4.4304	0.22571	0.02041	49.006	0.09041	11.061	7.8725
23	4.7405	0.21095	0.01871	53.436	0.08871	11.272	8.1369
24	5.0724	0.19715	0.01719	58.177	0.08719	11.469	8.3923
25	5.4274	0.18425	0.01581	63.249	0.08581	11.654	8.6391
26	5.8074	0.17220	0.01456	68.676	0.08456	11.826	8.8773
27	6.2139	0.16093	0.01343	74.484	0.08343	11.987	9.1072
28	6.6488	0.15040	0.01239	80.698	0.08239	12.137	9.3289
29	7.1143	0.14056	0.01145	87.347	0.08145	12.278	9.5427
30	7.6123	0.13137	0.01059	94.461	0.08059	12.409	9.7487
31	8.1451	0.12277	0.00980	102.07	0.07980	12.532	9.9471
32	8.7153	0.11474	0.00907	110.22	0.07907	12.647	10.138
33	9.3253	0.10723	0.00841	118.93	0.07841	12.754	10.322
34	9.9781	0.10022	0.00780	128.26	0.07780	12.854	10.499
35	10.677	0.09366	0.00723	138.24	0.07723	12.948	10.669
40	14.974	0.06678	0.00501	199.64	0.07501	13.332	11.423
45	21.002	0.04761	0.00350	285.75	0.07350	13.606	12.036
50	29.457	0.03395	0.00246	406.53	0.07246	13.801	12.529
55	41.315	0.02420	0.00174	575.93	0.07174	13.940	12.921
60	57.946	0.01726	0.00123	813.52	0.07123	14.039	13.232
65	81.273	0.01230	0.00087	1146.8	0.07087	14.110	13.476
70	113.99	0.00877	0.00062	1614.1	0.07062	14.160	13.666
75	159.88	0.00625	0.00044	2269.7	0.07044	14.196	13.814
80	224.23	0.00446	0.00031	3189.1	0.07031	14.222	13.927
85	314.50	0.00318	0.00022	4478.6	0.07022	14.240	14.015
90	441.10	0.00227	0.00016	6287.2	0.07016	14.253	14.081
95	618.67	0.00162	0.00011	8823.9	0.07011	14.263	14.132
100	867.72	0.00115	0.00008	12 382.0	0.07008	14.269	14.170

i = 8%   **Discrete Compounding, Discrete Cash Flows**

	SINGLE PAYMENT		**UNIFORM SERIES**				**Arithmetic Gradient Series Factor**
	Compound Amount Factor	Present Worth Factor	Sinking Fund Factor	Uniform Series Factor	Capital Recovery Factor	Series Present Worth Factor	
N	(*F/P,i,N*)	(*P/F,i,N*)	(*A/F,i,N*)	(*F/A,i,N*)	(*A/P,i,N*)	(*P/A,i,N*)	(*A/G,i,N*)
1	1.0800	0.92593	1.0000	1.0000	1.0800	0.92593	0.00000
2	1.1664	0.85734	0.48077	2.0800	0.56077	1.7833	0.48077
3	1.2597	0.79383	0.30803	3.2464	0.38803	2.5771	0.94874
4	1.3605	0.73503	0.22192	4.5061	0.30192	3.3121	1.4040
5	1.4693	0.68058	0.17046	5.8666	0.25046	3.9927	1.8465
6	1.5869	0.63017	0.13632	7.3359	0.21632	4.6229	2.2763
7	1.7138	0.58349	0.11207	8.9228	0.19207	5.2064	2.6937
8	1.8509	0.54027	0.09401	10.637	0.17401	5.7466	3.0985
9	1.9990	0.50025	0.08008	12.488	0.16008	6.2469	3.4910
10	2.1589	0.46319	0.06903	14.487	0.14903	6.7101	3.8713
11	2.3316	0.42888	0.06008	16.645	0.14008	7.1390	4.2395
12	2.5182	0.39711	0.05270	18.977	0.13270	7.5361	4.5957
13	2.7196	0.36770	0.04652	21.495	0.12652	7.9038	4.9402
14	2.9372	0.34046	0.04130	24.215	0.12130	8.2442	5.2731
15	3.1722	0.31524	0.03683	27.152	0.11683	8.5595	5.5945
16	3.4259	0.29189	0.03298	30.324	0.11298	8.8514	5.9046
17	3.7000	0.27027	0.02963	33.750	0.10963	9.1216	6.2037
18	3.9960	0.25025	0.02670	37.450	0.10670	9.3719	6.4920
19	4.3157	0.23171	0.02413	41.446	0.10413	9.6036	6.7697
20	4.6610	0.21455	0.02185	45.762	0.10185	9.8181	7.0369
21	5.0338	0.19866	0.01983	50.423	0.09983	10.017	7.2940
22	5.4365	0.18394	0.01803	55.457	0.09803	10.201	7.5412
23	5.8715	0.17032	0.01642	60.893	0.09642	10.371	7.7786
24	6.3412	0.15770	0.01498	66.765	0.09498	10.529	8.0066
25	6.8485	0.14602	0.01368	73.106	0.09368	10.675	8.2254
26	7.3964	0.13520	0.01251	79.954	0.09251	10.810	8.4352
27	7.9881	0.12519	0.01145	87.351	0.09145	10.935	8.6363
28	8.6271	0.11591	0.01049	95.339	0.09049	11.051	8.8289
29	9.3173	0.10733	0.00962	103.97	0.08962	11.158	9.0133
30	10.063	0.09938	0.00883	113.28	0.08883	11.258	9.1897
31	10.868	0.09202	0.00811	123.35	0.08811	11.350	9.3584
32	11.737	0.08520	0.00745	134.21	0.08745	11.435	9.5197
33	12.676	0.07889	0.00685	145.95	0.08685	11.514	9.6737
34	13.690	0.07305	0.00630	158.63	0.08630	11.587	9.8208
35	14.785	0.06763	0.00580	172.32	0.08580	11.655	9.9611
40	21.725	0.04603	0.00386	259.06	0.08386	11.925	10.570
45	31.920	0.03133	0.00259	386.51	0.08259	12.108	11.045
50	46.902	0.02132	0.00174	573.77	0.08174	12.233	11.411
55	68.914	0.01451	0.00118	848.92	0.08118	12.319	11.690
60	101.26	0.00988	0.00080	1253.2	0.08080	12.377	11.902
65	148.78	0.00672	0.00054	1847.2	0.08054	12.416	12.060
70	218.61	0.00457	0.00037	2720.1	0.08037	12.443	12.178
75	321.20	0.00311	0.00025	4002.6	0.08025	12.461	12.266
80	471.95	0.00212	0.00017	5886.9	0.08017	12.474	12.330
85	693.46	0.00144	0.00012	8655.7	0.08012	12.482	12.377
90	1018.9	0.00098	0.00008	12724.0	0.08008	12.488	12.412
95	1497.1	0.00067	0.00005	18702.0	0.08005	12.492	12.437
100	2199.8	0.00045	0.00004	27485.0	0.08004	12.494	12.455

$i = 9\%$　　　　　　　　　　　　　　　Discrete Compounding, Discrete Cash Flows

	SINGLE PAYMENT		UNIFORM SERIES				Arithmetic Gradient Series Factor
	Compound Amount Factor	Present Worth Factor	Sinking Fund Factor	Uniform Series Factor	Capital Recovery Factor	Series Present Worth Factor	
N	$(F/P,i,N)$	$(P/F,i,N)$	$(A/F,i,N)$	$(F/A,i,N)$	$(A/P,i,N)$	$(P/A,i,N)$	$(A/G,i,N)$
1	1.0900	0.91743	1.0000	1.0000	1.0900	0.91743	0.00000
2	1.1881	0.84168	0.47847	2.0900	0.56847	1.7591	0.47847
3	1.2950	0.77218	0.30505	3.2781	0.39505	2.5313	0.94262
4	1.4116	0.70843	0.21867	4.5731	0.30867	3.2397	1.3925
5	1.5386	0.64993	0.16709	5.9847	0.25709	3.8897	1.8282
6	1.6771	0.59627	0.13292	7.5233	0.22292	4.4859	2.2498
7	1.8280	0.54703	0.10869	9.2004	0.19869	5.0330	2.6574
8	1.9926	0.50187	0.09067	11.028	0.18067	5.5348	3.0512
9	2.1719	0.46043	0.07680	13.021	0.16680	5.9952	3.4312
10	2.3674	0.42241	0.06582	15.193	0.15582	6.4177	3.7978
11	2.5804	0.38753	0.05695	17.560	0.14695	6.8052	4.1510
12	2.8127	0.35553	0.04965	20.141	0.13965	7.1607	4.4910
13	3.0658	0.32618	0.04357	22.953	0.13357	7.4869	4.8182
14	3.3417	0.29925	0.03843	26.019	0.12843	7.7862	5.1326
15	3.6425	0.27454	0.03406	29.361	0.12406	8.0607	5.4346
16	3.9703	0.25187	0.03030	33.003	0.12030	8.3126	5.7245
17	4.3276	0.23107	0.02705	36.974	0.11705	8.5436	6.0024
18	4.7171	0.21199	0.02421	41.301	0.11421	8.7556	6.2687
19	5.1417	0.19449	0.02173	46.018	0.11173	8.9501	6.5236
20	5.6044	0.17843	0.01955	51.160	0.10955	9.1285	6.7674
21	6.1088	0.16370	0.01762	56.765	0.10762	9.2922	7.0006
22	6.6586	0.15018	0.01590	62.873	0.10590	9.4424	7.2232
23	7.2579	0.13778	0.01438	69.532	0.10438	9.5802	7.4357
24	7.9111	0.12640	0.01302	76.790	0.10302	9.7066	7.6384
25	8.6231	0.11597	0.01181	84.701	0.10181	9.8226	7.8316
26	9.3992	0.10639	0.01072	93.324	0.10072	9.9290	8.0156
27	10.245	0.09761	0.00973	102.72	0.09973	10.027	8.1906
28	11.167	0.08955	0.00885	112.97	0.09885	10.116	8.3571
29	12.172	0.08215	0.00806	124.14	0.09806	10.198	8.5154
30	13.268	0.07537	0.00734	136.31	0.09734	10.274	8.6657
31	14.462	0.06915	0.00669	149.58	0.09669	10.343	8.8083
32	15.763	0.06344	0.00610	164.04	0.09610	10.406	8.9436
33	17.182	0.05820	0.00556	179.80	0.09556	10.464	9.0718
34	18.728	0.05339	0.00508	196.98	0.09508	10.518	9.1933
35	20.414	0.04899	0.00464	215.71	0.09464	10.567	9.3083
40	31.409	0.03184	0.00296	337.88	0.09296	10.757	9.7957
45	48.327	0.02069	0.00190	525.86	0.09190	10.881	10.160
50	74.358	0.01345	0.00123	815.08	0.09123	10.962	10.430
55	114.41	0.00874	0.00079	1260.1	0.09079	11.014	10.626
60	176.03	0.00568	0.00051	1944.8	0.09051	11.048	10.768
65	270.85	0.00369	0.00033	2998.3	0.09033	11.070	10.870
70	416.73	0.00240	0.00022	4619.2	0.09022	11.084	10.943
75	641.19	0.00156	0.00014	7113.2	0.09014	11.094	10.994
80	986.55	0.00101	0.00009	10951.0	0.09009	11.100	11.030
85	1517.9	0.00066	0.00006	16855.0	0.09006	11.104	11.055
90	2335.5	0.00043	0.00004	25939.0	0.09004	11.106	11.073
95	3593.5	0.00028	0.00003	39917.0	0.09003	11.108	11.085
100	5529.0	0.00018	0.00002	61423.0	0.09002	11.109	11.093

$i = 10\%$ **Discrete Compounding, Discrete Cash Flows**

	SINGLE PAYMENT		UNIFORM SERIES				Arithmetic Gradient Series Factor
	Compound Amount Factor	Present Worth Factor	Sinking Fund Factor	Uniform Series Factor	Capital Recovery Factor	Series Present Worth Factor	
N	(F/P,i,N)	(P/F,i,N)	(A/F,i,N)	(F/A,i,N)	(A/P,i,N)	(P/A,i,N)	(A/G,i,N)
1	1.1000	0.90909	1.0000	1.0000	1.1000	0.90909	0.00000
2	1.2100	0.82645	0.47619	2.1000	0.57619	1.7355	0.47619
3	1.3310	0.75131	0.30211	3.3100	0.40211	2.4869	0.93656
4	1.4641	0.68301	0.21547	4.6410	0.31547	3.1699	1.3812
5	1.6105	0.62092	0.16380	6.1051	0.26380	3.7908	1.8101
6	1.7716	0.56447	0.12961	7.7156	0.22961	4.3553	2.2236
7	1.9487	0.51316	0.10541	9.4872	0.20541	4.8684	2.6216
8	2.1436	0.46651	0.08744	11.436	0.18744	5.3349	3.0045
9	2.3579	0.42410	0.07364	13.579	0.17364	5.7590	3.3724
10	2.5937	0.38554	0.06275	15.937	0.16275	6.1446	3.7255
11	2.8531	0.35049	0.05396	18.531	0.15396	6.4951	4.0641
12	3.1384	0.31863	0.04676	21.384	0.14676	6.8137	4.3884
13	3.4523	0.28966	0.04078	24.523	0.14078	7.1034	4.6988
14	3.7975	0.26333	0.03575	27.975	0.13575	7.3667	4.9955
15	4.1772	0.23939	0.03147	31.772	0.13147	7.6061	5.2789
16	4.5950	0.21763	0.02782	35.950	0.12782	7.8237	5.5493
17	5.0545	0.19784	0.02466	40.545	0.12466	8.0216	5.8071
18	5.5599	0.17986	0.02193	45.599	0.12193	8.2014	6.0526
19	6.1159	0.16351	0.01955	51.159	0.11955	8.3649	6.2861
20	6.7275	0.14864	0.01746	57.275	0.11746	8.5136	6.5081
21	7.4002	0.13513	0.01562	64.002	0.11562	8.6487	6.7189
22	8.1403	0.12285	0.01401	71.403	0.11401	8.7715	6.9189
23	8.9543	0.11168	0.01257	79.543	0.11257	8.8832	7.1085
24	9.8497	0.10153	0.01130	88.497	0.11130	8.9847	7.2881
25	10.835	0.09230	0.01017	98.347	0.11017	9.0770	7.4580
26	11.918	0.08391	0.00916	109.18	0.10916	9.1609	7.6186
27	13.110	0.07628	0.00826	121.10	0.10826	9.2372	7.7704
28	14.421	0.06934	0.00745	134.21	0.10745	9.3066	7.9137
29	15.863	0.06304	0.00673	148.63	0.10673	9.3696	8.0489
30	17.449	0.05731	0.00608	164.49	0.10608	9.4269	8.1762
31	19.194	0.05210	0.00550	181.94	0.10550	9.4790	8.2962
32	21.114	0.04736	0.00497	201.14	0.10497	9.5264	8.4091
33	23.225	0.04306	0.00450	222.25	0.10450	9.5694	8.5152
34	25.548	0.03914	0.00407	245.48	0.10407	9.6086	8.6149
35	28.102	0.03558	0.00369	271.02	0.10369	9.6442	8.7086
40	45.259	0.02209	0.00226	442.59	0.10226	9.7791	9.0962
45	72.890	0.01372	0.00139	718.90	0.10139	9.8628	9.3740
50	117.39	0.00852	0.00086	1163.9	0.10086	9.9148	9.5704
55	189.06	0.00529	0.00053	1880.6	0.10053	9.9471	9.7075
60	304.48	0.00328	0.00033	3034.8	0.10033	9.9672	9.8023
65	490.37	0.00204	0.00020	4893.7	0.10020	9.9796	9.8672
70	789.75	0.00127	0.00013	7887.5	0.10013	9.9873	9.9113
75	1271.9	0.00079	0.00008	12 709.0	0.10008	9.9921	9.9410

$i = 11\%$ Discrete Compounding, Discrete Cash Flows

| | SINGLE PAYMENT | | UNIFORM SERIES | | | | Arithmetic Gradient Series Factor |
| | Compound Amount Factor | Present Worth Factor | Sinking Fund Factor | Uniform Series Factor | Capital Recovery Factor | Series Present Worth Factor | |
N	$(F/P,i,N)$	$(P/F,i,N)$	$(A/F,i,N)$	$(F/A,i,N)$	$(A/P,i,N)$	$(P/A,i,N)$	$(A/G,i,N)$
1	1.1100	0.90090	1.0000	1.0000	1.1100	0.90090	0.00000
2	1.2321	0.81162	0.47393	2.1100	0.58393	1.7125	0.47393
3	1.3676	0.73119	0.29921	3.3421	0.40921	2.4437	0.93055
4	1.5181	0.65873	0.21233	4.7097	0.32233	3.1024	1.3700
5	1.6851	0.59345	0.16057	6.2278	0.27057	3.6959	1.7923
6	1.8704	0.53464	0.12638	7.9129	0.23638	4.2305	2.1976
7	2.0762	0.48166	0.10222	9.783	0.21222	4.7122	2.5863
8	2.3045	0.43393	0.08432	11.859	0.19432	5.1461	2.9585
9	2.5580	0.39092	0.07060	14.164	0.18060	5.5370	3.3144
10	2.8394	0.35218	0.05980	16.722	0.16980	5.8892	3.6544
11	3.1518	0.31728	0.05112	19.561	0.16112	6.2065	3.9788
12	3.4985	0.28584	0.04403	22.713	0.15403	6.4924	4.2879
13	3.8833	0.25751	0.03815	26.212	0.14815	6.7499	4.5822
14	4.3104	0.23199	0.03323	30.095	0.14323	6.9819	4.8619
15	4.7846	0.20900	0.02907	34.405	0.13907	7.1909	5.1275
16	5.3109	0.18829	0.02552	39.190	0.13552	7.3792	5.3794
17	5.8951	0.16963	0.02247	44.501	0.13247	7.5488	5.6180
18	6.5436	0.15282	0.01984	50.396	0.12984	7.7016	5.8439
19	7.2633	0.13768	0.01756	56.939	0.12756	7.8393	6.0574
20	8.0623	0.12403	0.01558	64.203	0.12558	7.9633	6.2590
21	8.949	0.11174	0.01384	72.265	0.12384	8.0751	6.4491
22	9.934	0.10067	0.01231	81.214	0.12231	8.1757	6.6283
23	11.026	0.09069	0.01097	91.15	0.12097	8.2664	6.7969
24	12.239	0.08170	0.00979	102.17	0.11979	8.3481	6.9555
25	13.585	0.07361	0.00874	114.41	0.11874	8.4217	7.1045
26	15.080	0.06631	0.00781	128.00	0.11781	8.4881	7.2443
27	16.739	0.05974	0.00699	143.08	0.11699	8.5478	7.3754
28	18.580	0.05382	0.00626	159.82	0.11626	8.6016	7.4982
29	20.624	0.04849	0.00561	178.40	0.11561	8.6501	7.6131
30	22.892	0.04368	0.00502	199.02	0.11502	8.6938	7.7206
31	25.410	0.03935	0.00451	221.91	0.11451	8.7331	7.8210
32	28.206	0.03545	0.00404	247.32	0.11404	8.7686	7.9147
33	31.308	0.03194	0.00363	275.53	0.11363	8.8005	8.0021
34	34.752	0.02878	0.00326	306.84	0.11326	8.8293	8.0836
35	38.575	0.02592	0.00293	341.59	0.11293	8.8552	8.1594
40	65.001	0.01538	0.00172	581.83	0.11172	8.9511	8.4659
45	109.53	0.00913	0.00101	986.6	0.11101	9.0079	8.6763
50	184.56	0.00542	0.00060	1668.8	0.11060	9.0417	8.8185
55	311.00	0.00322	0.00035	2818.2	0.11035	9.0617	8.9135

i = 12%   **Discrete Compounding, Discrete Cash Flows**

	SINGLE PAYMENT		UNIFORM SERIES				Arithmetic Gradient Series Factor
	Compound Amount Factor	Present Worth Factor	Sinking Fund Factor	Uniform Series Factor	Capital Recovery Factor	Series Present Worth Factor	
N	(*F/P,i,N*)	(*P/F,i,N*)	(*A/F,i,N*)	(*F/A,i,N*)	(*A/P,i,N*)	(*P/A,i,N*)	(*A/G,i,N*)
1	1.1200	0.89286	1.0000	1.0000	1.1200	0.89286	0.00000
2	1.2544	0.79719	0.47170	2.1200	0.59170	1.6901	0.47170
3	1.4049	0.71178	0.29635	3.3744	0.41635	2.4018	0.92461
4	1.5735	0.63552	0.20923	4.7793	0.32923	3.0373	1.3589
5	1.7623	0.56743	0.15741	6.3528	0.27741	3.6048	1.7746
6	1.9738	0.50663	0.12323	8.1152	0.24323	4.1114	2.1720
7	2.2107	0.45235	0.09912	10.089	0.21912	4.5638	2.5515
8	2.4760	0.40388	0.08130	12.300	0.20130	4.9676	2.9131
9	2.7731	0.36061	0.06768	14.776	0.18768	5.3282	3.2574
10	3.1058	0.32197	0.05698	17.549	0.17698	5.6502	3.5847
11	3.4785	0.28748	0.04842	20.655	0.16842	5.9377	3.8953
12	3.8960	0.25668	0.04144	24.133	0.16144	6.1944	4.1897
13	4.3635	0.22917	0.03568	28.029	0.15568	6.4235	4.4683
14	4.8871	0.20462	0.03087	32.393	0.15087	6.6282	4.7317
15	5.4736	0.18270	0.02682	37.280	0.14682	6.8109	4.9803
16	6.1304	0.16312	0.02339	42.753	0.14339	6.9740	5.2147
17	6.8660	0.14564	0.02046	48.884	0.14046	7.1196	5.4353
18	7.6900	0.13004	0.01794	55.750	0.13794	7.2497	5.6427
19	8.6128	0.11611	0.01576	63.440	0.13576	7.3658	5.8375
20	9.6463	0.10367	0.01388	72.052	0.13388	7.4694	6.0202
21	10.804	0.09256	0.01224	81.699	0.13224	7.5620	6.1913
22	12.100	0.08264	0.01081	92.503	0.13081	7.6446	6.3514
23	13.552	0.07379	0.00956	104.60	0.12956	7.7184	6.5010
24	15.179	0.06588	0.00846	118.16	0.12846	7.7843	6.6406
25	17.000	0.05882	0.00750	133.33	0.12750	7.8431	6.7708
26	19.040	0.05252	0.00665	150.33	0.12665	7.8957	6.8921
27	21.325	0.04689	0.00590	169.37	0.12590	7.9426	7.0049
28	23.884	0.04187	0.00524	190.70	0.12524	7.9844	7.1098
29	26.750	0.03738	0.00466	214.58	0.12466	8.0218	7.2071
30	29.960	0.03338	0.00414	241.33	0.12414	8.0552	7.2974
31	33.555	0.02980	0.00369	271.29	0.12369	8.0850	7.3811
32	37.582	0.02661	0.00328	304.85	0.12328	8.1116	7.4586
33	42.092	0.02376	0.00292	342.43	0.12292	8.1354	7.5302
34	47.143	0.02121	0.00260	384.52	0.12260	8.1566	7.5965
35	52.800	0.01894	0.00232	431.66	0.12232	8.1755	7.6577
40	93.051	0.01075	0.00130	767.09	0.12130	8.2438	7.8988
45	163.99	0.00610	0.00074	1358.2	0.12074	8.2825	8.0572
50	289.00	0.00346	0.00042	2400.0	0.12042	8.3045	8.1597
55	509.32	0.00196	0.00024	4236.0	0.12024	8.3170	8.2251

$i = 13\%$ **Discrete Compounding, Discrete Cash Flows**

	SINGLE PAYMENT		UNIFORM SERIES				Arithmetic Gradient Series Factor
	Compound Amount Factor	Present Worth Factor	Sinking Fund Factor	Uniform Series Factor	Capital Recovery Factor	Series Present Worth Factor	
N	(F/P,i,N)	(P/F,i,N)	(A/F,i,N)	(F/A,i,N)	(A/P,i,N)	(P/A,i,N)	(A/G,i,N)
1	1.1300	0.88496	1.0000	1.0000	1.1300	0.88496	0.00000
2	1.2769	0.78315	0.46948	2.1300	0.59948	1.6681	0.46948
3	1.4429	0.69305	0.29352	3.4069	0.42352	2.3612	0.91872
4	1.6305	0.61332	0.20619	4.8498	0.33619	2.9745	1.3479
5	1.8424	0.54276	0.15431	6.4803	0.28431	3.5172	1.7571
6	2.0820	0.48032	0.12015	8.3227	0.25015	3.9975	2.1468
7	2.3526	0.42506	0.09611	10.405	0.22611	4.4226	2.5171
8	2.6584	0.37616	0.07839	12.757	0.20839	4.7988	2.8685
9	3.0040	0.33288	0.06487	15.416	0.19487	5.1317	3.2014
10	3.3946	0.29459	0.05429	18.420	0.18429	5.4262	3.5162
11	3.8359	0.26070	0.04584	21.814	0.17584	5.6869	3.8134
12	4.3345	0.23071	0.03899	25.650	0.16899	5.9176	4.0936
13	4.8980	0.20416	0.03335	29.985	0.16335	6.1218	4.3573
14	5.5348	0.18068	0.02867	34.883	0.15867	6.3025	4.6050
15	6.2543	0.15989	0.02474	40.417	0.15474	6.4624	4.8375
16	7.0673	0.14150	0.02143	46.672	0.15143	6.6039	5.0552
17	7.9861	0.12522	0.01861	53.739	0.14861	6.7291	5.2589
18	9.0243	0.11081	0.01620	61.725	0.14620	6.8399	5.4491
19	10.197	0.09806	0.01413	70.749	0.14413	6.9380	5.6265
20	11.523	0.08678	0.01235	80.947	0.14235	7.0248	5.7917
21	13.021	0.07680	0.01081	92.470	0.14081	7.1016	5.9454
22	14.714	0.06796	0.00948	105.49	0.13948	7.1695	6.0881
23	16.627	0.06014	0.00832	120.20	0.13832	7.2297	6.2205
24	18.788	0.05323	0.00731	136.83	0.13731	7.2829	6.3431
25	21.231	0.04710	0.00643	155.62	0.13643	7.3300	6.4566
26	23.991	0.04168	0.00565	176.85	0.13565	7.3717	6.5614
27	27.109	0.03689	0.00498	200.84	0.13498	7.4086	6.6582
28	30.633	0.03264	0.00439	227.95	0.13439	7.4412	6.7474
29	34.616	0.02889	0.00387	258.58	0.13387	7.4701	6.8296
30	39.116	0.02557	0.00341	293.20	0.13341	7.4957	6.9052
31	44.201	0.02262	0.00301	332.32	0.13301	7.5183	6.9747
32	49.947	0.02002	0.00266	376.52	0.13266	7.5383	7.0385
33	56.440	0.01772	0.00234	426.46	0.13234	7.5560	7.0971
34	63.777	0.01568	0.00207	482.90	0.13207	7.5717	7.1507
35	72.069	0.01388	0.00183	546.68	0.13183	7.5856	7.1998
40	132.78	0.00753	0.00099	1013.7	0.13099	7.6344	7.3888
45	244.64	0.00409	0.00053	1874.2	0.13053	7.6609	7.5076
50	450.74	0.00222	0.00029	3459.5	0.13029	7.6752	7.5811
55	830.45	0.00120	0.00016	6380.4	0.13016	7.6830	7.6260

i = 14%   **Discrete Compounding, Discrete Cash Flows**

	SINGLE PAYMENT		UNIFORM SERIES				Arithmetic Gradient Series Factor
	Compound Amount Factor	Present Worth Factor	Sinking Fund Factor	Uniform Series Factor	Capital Recovery Factor	Series Present Worth Factor	
N	(*F/P,i,N*)	(*P/F,i,N*)	(*A/F,i,N*)	(*F/A,i,N*)	(*A/P,i,N*)	(*P/A,i,N*)	(*A/G,i,N*)
1	1.1400	0.87719	1.0000	1.0000	1.1400	0.87719	0.00000
2	1.2996	0.76947	0.46729	2.1400	0.60729	1.6467	0.46729
3	1.4815	0.67497	0.29073	3.4396	0.43073	2.3216	0.91290
4	1.6890	0.59208	0.20320	4.9211	0.34320	2.9137	1.3370
5	1.9254	0.51937	0.15128	6.6101	0.29128	3.4331	1.7399
6	2.1950	0.45559	0.11716	8.5355	0.25716	3.8887	2.1218
7	2.5023	0.39964	0.09319	10.730	0.23319	4.2883	2.4832
8	2.8526	0.35056	0.07557	13.233	0.21557	4.6389	2.8246
9	3.2519	0.30751	0.06217	16.085	0.20217	4.9464	3.1463
10	3.7072	0.26974	0.05171	19.337	0.19171	5.2161	3.4490
11	4.2262	0.23662	0.04339	23.045	0.18339	5.4527	3.7333
12	4.8179	0.20756	0.03667	27.271	0.17667	5.6603	3.9998
13	5.4924	0.18207	0.03116	32.089	0.17116	5.8424	4.2491
14	6.2613	0.15971	0.02661	37.581	0.16661	6.0021	4.4819
15	7.1379	0.14010	0.02281	43.842	0.16281	6.1422	4.6990
16	8.1372	0.12289	0.01962	50.980	0.15962	6.2651	4.9011
17	9.2765	0.10780	0.01692	59.118	0.15692	6.3729	5.0888
18	10.575	0.09456	0.01462	68.394	0.15462	6.4674	5.2630
19	12.056	0.08295	0.01266	78.969	0.15266	6.5504	5.4243
20	13.743	0.07276	0.01099	91.025	0.15099	6.6231	5.5734
21	15.668	0.06383	0.00954	104.77	0.14954	6.6870	5.7111
22	17.861	0.05599	0.00830	120.44	0.14830	6.7429	5.8381
23	20.362	0.04911	0.00723	138.30	0.14723	6.7921	5.9549
24	23.212	0.04308	0.00630	158.66	0.14630	6.8351	6.0624
25	26.462	0.03779	0.00550	181.87	0.14550	6.8729	6.1610
26	30.167	0.03315	0.00480	208.33	0.14480	6.9061	6.2514
27	34.390	0.02908	0.00419	238.50	0.14419	6.9352	6.3342
28	39.204	0.02551	0.00366	272.89	0.14366	6.9607	6.4100
29	44.693	0.02237	0.00320	312.09	0.14320	6.9830	6.4791
30	50.950	0.01963	0.00280	356.79	0.14280	7.0027	6.5423
31	58.083	0.01722	0.00245	407.74	0.14245	7.0199	6.5998
32	66.215	0.01510	0.00215	465.82	0.14215	7.0350	6.6522
33	75.485	0.01325	0.00188	532.04	0.14188	7.0482	6.6998
34	86.053	0.01162	0.00165	607.52	0.14165	7.0599	6.7431
35	98.100	0.01019	0.00144	693.57	0.14144	7.0700	6.7824
40	188.88	0.00529	0.00075	1342.0	0.14075	7.1050	6.9300
45	363.68	0.00275	0.00039	2590.6	0.14039	7.1232	7.0188
50	700.23	0.00143	0.00020	4994.5	0.14020	7.1327	7.0714
55	1348.2	0.00074	0.00010	9623.1	0.14010	7.1376	7.1020

$i = 15\%$ Discrete Compounding, Discrete Cash Flows

	SINGLE PAYMENT		UNIFORM SERIES				Arithmetic Gradient Series Factor
	Compound Amount Factor	Present Worth Factor	Sinking Fund Factor	Uniform Series Factor	Capital Recovery Factor	Series Present Worth Factor	
N	(F/P,i,N)	(P/F,i,N)	(A/F,i,N)	(F/A,i,N)	(A/P,i,N)	(P/A,i,N)	(A/G,i,N)
1	1.1500	0.86957	1.0000	1.0000	1.1500	0.86957	0.00000
2	1.3225	0.75614	0.46512	2.1500	0.61512	1.6257	0.46512
3	1.5209	0.65752	0.28798	3.4725	0.43798	2.2832	0.90713
4	1.7490	0.57175	0.20027	4.9934	0.35027	2.8550	1.3263
5	2.0114	0.49718	0.14832	6.7424	0.29832	3.3522	1.7228
6	2.3131	0.43233	0.11424	8.7537	0.26424	3.7845	2.0972
7	2.6600	0.37594	0.09036	11.067	0.24036	4.1604	2.4498
8	3.0590	0.32690	0.07285	13.727	0.22285	4.4873	2.7813
9	3.5179	0.28426	0.05957	16.786	0.20957	4.7716	3.0922
10	4.0456	0.24718	0.04925	20.304	0.19925	5.0188	3.3832
11	4.6524	0.21494	0.04107	24.349	0.19107	5.2337	3.6549
12	5.3503	0.18691	0.03448	29.002	0.18448	5.4206	3.9082
13	6.1528	0.16253	0.02911	34.352	0.17911	5.5831	4.1438
14	7.0757	0.14133	0.02469	40.505	0.17469	5.7245	4.3624
15	8.1371	0.12289	0.02102	47.580	0.17102	5.8474	4.5650
16	9.3576	0.10686	0.01795	55.717	0.16795	5.9542	4.7522
17	10.761	0.09293	0.01537	65.075	0.16537	6.0472	4.9251
18	12.375	0.08081	0.01319	75.836	0.16319	6.1280	5.0843
19	14.232	0.07027	0.01134	88.212	0.16134	6.1982	5.2307
20	16.367	0.06110	0.00976	102.44	0.15976	6.2593	5.3651
21	18.822	0.05313	0.00842	118.81	0.15842	6.3125	5.4883
22	21.645	0.04620	0.00727	137.63	0.15727	6.3587	5.6010
23	24.891	0.04017	0.00628	159.28	0.15628	6.3988	5.7040
24	28.625	0.03493	0.00543	184.17	0.15543	6.4338	5.7979
25	32.919	0.03038	0.00470	212.79	0.15470	6.4641	5.8834
26	37.857	0.02642	0.00407	245.71	0.15407	6.4906	5.9612
27	43.535	0.02297	0.00353	283.57	0.15353	6.5135	6.0319
28	50.066	0.01997	0.00306	327.10	0.15306	6.5335	6.0960
29	57.575	0.01737	0.00265	377.17	0.15265	6.5509	6.1541
30	66.212	0.01510	0.00230	434.75	0.15230	6.5660	6.2066
31	76.144	0.01313	0.00200	500.96	0.15200	6.5791	6.2541
32	87.565	0.01142	0.00173	577.10	0.15173	6.5905	6.2970
33	100.70	0.00993	0.00150	664.67	0.15150	6.6005	6.3357
34	115.80	0.00864	0.00131	765.37	0.15131	6.6091	6.3705
35	133.18	0.00751	0.00113	881.17	0.15113	6.6166	6.4019
40	267.86	0.00373	0.00056	1779.1	0.15056	6.6418	6.5168
45	538.77	0.00186	0.00028	3585.1	0.15028	6.6543	6.5830
50	1083.7	0.00092	0.00014	7217.7	0.15014	6.6605	6.6205
55	2179.6	0.00046	0.00007	14524.0	0.15007	6.6636	6.6414

i = 20%   **Discrete Compounding, Discrete Cash Flows**

	SINGLE PAYMENT		UNIFORM SERIES				Arithmetic Gradient Series Factor
	Compound Amount Factor	Present Worth Factor	Sinking Fund Factor	Uniform Series Factor	Capital Recovery Factor	Series Present Worth Factor	
N	(F/P,i,N)	(P/F,i,N)	(A/F,i,N)	(F/A,i,N)	(A/P,i,N)	(P/A,i,N)	(A/G,i,N)
1	1.2000	0.83333	1.0000	1.0000	1.2000	0.83333	0.00000
2	1.4400	0.69444	0.45455	2.2000	0.65455	1.5278	0.45455
3	1.7280	0.57870	0.27473	3.6400	0.47473	2.1065	0.87912
4	2.0736	0.48225	0.18629	5.3680	0.38629	2.5887	1.2742
5	2.4883	0.40188	0.13438	7.4416	0.33438	2.9906	1.6405
6	2.9860	0.33490	0.10071	9.9299	0.30071	3.3255	1.9788
7	3.5832	0.27908	0.07742	12.916	0.27742	3.6046	2.2902
8	4.2998	0.23257	0.06061	16.499	0.26061	3.8372	2.5756
9	5.1598	0.19381	0.04808	20.799	0.24808	4.0310	2.8364
10	6.1917	0.16151	0.03852	25.959	0.23852	4.1925	3.0739
11	7.4301	0.13459	0.03110	32.150	0.23110	4.3271	3.2893
12	8.9161	0.11216	0.02526	39.581	0.22526	4.4392	3.4841
13	10.699	0.09346	0.02062	48.497	0.22062	4.5327	3.6597
14	12.839	0.07789	0.01689	59.196	0.21689	4.6106	3.8175
15	15.407	0.06491	0.01388	72.035	0.21388	4.6755	3.9588
16	18.488	0.05409	0.01144	87.442	0.21144	4.7296	4.0851
17	22.186	0.04507	0.00944	105.93	0.20944	4.7746	4.1976
18	26.623	0.03756	0.00781	128.12	0.20781	4.8122	4.2975
19	31.948	0.03130	0.00646	154.74	0.20646	4.8435	4.3861
20	38.338	0.02608	0.00536	186.69	0.20536	4.8696	4.4643
21	46.005	0.02174	0.00444	225.03	0.20444	4.8913	4.5334
22	55.206	0.01811	0.00369	271.03	0.20369	4.9094	4.5941
23	66.247	0.01509	0.00307	326.24	0.20307	4.9245	4.6475
24	79.497	0.01258	0.00255	392.48	0.20255	4.9371	4.6943
25	95.396	0.01048	0.00212	471.98	0.20212	4.9476	4.7352
26	114.48	0.00874	0.00176	567.38	0.20176	4.9563	4.7709
27	137.37	0.00728	0.00147	681.85	0.20147	4.9636	4.8020
28	164.84	0.00607	0.00122	819.22	0.20122	4.9697	4.8291
29	197.81	0.00506	0.00102	984.07	0.20102	4.9747	4.8527
30	237.38	0.00421	0.00085	1181.9	0.20085	4.9789	4.8731
31	284.85	0.00351	0.00070	1419.3	0.20070	4.9824	4.8908
32	341.82	0.00293	0.00059	1704.1	0.20059	4.9854	4.9061
33	410.19	0.00244	0.00049	2045.9	0.20049	4.9878	4.9194
34	492.22	0.00203	0.00041	2456.1	0.20041	4.9898	4.9308
35	590.67	0.00169	0.00034	2948.3	0.20034	4.9915	4.9406

$i = 25\%$ Discrete Compounding, Discrete Cash Flows

	SINGLE PAYMENT		UNIFORM SERIES				Arithmetic Gradient Series Factor
	Compound Amount Factor	Present Worth Factor	Sinking Fund Factor	Uniform Series Factor	Capital Recovery Factor	Series Present Worth Factor	
N	(F/P,i,N)	(P/F,i,N)	(A/F,i,N)	(F/A,i,N)	(A/P,i,N)	(P/A,i,N)	(A/G,i,N)
1	1.2500	0.80000	1.0000	1.0000	1.2500	0.80000	0.00000
2	1.5625	0.64000	0.44444	2.2500	0.69444	1.4400	0.44444
3	1.9531	0.51200	0.26230	3.8125	0.51230	1.9520	0.85246
4	2.4414	0.40960	0.17344	5.7656	0.42344	2.3616	1.2249
5	3.0518	0.32768	0.12185	8.2070	0.37185	2.6893	1.5631
6	3.8147	0.26214	0.08882	11.259	0.33882	2.9514	1.8683
7	4.7684	0.20972	0.06634	15.073	0.31634	3.1611	2.1424
8	5.9605	0.16777	0.05040	19.842	0.30040	3.3289	2.3872
9	7.4506	0.13422	0.03876	25.802	0.28876	3.4631	2.6048
10	9.3132	0.10737	0.03007	33.253	0.28007	3.5705	2.7971
11	11.642	0.08590	0.02349	42.566	0.27349	3.6564	2.9663
12	14.552	0.06872	0.01845	54.208	0.26845	3.7251	3.1145
13	18.190	0.05498	0.01454	68.760	0.26454	3.7801	3.2437
14	22.737	0.04398	0.01150	86.949	0.26150	3.8241	3.3559
15	28.422	0.03518	0.00912	109.69	0.25912	3.8593	3.4530
16	35.527	0.02815	0.00724	138.11	0.25724	3.8874	3.5366
17	44.409	0.02252	0.00576	173.64	0.25576	3.9099	3.6084
18	55.511	0.01801	0.00459	218.04	0.25459	3.9279	3.6698
19	69.389	0.01441	0.00366	273.56	0.25366	3.9424	3.7222
20	86.736	0.01153	0.00292	342.94	0.25292	3.9539	3.7667
21	108.42	0.00922	0.00233	429.68	0.25233	3.9631	3.8045
22	135.53	0.00738	0.00186	538.10	0.25186	3.9705	3.8365
23	169.41	0.00590	0.00148	673.63	0.25148	3.9764	3.8634
24	211.76	0.00472	0.00119	843.03	0.25119	3.9811	3.8861
25	264.70	0.00378	0.00095	1054.8	0.25095	3.9849	3.9052
26	330.87	0.00302	0.00076	1319.5	0.25076	3.9879	3.9212
27	413.59	0.00242	0.00061	1650.4	0.25061	3.9903	3.9346
28	516.99	0.00193	0.00048	2064.0	0.25048	3.9923	3.9457
29	646.23	0.00155	0.00039	2580.9	0.25039	3.9938	3.9551
30	807.79	0.00124	0.00031	3227.2	0.25031	3.9950	3.9628
31	1009.7	0.00099	0.00025	4035.0	0.25025	3.9960	3.9693
32	1262.2	0.00079	0.00020	5044.7	0.25020	3.9968	3.9746
33	1577.7	0.00063	0.00016	6306.9	0.25016	3.9975	3.9791
34	1972.2	0.00051	0.00013	7884.6	0.25013	3.9980	3.9828
35	2465.2	0.00041	0.00010	9856.8	0.25010	3.9984	3.9858

i = 30%   **Discrete Compounding, Discrete Cash Flows**

	SINGLE PAYMENT		**UNIFORM SERIES**				**Arithmetic Gradient Series Factor**
	Compound Amount Factor	Present Worth Factor	Sinking Fund Factor	Uniform Series Factor	Capital Recovery Factor	Series Present Worth Factor	
N	(*F/P,i,N*)	(*P/F,i,N*)	(*A/F,i,N*)	(*F/A,i,N*)	(*A/P,i,N*)	(*P/A,i,N*)	(*A/G,i,N*)
1	1.3000	0.76923	1.0000	1.0000	1.3000	0.76923	0.00000
2	1.6900	0.59172	0.43478	2.3000	0.73478	1.3609	0.43478
3	2.1970	0.45517	0.25063	3.9900	0.55063	1.8161	0.82707
4	2.8561	0.35013	0.16163	6.1870	0.46163	2.1662	1.1783
5	3.7129	0.26933	0.11058	9.0431	0.41058	2.4356	1.4903
6	4.8268	0.20718	0.07839	12.756	0.37839	2.6427	1.7654
7	6.2749	0.15937	0.05687	17.583	0.35687	2.8021	2.0063
8	8.1573	0.12259	0.04192	23.858	0.34192	2.9247	2.2156
9	10.604	0.09430	0.03124	32.015	0.33124	3.0190	2.3963
10	13.786	0.07254	0.02346	42.619	0.32346	3.0915	2.5512
11	17.922	0.05580	0.01773	56.405	0.31773	3.1473	2.6833
12	23.298	0.04292	0.01345	74.327	0.31345	3.1903	2.7952
13	30.288	0.03302	0.01024	97.625	0.31024	3.2233	2.8895
14	39.374	0.02540	0.00782	127.91	0.30782	3.2487	2.9685
15	51.186	0.01954	0.00598	167.29	0.30598	3.2682	3.0344
16	66.542	0.01503	0.00458	218.47	0.30458	3.2832	3.0892
17	86.504	0.01156	0.00351	285.01	0.30351	3.2948	3.1345
18	112.46	0.00889	0.00269	371.52	0.30269	3.3037	3.1718
19	146.19	0.00684	0.00207	483.97	0.30207	3.3105	3.2025
20	190.05	0.00526	0.00159	630.17	0.30159	3.3158	3.2275
21	247.06	0.00405	0.00122	820.22	0.30122	3.3198	3.2480
22	321.18	0.00311	0.00094	1067.3	0.30094	3.3230	3.2646
23	417.54	0.00239	0.00072	1388.5	0.30072	3.3254	3.2781
24	542.80	0.00184	0.00055	1806.0	0.30055	3.3272	3.2890
25	705.64	0.00142	0.00043	2348.8	0.30043	3.3286	3.2979
26	917.33	0.00109	0.00033	3054.4	0.30033	3.3297	3.3050
27	1192.5	0.00084	0.00025	3971.8	0.30025	3.3305	3.3107
28	1550.3	0.00065	0.00019	5164.3	0.30019	3.3312	3.3153
29	2015.4	0.00050	0.00015	6714.6	0.30015	3.3317	3.3189
30	2620.0	0.00038	0.00011	8730.0	0.30011	3.3321	3.3219
31	3406.0	0.00029	0.00009	11 350.0	0.30009	3.3324	3.3242
32	4427.8	0.00023	0.00007	14 756.0	0.30007	3.3326	3.3261
33	5756.1	0.00017	0.00005	19 184.0	0.30005	3.3328	3.3276
34	7483.0	0.00013	0.00004	24 940.0	0.30004	3.3329	3.3288
35	9727.9	0.00010	0.00003	32 423.0	0.30003	3.3330	3.3297

i = 40%   Discrete Compounding, Discrete Cash Flows

	SINGLE PAYMENT		UNIFORM SERIES				Arithmetic Gradient Series Factor
	Compound Amount Factor	Present Worth Factor	Sinking Fund Factor	Uniform Series Factor	Capital Recovery Factor	Series Present Worth Factor	
N	(F/P,i,N)	(P/F,i,N)	(A/F,i,N)	(F/A,i,N)	(A/P,i,N)	(P/A,i,N)	(A/G,i,N)
1	1.4000	0.71429	1.0000	1.0000	1.4000	0.71429	0.00000
2	1.9600	0.51020	0.41667	2.4000	0.81667	1.2245	0.41667
3	2.7440	0.36443	0.22936	4.3600	0.62936	1.5889	0.77982
4	3.8416	0.26031	0.14077	7.1040	0.54077	1.8492	1.0923
5	5.3782	0.18593	0.09136	10.946	0.49136	2.0352	1.3580
6	7.5295	0.13281	0.06126	16.324	0.46126	2.1680	1.5811
7	10.541	0.09486	0.04192	23.853	0.44192	2.2628	1.7664
8	14.758	0.06776	0.02907	34.395	0.42907	2.3306	1.9185
9	20.661	0.04840	0.02034	49.153	0.42034	2.3790	2.0422
10	28.925	0.03457	0.01432	69.814	0.41432	2.4136	2.1419
11	40.496	0.02469	0.01013	98.739	0.41013	2.4383	2.2215
12	56.694	0.01764	0.00718	139.23	0.40718	2.4559	2.2845
13	79.371	0.01260	0.00510	195.93	0.40510	2.4685	2.3341
14	111.12	0.00900	0.00363	275.30	0.40363	2.4775	2.3729
15	155.57	0.00643	0.00259	386.42	0.40259	2.4839	2.4030
16	217.80	0.00459	0.00185	541.99	0.40185	2.4885	2.4262
17	304.91	0.00328	0.00132	759.78	0.40132	2.4918	2.4441
18	426.88	0.00234	0.00094	1064.70	0.40094	2.4941	2.4577
19	597.63	0.00167	0.00067	1491.58	0.40067	2.4958	2.4682
20	836.68	0.00120	0.00048	2089.21	0.40048	2.4970	2.4761
21	1171.36	0.00085	0.00034	2925.89	0.40034	2.4979	2.4821
22	1639.90	0.00061	0.00024	4097.24	0.40024	2.4985	2.4866
23	2295.86	0.00044	0.00017	5737.14	0.40017	2.4989	2.4900
24	3214.20	0.00031	0.00012	8033.00	0.40012	2.4992	2.4925
25	4499.88	0.00022	0.00009	11 247.0	0.40009	2.4994	2.4944
26	6299.83	0.00016	0.00006	15 747.0	0.40006	2.4996	2.4959
27	8819.76	0.00011	0.00005	22 047.0	0.40005	2.4997	2.4969
28	12 348.0	0.00008	0.00003	30 867.0	0.40003	2.4998	2.4977
29	17 287.0	0.00006	0.00002	43 214.0	0.40002	2.4999	2.4983
30	24 201.0	0.00004	0.00002	60 501.0	0.40002	2.4999	2.4988
31	33 882.0	0.00003	0.00001	84 703.0	0.40001	2.4999	2.4991
32	47 435.0	0.00002	0.00001	118 585.0	0.40001	2.4999	2.4993
33	66 409.0	0.00002	0.00001	166 019.0	0.40001	2.5000	2.4995
34	92 972.0	0.00001	0.00000	232 428.0	0.40000	2.5000	2.4996
35	130 161.0	0.00001	0.00000	325 400.0	0.40000	2.5000	2.4997

$i = 50\%$ **Discrete Compounding, Discrete Cash Flows**

	SINGLE PAYMENT		UNIFORM SERIES				Arithmetic Gradient Series Factor
	Compound Amount Factor	Present Worth Factor	Sinking Fund Factor	Uniform Series Factor	Capital Recovery Factor	Series Present Worth Factor	
N	(F/P,i,N)	(P/F,i,N)	(A/F,i,N)	(F/A,i,N)	(A/P,i,N)	(P/A,i,N)	(A/G,i,N)
1	1.5000	0.66667	1.0000	1.0000	1.5000	0.66667	0.00000
2	2.2500	0.44444	0.40000	2.5000	0.90000	1.1111	0.40000
3	3.3750	0.29630	0.21053	4.7500	0.71053	1.4074	0.73684
4	5.0625	0.19753	0.12308	8.1250	0.62308	1.6049	1.0154
5	7.5938	0.13169	0.07583	13.1875	0.57583	1.7366	1.2417
6	11.3906	0.08779	0.04812	20.781	0.54812	1.8244	1.4226
7	17.0859	0.05853	0.03108	32.172	0.53108	1.8829	1.5648
8	25.6289	0.03902	0.02030	49.258	0.52030	1.9220	1.6752
9	38.443	0.02601	0.01335	74.887	0.51335	1.9480	1.7596
10	57.665	0.01734	0.00882	113.330	0.50882	1.9653	1.8235
11	86.498	0.01156	0.00585	170.995	0.50585	1.9769	1.8713
12	129.746	0.00771	0.00388	257.493	0.50388	1.9846	1.9068
13	194.620	0.00514	0.00258	387.239	0.50258	1.9897	1.9329
14	291.929	0.00343	0.00172	581.86	0.50172	1.9931	1.9519
15	437.894	0.00228	0.00114	873.79	0.50114	1.9954	1.9657
16	656.841	0.00152	0.00076	1311.68	0.50076	1.9970	1.9756
17	985.261	0.00101	0.00051	1968.52	0.50051	1.9980	1.9827
18	1477.89	0.00068	0.00034	2953.78	0.50034	1.9986	1.9878
19	2216.84	0.00045	0.00023	4431.68	0.50023	1.9991	1.9914
20	3325.26	0.00030	0.00015	6648.51	0.50015	1.9994	1.9940
21	4987.89	0.00020	0.00010	9973.77	0.50010	1.9996	1.9958
22	7481.83	0.00013	0.00007	14962.0	0.50007	1.9997	1.9971
23	11223.0	0.00009	0.00004	22443.0	0.50004	1.9998	1.9980
24	16834.0	0.00006	0.00003	33666.0	0.50003	1.9999	1.9986
25	25251.0	0.00004	0.00002	50500.0	0.50002	1.9999	1.9990
26	37877.0	0.00003	0.00001	75752.0	0.50001	1.9999	1.9993
27	56815.0	0.00002	0.00001	113628.0	0.50001	2.0000	1.9995
28	85223.0	0.00001	0.00001	170443.0	0.50001	2.0000	1.9997
29	127834.0	0.00001	0.00000	255666.0	0.50000	2.0000	1.9998
30	191751.0	0.00001	0.00000	383500.0	0.50000	2.0000	1.9998
31	287627.0	0.00000	0.00000	575251.0	0.50000	2.0000	1.9999
32	431440.0	0.00000	0.00000	862878.0	0.50000	2.0000	1.9999
33	647160.0	0.00000	0.00000	1294318.0	0.50000	2.0000	1.9999
34	970740.0	0.00000	0.00000	1941477.0	0.50000	2.0000	2.0000
35	1456110.0	0.00000	0.00000	2912217.0	0.50000	2.0000	2.0000

B

Compound Interest Factors for Continuous Compounding, Discrete Cash Flows

$r = 1\%$ **Continuous Compounding, Discrete Cash Flows**

	SINGLE PAYMENT		UNIFORM SERIES				Arithmetic Gradient Series Factor
	Compound Amount Factor	Present Worth Factor	Sinking Fund Factor	Uniform Series Factor	Capital Recovery Factor	Series Present Worth Factor	
N	$(F/P,r,N)$	$(P/F,r,N)$	$(A/F,r,N)$	$(F/A,r,N)$	$(A/P,r,N)$	$(P/A,r,N)$	$(A/G,r,N)$
1	1.0101	0.99005	1.0000	1.0000	1.0101	0.99005	0.00000
2	1.0202	0.98020	0.49750	2.0101	0.50755	1.97025	0.49750
3	1.0305	0.97045	0.33001	3.0303	0.34006	2.94069	0.99333
4	1.0408	0.96079	0.24626	4.0607	0.25631	3.90148	1.48750
5	1.0513	0.95123	0.19602	5.1015	0.20607	4.85271	1.98000
6	1.0618	0.94176	0.16253	6.1528	0.17258	5.79448	2.47084
7	1.0725	0.93239	0.13861	7.2146	0.14866	6.72687	2.96000
8	1.0833	0.92312	0.12067	8.2871	0.13072	7.64999	3.44751
9	1.0942	0.91393	0.10672	9.3704	0.11677	8.56392	3.93334
10	1.1052	0.90484	0.09556	10.4646	0.10561	9.46876	4.41751
11	1.1163	0.89583	0.08643	11.5698	0.09648	10.36459	4.90002
12	1.1275	0.88692	0.07883	12.6860	0.08888	11.25151	5.38086
13	1.1388	0.87810	0.07239	13.8135	0.08244	12.12961	5.86004
14	1.1503	0.86936	0.06688	14.9524	0.07693	12.99896	6.33755
15	1.1618	0.86071	0.06210	16.1026	0.07215	13.85967	6.81340
16	1.1735	0.85214	0.05792	17.2645	0.06797	14.71182	7.28759
17	1.1853	0.84366	0.05424	18.4380	0.06429	15.55548	7.76012
18	1.1972	0.83527	0.05096	19.6233	0.06101	16.39075	8.23098
19	1.2092	0.82696	0.04803	20.8205	0.05808	17.21771	8.70018
20	1.2214	0.81873	0.04539	22.0298	0.05544	18.03644	9.16772
21	1.2337	0.81058	0.04301	23.2512	0.05306	18.84703	9.63360
22	1.2461	0.80252	0.04084	24.4848	0.05089	19.64954	10.09782
23	1.2586	0.79453	0.03886	25.7309	0.04891	20.44408	10.56039
24	1.2712	0.78663	0.03705	26.9895	0.04710	21.23071	11.02129
25	1.2840	0.77880	0.03538	28.2608	0.04543	22.00951	11.48054
26	1.2969	0.77105	0.03385	29.5448	0.04390	22.78056	11.93813
27	1.3100	0.76338	0.03242	30.8417	0.04247	23.54394	12.39407
28	1.3231	0.75578	0.03110	32.1517	0.04115	24.29972	12.84835
29	1.3364	0.74826	0.02987	33.4748	0.03992	25.04798	13.30098
30	1.3499	0.74082	0.02873	34.8112	0.03878	25.78880	13.75196
31	1.3634	0.73345	0.02765	36.1611	0.03770	26.52225	14.20128
32	1.3771	0.72615	0.02665	37.5245	0.03670	27.24840	14.64895
33	1.3910	0.71892	0.02571	38.9017	0.03576	27.96732	15.09498
34	1.4049	0.71177	0.02482	40.2926	0.03487	28.67909	15.53935
35	1.4191	0.70469	0.02398	41.6976	0.03403	29.38378	15.98208
40	1.4918	0.67032	0.02043	48.9370	0.03048	32.80343	18.17104
45	1.5683	0.63763	0.01768	56.5475	0.02773	36.05630	20.31900
50	1.6487	0.60653	0.01549	64.5483	0.02554	39.15053	22.42613
55	1.7333	0.57695	0.01371	72.9593	0.02376	42.09385	24.49262
60	1.8221	0.54881	0.01222	81.8015	0.02227	44.89362	26.51868
65	1.9155	0.52205	0.01098	91.0971	0.02103	47.55684	28.50455
70	2.0138	0.49659	0.00991	100.869	0.01996	50.09018	30.45046
75	2.1170	0.47237	0.00900	111.142	0.01905	52.49997	32.35670
80	2.2255	0.44933	0.00820	121.942	0.01825	54.79223	34.22354
85	2.3396	0.42741	0.00750	133.296	0.01755	56.97269	36.05128
90	2.4596	0.40657	0.00689	145.232	0.01694	59.04681	37.84024
95	2.5857	0.38674	0.00634	157.779	0.01639	61.01978	39.59075
100	2.7183	0.36788	0.00585	170.970	0.01582	63.21206	41.30316

$r = 2\%$ **Continuous Compounding, Discrete Cash Flows**

	SINGLE PAYMENT		UNIFORM SERIES				Arithmetic Gradient Series Factor
	Compound Amount Factor	Present Worth Factor	Sinking Fund Factor	Uniform Series Factor	Capital Recovery Factor	Series Present Worth Factor	
N	(F/P,r,N)	(P/F,r,N)	(A/F,r,N)	(F/A,r,N)	(A/P,r,N)	(P/A,r,N)	(A/G,r,N)
1	1.0202	0.98020	1.0000	1.0000	1.0202	0.98020	0.00000
2	1.0408	0.96079	0.49500	2.0202	0.51520	1.94099	0.49500
3	1.0618	0.94176	0.32669	3.0610	0.34689	2.88275	0.98667
4	1.0833	0.92312	0.24255	4.1228	0.26275	3.80587	1.47500
5	1.1052	0.90484	0.19208	5.2061	0.21228	4.71071	1.96001
6	1.1275	0.88692	0.15845	6.3113	0.17865	5.59763	2.44168
7	1.1503	0.86936	0.13443	7.4388	0.15463	6.46699	2.92003
8	1.1735	0.85214	0.11643	8.5891	0.13663	7.31913	3.39505
9	1.1972	0.83527	0.10243	9.7626	0.12263	8.15440	3.86674
10	1.2214	0.81873	0.09124	10.9598	0.11144	8.97313	4.33511
11	1.2461	0.80252	0.08209	12.1812	0.10230	9.77565	4.80016
12	1.2712	0.78663	0.07448	13.4273	0.09468	10.56228	5.26190
13	1.2969	0.77105	0.06803	14.6985	0.08824	11.33333	5.72032
14	1.3231	0.75578	0.06252	15.9955	0.08272	12.08911	6.17543
15	1.3499	0.74082	0.05774	17.3186	0.07794	12.82993	6.62723
16	1.3771	0.72615	0.05357	18.6685	0.07377	13.55608	7.07573
17	1.4049	0.71177	0.04989	20.0456	0.07009	14.26785	7.52093
18	1.4333	0.69768	0.04662	21.4505	0.06682	14.96553	7.96283
19	1.4623	0.68386	0.04370	22.8839	0.06390	15.64939	8.40144
20	1.4918	0.67032	0.04107	24.3461	0.06128	16.31971	8.83677
21	1.5220	0.65705	0.03870	25.8380	0.05890	16.97675	9.26882
22	1.5527	0.64404	0.03655	27.3599	0.05675	17.62079	9.69759
23	1.5841	0.63128	0.03459	28.9126	0.05479	18.25207	10.12309
24	1.6161	0.61878	0.03279	30.4967	0.05299	18.87086	10.54533
25	1.6487	0.60653	0.03114	32.1128	0.05134	19.47739	10.96431
26	1.6820	0.59452	0.02962	33.7615	0.04982	20.07191	11.38005
27	1.7160	0.58275	0.02821	35.4435	0.04842	20.65466	11.79253
28	1.7507	0.57121	0.02691	37.1595	0.04711	21.22587	12.20178
29	1.7860	0.55990	0.02570	38.9102	0.04590	21.78576	12.60780
30	1.8221	0.54881	0.02457	40.6963	0.04477	22.33458	13.01059
31	1.8589	0.53794	0.02352	42.5184	0.04372	22.87252	13.41017
32	1.8965	0.52729	0.02253	44.3773	0.04274	23.39981	13.80654
33	1.9348	0.51685	0.02161	46.2738	0.04181	23.91666	14.19971
34	1.9739	0.50662	0.02074	48.2086	0.04094	24.42328	14.58969
35	2.0138	0.49659	0.01993	50.1824	0.04013	24.91987	14.97648
40	2.2255	0.44933	0.01648	60.6663	0.03668	27.25913	16.86302
45	2.4596	0.40657	0.01384	72.2528	0.03404	29.37579	18.67137
50	2.7183	0.36788	0.01176	85.0578	0.03196	31.29102	20.40283
55	3.0042	0.33287	0.01008	99.2096	0.03028	33.02399	22.05883
60	3.3201	0.30119	0.00871	114.850	0.02891	34.59205	23.64090
65	3.6693	0.27253	0.00757	132.135	0.02777	36.01089	25.15068
70	4.0552	0.24660	0.00661	151.237	0.02681	37.29471	26.58991
75	4.4817	0.22313	0.00580	172.349	0.02600	38.45635	27.96040
80	4.9530	0.20190	0.00511	195.682	0.02531	39.50745	29.26404
85	5.4739	0.18268	0.00452	221.468	0.02472	40.45853	30.50278
90	6.0496	0.16530	0.00400	249.966	0.02420	41.31910	31.67864
95	6.6859	0.14957	0.00355	281.461	0.02375	42.09777	32.79365
100	7.3891	0.13534	0.00316	316.269	0.02336	42.80234	33.84990

$r = 3\%$ Continuous Compounding, Discrete Cash Flows

	SINGLE PAYMENT		UNIFORM SERIES				Arithmetic Gradient Series Factor
	Compound Amount Factor	Present Worth Factor	Sinking Fund Factor	Uniform Series Factor	Capital Recovery Factor	Series Present Worth Factor	
N	(F/P,r,N)	(P/F,r,N)	(A/F,r,N)	(F/A,r,N)	(A/P,r,N)	(P/A,r,N)	(A/G,r,N)
1	1.0305	0.97045	1.0000	1.0000	1.0305	0.97045	0.00000
2	1.0618	0.94176	0.49250	2.0305	0.52296	1.91221	0.49250
3	1.0942	0.91393	0.32338	3.0923	0.35384	2.82614	0.98000
4	1.1275	0.88692	0.23886	4.1865	0.26932	3.71306	1.46251
5	1.1618	0.86071	0.18818	5.3140	0.21864	4.57377	1.94002
6	1.1972	0.83527	0.15442	6.4758	0.18488	5.40904	2.41255
7	1.2337	0.81058	0.13033	7.6730	0.16078	6.21962	2.88009
8	1.2712	0.78663	0.11228	8.9067	0.14273	7.00625	3.34265
9	1.3100	0.76338	0.09825	10.1779	0.12871	7.76963	3.80025
10	1.3499	0.74082	0.08705	11.4879	0.11750	8.51045	4.25287
11	1.3910	0.71892	0.07790	12.8378	0.10835	9.22937	4.70055
12	1.4333	0.69768	0.07028	14.2287	0.10073	9.92705	5.14328
13	1.4770	0.67706	0.06385	15.6621	0.09430	10.60411	5.58107
14	1.5220	0.65705	0.05835	17.1390	0.08880	11.26115	6.01393
15	1.5683	0.63763	0.05359	18.6610	0.08404	11.89878	6.44189
16	1.6161	0.61878	0.04943	20.2293	0.07989	12.51756	6.86494
17	1.6653	0.60050	0.04578	21.8454	0.07623	13.11806	7.28311
18	1.7160	0.58275	0.04253	23.5107	0.07299	13.70081	7.69641
19	1.7683	0.56553	0.03964	25.2267	0.07010	14.26633	8.10485
20	1.8221	0.54881	0.03704	26.9950	0.06750	14.81515	8.50845
21	1.8776	0.53259	0.03470	28.8171	0.06516	15.34774	8.90722
22	1.9348	0.51685	0.03258	30.6947	0.06303	15.86459	9.30119
23	1.9937	0.50158	0.03065	32.6295	0.06110	16.36617	9.69038
24	2.0544	0.48675	0.02888	34.6232	0.05934	16.85292	10.07479
25	2.1170	0.47237	0.02726	36.6776	0.05772	17.32528	10.45445
26	2.1815	0.45841	0.02578	38.7946	0.05623	17.78369	10.82939
27	2.2479	0.44486	0.02440	40.9761	0.05486	18.22855	11.19962
28	2.3164	0.43171	0.02314	43.2240	0.05359	18.66026	11.56517
29	2.3869	0.41895	0.02196	45.5404	0.05241	19.07921	11.92605
30	2.4596	0.40657	0.02086	47.9273	0.05132	19.48578	12.28230
31	2.5345	0.39455	0.01985	50.3869	0.05030	19.88033	12.63393
32	2.6117	0.38289	0.01890	52.9214	0.04935	20.26323	12.98098
33	2.6912	0.37158	0.01801	55.5331	0.04846	20.63480	13.32346
34	2.7732	0.36059	0.01717	58.2243	0.04763	20.99540	13.66140
35	2.8577	0.34994	0.01639	60.9975	0.04685	21.34534	13.99484
40	3.3201	0.30119	0.01313	76.1830	0.04358	22.94587	15.59532
45	3.8574	0.25924	0.01066	93.8259	0.04111	24.32346	17.08739
50	4.4817	0.22313	0.00875	114.324	0.03920	25.50917	18.47499
55	5.2070	0.19205	0.00724	138.140	0.03769	26.52971	19.76232
60	6.0496	0.16530	0.00603	165.809	0.03649	27.40811	20.95382
65	7.0287	0.14227	0.00505	197.957	0.03551	28.16415	22.05405
70	8.1662	0.12246	0.00425	235.307	0.03470	28.81487	23.06771
75	9.4877	0.10540	0.00359	278.702	0.03404	29.37496	23.99955
80	11.0232	0.09072	0.00304	329.119	0.03349	29.85703	24.85433
85	12.8071	0.07808	0.00258	387.696	0.03303	30.27196	25.63678
90	14.8797	0.06721	0.00219	455.753	0.03265	30.62908	26.35156
95	17.2878	0.05784	0.00187	534.823	0.03232	30.93647	27.00324
100	20.0855	0.04979	0.00160	626.690	0.03205	31.20103	27.59626

$r = 4\%$ **Continuous Compounding, Discrete Cash Flows**

	SINGLE PAYMENT		UNIFORM SERIES				Arithmetic Gradient Series Factor
	Compound Amount Factor	Present Worth Factor	Sinking Fund Factor	Uniform Series Factor	Capital Recovery Factor	Series Present Worth Factor	Arithmetic Gradient Series Factor
N	$(F/P,r,N)$	$(P/F,r,N)$	$(A/F,r,N)$	$(F/A,r,N)$	$(A/P,r,N)$	$(P/A,r,N)$	$(A/G,r,N)$
1	1.0408	0.96079	1.0000	1.0000	1.0408	0.96079	0.00000
2	1.0833	0.92312	0.49000	2.0408	0.53081	1.88391	0.49000
3	1.1275	0.88692	0.32009	3.1241	0.36090	2.77083	0.97334
4	1.1735	0.85214	0.23521	4.2516	0.27602	3.62297	1.45002
5	1.2214	0.81873	0.18433	5.4251	0.22514	4.44170	1.92006
6	1.2712	0.78663	0.15045	6.6465	0.19127	5.22833	2.38345
7	1.3231	0.75578	0.12630	7.9178	0.16711	5.98411	2.84021
8	1.3771	0.72615	0.10821	9.2409	0.14903	6.71026	3.29036
9	1.4333	0.69768	0.09418	10.6180	0.13499	7.40794	3.73391
10	1.4918	0.67032	0.08298	12.0513	0.12379	8.07826	4.17089
11	1.5527	0.64404	0.07384	13.5432	0.11465	8.72229	4.60130
12	1.6161	0.61878	0.06624	15.0959	0.10705	9.34108	5.02517
13	1.6820	0.59452	0.05984	16.7120	0.10065	9.93560	5.44252
14	1.7507	0.57121	0.05437	18.3940	0.09518	10.50681	5.85339
15	1.8221	0.54881	0.04964	20.1447	0.09045	11.05562	6.25780
16	1.8965	0.52729	0.04552	21.9668	0.08633	11.58291	6.65577
17	1.9739	0.50662	0.04191	23.8633	0.08272	12.08953	7.04734
18	2.0544	0.48675	0.03870	25.8371	0.07951	12.57628	7.43255
19	2.1383	0.46767	0.03585	27.8916	0.07666	13.04395	7.81143
20	2.2255	0.44933	0.03330	30.0298	0.07411	13.49328	8.18401
21	2.3164	0.43171	0.03100	32.2554	0.07181	13.92499	8.55034
22	2.4109	0.41478	0.02893	34.5717	0.06974	14.33977	8.91045
23	2.5093	0.39852	0.02704	36.9826	0.06785	14.73829	9.26438
24	2.6117	0.38289	0.02532	39.4919	0.06613	15.12118	9.61219
25	2.7183	0.36788	0.02375	42.1036	0.06456	15.48906	9.95392
26	2.8292	0.35345	0.02231	44.8219	0.06312	15.84252	10.28960
27	2.9447	0.33960	0.02099	47.6511	0.06180	16.18211	10.61930
28	3.0649	0.32628	0.01976	50.5958	0.06058	16.50839	10.94305
29	3.1899	0.31349	0.01864	53.6607	0.05945	16.82188	11.26092
30	3.3201	0.30119	0.01759	56.8506	0.05840	17.12307	11.57295
31	3.4556	0.28938	0.01662	60.1707	0.05743	17.41246	11.87920
32	3.5966	0.27804	0.01572	63.6263	0.05653	17.69049	12.17971
33	3.7434	0.26714	0.01488	67.2230	0.05569	17.95763	12.47456
34	3.8962	0.25666	0.01409	70.9664	0.05490	18.21429	12.76379
35	4.0552	0.24660	0.01336	74.8626	0.05417	18.46089	13.04745
40	4.9530	0.20190	0.01032	96.8625	0.05113	19.55620	14.38452
45	6.0496	0.16530	0.00808	123.733	0.04889	20.45296	15.59182
50	7.3891	0.13534	0.00639	156.553	0.04720	21.18717	16.67745
55	9.0250	0.11080	0.00509	196.640	0.04590	21.78829	17.64976
60	11.0232	0.09072	0.00407	245.601	0.04488	22.28044	18.51721
65	13.4637	0.07427	0.00327	305.403	0.04409	22.68338	19.28820
70	16.4446	0.06081	0.00264	378.445	0.04345	23.01328	19.97102
75	20.0855	0.04979	0.00214	467.659	0.04295	23.28338	20.57366
80	24.5325	0.04076	0.00173	576.625	0.04255	23.50452	21.10378
85	29.9641	0.03337	0.00141	709.717	0.04222	23.68558	21.56867
90	36.5982	0.02732	0.00115	872.275	0.04196	23.83381	21.97512
95	44.7012	0.02237	0.00093	1070.82	0.04174	23.95517	22.32948
100	54.5982	0.01832	0.00076	1313.33	0.04157	24.05454	22.63760

r = 5%   Continuous Compounding, Discrete Cash Flows

	SINGLE PAYMENT		UNIFORM SERIES				Arithmetic Gradient Series Factor
	Compound Amount Factor	Present Worth Factor	Sinking Fund Factor	Uniform Series Factor	Capital Recovery Factor	Series Present Worth Factor	
N	(F/P,r,N)	(P/F,r,N)	(A/F,r,N)	(F/A,r,N)	(A/P,r,N)	(P/A,r,N)	(A/G,r,N)
1	1.0513	0.95123	1.0000	1.0000	1.0513	0.95123	0.00000
2	1.1052	0.90484	0.48750	2.0513	0.53877	1.85607	0.48750
3	1.1618	0.86071	0.31681	3.1564	0.36808	2.71677	0.96668
4	1.2214	0.81873	0.23157	4.3183	0.28284	3.53551	1.43754
5	1.2840	0.77880	0.18052	5.5397	0.23179	4.31431	1.90011
6	1.3499	0.74082	0.14655	6.8237	0.19782	5.05512	2.35439
7	1.4191	0.70469	0.12235	8.1736	0.17362	5.75981	2.80042
8	1.4918	0.67032	0.10425	9.5926	0.15552	6.43013	3.23821
9	1.5683	0.63763	0.09022	11.0845	0.14149	7.06776	3.66780
10	1.6487	0.60653	0.07903	12.6528	0.13031	7.67429	4.08923
11	1.7333	0.57695	0.06992	14.3015	0.12119	8.25124	4.50252
12	1.8221	0.54881	0.06236	16.0347	0.11364	8.80005	4.90774
13	1.9155	0.52205	0.05600	17.8569	0.10727	9.32210	5.30491
14	2.0138	0.49659	0.05058	19.7724	0.10185	9.81868	5.69409
15	2.1170	0.47237	0.04590	21.7862	0.09717	10.29105	6.07534
16	2.2255	0.44933	0.04184	23.9032	0.09311	10.74038	6.44871
17	2.3396	0.42741	0.03827	26.1287	0.08954	11.16779	6.81425
18	2.4596	0.40657	0.03513	28.4683	0.08640	11.57436	7.17205
19	2.5857	0.38674	0.03233	30.9279	0.08360	11.96111	7.52215
20	2.7183	0.36788	0.02984	33.5137	0.08111	12.32898	7.86463
21	2.8577	0.34994	0.02760	36.2319	0.07887	12.67892	8.19957
22	3.0042	0.33287	0.02558	39.0896	0.07685	13.01179	8.52703
23	3.1582	0.31664	0.02376	42.0938	0.07503	13.32843	8.84710
24	3.3201	0.30119	0.02210	45.2519	0.07337	13.62962	9.15986
25	3.4903	0.28650	0.02059	48.5721	0.07186	13.91613	9.46539
26	3.6693	0.27253	0.01921	52.0624	0.07048	14.18866	9.76377
27	3.8574	0.25924	0.01794	55.7317	0.06921	14.44790	10.05510
28	4.0552	0.24660	0.01678	59.5891	0.06805	14.69450	10.33946
29	4.2631	0.23457	0.01571	63.6443	0.06698	14.92907	10.61695
30	4.4817	0.22313	0.01473	67.9074	0.06600	15.15220	10.88766
31	4.7115	0.21225	0.01381	72.3891	0.06509	15.36445	11.15168
32	4.9530	0.20190	0.01297	77.1006	0.06424	15.56634	11.40912
33	5.2070	0.19205	0.01219	82.0536	0.06346	15.75839	11.66006
34	5.4739	0.18268	0.01146	87.2606	0.06273	15.94108	11.90461
35	5.7546	0.17377	0.01078	92.7346	0.06205	16.11485	12.14288
40	7.3891	0.13534	0.00802	124.613	0.05930	16.86456	13.24346
45	9.4877	0.10540	0.00604	165.546	0.05731	17.44844	14.20240
50	12.1825	0.08208	0.00458	218.105	0.05586	17.90317	15.03289
55	15.6426	0.06393	0.00350	285.592	0.05477	18.25731	15.74801
60	20.0855	0.04979	0.00269	372.247	0.05396	18.53311	16.36042
65	25.7903	0.03877	0.00207	483.515	0.05334	18.74791	16.88218
70	33.1155	0.03020	0.00160	626.385	0.05287	18.91519	17.32453
75	42.5211	0.02352	0.00123	809.834	0.05251	19.04547	17.69786
80	54.5982	0.01832	0.00096	1045.39	0.05223	19.14694	18.01158
85	70.1054	0.01426	0.00074	1347.84	0.05201	19.22595	18.27416
90	90.0171	0.01111	0.00058	1736.20	0.05185	19.28749	18.49313
95	115.584	0.00865	0.00045	2234.87	0.05172	19.33542	18.67508
100	148.413	0.00674	0.00035	2875.17	0.05162	19.37275	18.82580

$r = 6\%$ **Continuous Compounding, Discrete Cash Flows**

	SINGLE PAYMENT		UNIFORM SERIES				Arithmetic Gradient Series Factor
	Compound Amount Factor	Present Worth Factor	Sinking Fund Factor	Uniform Series Factor	Capital Recovery Factor	Series Present Worth Factor	
N	*(F/P,r,N)*	*(P/F,r,N)*	*(A/F,r,N)*	*(F/A,r,N)*	*(A/P,r,N)*	*(P/A,r,N)*	*(A/G,r,N)*
1	1.0618	0.94176	1.0000	1.0000	1.0618	0.94176	0.00000
2	1.1275	0.88692	0.48500	2.0618	0.54684	1.82868	0.48500
3	1.1972	0.83527	0.31355	3.1893	0.37538	2.66396	0.96002
4	1.2712	0.78663	0.22797	4.3866	0.28981	3.45058	1.42508
5	1.3499	0.74082	0.17675	5.6578	0.23858	4.19140	1.88019
6	1.4333	0.69768	0.14270	7.0077	0.20454	4.88908	2.32539
7	1.5220	0.65705	0.11847	8.4410	0.18031	5.54612	2.76072
8	1.6161	0.61878	0.10037	9.9629	0.16221	6.16491	3.18622
9	1.7160	0.58275	0.08636	11.5790	0.14820	6.74766	3.60195
10	1.8221	0.54881	0.07522	13.2950	0.13705	7.29647	4.00797
11	1.9348	0.51685	0.06615	15.1171	0.12799	7.81332	4.40435
12	2.0544	0.48675	0.05864	17.0519	0.12048	8.30007	4.79114
13	2.1815	0.45841	0.05234	19.1064	0.11418	8.75848	5.16845
14	2.3164	0.43171	0.04698	21.2878	0.10881	9.19019	5.53633
15	2.4596	0.40657	0.04237	23.6042	0.10420	9.59676	5.89490
16	2.6117	0.38289	0.03837	26.0638	0.10020	9.97965	6.24424
17	2.7732	0.36059	0.03487	28.6755	0.09671	10.34025	6.58445
18	2.9447	0.33960	0.03180	31.4487	0.09363	10.67984	6.91564
19	3.1268	0.31982	0.02908	34.3934	0.09091	10.99966	7.23792
20	3.3201	0.30119	0.02665	37.5202	0.08849	11.30085	7.55141
21	3.5254	0.28365	0.02449	40.8403	0.08632	11.58451	7.85622
22	3.7434	0.26714	0.02254	44.3657	0.08438	11.85164	8.15248
23	3.9749	0.25158	0.02079	48.1091	0.08262	12.10322	8.44032
24	4.2207	0.23693	0.01920	52.0840	0.08104	12.34015	8.71986
25	4.4817	0.22313	0.01776	56.3047	0.07960	12.56328	8.99124
26	4.7588	0.21014	0.01645	60.7864	0.07829	12.77342	9.25460
27	5.0531	0.19790	0.01526	65.5452	0.07709	12.97131	9.51008
28	5.3656	0.18637	0.01416	70.5983	0.07600	13.15769	9.75782
29	5.6973	0.17552	0.01316	75.9639	0.07500	13.33321	9.99796
30	6.0496	0.16530	0.01225	81.6612	0.07408	13.49851	10.23066
31	6.4237	0.15567	0.01140	87.7109	0.07324	13.65418	10.45605
32	6.8210	0.14661	0.01062	94.1346	0.07246	13.80079	10.67429
33	7.2427	0.13807	0.00991	100.956	0.07174	13.93886	10.88553
34	7.6906	0.13003	0.00924	108.198	0.07108	14.06889	11.08992
35	8.1662	0.12246	0.00863	115.889	0.07047	14.19134	11.28761
40	11.0232	0.09072	0.00617	162.091	0.06801	14.70461	12.18092
45	14.8797	0.06721	0.00446	224.458	0.06629	15.08484	12.92953
50	20.0855	0.04979	0.00324	308.645	0.06508	15.36653	13.55188
55	27.1126	0.03688	0.00237	422.285	0.06420	15.57520	14.06541
60	36.5982	0.02732	0.00174	575.683	0.06357	15.72980	14.48619
65	49.4024	0.02024	0.00128	782.748	0.06311	15.84432	14.82876
70	66.6863	0.01500	0.00094	1062.26	0.06278	15.92916	15.10600
75	90.0171	0.01111	0.00069	1439.56	0.06253	15.99202	15.32913
80	121.510	0.00823	0.00051	1948.85	0.06235	16.03858	15.50782
85	164.022	0.00610	0.00038	2636.34	0.06222	16.07307	15.65026
90	221.406	0.00452	0.00028	3564.34	0.06212	16.09863	15.76333
95	298.867	0.00335	0.00021	4817.01	0.06204	16.11756	15.85273
100	403.429	0.00248	0.00015	6507.94	0.06199	16.13158	15.92318

$r = 7\%$ Continuous Compounding, Discrete Cash Flows

| | SINGLE PAYMENT | | UNIFORM SERIES | | | | Arithmetic Gradient Series Factor |
| | Compound Amount Factor | Present Worth Factor | Sinking Fund Factor | Uniform Series Factor | Capital Recovery Factor | Series Present Worth Factor | |
N	(F/P,r,N)	(P/F,r,N)	(A/F,r,N)	(F/A,r,N)	(A/P,r,N)	(P/A,r,N)	(A/G,r,N)
1	1.0725	0.93239	1.0000	1.0000	1.0725	0.93239	0.00000
2	1.1503	0.86936	0.48251	2.0725	0.55502	1.80175	0.48251
3	1.2337	0.81058	0.31029	3.2228	0.38280	2.61234	0.95337
4	1.3231	0.75578	0.22439	4.4565	0.29690	3.36812	1.41262
5	1.4191	0.70469	0.17302	5.7796	0.24553	4.07281	1.86030
6	1.5220	0.65705	0.13891	7.1987	0.21142	4.72985	2.29645
7	1.6323	0.61263	0.11467	8.7206	0.18718	5.34248	2.72114
8	1.7507	0.57121	0.09659	10.3529	0.16910	5.91369	3.13444
9	1.8776	0.53259	0.08262	12.1036	0.15513	6.44628	3.53643
10	2.0138	0.49659	0.07152	13.9812	0.14403	6.94287	3.92721
11	2.1598	0.46301	0.06252	15.9950	0.13503	7.40588	4.30688
12	2.3164	0.43171	0.05508	18.1547	0.12759	7.83759	4.67555
13	2.4843	0.40252	0.04885	20.4711	0.12136	8.24012	5.03334
14	2.6645	0.37531	0.04356	22.9554	0.11607	8.61543	5.38039
15	2.8577	0.34994	0.03903	25.6199	0.11154	8.96536	5.71683
16	3.0649	0.32628	0.03512	28.4775	0.10762	9.29164	6.04282
17	3.2871	0.30422	0.03170	31.5424	0.10421	9.59587	6.35849
18	3.5254	0.28365	0.02871	34.8295	0.10122	9.87952	6.66402
19	3.7810	0.26448	0.02607	38.3549	0.09858	10.14400	6.95958
20	4.0552	0.24660	0.02373	42.1359	0.09624	10.39059	7.24533
21	4.3492	0.22993	0.02165	46.1911	0.09416	10.62052	7.52146
22	4.6646	0.21438	0.01979	50.5404	0.09229	10.83490	7.78815
23	5.0028	0.19989	0.01811	55.2050	0.09062	11.03479	8.04559
24	5.3656	0.18637	0.01661	60.2078	0.08912	11.22116	8.29397
25	5.7546	0.17377	0.01525	65.5733	0.08776	11.39494	8.53348
26	6.1719	0.16203	0.01402	71.3279	0.08653	11.55696	8.76434
27	6.6194	0.15107	0.01290	77.4998	0.08541	11.70803	8.98674
28	7.0993	0.14086	0.01189	84.1192	0.08440	11.84889	9.20088
29	7.6141	0.13134	0.01096	91.2185	0.08347	11.98023	9.40697
30	8.1662	0.12246	0.01012	98.8326	0.08263	12.10268	9.60521
31	8.7583	0.11418	0.00935	106.999	0.08185	12.21686	9.79582
32	9.3933	0.10646	0.00864	115.757	0.08115	12.32332	9.97900
33	10.0744	0.09926	0.00799	125.150	0.08050	12.42258	10.15495
34	10.8049	0.09255	0.00740	135.225	0.07990	12.51513	10.32389
35	11.5883	0.08629	0.00685	146.030	0.07936	12.60143	10.48603
40	16.4446	0.06081	0.00469	213.006	0.07720	12.95288	11.20165
45	23.3361	0.04285	0.00325	308.049	0.07575	13.20055	11.77687
50	33.1155	0.03020	0.00226	442.922	0.07477	13.37508	12.23466
55	46.9931	0.02128	0.00158	634.315	0.07408	13.49807	12.59571
60	66.6863	0.01500	0.00110	905.916	0.07361	13.58473	12.87812
65	94.6324	0.01057	0.00077	1291.34	0.07328	13.64581	13.09734
70	134.290	0.00745	0.00054	1838.27	0.07305	13.68885	13.26638
75	190.566	0.00525	0.00038	2614.41	0.07289	13.71918	13.39591
80	270.426	0.00370	0.00027	3715.81	0.07278	13.74055	13.49462
85	383.753	0.00261	0.00019	5278.76	0.07270	13.75561	13.56947
90	544.572	0.00184	0.00013	7496.70	0.07264	13.76622	13.62598
95	772.784	0.00129	0.00009	10 644.0	0.07260	13.77370	13.66846
100	1096.63	0.00091	0.00007	15 110.0	0.07257	13.77897	13.70028

$r = 8\%$ **Continuous Compounding, Discrete Cash Flows**

	SINGLE PAYMENT		UNIFORM SERIES				Arithmetic Gradient Series Factor
	Compound Amount Factor	Present Worth Factor	Sinking Fund Factor	Uniform Series Factor	Capital Recovery Factor	Series Present Worth Factor	
N	(*F/P,r,N*)	(*P/F,r,N*)	(*A/F,r,N*)	(*F/A,r,N*)	(*A/P,r,N*)	(*P/A,r,N*)	(*A/G,r,N*)
1	1.0833	0.92312	1.0000	1.0000	1.0833	0.92312	0.00000
2	1.1735	0.85214	0.48001	2.0833	0.56330	1.77526	0.48001
3	1.2712	0.78663	0.30705	3.2568	0.39034	2.56189	0.94672
4	1.3771	0.72615	0.22085	4.5280	0.30413	3.28804	1.40018
5	1.4918	0.67032	0.16934	5.9052	0.25263	3.95836	1.84044
6	1.6161	0.61878	0.13519	7.3970	0.21848	4.57714	2.26758
7	1.7507	0.57121	0.11095	9.0131	0.19424	5.14835	2.68169
8	1.8965	0.52729	0.09290	10.7637	0.17619	5.67564	3.08288
9	2.0544	0.48675	0.07899	12.6602	0.16227	6.16239	3.47127
10	2.2255	0.44933	0.06796	14.7147	0.15125	6.61172	3.84700
11	2.4109	0.41478	0.05903	16.9402	0.14232	7.02651	4.21022
12	2.6117	0.38289	0.05168	19.3511	0.13496	7.40940	4.56110
13	2.8292	0.35345	0.04553	21.9628	0.12882	7.76285	4.89980
14	3.0649	0.32628	0.04034	24.7920	0.12362	8.08913	5.22653
15	3.3201	0.30119	0.03590	27.8569	0.11918	8.39033	5.54147
16	3.5966	0.27804	0.03207	31.1770	0.11536	8.66836	5.84486
17	3.8962	0.25666	0.02876	34.7736	0.11204	8.92503	6.13689
18	4.2207	0.23693	0.02586	38.6698	0.10915	9.16195	6.41781
19	4.5722	0.21871	0.02332	42.8905	0.10660	9.38067	6.68785
20	4.9530	0.20190	0.02107	47.4627	0.10436	9.58256	6.94726
21	5.3656	0.18637	0.01908	52.4158	0.10237	9.76894	7.19628
22	5.8124	0.17204	0.01731	57.7813	0.10059	9.94098	7.43518
23	6.2965	0.15882	0.01572	63.5938	0.09901	10.09980	7.66421
24	6.8210	0.14661	0.01431	69.8903	0.09760	10.24641	7.88363
25	7.3891	0.13534	0.01304	76.7113	0.09632	10.38174	8.09372
26	8.0045	0.12493	0.01189	84.1003	0.09518	10.50667	8.29475
27	8.6711	0.11533	0.01086	92.1048	0.09414	10.62200	8.48698
28	9.3933	0.10646	0.00992	100.776	0.09321	10.72845	8.67068
29	10.1757	0.09827	0.00908	110.169	0.09236	10.82673	8.84614
30	11.0232	0.09072	0.00831	120.345	0.09160	10.91745	9.01360
31	11.9413	0.08374	0.00761	131.368	0.09090	11.00119	9.17336
32	12.9358	0.07730	0.00698	143.309	0.09026	11.07849	9.32566
33	14.0132	0.07136	0.00640	156.245	0.08969	11.14986	9.47078
34	15.1803	0.06587	0.00587	170.258	0.08916	11.21573	9.60898
35	16.4446	0.06081	0.00539	185.439	0.08868	11.27654	9.74051
40	24.5325	0.04076	0.00354	282.547	0.08683	11.51725	10.30689
45	36.5982	0.02732	0.00234	427.416	0.08563	11.67860	10.74256
50	54.5982	0.01832	0.00155	643.535	0.08484	11.78676	11.07380
55	81.4509	0.01228	0.00104	965.947	0.08432	11.85926	11.32302
60	121.510	0.00823	0.00069	1446.93	0.08398	11.90785	11.50878
65	181.272	0.00552	0.00046	2164.47	0.08375	11.94043	11.64610
70	270.426	0.00370	0.00031	3234.91	0.08360	11.96227	11.74685
75	403.429	0.00248	0.00021	4831.83	0.08349	11.97690	11.82030
80	601.845	0.00166	0.00014	7214.15	0.08343	11.98672	11.87352
85	897.847	0.00111	0.00009	10 768.0	0.08338	11.99329	11.91189
90	1339.43	0.00075	0.00006	16 070.0	0.08335	11.99770	11.93942
95	1998.20	0.00050	0.00004	23 980.0	0.08333	12.00066	11.95910
100	2980.96	0.00034	0.00003	35 779.0	0.08332	12.00264	11.97311

r = 9%   Continuous Compounding, Discrete Cash Flows

	SINGLE PAYMENT		UNIFORM SERIES				Arithmetic Gradient Series Factor
	Compound Amount Factor	Present Worth Factor	Sinking Fund Factor	Uniform Series Factor	Capital Recovery Factor	Series Present Worth Factor	
N	(F/P,r,N)	(P/F,r,N)	(A/F,r,N)	(F/A,r,N)	(A/P,r,N)	(P/A,r,N)	(A/G,r,N)
1	1.0942	0.91393	1.0000	1.0000	1.0942	0.91393	0.00000
2	1.1972	0.83527	0.47752	2.0942	0.57169	1.74920	0.47752
3	1.3100	0.76338	0.30382	3.2914	0.39800	2.51258	0.94008
4	1.4333	0.69768	0.21733	4.6014	0.31150	3.21026	1.38776
5	1.5683	0.63763	0.16571	6.0347	0.25988	3.84789	1.82063
6	1.7160	0.58275	0.13153	7.6030	0.22570	4.43063	2.23880
7	1.8776	0.53259	0.10731	9.3190	0.20148	4.96323	2.64241
8	2.0544	0.48675	0.08931	11.1966	0.18349	5.44998	3.03160
9	2.2479	0.44486	0.07547	13.2510	0.16964	5.89484	3.40654
10	2.4596	0.40657	0.06452	15.4990	0.15869	6.30141	3.76743
11	2.6912	0.37158	0.05568	17.9586	0.14986	6.67298	4.11449
12	2.9447	0.33960	0.04843	20.6498	0.14260	7.01258	4.44793
13	3.2220	0.31037	0.04238	23.5945	0.13656	7.32294	4.76801
14	3.5254	0.28365	0.03729	26.8165	0.13146	7.60660	5.07498
15	3.8574	0.25924	0.03296	30.3419	0.12713	7.86584	5.36913
16	4.2207	0.23693	0.02924	34.1993	0.12341	8.10277	5.65074
17	4.6182	0.21654	0.02603	38.4200	0.12020	8.31930	5.92011
18	5.0531	0.19790	0.02324	43.0382	0.11741	8.51720	6.17755
19	5.5290	0.18087	0.02079	48.0913	0.11497	8.69807	6.42339
20	6.0496	0.16530	0.01865	53.6202	0.11282	8.86337	6.65794
21	6.6194	0.15107	0.01676	59.6699	0.11093	9.01444	6.88154
22	7.2427	0.13807	0.01509	66.2893	0.10926	9.15251	7.09452
23	7.9248	0.12619	0.01360	73.5320	0.10777	9.27869	7.29723
24	8.6711	0.11533	0.01228	81.4568	0.10645	9.39402	7.49000
25	9.4877	0.10540	0.01110	90.1280	0.10527	9.49942	7.67318
26	10.3812	0.09633	0.01004	99.6157	0.10421	9.59574	7.84712
27	11.3589	0.08804	0.00909	109.997	0.10327	9.68378	8.01215
28	12.4286	0.08046	0.00824	121.356	0.10241	9.76424	8.16862
29	13.5991	0.07353	0.00747	133.784	0.10165	9.83778	8.31685
30	14.8797	0.06721	0.00679	147.383	0.10096	9.90498	8.45719
31	16.2810	0.06142	0.00616	162.263	0.10034	9.96640	8.58995
32	17.8143	0.05613	0.00560	178.544	0.09978	10.02254	8.71547
33	19.4919	0.05130	0.00509	196.358	0.09927	10.07384	8.83405
34	21.3276	0.04689	0.00463	215.850	0.09881	10.12073	8.94600
35	23.3361	0.04285	0.00422	237.178	0.09839	10.16358	9.05164
40	36.5982	0.02732	0.00265	378.004	0.09682	10.32847	9.49496
45	57.3975	0.01742	0.00167	598.863	0.09584	10.43361	9.82070
50	90.0171	0.01111	0.00106	945.238	0.09523	10.50065	10.05692
55	141.175	0.00708	0.00067	1488.46	0.09485	10.54339	10.22624
60	221.406	0.00452	0.00043	2340.41	0.09460	10.57065	10.34639
65	347.234	0.00288	0.00027	3676.53	0.09445	10.58803	10.43088
70	544.572	0.00184	0.00017	5771.98	0.09435	10.59911	10.48983
75	854.059	0.00117	0.00011	9058.30	0.09428	10.60618	10.53069
80	1339.43	0.00075	0.00007	14212.0	0.09424	10.61068	10.55884
85	2100.65	0.00048	0.00004	22295.0	0.09422	10.61356	10.57813
90	3294.47	0.00030	0.00003	34972.0	0.09420	10.61539	10.59128
95	5166.75	0.00019	0.00002	54853.0	0.09419	10.61655	10.60022
100	8103.08	0.00012	0.00001	86033.0	0.09419	10.61730	10.60627

$r = 10\%$ **Continuous Compounding, Discrete Cash Flows**

	SINGLE PAYMENT		UNIFORM SERIES				Arithmetic Gradient Series Factor
	Compound Amount Factor	Present Worth Factor	Sinking Fund Factor	Uniform Series Factor	Capital Recovery Factor	Series Present Worth Factor	
N	(F/P,r,N)	(P/F,r,N)	(A/F,r,N)	(F/A,r,N)	(A/P,r,N)	(P/A,r,N)	(A/G,r,N)
1	1.1052	0.90484	1.0000	1.0000	1.1052	0.90484	0.00000
2	1.2214	0.81873	0.47502	2.1052	0.58019	1.72357	0.47502
3	1.3499	0.74082	0.30061	3.3266	0.40578	2.46439	0.93344
4	1.4918	0.67032	0.21384	4.6764	0.31901	3.13471	1.37535
5	1.6487	0.60653	0.16212	6.1683	0.26729	3.74124	1.80086
6	1.8221	0.54881	0.12793	7.8170	0.23310	4.29005	2.21012
7	2.0138	0.49659	0.10374	9.6391	0.20892	4.78663	2.60329
8	2.2255	0.44933	0.08582	11.6528	0.19099	5.23596	2.98060
9	2.4596	0.40657	0.07205	13.8784	0.17723	5.64253	3.34227
10	2.7183	0.36788	0.06121	16.3380	0.16638	6.01041	3.68856
11	3.0042	0.33287	0.05248	19.0563	0.15765	6.34328	4.01976
12	3.3201	0.30119	0.04533	22.0604	0.15050	6.64448	4.33618
13	3.6693	0.27253	0.03940	25.3806	0.14457	6.91701	4.63814
14	4.0552	0.24660	0.03442	29.0499	0.13959	7.16361	4.92598
15	4.4817	0.22313	0.03021	33.1051	0.13538	7.38674	5.20008
16	4.9530	0.20190	0.02661	37.5867	0.13178	7.58863	5.46081
17	5.4739	0.18268	0.02351	42.5398	0.12868	7.77132	5.70856
18	6.0496	0.16530	0.02083	48.0137	0.12600	7.93662	5.94373
19	6.6859	0.14957	0.01850	54.0634	0.12367	8.08618	6.16673
20	7.3891	0.13534	0.01646	60.7493	0.12163	8.22152	6.37798
21	8.1662	0.12246	0.01468	68.1383	0.11985	8.34398	6.57790
22	9.0250	0.11080	0.01311	76.3045	0.11828	8.45478	6.76690
23	9.9742	0.10026	0.01172	85.3295	0.11689	8.55504	6.94542
24	11.0232	0.09072	0.01049	95.3037	0.11566	8.64576	7.11388
25	12.1825	0.08208	0.00940	106.327	0.11458	8.72784	7.27269
26	13.4637	0.07427	0.00844	118.509	0.11361	8.80211	7.42228
27	14.8797	0.06721	0.00758	131.973	0.11275	8.86932	7.56305
28	16.4446	0.06081	0.00681	146.853	0.11198	8.93013	7.69541
29	18.1741	0.05502	0.00612	163.297	0.11129	8.98515	7.81975
30	20.0855	0.04979	0.00551	181.472	0.11068	9.03494	7.93646
31	22.1980	0.04505	0.00496	201.557	0.11013	9.07999	8.04593
32	24.5325	0.04076	0.00447	223.755	0.10964	9.12075	8.14851
33	27.1126	0.03688	0.00403	248.288	0.10920	9.15763	8.24458
34	29.9641	0.03337	0.00363	275.400	0.10880	9.19101	8.33446
35	33.1155	0.03020	0.00327	305.364	0.10845	9.22121	8.41851
40	54.5982	0.01832	0.00196	509.629	0.10713	9.33418	8.76204
45	90.0171	0.01111	0.00118	846.404	0.10635	9.40270	9.00281
50	148.413	0.00674	0.00071	1401.65	0.10588	9.44427	9.16915
55	244.692	0.00409	0.00043	2317.10	0.10560	9.46947	9.28264
60	403.429	0.00248	0.00026	3826.43	0.10543	9.48476	9.35924
65	665.142	0.00150	0.00016	6314.88	0.10533	9.49404	9.41046
70	1096.63	0.00091	0.00010	10 418.0	0.10527	9.49966	9.44444
75	1808.04	0.00055	0.00006	17 182.0	0.10523	9.50307	9.46683

$r = 11\%$ Continuous Compounding, Discrete Cash Flows

	SINGLE PAYMENT		UNIFORM SERIES				Arithmetic Gradient Series Factor
	Compound Amount Factor	Present Worth Factor	Sinking Fund Factor	Uniform Series Factor	Capital Recovery Factor	Series Present Worth Factor	
N	(F/P,r,N)	(P/F,r,N)	(A/F,r,N)	(F/A,r,N)	(A/P,r,N)	(P/A,r,N)	(A/G,r,N)
1	1.1163	0.89583	1.0000	1.0000	1.1163	0.89583	0.00000
2	1.2461	0.80252	0.47253	2.1163	0.58881	1.69835	0.47253
3	1.3910	0.71892	0.29741	3.3624	0.41369	2.41728	0.92681
4	1.5527	0.64404	0.21038	4.7533	0.32666	3.06131	1.36297
5	1.7333	0.57695	0.15858	6.3060	0.27486	3.63826	1.78115
6	1.9348	0.51685	0.12439	8.0393	0.24067	4.15511	2.18154
7	2.1598	0.46301	0.10026	9.9741	0.21654	4.61813	2.56437
8	2.4109	0.41478	0.08241	12.1338	0.19869	5.03291	2.92993
9	2.6912	0.37158	0.06875	14.5447	0.18503	5.40449	3.27852
10	3.0042	0.33287	0.05802	17.2360	0.17430	5.73736	3.61047
11	3.3535	0.29820	0.04941	20.2401	0.16568	6.03556	3.92615
12	3.7434	0.26714	0.04238	23.5936	0.15866	6.30269	4.22597
13	4.1787	0.23931	0.03658	27.3370	0.15286	6.54200	4.51035
14	4.6646	0.21438	0.03173	31.5157	0.14801	6.75638	4.77973
15	5.2070	0.19205	0.02764	36.1803	0.14392	6.94843	5.03457
16	5.8124	0.17204	0.02416	41.3873	0.14044	7.12048	5.27536
17	6.4883	0.15412	0.02119	47.1998	0.13746	7.27460	5.50257
18	7.2427	0.13807	0.01863	53.6881	0.13490	7.41267	5.71673
19	8.0849	0.12369	0.01641	60.9308	0.13269	7.53636	5.91832
20	9.0250	0.11080	0.01449	69.0157	0.13077	7.64716	6.10787
21	10.0744	0.09926	0.01281	78.0407	0.12909	7.74642	6.28588
22	11.2459	0.08892	0.01135	88.1151	0.12763	7.83534	6.45287
23	12.5535	0.07966	0.01006	99.3610	0.12634	7.91500	6.60934
24	14.0132	0.07136	0.00894	111.915	0.12521	7.98636	6.75579
25	15.6426	0.06393	0.00794	125.928	0.12422	8.05029	6.89273
26	17.4615	0.05727	0.00706	141.570	0.12334	8.10756	7.02063
27	19.4919	0.05130	0.00629	159.032	0.12257	8.15886	7.13998
28	21.7584	0.04596	0.00560	178.524	0.12188	8.20482	7.25122
29	24.2884	0.04117	0.00499	200.282	0.12127	8.24599	7.35482
30	27.1126	0.03688	0.00445	224.571	0.12073	8.28288	7.45120
31	30.2652	0.03304	0.00397	251.683	0.12025	8.31592	7.54080
32	33.7844	0.02960	0.00355	281.949	0.11982	8.34552	7.62400
33	37.7128	0.02652	0.00317	315.733	0.11945	8.37203	7.70121
34	42.0980	0.02375	0.00283	353.446	0.11911	8.39579	7.77278
35	46.9931	0.02128	0.00253	395.544	0.11881	8.41707	7.83909
40	81.4509	0.01228	0.00145	691.883	0.11772	8.49449	8.10288
45	141.175	0.00708	0.00083	1205.52	0.11711	8.53916	8.27905
50	244.692	0.00409	0.00048	2095.77	0.11676	8.56493	8.39490
55	424.113	0.00236	0.00027	3638.80	0.11655	8.57980	8.47009

$r = 12\%$ **Continuous Compounding, Discrete Cash Flows**

	SINGLE PAYMENT		UNIFORM SERIES				Arithmetic Gradient Series Factor
	Compound Amount Factor	Present Worth Factor	Sinking Fund Factor	Uniform Series Factor	Capital Recovery Factor	Series Present Worth Factor	
N	(F/P,r,N)	(P/F,r,N)	(A/F,r,N)	(F/A,r,N)	(A/P,r,N)	(P/A,r,N)	(A/G,r,N)
1	1.1275	0.88692	1.0000	1.0000	1.1275	0.88692	0.00000
2	1.2712	0.78663	0.47004	2.1275	0.59753	1.67355	0.47004
3	1.4333	0.69768	0.29423	3.3987	0.42172	2.37122	0.92019
4	1.6161	0.61878	0.20695	4.8321	0.33445	2.99001	1.35061
5	1.8221	0.54881	0.15508	6.4481	0.28258	3.53882	1.76148
6	2.0544	0.48675	0.12092	8.2703	0.24841	4.02557	2.15307
7	2.3164	0.43171	0.09686	10.3247	0.22435	4.45728	2.52566
8	2.6117	0.38289	0.07911	12.6411	0.20660	4.84018	2.87962
9	2.9447	0.33960	0.06556	15.2528	0.19306	5.17977	3.21532
10	3.3201	0.30119	0.05495	18.1974	0.18245	5.48097	3.53320
11	3.7434	0.26714	0.04647	21.5176	0.17397	5.74810	3.83374
12	4.2207	0.23693	0.03959	25.2610	0.16708	5.98503	4.11743
13	4.7588	0.21014	0.03392	29.4817	0.16142	6.19516	4.38480
14	5.3656	0.18637	0.02921	34.2405	0.15670	6.38154	4.63641
15	6.0496	0.16530	0.02525	39.6061	0.15275	6.54684	4.87283
16	6.8210	0.14661	0.02190	45.6557	0.14940	6.69344	5.09464
17	7.6906	0.13003	0.01906	52.4767	0.14655	6.82347	5.30246
18	8.6711	0.11533	0.01662	60.1673	0.14412	6.93880	5.49687
19	9.7767	0.10228	0.01453	68.8384	0.14202	7.04108	5.67850
20	11.0232	0.09072	0.01272	78.6151	0.14022	7.13180	5.84796
21	12.4286	0.08046	0.01116	89.6383	0.13865	7.21226	6.00583
22	14.0132	0.07136	0.00980	102.067	0.13729	7.28362	6.15274
23	15.7998	0.06329	0.00861	116.080	0.13611	7.34691	6.28926
24	17.8143	0.05613	0.00758	131.880	0.13508	7.40305	6.41597
25	20.0855	0.04979	0.00668	149.694	0.13418	7.45283	6.53344
26	22.6464	0.04416	0.00589	169.780	0.13339	7.49699	6.64221
27	25.5337	0.03916	0.00520	192.426	0.13269	7.53616	6.74280
28	28.7892	0.03474	0.00459	217.960	0.13208	7.57089	6.83574
29	32.4597	0.03081	0.00405	246.749	0.13155	7.60170	6.92152
30	36.5982	0.02732	0.00358	279.209	0.13108	7.62902	7.00059
31	41.2644	0.02423	0.00317	315.807	0.13066	7.65326	7.07342
32	46.5255	0.02149	0.00280	357.071	0.13030	7.67475	7.14043
33	52.4573	0.01906	0.00248	403.597	0.12997	7.69381	7.20202
34	59.1455	0.01691	0.00219	456.054	0.12969	7.71072	7.25859
35	66.6863	0.01500	0.00194	515.200	0.12944	7.72572	7.31050
40	121.510	0.00823	0.00106	945.203	0.12855	7.77878	7.51141
45	221.406	0.00452	0.00058	1728.72	0.12808	7.80791	7.63916
50	403.429	0.00248	0.00032	3156.38	0.12781	7.82389	7.71909
55	735.095	0.00136	0.00017	5757.75	0.12767	7.83266	7.76841

$r = 13\%$ Continuous Compounding, Discrete Cash Flows

	SINGLE PAYMENT		UNIFORM SERIES				Arithmetic Gradient Series Factor
	Compound Amount Factor	Present Worth Factor	Sinking Fund Factor	Uniform Series Factor	Capital Recovery Factor	Series Present Worth Factor	
N	$(F/P,r,N)$	$(P/F,r,N)$	$(A/F,r,N)$	$(F/A,r,N)$	$(A/P,r,N)$	$(P/A,r,N)$	$(A/G,r,N)$
1	1.1388	0.87810	1.0000	1.0000	1.1388	0.87810	0.00000
2	1.2969	0.77105	0.46755	2.1388	0.60637	1.64915	0.46755
3	1.4770	0.67706	0.29106	3.4358	0.42988	2.32620	0.91358
4	1.6820	0.59452	0.20355	4.9127	0.34238	2.92072	1.33827
5	1.9155	0.52205	0.15164	6.5948	0.29046	3.44277	1.74189
6	2.1815	0.45841	0.11750	8.5103	0.25633	3.90118	2.12473
7	2.4843	0.40252	0.09353	10.6918	0.23236	4.30370	2.48718
8	2.8292	0.35345	0.07589	13.1761	0.21472	4.65716	2.82968
9	3.2220	0.31037	0.06248	16.0053	0.20131	4.96752	3.15272
10	3.6693	0.27253	0.05201	19.2273	0.19084	5.24005	3.45683
11	4.1787	0.23931	0.04367	22.8966	0.18250	5.47936	3.74260
12	4.7588	0.21014	0.03693	27.0753	0.17576	5.68950	4.01065
13	5.4195	0.18452	0.03141	31.8341	0.17024	5.87402	4.26162
14	6.1719	0.16203	0.02684	37.2536	0.16567	6.03604	4.49618
15	7.0287	0.14227	0.02303	43.4255	0.16186	6.17832	4.71503
16	8.0045	0.12493	0.01982	50.4542	0.15865	6.30325	4.91888
17	9.1157	0.10970	0.01711	58.4586	0.15593	6.41295	5.10844
18	10.3812	0.09633	0.01480	67.5743	0.15363	6.50928	5.28441
19	11.8224	0.08458	0.01283	77.9556	0.15166	6.59386	5.44753
20	13.4637	0.07427	0.01114	89.7780	0.14997	6.66814	5.59848
21	15.3329	0.06522	0.00969	103.242	0.14851	6.73335	5.73798
22	17.4615	0.05727	0.00843	118.575	0.14726	6.79062	5.86669
23	19.8857	0.05029	0.00735	136.036	0.14618	6.84091	5.98528
24	22.6464	0.04416	0.00641	155.922	0.14524	6.88507	6.09441
25	25.7903	0.03877	0.00560	178.568	0.14443	6.92384	6.19468
26	29.3708	0.03405	0.00489	204.359	0.14372	6.95789	6.28670
27	33.4483	0.02990	0.00428	233.729	0.14311	6.98779	6.37104
28	38.0918	0.02625	0.00374	267.178	0.14257	7.01404	6.44825
29	43.3801	0.02305	0.00328	305.269	0.14210	7.03709	6.51885
30	49.4024	0.02024	0.00287	348.650	0.14170	7.05733	6.58333
31	56.2609	0.01777	0.00251	398.052	0.14134	7.07511	6.64216
32	64.0715	0.01561	0.00220	454.313	0.14103	7.09071	6.69578
33	72.9665	0.01370	0.00193	518.384	0.14076	7.10442	6.74459
34	83.0963	0.01203	0.00169	591.351	0.14052	7.11645	6.78899
35	94.6324	0.01057	0.00148	674.447	0.14031	7.12702	6.82934
40	181.272	0.00552	0.00077	1298.53	0.13960	7.16340	6.98125
45	347.234	0.00288	0.00040	2493.97	0.13923	7.18239	7.07317
50	665.142	0.00150	0.00021	4783.90	0.13904	7.19231	7.12785
55	1274.11	0.00078	0.00011	9170.36	0.13894	7.19748	7.15994

$r = 14\%$ **Continuous Compounding, Discrete Cash Flows**

	SINGLE PAYMENT		UNIFORM SERIES				Arithmetic Gradient Series Factor
	Compound Amount Factor	Present Worth Factor	Sinking Fund Factor	Uniform Series Factor	Capital Recovery Factor	Series Present Worth Factor	
N	(F/P,r,N)	(P/F,r,N)	(A/F,r,N)	(F/A,r,N)	(A/P,r,N)	(P/A,r,N)	(A/G,r,N)
1	1.1503	0.86936	1.0000	1.0000	1.1503	0.86936	0.00000
2	1.3231	0.75578	0.46506	2.1503	0.61533	1.62514	0.46506
3	1.5220	0.65705	0.28790	3.4734	0.43818	2.28219	0.90697
4	1.7507	0.57121	0.20019	4.9954	0.35046	2.85340	1.32596
5	2.0138	0.49659	0.14824	6.7460	0.29851	3.34998	1.72235
6	2.3164	0.43171	0.11416	8.7598	0.26443	3.78169	2.09652
7	2.6645	0.37531	0.09028	11.0762	0.24056	4.15700	2.44894
8	3.0649	0.32628	0.07278	13.7406	0.22305	4.48328	2.78015
9	3.5254	0.28365	0.05950	16.8055	0.20978	4.76694	3.09076
10	4.0552	0.24660	0.04919	20.3309	0.19946	5.01354	3.38141
11	4.6646	0.21438	0.04101	24.3861	0.19128	5.22792	3.65282
12	5.3656	0.18637	0.03442	29.0507	0.18470	5.41429	3.90573
13	6.1719	0.16203	0.02906	34.4162	0.17933	5.57632	4.14092
14	7.0993	0.14086	0.02464	40.5881	0.17491	5.71717	4.35918
15	8.1662	0.12246	0.02097	47.6874	0.17124	5.83963	4.56135
16	9.3933	0.10646	0.01790	55.8536	0.16818	5.94609	4.74824
17	10.8049	0.09255	0.01533	65.2469	0.16560	6.03864	4.92069
18	12.4286	0.08046	0.01315	76.0518	0.16342	6.11910	5.07952
19	14.2963	0.06995	0.01130	88.4804	0.16158	6.18905	5.22555
20	16.4446	0.06081	0.00973	102.777	0.16000	6.24986	5.35957
21	18.9158	0.05287	0.00839	119.221	0.15866	6.30272	5.48237
22	21.7584	0.04596	0.00724	138.137	0.15751	6.34868	5.59471
23	25.0281	0.03996	0.00625	159.896	0.15653	6.38864	5.69731
24	28.7892	0.03474	0.00541	184.924	0.15568	6.42337	5.79087
25	33.1155	0.03020	0.00468	213.713	0.15495	6.45357	5.87608
26	38.0918	0.02625	0.00405	246.828	0.15433	6.47982	5.95356
27	43.8160	0.02282	0.00351	284.920	0.15378	6.50265	6.02392
28	50.4004	0.01984	0.00304	328.736	0.15332	6.52249	6.08772
29	57.9743	0.01725	0.00264	379.137	0.15291	6.53974	6.14552
30	66.6863	0.01500	0.00229	437.111	0.15256	6.55473	6.19780
31	76.7075	0.01304	0.00198	503.797	0.15226	6.56777	6.24505
32	88.2347	0.01133	0.00172	580.505	0.15200	6.57910	6.28769
33	101.494	0.00985	0.00150	668.740	0.15177	6.58895	6.32614
34	116.746	0.00857	0.00130	770.234	0.15157	6.59752	6.36077
35	134.290	0.00745	0.00113	886.980	0.15140	6.60497	6.39193
40	270.426	0.00370	0.00056	1792.90	0.15083	6.62991	6.50606
45	544.572	0.00184	0.00028	3617.21	0.15055	6.64230	6.57173
50	1096.63	0.00091	0.00014	7290.91	0.15041	6.64845	6.60888
55	2208.35	0.00045	0.00007	14689.0	0.15034	6.65151	6.62960

r = 15%   Continuous Compounding, Discrete Cash Flows

	SINGLE PAYMENT		UNIFORM SERIES				Arithmetic Gradient Series Factor
	Compound Amount Factor	Present Worth Factor	Sinking Fund Factor	Uniform Series Factor	Capital Recovery Factor	Series Present Worth Factor	
N	(F/P,r,N)	(P/F,r,N)	(A/F,r,N)	(F/A,r,N)	(A/P,r,N)	(P/A,r,N)	(A/G,r,N)
1	1.1618	0.86071	1.0000	1.0000	1.1618	0.86071	0.00000
2	1.3499	0.74082	0.46257	2.1618	0.62440	1.60153	0.46257
3	1.5683	0.63763	0.28476	3.5117	0.44660	2.23915	0.90037
4	1.8221	0.54881	0.19685	5.0800	0.35868	2.78797	1.31369
5	2.1170	0.47237	0.14488	6.9021	0.30672	3.26033	1.70289
6	2.4596	0.40657	0.11088	9.0191	0.27271	3.66690	2.06846
7	2.8577	0.34994	0.08712	11.4787	0.24895	4.01684	2.41096
8	3.3201	0.30119	0.06975	14.3364	0.23159	4.31803	2.73106
9	3.8574	0.25924	0.05664	17.6565	0.21847	4.57727	3.02947
10	4.4817	0.22313	0.04648	21.5139	0.20832	4.80040	3.30699
11	5.2070	0.19205	0.03847	25.9956	0.20030	4.99245	3.56446
12	6.0496	0.16530	0.03205	31.2026	0.19388	5.15775	3.80276
13	7.0287	0.14227	0.02684	37.2522	0.18868	5.30003	4.02281
14	8.1662	0.12246	0.02258	44.2809	0.18442	5.42248	4.22554
15	9.4877	0.10540	0.01907	52.4471	0.18090	5.52788	4.41191
16	11.0232	0.09072	0.01615	61.9348	0.17798	5.61860	4.58286
17	12.8071	0.07808	0.01371	72.9580	0.17554	5.69668	4.73935
18	14.8797	0.06721	0.01166	85.7651	0.17349	5.76389	4.88231
19	17.2878	0.05784	0.00994	100.645	0.17177	5.82173	5.01264
20	20.0855	0.04979	0.00848	117.933	0.17031	5.87152	5.13125
21	23.3361	0.04285	0.00725	138.018	0.16908	5.91437	5.23898
22	27.1126	0.03688	0.00620	161.354	0.16803	5.95125	5.33666
23	31.5004	0.03175	0.00531	188.467	0.16714	5.98300	5.42507
24	36.5982	0.02732	0.00455	219.967	0.16638	6.01032	5.50497
25	42.5211	0.02352	0.00390	256.565	0.16573	6.03384	5.57706
26	49.4024	0.02024	0.00334	299.087	0.16518	6.05408	5.64200
27	57.3975	0.01742	0.00287	348.489	0.16470	6.07151	5.70042
28	66.6863	0.01500	0.00246	405.886	0.16430	6.08650	5.75289
29	77.4785	0.01291	0.00212	472.573	0.16395	6.09941	5.79997
30	90.0171	0.01111	0.00182	550.051	0.16365	6.11052	5.84215
31	104.585	0.00956	0.00156	640.068	0.16340	6.12008	5.87989
32	121.510	0.00823	0.00134	744.653	0.16318	6.12831	5.91362
33	141.175	0.00708	0.00115	866.164	0.16299	6.13539	5.94374
34	164.022	0.00610	0.00099	1007.34	0.16283	6.14149	5.97060
35	190.566	0.00525	0.00085	1171.36	0.16269	6.14674	5.99453

$r = 20\%$ **Continuous Compounding, Discrete Cash Flows**

	SINGLE PAYMENT		UNIFORM SERIES				Arithmetic Gradient Series Factor
	Compound Amount Factor	Present Worth Factor	Sinking Fund Factor	Uniform Series Factor	Capital Recovery Factor	Series Present Worth Factor	
N	$(F/P,r,N)$	$(P/F,r,N)$	$(A/F,r,N)$	$(F/A,r,N)$	$(A/P,r,N)$	$(P/A,r,N)$	$(A/G,r,N)$
1	1.2214	0.81873	1.0000	1.0000	1.2214	0.81873	0.00000
2	1.4918	0.67032	0.45017	2.2214	0.67157	1.48905	0.45017
3	1.8221	0.54881	0.26931	3.7132	0.49071	2.03786	0.86755
4	2.2255	0.44933	0.18066	5.5353	0.40206	2.48719	1.25279
5	2.7183	0.36788	0.12885	7.7609	0.35025	2.85507	1.60677
6	3.3201	0.30119	0.09543	10.4792	0.31683	3.15627	1.93058
7	4.0552	0.24660	0.07247	13.7993	0.29387	3.40286	2.22548
8	4.9530	0.20190	0.05601	17.8545	0.27741	3.60476	2.49289
9	6.0496	0.16530	0.04385	22.8075	0.26525	3.77006	2.73435
10	7.3891	0.13534	0.03465	28.8572	0.25606	3.90539	2.95148
11	9.0250	0.11080	0.02759	36.2462	0.24899	4.01620	3.14594
12	11.0232	0.09072	0.02209	45.2712	0.24349	4.10691	3.31943
13	13.4637	0.07427	0.01776	56.2944	0.23917	4.18119	3.47363
14	16.4446	0.06081	0.01434	69.7581	0.23574	4.24200	3.61019
15	20.0855	0.04979	0.01160	86.2028	0.23300	4.29178	3.73072
16	24.5325	0.04076	0.00941	106.288	0.23081	4.33255	3.83675
17	29.9641	0.03337	0.00764	130.821	0.22905	4.36592	3.92972
18	36.5982	0.02732	0.00622	160.785	0.22762	4.39324	4.01101
19	44.7012	0.02237	0.00507	197.383	0.22647	4.41561	4.08188
20	54.5982	0.01832	0.00413	242.084	0.22553	4.43393	4.14351
21	66.6863	0.01500	0.00337	296.683	0.22477	4.44893	4.19695
22	81.4509	0.01228	0.00275	363.369	0.22415	4.46120	4.24320
23	99.4843	0.01005	0.00225	444.820	0.22365	4.47125	4.28312
24	121.510	0.00823	0.00184	544.304	0.22324	4.47948	4.31750
25	148.413	0.00674	0.00150	665.814	0.22290	4.48622	4.34706
26	181.272	0.00552	0.00123	814.228	0.22263	4.49174	4.37243
27	221.406	0.00452	0.00100	995.500	0.22241	4.49626	4.39415
28	270.426	0.00370	0.00082	1216.91	0.22222	4.49995	4.41273
29	330.300	0.00303	0.00067	1487.33	0.22208	4.50298	4.42859
30	403.429	0.00248	0.00055	1817.63	0.22195	4.50546	4.44211
31	492.749	0.00203	0.00045	2221.06	0.22185	4.50749	4.45362
32	601.845	0.00166	0.00037	2713.81	0.22177	4.50915	4.46340
33	735.095	0.00136	0.00030	3315.66	0.22170	4.51051	4.47170
34	897.847	0.00111	0.00025	4050.75	0.22165	4.51163	4.47874
35	1096.63	0.00091	0.00020	4948.60	0.22160	4.51254	4.48471

$r = 25\%$ **Continuous Compounding, Discrete Cash Flows**

	SINGLE PAYMENT		UNIFORM SERIES				Arithmetic Gradient Series Factor
	Compound Amount Factor	Present Worth Factor	Sinking Fund Factor	Uniform Series Factor	Capital Recovery Factor	Series Present Worth Factor	
N	$(F/P,r,N)$	$(P/F,r,N)$	$(A/F,r,N)$	$(F/A,r,N)$	$(A/P,r,N)$	$(P/A,r,N)$	$(A/G,r,N)$
1	1.2840	0.77880	1.0000	1.0000	1.2840	0.77880	0.00000
2	1.6487	0.60653	0.43782	2.2840	0.72185	1.38533	0.43782
3	2.1170	0.47237	0.25428	3.9327	0.53830	1.85770	0.83505
4	2.7183	0.36788	0.16530	6.0497	0.44932	2.22558	1.19290
5	3.4903	0.28650	0.11405	8.7680	0.39808	2.51208	1.51306
6	4.4817	0.22313	0.08158	12.2584	0.36560	2.73521	1.79751
7	5.7546	0.17377	0.05974	16.7401	0.34376	2.90899	2.04855
8	7.3891	0.13534	0.04445	22.4947	0.32848	3.04432	2.26867
9	9.4877	0.10540	0.03346	29.8837	0.31749	3.14972	2.46046
10	12.1825	0.08208	0.02540	39.3715	0.30942	3.23181	2.62656
11	15.6426	0.06393	0.01940	51.5539	0.30342	3.29573	2.76958
12	20.0855	0.04979	0.01488	67.1966	0.29891	3.34552	2.89206
13	25.7903	0.03877	0.01146	87.2821	0.29548	3.38429	2.99641
14	33.1155	0.03020	0.00884	113.072	0.29287	3.41449	3.08488
15	42.5211	0.02352	0.00684	146.188	0.29087	3.43801	3.15955
16	54.5982	0.01832	0.00530	188.709	0.28932	3.45633	3.22229
17	70.1054	0.01426	0.00411	243.307	0.28814	3.47059	3.27481
18	90.0171	0.01111	0.00319	313.413	0.28722	3.48170	3.31860
19	115.584	0.00865	0.00248	403.430	0.28650	3.49035	3.35499
20	148.413	0.00674	0.00193	519.014	0.28595	3.49709	3.38514
21	190.566	0.00525	0.00150	667.427	0.28552	3.50234	3.41003
22	244.692	0.00409	0.00117	857.993	0.28519	3.50642	3.43053
23	314.191	0.00318	0.00091	1102.69	0.28493	3.50961	3.44737
24	403.429	0.00248	0.00071	1416.88	0.28473	3.51208	3.46117
25	518.013	0.00193	0.00055	1820.30	0.28457	3.51401	3.47246
26	665.142	0.00150	0.00043	2338.32	0.28445	3.51552	3.48166
27	854.059	0.00117	0.00033	3003.46	0.28436	3.51669	3.48916
28	1096.63	0.00091	0.00026	3857.52	0.28428	3.51760	3.49526
29	1408.10	0.00071	0.00020	4954.15	0.28423	3.51831	3.50020
30	1808.04	0.00055	0.00016	6362.26	0.28418	3.51886	3.50421
31	2321.57	0.00043	0.00012	8170.30	0.28415	3.51930	3.50745
32	2980.96	0.00034	0.00010	10 492.0	0.28412	3.51963	3.51007
33	3827.63	0.00026	0.00007	13 473.0	0.28410	3.51989	3.51219
34	4914.77	0.00020	0.00006	17 300.0	0.28408	3.52010	3.51389
35	6310.69	0.00016	0.00005	22 215.0	0.28407	3.52025	3.51526

Compound Interest Factors for Continuous Compounding, Continuous Compounding Periods

r = 1% **Continuous Compounding, Continuous Compounding Periods**

T	Sinking Fund Factor $(A/F,r,T)$	Uniform Series Factor $(F/A,r,T)$	Capital Recovery Factor $(A/P,r,T)$	Series Present Worth Factor $(P/A,r,T)$
1	0.99501	1.0050	1.0050	0.99502
2	0.49502	2.0201	0.50502	1.9801
3	0.32836	3.0455	0.33836	2.9554
4	0.24503	4.0811	0.25503	3.9211
5	0.19504	5.1271	0.20504	4.8771
6	0.16172	6.1837	0.17172	5.8235
7	0.13792	7.2508	0.14792	6.7606
8	0.12007	8.3287	0.13007	7.6884
9	0.10619	9.4174	0.11619	8.6069
10	0.09508	10.5171	0.10508	9.5163
11	0.08600	11.6278	0.09600	10.4166
12	0.07843	12.7497	0.08843	11.3080
13	0.07203	13.8828	0.08203	12.1905
14	0.06655	15.0274	0.07655	13.0642
15	0.06179	16.1834	0.07179	13.9292
16	0.05763	17.3511	0.06763	14.7856
17	0.05397	18.5305	0.06397	15.6335
18	0.05071	19.7217	0.06071	16.4730
19	0.04779	20.9250	0.05779	17.3041
20	0.04517	22.1403	0.05517	18.1269
21	0.04279	23.3678	0.05279	18.9416
22	0.04064	24.6077	0.05064	19.7481
23	0.03867	25.8600	0.04867	20.5466
24	0.03687	27.1249	0.04687	21.3372
25	0.03521	28.4025	0.04521	22.1199
26	0.03368	29.6930	0.04368	22.8948
27	0.03226	30.9964	0.04226	23.6621
28	0.03095	32.3130	0.04095	24.4216
29	0.02972	33.6427	0.03972	25.1736
30	0.02858	34.9859	0.03858	25.9182
31	0.02752	36.3425	0.03752	26.6553
32	0.02652	37.7128	0.03652	27.3851
33	0.02558	39.0968	0.03558	28.1076
34	0.02469	40.4948	0.03469	28.8230
35	0.02386	41.9068	0.03386	29.5312
40	0.02033	49.1825	0.03033	32.9680
45	0.01760	56.8312	0.02760	36.2372
50	0.01541	64.8721	0.02541	39.3469
55	0.01364	73.3253	0.02364	42.3050
60	0.01216	82.2119	0.02216	45.1188
65	0.01092	91.5541	0.02092	47.7954
70	0.00986	101.375	0.01986	50.3415
75	0.00895	111.700	0.01895	52.7633
80	0.00816	122.554	0.01816	55.0671
85	0.00746	133.965	0.01746	57.2585
90	0.00685	145.960	0.01685	59.3430
95	0.00631	158.571	0.01631	61.3259
100	0.00582	171.828	0.01582	63.2121

	Sinking Fund Factor	Uniform Series Factor	Capital Recovery Factor	Series Present Worth Factor
T	$(A/F,r,T)$	$(F/A,r,T)$	$(A/P,r,T)$	$(P/A,r,T)$
1	0.99003	1.0101	1.0100	0.99007
2	0.49007	2.0405	0.51007	1.9605
3	0.32343	3.0918	0.34343	2.9118
4	0.24013	4.1644	0.26013	3.8442
5	0.19017	5.2585	0.21017	4.7581
6	0.15687	6.3748	0.17687	5.6540
7	0.13309	7.5137	0.15309	6.5321
8	0.11527	8.6755	0.13527	7.3928
9	0.10141	9.8609	0.12141	8.2365
10	0.09033	11.0701	0.11033	9.0635
11	0.08128	12.3038	0.10128	9.8741
12	0.07373	13.5625	0.09373	10.6686
13	0.06736	14.8465	0.08736	11.4474
14	0.06189	16.1565	0.08189	12.2108
15	0.05717	17.4929	0.07717	12.9591
16	0.05303	18.8564	0.07303	13.6925
17	0.04939	20.2474	0.06939	14.4115
18	0.04615	21.6665	0.06615	15.1162
19	0.04326	23.1142	0.06326	15.8069
20	0.04066	24.5912	0.06066	16.4840
21	0.03832	26.0981	0.05832	17.1477
22	0.03619	27.6354	0.05619	17.7982
23	0.03424	29.2037	0.05424	18.4358
24	0.03246	30.8037	0.05246	19.0608
25	0.03083	32.4361	0.05083	19.6735
26	0.02932	34.1014	0.04932	20.2740
27	0.02793	35.8003	0.04793	20.8626
28	0.02664	37.5336	0.04664	21.4395
29	0.02544	39.3019	0.04544	22.0051
30	0.02433	41.1059	0.04433	22.5594
31	0.02328	42.9464	0.04328	23.1028
32	0.02231	44.8240	0.04231	23.6354
33	0.02140	46.7396	0.04140	24.1574
34	0.02054	48.6939	0.04054	24.6692
35	0.01973	50.6876	0.03973	25.1707
40	0.01632	61.2770	0.03632	27.5336
45	0.01370	72.9802	0.03370	29.6715
50	0.01164	85.9141	0.03164	31.6060
55	0.00998	100.208	0.02998	33.3564
60	0.00862	116.006	0.02862	34.9403
65	0.00749	133.465	0.02749	36.3734
70	0.00655	152.760	0.02655	37.6702
75	0.00574	174.084	0.02574	38.8435
80	0.00506	197.652	0.02506	39.9052
85	0.00447	223.697	0.02447	40.8658
90	0.00396	252.482	0.02396	41.7351
95	0.00352	284.295	0.02352	42.5216
100	0.00313	319.453	0.02313	43.2332

$r = 2\%$ **Continuous Compounding, Continuous Compounding Periods**

$r = 3\%$ **Continuous Compounding, Continuous Compounding Periods**

T	Sinking Fund Factor $(A/F,r,T)$	Uniform Series Factor $(F/A,r,T)$	Capital Recovery Factor $(A/P,r,T)$	Series Present Worth Factor $(P/A,r,T)$
1	0.98507	1.0152	1.0151	0.98515
2	0.48515	2.0612	0.51515	1.9412
3	0.31856	3.1391	0.34856	2.8690
4	0.23530	4.2499	0.26530	3.7693
5	0.18537	5.3945	0.21537	4.6431
6	0.15212	6.5739	0.18212	5.4910
7	0.12838	7.7893	0.15838	6.3139
8	0.11060	9.0416	0.14060	7.1124
9	0.09679	10.3321	0.12679	7.8874
10	0.08575	11.6620	0.11575	8.6394
11	0.07673	13.0323	0.10673	9.3692
12	0.06923	14.4443	0.09923	10.0775
13	0.06290	15.8994	0.09290	10.7648
14	0.05748	17.3987	0.08748	11.4318
15	0.05279	18.9437	0.08279	12.0791
16	0.04870	20.5358	0.07870	12.7072
17	0.04509	22.1764	0.07509	13.3168
18	0.04190	23.8669	0.07190	13.9084
19	0.03905	25.6089	0.06905	14.4825
20	0.03649	27.4040	0.06649	15.0396
21	0.03418	29.2537	0.06418	15.5803
22	0.03209	31.1597	0.06209	16.1050
23	0.03019	33.1239	0.06019	16.6141
24	0.02845	35.1478	0.05845	17.1083
25	0.02686	37.2333	0.05686	17.5878
26	0.02539	39.3824	0.05539	18.0531
27	0.02404	41.5969	0.05404	18.5047
28	0.02279	43.8789	0.05279	18.9430
29	0.02163	46.2304	0.05163	19.3683
30	0.02055	48.6534	0.05055	19.7810
31	0.01955	51.1503	0.04955	20.1815
32	0.01861	53.7232	0.04861	20.5702
33	0.01774	56.3745	0.04774	20.9474
34	0.01692	59.1065	0.04692	21.3135
35	0.01615	61.9217	0.04615	21.6687
40	0.01293	77.3372	0.04293	23.2935
45	0.01050	95.2475	0.04050	24.6920
50	0.00862	116.056	0.03862	25.8957
55	0.00713	140.233	0.03713	26.9317
60	0.00594	168.322	0.03594	27.8234
65	0.00498	200.956	0.03498	28.5909
70	0.00419	238.872	0.03419	29.2515
75	0.00353	282.925	0.03353	29.8200
80	0.00299	334.106	0.03299	30.3094
85	0.00254	393.570	0.03254	30.7306
90	0.00216	462.658	0.03216	31.0931
95	0.00184	542.926	0.03184	31.4052
100	0.00157	636.185	0.03157	31.6738

r = 4%   **Continuous Compounding, Continuous Compounding Periods**

T	Sinking Fund Factor (A/F,r,T)	Uniform Series Factor (F/A,r,T)	Capital Recovery Factor (A/P,r,T)	Series Present Worth Factor (P/A,r,T)
1	0.98013	1.0203	1.0201	0.98026
2	0.48027	2.0822	0.52027	1.9221
3	0.31373	3.1874	0.35373	2.8270
4	0.23053	4.3378	0.27053	3.6964
5	0.18067	5.5351	0.22067	4.5317
6	0.14747	6.7812	0.18747	5.3343
7	0.12379	8.0782	0.16379	6.1054
8	0.10606	9.4282	0.14606	6.8463
9	0.09231	10.8332	0.13231	7.5581
10	0.08133	12.2956	0.12133	8.2420
11	0.07237	13.8177	0.11237	8.8991
12	0.06493	15.4019	0.10493	9.5304
13	0.05865	17.0507	0.09865	10.1370
14	0.05329	18.7668	0.09329	10.7198
15	0.04865	20.5530	0.08865	11.2797
16	0.04462	22.4120	0.08462	11.8177
17	0.04107	24.3469	0.08107	12.3346
18	0.03794	26.3608	0.07794	12.8312
19	0.03514	28.4569	0.07514	13.3083
20	0.03264	30.6385	0.07264	13.7668
21	0.03039	32.9092	0.07039	14.2072
22	0.02835	35.2725	0.06835	14.6304
23	0.02650	37.7323	0.06650	15.0370
24	0.02482	40.2924	0.06482	15.4277
25	0.02328	42.9570	0.06328	15.8030
26	0.02187	45.7304	0.06187	16.1636
27	0.02057	48.6170	0.06057	16.5101
28	0.01937	51.6214	0.05937	16.8430
29	0.01827	54.7483	0.05827	17.1628
30	0.01724	58.0029	0.05724	17.4701
31	0.01629	61.3903	0.05629	17.7654
32	0.01540	64.9160	0.05540	18.0491
33	0.01458	68.5855	0.05458	18.3216
34	0.01381	72.4048	0.05381	18.5835
35	0.01309	76.3800	0.05309	18.8351
40	0.01012	98.8258	0.05012	19.9526
45	0.00792	126.241	0.04792	20.8675
50	0.00626	159.726	0.04626	21.6166
55	0.00498	200.625	0.04498	22.2299
60	0.00399	250.579	0.04399	22.7321
65	0.00321	311.593	0.04321	23.1432
70	0.00259	386.116	0.04259	23.4797
75	0.00210	477.138	0.04210	23.7553
80	0.00170	588.313	0.04170	23.9809
85	0.00138	724.103	0.04138	24.1657
90	0.00112	889.956	0.04112	24.3169
95	0.00092	1092.53	0.04092	24.4407
100	0.00075	1339.95	0.04075	24.5421

$r = 5\%$ **Continuous Compounding, Continuous Compounding Periods**

T	Sinking Fund Factor $(A/F,r,T)$	Uniform Series Factor $(F/A,r,T)$	Capital Recovery Factor $(A/P,r,T)$	Series Present Worth Factor $(P/A,r,T)$
1	0.97521	1.0254	1.0252	0.97541
2	0.47542	2.1034	0.52542	1.9033
3	0.30896	3.2367	0.35896	2.7858
4	0.22583	4.4281	0.27583	3.6254
5	0.17604	5.6805	0.22604	4.4240
6	0.14291	6.9972	0.19291	5.1836
7	0.11931	8.3814	0.16931	5.9062
8	0.10166	9.8365	0.15166	6.5936
9	0.08798	11.3662	0.13798	7.2474
10	0.07707	12.9744	0.12707	7.8694
11	0.06819	14.6651	0.11819	8.4610
12	0.06082	16.4424	0.11082	9.0238
13	0.05461	18.3108	0.10461	9.5591
14	0.04932	20.2751	0.09932	10.0683
15	0.04476	22.3400	0.09476	10.5527
16	0.04080	24.5108	0.09080	11.0134
17	0.03732	26.7929	0.08732	11.4517
18	0.03426	29.1921	0.08426	11.8686
19	0.03153	31.7142	0.08153	12.2652
20	0.02910	34.3656	0.07910	12.6424
21	0.02692	37.1530	0.07692	13.0012
22	0.02495	40.0833	0.07495	13.3426
23	0.02317	43.1639	0.07317	13.6673
24	0.02155	46.4023	0.07155	13.9761
25	0.02008	49.8069	0.07008	14.2699
26	0.01873	53.3859	0.06873	14.5494
27	0.01750	57.1485	0.06750	14.8152
28	0.01637	61.1040	0.06637	15.0681
29	0.01532	65.2623	0.06532	15.3086
30	0.01436	69.6338	0.06436	15.5374
31	0.01347	74.2294	0.06347	15.7550
32	0.01265	79.0606	0.06265	15.9621
33	0.01189	84.1396	0.06189	16.1590
34	0.01118	89.4789	0.06118	16.3463
35	0.01052	95.0921	0.06052	16.5245
40	0.00783	127.781	0.05783	17.2933
45	0.00589	169.755	0.05589	17.8920
50	0.00447	223.650	0.05447	18.3583
55	0.00341	292.853	0.05341	18.7214
60	0.00262	381.711	0.05262	19.0043
65	0.00202	495.807	0.05202	19.2245
70	0.00156	642.309	0.05156	19.3961
75	0.00120	830.422	0.05120	19.5296
80	0.00093	1071.96	0.05093	19.6337
85	0.00072	1382.11	0.05072	19.7147
90	0.00056	1780.34	0.05056	19.7778
95	0.00044	2291.69	0.05044	19.8270
100	0.00034	2948.26	0.05034	19.8652

r = 6%   **Continuous Compounding, Continuous Compounding Periods**

T	Sinking Fund Factor (A/F,r,T)	Uniform Series Factor (F/A,r,T)	Capital Recovery Factor (A/P,r,T)	Series Present Worth Factor (P/A,r,T)
1	0.97030	1.0306	1.0303	0.97059
2	0.47060	2.1249	0.53060	1.8847
3	0.30423	3.2870	0.36423	2.7455
4	0.22120	4.5208	0.28120	3.5562
5	0.17150	5.8310	0.23150	4.3197
6	0.13846	7.2222	0.19846	5.0387
7	0.11495	8.6994	0.17495	5.7159
8	0.09739	10.2679	0.15739	6.3536
9	0.08380	11.9334	0.14380	6.9542
10	0.07298	13.7020	0.13298	7.5198
11	0.06419	15.5799	0.12419	8.0525
12	0.05690	17.5739	0.11690	8.5541
13	0.05078	19.6912	0.11078	9.0266
14	0.04558	21.9394	0.10558	9.4715
15	0.04111	24.3267	0.10111	9.8905
16	0.03723	26.8616	0.09723	10.2851
17	0.03384	29.5532	0.09384	10.6568
18	0.03085	32.4113	0.09085	11.0067
19	0.02821	35.4461	0.08821	11.3363
20	0.02586	38.6686	0.08586	11.6468
21	0.02376	42.0904	0.08376	11.9391
22	0.02187	45.7237	0.08187	12.2144
23	0.02017	49.5817	0.08017	12.4737
24	0.01863	53.6783	0.07863	12.7179
25	0.01723	58.0282	0.07723	12.9478
26	0.01596	62.6470	0.07596	13.1644
27	0.01480	67.5515	0.07480	13.3684
28	0.01374	72.7593	0.07374	13.5604
29	0.01277	78.2891	0.07277	13.7413
30	0.01188	84.1608	0.07188	13.9117
31	0.01106	90.3956	0.07106	14.0721
32	0.01031	97.0160	0.07031	14.2232
33	0.00961	104.046	0.06961	14.3655
34	0.00897	111.510	0.06897	14.4995
35	0.00837	119.436	0.06837	14.6257
40	0.00599	167.053	0.06599	15.1547
45	0.00432	231.329	0.06432	15.5466
50	0.00314	318.092	0.06314	15.8369
55	0.00230	435.211	0.06230	16.0519
60	0.00169	593.304	0.06169	16.2113
65	0.00124	806.707	0.06124	16.3293
70	0.00091	1094.77	0.06091	16.4167
75	0.00067	1483.62	0.06067	16.4815
80	0.00050	2008.51	0.06050	16.5295
85	0.00037	2717.03	0.06037	16.5651
90	0.00027	3673.44	0.06027	16.5914
95	0.00020	4964.46	0.06020	16.6109
100	0.00015	6707.15	0.06015	16.6254

$r = 7\%$ **Continuous Compounding, Continuous Compounding Periods**

T	Sinking Fund Factor $(A/F,r,T)$	Uniform Series Factor $(F/A,r,T)$	Capital Recovery Factor $(A/P,r,T)$	Series Present Worth Factor $(P/A,r,T)$
1	0.96541	1.0358	1.0354	0.96580
2	0.46582	2.1468	0.53582	1.8663
3	0.29956	3.3383	0.36956	2.7059
4	0.21663	4.6161	0.28663	3.4888
5	0.16704	5.9867	0.23704	4.2187
6	0.13411	7.4566	0.20411	4.8993
7	0.11070	9.0331	0.18070	5.5339
8	0.09325	10.7239	0.16325	6.1256
9	0.07976	12.5373	0.14976	6.6773
10	0.06905	14.4822	0.13905	7.1916
11	0.06036	16.5681	0.13036	7.6712
12	0.05318	18.8052	0.12318	8.1184
13	0.04716	21.2046	0.11716	8.5354
14	0.04206	23.7779	0.11206	8.9241
15	0.03768	26.5379	0.10768	9.2866
16	0.03390	29.4979	0.10390	9.6246
17	0.03061	32.6726	0.10061	9.9397
18	0.02772	36.0774	0.09772	10.2335
19	0.02517	39.7292	0.09517	10.5075
20	0.02291	43.6457	0.09291	10.7629
21	0.02090	47.8462	0.09090	11.0011
22	0.01910	52.3513	0.08910	11.2231
23	0.01749	57.1830	0.08749	11.4302
24	0.01603	62.3651	0.08603	11.6232
25	0.01472	67.9229	0.08472	11.8032
26	0.01353	73.8837	0.08353	11.9711
27	0.01246	80.2767	0.08246	12.1275
28	0.01148	87.1332	0.08148	12.2735
29	0.01058	94.4869	0.08058	12.4095
30	0.00977	102.374	0.07977	12.5363
31	0.00902	110.833	0.07902	12.6546
32	0.00834	119.905	0.07834	12.7649
33	0.00771	129.635	0.07771	12.8677
34	0.00714	140.070	0.07714	12.9636
35	0.00661	151.262	0.07661	13.0529
40	0.00453	220.638	0.07453	13.4170
45	0.00313	319.087	0.07313	13.6735
50	0.00218	458.792	0.07218	13.8543
55	0.00152	657.044	0.07152	13.9817
60	0.00107	938.376	0.07107	14.0715
65	0.00075	1337.61	0.07075	14.1348
70	0.00053	1904.14	0.07053	14.1793
75	0.00037	2708.09	0.07037	14.2107
80	0.00026	3848.95	0.07026	14.2329
85	0.00018	5467.90	0.07018	14.2485
90	0.00013	7765.31	0.07013	14.2595
95	0.00009	11 025.0	0.07009	14.2672
100	0.00006	15 652.0	0.07006	14.2727

r = 8% **Continuous Compounding, Continuous Compounding Periods**

T	Sinking Fund Factor (A/F,r,T)	Uniform Series Factor (F/A,r,T)	Capital Recovery Factor (A/P,r,T)	Series Present Worth Factor (P/A,r,T)
1	0.96053	1.0411	1.0405	0.96105
2	0.46107	2.1689	0.54107	1.8482
3	0.29493	3.3906	0.37493	2.6672
4	0.21213	4.7141	0.29213	3.4231
5	0.16266	6.1478	0.24266	4.1210
6	0.12985	7.7009	0.20985	4.7652
7	0.10657	9.3834	0.18657	5.3599
8	0.08924	11.2060	0.16924	5.9088
9	0.07587	13.1804	0.15587	6.4156
10	0.06528	15.3193	0.14528	6.8834
11	0.05670	17.6362	0.13670	7.3152
12	0.04964	20.1462	0.12964	7.7138
13	0.04373	22.8652	0.12373	8.0818
14	0.03874	25.8107	0.11874	8.4215
15	0.03448	29.0015	0.11448	8.7351
16	0.03081	32.4580	0.11081	9.0245
17	0.02762	36.2024	0.10762	9.2917
18	0.02484	40.2587	0.10484	9.5384
19	0.02240	44.6528	0.10240	9.7661
20	0.02024	49.4129	0.10024	9.9763
21	0.01833	54.5694	0.09833	10.1703
22	0.01662	60.1555	0.09662	10.3494
23	0.01510	66.2067	0.09510	10.5148
24	0.01374	72.7620	0.09374	10.6674
25	0.01252	79.8632	0.09252	10.8083
26	0.01142	87.5559	0.09142	10.9384
27	0.01043	95.8892	0.09043	11.0584
28	0.00953	104.917	0.08953	11.1693
29	0.00872	114.696	0.08872	11.2716
30	0.00798	125.290	0.08798	11.3660
31	0.00731	136.766	0.08731	11.4532
32	0.00670	149.198	0.08670	11.5337
33	0.00615	162.665	0.08615	11.6080
34	0.00564	177.254	0.08564	11.6766
35	0.00518	193.058	0.08518	11.7399
40	0.00340	294.157	0.08340	11.9905
45	0.00225	444.978	0.08225	12.1585
50	0.00149	669.977	0.08149	12.2711
55	0.00099	1005.64	0.08099	12.3465
60	0.00066	1506.38	0.08066	12.3971
65	0.00044	2253.40	0.08044	12.4310
70	0.00030	3367.83	0.08030	12.4538
75	0.00020	5030.36	0.08020	12.4690
80	0.00013	7510.56	0.08013	12.4792
85	0.00009	11 211.0	0.08009	12.4861
90	0.00006	16 730.0	0.08006	12.4907
95	0.00004	24 965.0	0.08004	12.4937
100	0.00003	37 249.0	0.08003	12.4958

r = 9% Continuous Compounding, Continuous Compounding Periods

T	Sinking Fund Factor (A/F,r,T)	Uniform Series Factor (F/A,r,T)	Capital Recovery Factor (A/P,r,T)	Series Present Worth Factor (P/A,r,T)
1	0.95567	1.0464	1.0457	0.95632
2	0.45635	2.1913	0.54635	1.8303
3	0.29036	3.4440	0.38036	2.6291
4	0.20769	4.8148	0.29769	3.3592
5	0.15836	6.3146	0.24836	4.0264
6	0.12570	7.9556	0.21570	4.6361
7	0.10255	9.7512	0.19255	5.1934
8	0.08535	11.7159	0.17535	5.7028
9	0.07212	13.8656	0.16212	6.1682
10	0.06166	16.2178	0.15166	6.5937
11	0.05322	18.7915	0.14322	6.9825
12	0.04628	21.6076	0.13628	7.3378
13	0.04050	24.6888	0.13050	7.6626
14	0.03564	28.0602	0.12564	7.9594
15	0.03150	31.7492	0.12150	8.2307
16	0.02794	35.7855	0.11794	8.4786
17	0.02487	40.2020	0.11487	8.7052
18	0.02221	45.0343	0.11221	8.9122
19	0.01987	50.3218	0.10987	9.1015
20	0.01782	56.1072	0.10782	9.2745
21	0.01602	62.4374	0.10602	9.4325
22	0.01442	69.3638	0.10442	9.5770
23	0.01300	76.9425	0.10300	9.7090
24	0.01173	85.2349	0.10173	9.8297
25	0.01060	94.3082	0.10060	9.9400
26	0.00959	104.236	0.09959	10.0408
27	0.00869	115.099	0.09869	10.1329
28	0.00787	126.984	0.09787	10.2171
29	0.00714	139.989	0.09714	10.2941
30	0.00648	154.219	0.09648	10.3644
31	0.00589	169.789	0.09589	10.4287
32	0.00535	186.825	0.09535	10.4874
33	0.00487	205.466	0.09487	10.5411
34	0.00443	225.862	0.09443	10.5901
35	0.00403	248.178	0.09403	10.6350
40	0.00253	395.536	0.09253	10.8075
45	0.00160	626.638	0.09160	10.9175
50	0.00101	989.079	0.09101	10.9877
55	0.00064	1557.50	0.09064	11.0324
60	0.00041	2448.96	0.09041	11.0609
65	0.00026	3847.05	0.09026	11.0791
70	0.00017	6039.69	0.09017	11.0907
75	0.00011	9478.43	0.09011	11.0981
80	0.00007	14 871.0	0.09007	11.1028
85	0.00004	23 329.0	0.09004	11.1058
90	0.00003	36 594.0	0.09003	11.1077
95	0.00002	57 397.0	0.09002	11.1090
100	0.00001	90 023.0	0.09001	11.1097

$r = 10\%$ 　　　　　　　**Continuous Compounding, Continuous Compounding Periods**

T	Sinking Fund Factor $(A/F,r,T)$	Uniform Series Factor $(F/A,r,T)$	Capital Recovery Factor $(A/P,r,T)$	Series Present Worth Factor $(P/A,r,T)$
1	0.95083	1.0517	1.0508	0.95163
2	0.45167	2.2140	0.55167	1.8127
3	0.28583	3.4986	0.38583	2.5918
4	0.20332	4.9182	0.30332	3.2968
5	0.15415	6.4872	0.25415	3.9347
6	0.12164	8.2212	0.22164	4.5119
7	0.09864	10.1375	0.19864	5.0341
8	0.08160	12.2554	0.18160	5.5067
9	0.06851	14.5960	0.16851	5.9343
10	0.05820	17.1828	0.15820	6.3212
11	0.04990	20.0417	0.14990	6.6713
12	0.04310	23.2012	0.14310	6.9881
13	0.03746	26.6930	0.13746	7.2747
14	0.03273	30.5520	0.13273	7.5340
15	0.02872	34.8169	0.12872	7.7687
16	0.02530	39.5303	0.12530	7.9810
17	0.02235	44.7395	0.12235	8.1732
18	0.01980	50.4965	0.11980	8.3470
19	0.01759	56.8589	0.11759	8.5043
20	0.01565	63.8906	0.11565	8.6466
21	0.01395	71.6617	0.11395	8.7754
22	0.01246	80.2501	0.11246	8.8920
23	0.01114	89.7418	0.11114	8.9974
24	0.00998	100.232	0.10998	9.0928
25	0.00894	111.825	0.10894	9.1792
26	0.00802	124.637	0.10802	9.2573
27	0.00720	138.797	0.10720	9.3279
28	0.00647	154.446	0.10647	9.3919
29	0.00582	171.741	0.10582	9.4498
30	0.00524	190.855	0.10524	9.5021
31	0.00472	211.980	0.10472	9.5495
32	0.00425	235.325	0.10425	9.5924
33	0.00383	261.126	0.10383	9.6312
34	0.00345	289.641	0.10345	9.6663
35	0.00311	321.155	0.10311	9.6980
40	0.00187	535.982	0.10187	9.8168
45	0.00112	890.171	0.10112	9.8889
50	0.00068	1474.13	0.10068	9.9326
55	0.00041	2436.92	0.10041	9.9591
60	0.00025	4024.29	0.10025	9.9752
65	0.00015	6641.42	0.10015	9.9850
70	0.00009	10 956.0	0.10009	9.9909
75	0.00006	18 070.0	0.10006	9.9945
80	0.00003	29 800.0	0.10003	9.9966
85	0.00002	49 138.0	0.10002	9.9980
90	0.00001	81 021.0	0.10001	9.9988
95	0.00001	133 587.0	0.10001	9.9993
100	0.00000	220 255.0	0.10000	9.9995

$r = 11\%$ Continuous Compounding, Continuous Compounding Periods

T	Sinking Fund Factor $(A/F,r,T)$	Uniform Series Factor $(F/A,r,T)$	Capital Recovery Factor $(A/P,r,T)$	Series Present Worth Factor $(P/A,r,T)$
1	0.94601	1.0571	1.0560	0.94696
2	0.44702	2.2371	0.55702	1.7953
3	0.28135	3.5543	0.39135	2.5552
4	0.19902	5.0246	0.30902	3.2360
5	0.15002	6.6659	0.26002	3.8459
6	0.11767	8.4981	0.22767	4.3923
7	0.09485	10.5433	0.20485	4.8817
8	0.07796	12.8264	0.18796	5.3202
9	0.06504	15.3749	0.17504	5.7129
10	0.05489	18.2197	0.16489	6.0648
11	0.04674	21.3953	0.15674	6.3800
12	0.04010	24.9402	0.15010	6.6624
13	0.03461	28.8973	0.14461	6.9154
14	0.03002	33.3145	0.14002	7.1420
15	0.02615	38.2453	0.13615	7.3450
16	0.02286	43.7494	0.13286	7.5269
17	0.02004	49.8936	0.13004	7.6898
18	0.01762	56.7522	0.12762	7.8357
19	0.01553	64.4083	0.12553	7.9665
20	0.01371	72.9547	0.12371	8.0836
21	0.01212	82.4948	0.12212	8.1885
22	0.01074	93.1442	0.12074	8.2825
23	0.00952	105.032	0.11952	8.3667
24	0.00845	118.302	0.11845	8.4422
25	0.00751	133.115	0.11751	8.5097
26	0.00668	149.650	0.11668	8.5703
27	0.00595	168.108	0.11595	8.6245
28	0.00530	188.713	0.11530	8.6731
29	0.00472	211.713	0.11472	8.7166
30	0.00421	237.388	0.11421	8.7556
31	0.00376	266.048	0.11376	8.7905
32	0.00336	298.040	0.11336	8.8218
33	0.00300	333.753	0.11300	8.8499
34	0.00268	373.618	0.11268	8.8750
35	0.00239	418.119	0.11239	8.8975
40	0.00137	731.372	0.11137	8.9793
45	0.00078	1274.32	0.11078	9.0265
50	0.00045	2215.38	0.11045	9.0538
55	0.00026	3846.48	0.11026	9.0695
60	0.00015	6 674.0	0.11015	9.0785
65	0.00009	11 574.0	0.11009	9.0838
70	0.00005	20 067.0	0.11005	9.0868
75	0.00003	34 788.0	0.11003	9.0885
80	0.00002	60302.218	0.11002	9.0895
85	0.00001	104525.668	0.11001	9.0901
90	0.00001	181176.095	0.11001	9.0905
95	0.00000	314030.679	0.11000	9.0906
100	0.00000	544301.288	0.11000	9.0908

r = 12%   **Continuous Compounding, Continuous Compounding Periods**

T	Sinking Fund Factor (A/F,r,T)	Uniform Series Factor (F/A,r,T)	Capital Recovery Factor (A/P,r,T)	Series Present Worth Factor (P/A,r,T)
1	0.94120	1.0625	1.0612	0.94233
2	0.44240	2.2604	0.56240	1.7781
3	0.27693	3.6111	0.39693	2.5194
4	0.19478	5.1340	0.31478	3.1768
5	0.14596	6.8510	0.26596	3.7599
6	0.11381	8.7869	0.23381	4.2771
7	0.09116	10.9697	0.21116	4.7357
8	0.07446	13.4308	0.19446	5.1426
9	0.06171	16.2057	0.18171	5.5034
10	0.05172	19.3343	0.17172	5.8234
11	0.04374	22.8618	0.16374	6.1072
12	0.03726	26.8391	0.15726	6.3589
13	0.03192	31.3235	0.15192	6.5822
14	0.02749	36.3796	0.14749	6.7802
15	0.02376	42.0804	0.14376	6.9558
16	0.02062	48.5080	0.14062	7.1116
17	0.01794	55.7551	0.13794	7.2498
18	0.01564	63.9261	0.13564	7.3723
19	0.01367	73.1390	0.13367	7.4810
20	0.01197	83.5265	0.13197	7.5774
21	0.01050	95.2383	0.13050	7.6628
22	0.00922	108.443	0.12922	7.7387
23	0.00811	123.332	0.12811	7.8059
24	0.00714	140.119	0.12714	7.8655
25	0.00629	159.046	0.12629	7.9184
26	0.00554	180.386	0.12554	7.9654
27	0.00489	204.448	0.12489	8.0070
28	0.00432	231.577	0.12432	8.0439
29	0.00381	262.164	0.12381	8.0766
30	0.00337	296.652	0.12337	8.1056
31	0.00298	335.537	0.12298	8.1314
32	0.00264	379.379	0.12264	8.1542
33	0.00233	428.811	0.12233	8.1745
34	0.00206	484.546	0.12206	8.1924
35	0.00183	547.386	0.12183	8.2084
40	0.00100	1004.25	0.12100	8.2648
45	0.00054	1836.72	0.12054	8.2957
50	0.00030	3353.57	0.12030	8.3127
55	0.00016	6117.46	0.12016	8.3220
60	0.00009	11 154.0	0.12009	8.3271
65	0.00005	20 330.0	0.12005	8.3299
70	0.00003	37 051.0	0.12003	8.3315
75	0.00001	67 517.0	0.12001	8.3323
80	0.00001	123 032.0	0.12001	8.3328
85	0.00000	224 185.0	0.12000	8.3330
90	0.00000	408 498.0	0.12000	8.3332
95	0.00000	744 339.0	0.12000	8.3332
100	0.00000	1 356 282.0	0.12000	8.3333

$r = 13\%$ **Continuous Compounding, Continuous Compounding Periods**

T	Sinking Fund Factor $(A/F,r,T)$	Uniform Series Factor $(F/A,r,T)$	Capital Recovery Factor $(A/P,r,T)$	Series Present Worth Factor $(P/A,r,T)$
1	0.93641	1.0679	1.0664	0.93773
2	0.43781	2.2841	0.56781	1.7611
3	0.27255	3.6691	0.40255	2.4842
4	0.19061	5.2464	0.32061	3.1191
5	0.14199	7.0426	0.27199	3.6766
6	0.11003	9.0882	0.24003	4.1661
7	0.08758	11.4179	0.21758	4.5960
8	0.07107	14.0709	0.20107	4.9734
9	0.05851	17.0923	0.18851	5.3049
10	0.04870	20.5331	0.17870	5.5959
11	0.04090	24.4515	0.17090	5.8515
12	0.03459	28.9140	0.16459	6.0759
13	0.02942	33.9960	0.15942	6.2729
14	0.02514	39.7835	0.15514	6.4460
15	0.02156	46.3745	0.15156	6.5979
16	0.01856	53.8805	0.14856	6.7313
17	0.01602	62.4286	0.14602	6.8485
18	0.01386	72.1634	0.14386	6.9513
19	0.01201	83.2496	0.14201	7.0417
20	0.01043	95.8749	0.14043	7.1210
21	0.00907	110.253	0.13907	7.1906
22	0.00790	126.627	0.13790	7.2518
23	0.00688	145.274	0.13688	7.3055
24	0.00601	166.511	0.13601	7.3526
25	0.00524	190.695	0.13524	7.3940
26	0.00458	218.237	0.13458	7.4304
27	0.00401	249.602	0.13401	7.4623
28	0.00350	285.322	0.13350	7.4904
29	0.00307	326.000	0.13307	7.5150
30	0.00269	372.327	0.13269	7.5366
31	0.00235	425.084	0.13235	7.5556
32	0.00206	485.166	0.13206	7.5722
33	0.00181	553.588	0.13181	7.5869
34	0.00158	631.510	0.13158	7.5997
35	0.00139	720.249	0.13139	7.6110
40	0.00072	1386.71	0.13072	7.6499
45	0.00038	2663.34	0.13038	7.6702
50	0.00020	5108.78	0.13020	7.6807
55	0.00010	9793.12	0.13010	7.6863
60	0.00005	18 766.0	0.13005	7.6892
65	0.00003	35 954.0	0.13003	7.6907
70	0.00001	68 879.0	0.13001	7.6914
75	0.00001	131 948.0	0.13001	7.6919
80	0.00000	252 759.0	0.13000	7.6921
85	0.00000	484 177.0	0.13000	7.6922
90	0.00000	927 467.0	0.13000	7.6922
95	0.00000	1 776 608.0	0.13000	7.6923
100	0.00000	3 403 172.0	0.13000	7.6923

r = 14%   **Continuous Compounding, Continuous Compounding Periods**

T	Sinking Fund Factor (A/F,r,T)	Uniform Series Factor (F/A,r,T)	Capital Recovery Factor (A/P,r,T)	Series Present Worth Factor (P/A,r,T)
1	0.93163	1.0734	1.0716	0.93316
2	0.43326	2.3081	0.57326	1.7444
3	0.26822	3.7283	0.40822	2.4497
4	0.18650	5.3619	0.32650	3.0628
5	0.13810	7.2411	0.27810	3.5958
6	0.10635	9.4026	0.24635	4.0592
7	0.08411	11.8890	0.22411	4.4621
8	0.06780	14.7490	0.20780	4.8123
9	0.05544	18.0387	0.19544	5.1168
10	0.04582	21.8229	0.18582	5.3815
11	0.03820	26.1756	0.17820	5.6116
12	0.03207	31.1825	0.17207	5.8116
13	0.02707	36.9418	0.16707	5.9855
14	0.02295	43.5666	0.16295	6.1367
15	0.01954	51.1869	0.15954	6.2682
16	0.01668	59.9524	0.15668	6.3824
17	0.01428	70.0350	0.15428	6.4818
18	0.01225	81.6328	0.15225	6.5681
19	0.01053	94.9735	0.15053	6.6432
20	0.00906	110.319	0.14906	6.7085
21	0.00781	127.970	0.14781	6.7652
22	0.00674	148.274	0.14674	6.8146
23	0.00583	171.629	0.14583	6.8575
24	0.00504	198.494	0.14504	6.8947
25	0.00436	229.396	0.14436	6.9272
26	0.00377	264.942	0.14377	6.9553
27	0.00327	305.829	0.14327	6.9798
28	0.00283	352.860	0.14283	7.0011
29	0.00246	406.959	0.14246	7.0196
30	0.00213	469.188	0.14213	7.0357
31	0.00185	540.768	0.14185	7.0497
32	0.00160	623.105	0.14160	7.0619
33	0.00139	717.815	0.14139	7.0725
34	0.00121	826.757	0.14121	7.0817
35	0.00105	952.070	0.14105	7.0897
40	0.00052	1924.47	0.14052	7.1164
45	0.00026	3882.66	0.14026	7.1297
50	0.00013	7825.95	0.14013	7.1363
55	0.00006	15 767.0	0.14006	7.1396
60	0.00003	31 758.0	0.14003	7.1413
65	0.00002	63 959.0	0.14002	7.1421
70	0.00001	128 805.0	0.14001	7.1425
75	0.00000	259 389.0	0.14000	7.1427
80	0.00000	522 353.0	0.14000	7.1428
85	0.00000	1 051 897.0	0.14000	7.1428
90	0.00000	2 118 268.0	0.14000	7.1428
95	0.00000	4 265 676.0	0.14000	7.1428
100	0.00000	8 590 023.0	0.14000	7.1429

$r = 15\%$ **Continuous Compounding, Continuous Compounding Periods**

T	Sinking Fund Factor $(A/F,r,T)$	Uniform Series Factor $(F/A,r,T)$	Capital Recovery Factor $(A/P,r,T)$	Series Present Worth Factor $(P/A,r,T)$
1	0.92687	1.0789	1.0769	0.92861
2	0.42874	2.3324	0.57874	1.7279
3	0.26394	3.7887	0.41394	2.4158
4	0.18246	5.4808	0.33246	3.0079
5	0.13429	7.4467	0.28429	3.5176
6	0.10277	9.7307	0.25277	3.9562
7	0.08075	12.3843	0.23075	4.3337
8	0.06465	15.4674	0.21465	4.6587
9	0.05249	19.0495	0.20249	4.9384
10	0.04308	23.2113	0.19308	5.1791
11	0.03566	28.0465	0.18566	5.3863
12	0.02971	33.6643	0.17971	5.5647
13	0.02488	40.1913	0.17488	5.7182
14	0.02093	47.7745	0.17093	5.8503
15	0.01767	56.5849	0.16767	5.9640
16	0.01497	66.8212	0.16497	6.0619
17	0.01270	78.7140	0.16270	6.1461
18	0.01081	92.5315	0.16081	6.2186
19	0.00921	108.585	0.15921	6.2810
20	0.00786	127.237	0.15786	6.3348
21	0.00672	148.907	0.15672	6.3810
22	0.00574	174.084	0.15574	6.4208
23	0.00492	203.336	0.15492	6.4550
24	0.00421	237.322	0.15421	6.4845
25	0.00361	276.807	0.15361	6.5099
26	0.00310	322.683	0.15310	6.5317
27	0.00266	375.983	0.15266	6.5505
28	0.00228	437.909	0.15228	6.5667
29	0.00196	509.856	0.15196	6.5806
30	0.00169	593.448	0.15169	6.5926
31	0.00145	690.567	0.15145	6.6029
32	0.00124	803.403	0.15124	6.6118
33	0.00107	934.500	0.15107	6.6194
34	0.00092	1086.81	0.15092	6.6260
35	0.00079	1263.78	0.15079	6.6317
40	0.00037	2682.86	0.15037	6.6501
45	0.00018	5687.06	0.15018	6.6589
50	0.00008	12 047.0	0.15008	6.6630
55	0.00004	25 511.0	0.15004	6.6649
60	0.00002	54 014.0	0.15002	6.6658
65	0.00001	114 355.0	0.15001	6.6663
70	0.00000	242 097.0	0.15000	6.6665
75	0.00000	512 526.0	0.15000	6.6666

r = 20%   **Continuous Compounding, Continuous Compounding Periods**

T	Sinking Fund Factor $(A/F,r,T)$	Uniform Series Factor $(F/A,r,T)$	Capital Recovery Factor $(A/P,r,T)$	Series Present Worth Factor $(P/A,r,T)$
1	0.90333	1.1070	1.1033	0.90635
2	0.40665	2.4591	0.60665	1.6484
3	0.24327	4.1106	0.44327	2.2559
4	0.16319	6.1277	0.36319	2.7534
5	0.11640	8.5914	0.31640	3.1606
6	0.08620	11.6006	0.28620	3.4940
7	0.06546	15.2760	0.26546	3.7670
8	0.05059	19.7652	0.25059	3.9905
9	0.03961	25.2482	0.23961	4.1735
10	0.03130	31.9453	0.23130	4.3233
11	0.02492	40.1251	0.22492	4.4460
12	0.01995	50.1159	0.21995	4.5464
13	0.01605	62.3187	0.21605	4.6286
14	0.01295	77.2232	0.21295	4.6959
15	0.01048	95.4277	0.21048	4.7511
16	0.00850	117.663	0.20850	4.7962
17	0.00691	144.821	0.20691	4.8331
18	0.00562	177.991	0.20562	4.8634
19	0.00458	218.506	0.20458	4.8881
20	0.00373	267.991	0.20373	4.9084
21	0.00304	328.432	0.20304	4.9250
22	0.00249	402.254	0.20249	4.9386
23	0.00203	492.422	0.20203	4.9497
24	0.00166	602.552	0.20166	4.9589
25	0.00136	737.066	0.20136	4.9663
26	0.00111	901.361	0.20111	4.9724
27	0.00091	1102.03	0.20091	4.9774
28	0.00074	1347.13	0.20074	4.9815
29	0.00061	1646.50	0.20061	4.9849
30	0.00050	2012.14	0.20050	4.9876
31	0.00041	2458.75	0.20041	4.9899
32	0.00033	3004.23	0.20033	4.9917
33	0.00027	3670.48	0.20027	4.9932
34	0.00022	4484.24	0.20022	4.9944
35	0.00018	5478.17	0.20018	4.9954
40	0.00007	14 900.0	0.20007	4.9983
45	0.00002	40 510.0	0.20002	4.9994
50	0.00001	110 127.0	0.20001	4.9998
55	0.00000	299 366.0	0.20000	4.9999
60	0.00000	813 769.0	0.20000	5.0000
65	0.00000	2 212 062.0	0.20000	5.0000
70	0.00000	6 013 016.0	0.20000	5.0000
75	0.00000	16 345 082.0	0.20000	5.0000

$r = 25\%$ Continuous Compounding, Continuous Compounding Periods

T	Sinking Fund Factor $(A/F,r,T)$	Uniform Series Factor $(F/A,r,T)$	Capital Recovery Factor $(A/P,r,T)$	Series Present Worth Factor $(P/A,r,T)$
1	0.88020	1.1361	1.1302	0.88480
2	0.38537	2.5949	0.63537	1.5739
3	0.22381	4.4680	0.47381	2.1105
4	0.14549	6.8731	0.39549	2.5285
5	0.10039	9.9614	0.35039	2.8540
6	0.07180	13.9268	0.32180	3.1075
7	0.05258	19.0184	0.30258	3.3049
8	0.03913	25.5562	0.28913	3.4587
9	0.02945	33.9509	0.27945	3.5784
10	0.02236	44.7300	0.27236	3.6717
11	0.01707	58.5705	0.26707	3.7443
12	0.01310	76.3421	0.26310	3.8009
13	0.01008	99.1614	0.26008	3.8449
14	0.00778	128.462	0.25778	3.8792
15	0.00602	166.084	0.25602	3.9059
16	0.00466	214.393	0.25466	3.9267
17	0.00362	276.422	0.25362	3.9429
18	0.00281	356.069	0.25281	3.9556
19	0.00218	458.337	0.25218	3.9654
20	0.00170	589.653	0.25170	3.9730
21	0.00132	758.265	0.25132	3.9790
22	0.00103	974.768	0.25103	3.9837
23	0.00080	1252.76	0.25080	3.9873
24	0.00062	1609.72	0.25062	3.9901
25	0.00048	2068.05	0.25048	3.9923
26	0.00038	2656.57	0.25038	3.9940
27	0.00029	3412.24	0.25029	3.9953
28	0.00023	4382.53	0.25023	3.9964
29	0.00018	5628.42	0.25018	3.9972
30	0.00014	7228.17	0.25014	3.9978
31	0.00011	9282.29	0.25011	3.9983
32	0.00008	11 920.0	0.25008	3.9987
33	0.00007	15 307.0	0.25007	3.9990
34	0.00005	19 655.0	0.25005	3.9992
35	0.00004	25 239.0	0.25004	3.9994
40	0.00001	88 102.0	0.25001	3.9998
45	0.00000	307 516.0	0.25000	3.9999
50	0.00000	1 073 345.0	0.25000	4.0000
55	0.00000	3 746 353.0	0.25000	4.0000

Answers to Selected Problems

CHAPTER 1

CHAPTER 2

2.1: $120

2.3: $150

2.5: 8%

2.7: $1210

2.9: 18.75%

2.11: $29 719

2.13 (a): 5 years

2.15 (a): $6728

2.17 (a): 26.6%

2.19: 6.18%

2.21 (c): The first

2.27: 162.54, 111.29

CHAPTER 3

3.1: 317.22

3.3: $74 790

3.5: $24 017

3.7: 94.13

3.9: $2663.53

3.11: 11.7%

3.13: 5.8 years

3.15: $99 484

3.17: $7046

3.19 (a): New plan

3.21: $(P/A, g, i, N) = ((1 + i^o)N$
$- 1\backslash i^o(1 + i^o)N)\backslash 1\backslash 1 + g$

3.23: $3 597 993

3.25: $74 514

3.27: No

3.29: $85 919 300

3.31: $122 316

3.33: $1 593

3.35 (b): $695 093

3.37: $1 818 040

3.39: $7425.80

3.41: $10 632

3A.1: $1701

3A.3: $8352.70

CHAPTER 4

4.1: B and C, C and D

4.5: No

4.7 (b): $236.47

4.9: 2

4.11: Metal frame and plastic liner

4.13: XJ3

4.15: No

4.17 (a): 1367 hours

4.19: A, $3036

4.21: X

4.23: 2, 2.5, 2.667

4.25: A is longer than B.

4.27: Landfill

4.29: Curtains

CHAPTER 5

5.1 (a): 9.2%

5.3: 12.4%

5.5: B

5.7 (b): 3

5.11: Yes

5.13 (c): 4.24%

5.17: E

5.19: Schedules

5.21: Annual Worth

5.23: Annual Worth

5.25: Payback Period on Annual Worth

5.27: IRR or Present Worth

5.29: Pay Back Period

5A1 (a): 12.57, No

CHAPTER 6

6.1 (b): $7714

6.3 (b): $5806

6.7: 12.04%

6.9: A

6.15 (b): Current ratio = 5.33

CHAPTER 7

7.1: 8, 18, 3

7.3 (c): 10 years

7.7 (a): 14

7.7 (b): $8138

7.9: No

7.11 (c): Immediately

7:13 (a): There are 10 alternatives.

7.17: Every 8 years

7.19: No

7.21 (a): Less than about $10 344

7.23 (a): 4 years, 7 years

7.25 (a): 12 years, 4 years

CHAPTER 8

8.1: $13 750

8.3: $−1683

8.5: $26 779

8.7 (a): 0.6552, 0.6694

8.9: 8.68%

8.11 (a): $132 000

8.13: $12 962

8:15: $−5656

8:17: 4%

8.19: $4189

8.21: $1074, $1208

8.23: 2

8.25: T

8.27: 20.64%, 14.67%, 11.08%

8.29: T

CHAPTER 9

9.1 (a): $6209

9.3 (b): 2.0%

9.5: 14.3%

9.7: $14 683

9.9: 14.4%

9.11 (a): $2 358 153

9.13 (a): 11.3%

9.15 (a): 22.4%

9.17 (a): $152 574

9.19 (b): $79 568

CHAPTER 10

10.3: The present worth of the project is most sensitive to changes in the annual maintenance and repair costs.

10.7: The annual worth is most sensitive to changes in the annual benefits of the network.

10.9: $1190

10.11 (a): $160 190, above

10.13: The breakeven quantity is 212 500.

10.15 (a): B

10.17: Don't buy it.

10.19: 46%

CHAPTER 11

11.1: 1.546, 2

11.3 (c): 0

11.5 (a): $1598.5

11.7: 212 500

11.11: $270 304

11.15: −311 052, −252 547

11.19: Choose projects 2, 6, 7, and 8.

CHAPTER 12

12.1: 4, 5, 6, 7, 8, 10

12.3 (b): P4

12.5 (b): $\begin{bmatrix} 1 & 1 & 5 & \frac{1}{3} \\ 1 & 1 & \frac{1}{3} & 2 \\ \frac{1}{5} & 3 & 1 & 2 \\ 3 & \frac{1}{2} & \frac{1}{2} & 1 \end{bmatrix}$

12.7: 1, 3, 7, 8

12.9: D, 57.5

12.11: $\begin{bmatrix} 1 & 1 & \frac{1}{3} & 5 & \frac{1}{5} \\ 1 & 1 & \frac{1}{3} & 5 & \frac{1}{5} \\ 3 & 3 & 1 & 5 & \frac{1}{3} \\ \frac{1}{5} & \frac{1}{5} & \frac{1}{5} & 1 & \frac{1}{5} \\ 5 & 5 & 3 & 5 & 1 \end{bmatrix}$

12.17: $[0.130 \quad 0.130 \quad 0.557 \quad 0.130 \quad 0.052]^{\mathrm{T}}$

12.23: C

12.25: $[0.051 \quad 0.171 \quad 0.171 \quad 0.606]^{\mathrm{T}}$

12.29: $\begin{bmatrix} 0.051 & 0.617 & 0.141 & 0.442 \\ 0.171 & 0.259 & 0.263 & 0.072 \\ 0.171 & 0.077 & 0.455 & 0.045 \\ 0.606 & 0.047 & 0.141 & 0.442 \end{bmatrix}$

12.31: $[0.235 \quad 0.196 \quad 0.171 \quad 0.398]^{\mathrm{T}}$

12A.1: CR = 0.0297

Glossary

acid-test ratio: The ratio of quick assets to current liabilities. Quick assets are cash, accounts receivable, and marketable securities — those current assets considered to be highly *liquid*. The acid-test ratio is also known as the "quick" ratio.

actual dollars: Monetary units at the time of payment.

actual interest rate: The stated, or observed, interest rate based on actual dollars; also the real interest rate which has been adjusted upwards to include the effect of inflation. If the real interest rate is i' and the inflation rate is f, the actual interest rate i is found by:

$$i = i' + f + i'f$$

actual internal rate of return, IRR$_A$: The internal rate of return on a project based on actual dollar cash flows associated with the project; also the real internal rate of return which has been adjusted upwards to include the effect of inflation.

actual MARR: The minimum acceptable rate of return for *actual dollar* cash flows. It is the *real MARR* adjusted upwards for inflation.

amortization period: The duration over which a loan is calculated to be repaid.

analytic hierarchy process (AHP): A multi-attribute utility theory (MAUT) approach used for large, complex decisions, which provides a method for establishing the criteria weights.

annual worth method: Comparing alternatives by converting all cash flows to a uniform series, i.e., an annuity.

annuity: A series of uniform-sized receipts or disbursements that start at the end of the first period and continue over a number, N, of regularly spaced time intervals.

annuity due: An annuity whose first of N receipts or disbursements is immediate, at time 0, rather than at the end of the first period.

arithmetic gradient series: A series of receipts or disbursements that start at zero at the end of the first period and then increase by a constant amount from period to period.

arithmetic gradient to annuity conversion factor: Denoted by $(A/G,i,N)$, gives the value of an annuity, A, that is equivalent to an arithmetic gradient series where the constant increase in receipts or disbursements is G per period, the interest rate is i, and the number of periods is N.

asset-management ratios: Financial ratios that assess how efficiently a firm is using its assets. Asset management ratios are also known as efficiency ratios. Inventory turnover is an example.

assets: The economic resources owned by an enterprise.

balance sheet: A financial statement which gives a snapshot of an enterprise's financial position at a particular point in time, normally the last day of an accounting period.

base period: A particular date associated with *real dollars* that is used as a reference point for price changes; also the period from which the expenditure shares are calculated in a Laspeyres price index.

base year: The year on which real dollars are based.

benefit-cost ratio: The ratio of the present worth (or annual worth) of benefits to the present worth (or annual worth) of costs. That is,

$$BCR = \frac{PW(benefits)}{PW(costs)}$$

bond: An investment that provides an annuity and a future value in return for a cost today. It has a "par" or "face" value, which is the amount for which it can be redeemed after a certain period of time. It also has a "coupon rate," meaning that the bearer is paid an annuity, usually semi-annually, calculated as a percentage of the face value.

book value: The depreciated value of an asset, as calculated with a depreciation model, for accounting purposes.

break-even analysis: The process of varying a parameter of a problem and determining what parameter value the performance measure to reach some threshold or "break-even" value.

capacity: The ability to produce, often measured in units of production per time period.

capital: Any form of wealth that can be used to create more wealth.

capital cost: The depreciation expense incurred by the difference between what is paid for the assets required for a particular capacity and what the assets could be resold for some time after purchase.

capital cost allowance (CCA): The maximum depreciation expense allowed for tax purposes on all assets belonging to an asset class.

capital cost allowance (CCA) asset class: A categorization of assets for which a specified CCA rate is used to compute CCA. Numerous CCA asset classes exist in the CCA system.

capital cost allowance (CCA) rate: The depreciation rate allowed for assets in a designated asset class within the CCA system.

capital cost allowance (CCA) system: The system established by the Canadian government whereby the amount and timing of depreciation expenses on capital assets is controlled.

capital cost tax factor (CCTF): A value that summarizes the effect of the future benefit of tax savings due to CCA and allows analysts to take these benefits into account when calculating the value of an asset. The *new* CCTF takes into account the "half-year rule" where only half of the capital cost of an asset can be used to calculate the CCA in the first year. This rule came into effect in November 1981. The *old* CCTF takes into account the entire amount of a capital expense in one year.

capital expense: The expenditure associated with the purchase of a long-term depreciable asset.

capital recovery factor: Denoted by $(A/P,i,N)$, gives the value, A, of the periodic payments or receipts that is equivalent to a present amount, P, when the interest rate is i and the number of periods is N.

capitalized value: The present worth of an infinitely long uniform series of cash flows.

cash flow diagram: A chart that summarizes the timing and magnitude of cash flows as they occur over time. The X axis represents time, measured in periods, and the Y axis represents the size and direction of the cash flows. Individual cash flows are indicated by arrows pointing up (positive cash flows, or receipts) or down (negative cash flows, or disbursements).

challenger: A potential replacement for an existing asset. See **defender**.

comparison methods: Methods of evaluating and comparing projects, such as present worth, annual worth, payback, and IRR.

compound amount factor: Denoted by $(F/P,i,N)$, gives the future amount, F, that is equivalent to a present amount, P, when the interest rate is i and the number of periods is N.

compound interest: The standard method of computing interest where interest accumulated in one interest period is added to the principal amount used to calculate interest in the next period.

compound interest factors: Functions that define the mathematical equivalence of certain common cash flow patterns.

compounding period: The interest period used with the compound interest method of computing interest.

consistency ratio: A measure of the consistency of the reported comparisons in a PCM. The consistency ratio ranges from 0 (perfect consistency) to 1(no consistency). A consistency ratio of 0.1 or less is considered acceptable.

constant dollars: See **real dollars**.

consumer price index (CPI):   The CPI relates the average price of a standard set of goods and services in some base period to the average price of the same set of goods and services in another period. Currently, Statistics Canada uses a base year of 1986 for the CPI.

continuous compounding: Compounding of interest which occurs continuously over time, i.e., as the length of the compounding period tends toward zero.

continuous models: Models that assume all cash flows and all compounding of cash flows occur continuously over time.

cost of capital: The minimum rate of return required to induce investors to invest in a business.

cost principle of accounting: A principle of accounting which states that assets are to be valued on the basis of their cost as opposed to market or other values.

current assets: Cash and those assets that could be converted to cash within a relatively short period of time, usually a year or less.

current dollars: See **actual dollars**.

current liabilities: Liabilities that are due within some short period of time, usually a year or less.

current ratio: The ratio of all current assets to all current liabilities. It is also known as the working capital ratio.

debt management ratio: See **leverage ratio**.

decision matrix: A multi-attribute utility theory (MAUT) method in which the rows of a matrix represent criteria, and the columns alternatives. There is an extra column for the weights of the criteria. The cells of the matrix (other than the criteria weights) contain an evaluation of the alternatives.

decisional equivalence: Decisional equivalence is a consequence of indifference on the part of a decision maker among available choices.

declining-balance method of depreciation: A method of modelling depreciation where the loss in value of an asset in a period is assumed to be a constant proportion (amount) of the asset's current value.

defender: An existing asset being assessed for possible replacement. See **challenger**.

deflation: The decrease, over time, in average prices. It can also be described as the increase in the purchasing power of money over time.

depreciation: The loss in value of an asset.

discrete models: Models that assume all cash flows and all compounding of cash flows occur at the ends of conventionally defined periods like months or years.

dominated: See **inefficient**.

economic life: The service life of an asset that minimizes its average cost of use.

economic regulation: The imposition of rules by government that are intended to modify behaviour, and that are backed by the use of penalties for failure to obey the rules.

effective interest rate: The actual but not usually stated interest rate, found by converting a given interest rate (with an arbitrary compounding period, normally less than a year) to an equivalent interest rate, with a one-year compounding period.

efficiency: A multi-criterion decision-making (MCDM) method which permits the identification of a subset of superior alternatives.

efficiency ratios: See **asset-management ratios**.

efficient: An alternative is **efficient** if there is no alternative which is valued as at least equal to it for all criteria and preferred to it for at least one.

engineering economics: That science which deals with techniques of quantitative analysis useful for selecting a preferable alternative from several technically viable ones.

equity ratio: A financial ratio, which is the ratio of total owners' equity to total assets. The smaller this ratio is, the more dependent the firm is on debt for its operations and the higher are the risks the company faces.

equivalence: A condition that exists when the value of a cost at one time is equivalent to the value of the related benefit.

equivalent annual cost (EAC): An annuity that is mathematically equivalent to a generally more complicated set of cash flows.

expensed: Term applied to an asset with a CCA rate of 100%. For all intents and purposes, this is the same as treating the cost of the asset as an operating cost rather than a capital cost.

external rate of return (ERR): The rate of return on a project where any cash flows that are not invested in the project are assumed to earn interest at a predetermined rate (such as the MARR).

extraordinary item: A gain or loss which does not typically result from a company's normal business activities and is therefore not a recurring item.

financial accounting: The process recording and organizing the financial data of a business. The data cover both flows over time, like revenues and expenses, and levels, like an enterprise's resources and the claims on those resources, at a given date.

financial analysis: Comparison of a firm's financial ratios with ratios computed for the same firm from previous financial statements and with industry standard ratios.

financial ratios: Ratios between key amounts taken from the financial statements of a firm. They give an analyst a framework for answering questions about the firm's liquidity, asset management, leverage, and profitability.

future worth: See the definition of **interest rate**.

future worth method: Comparing alternatives by taking all cash flows to a future worth.

geometric gradient series: A set of disbursements or receipts that change by a constant *proportion* from one period to the next in a sequence of periods.

geometric gradient to present worth conversion factor: Denoted by $(P/A,g,i,N)$, gives the present worth, P, that is equivalent to a geometric gradient series where the base receipt or disbursement is A, and where the rate of growth is g, the interest rate is i, and the number of periods is N.

goal: The decision to be made in AHP.

growth adjusted interest rate, $i°$:

$$i° = \frac{1+i}{1+g} - 1 \quad so\ that \quad \frac{1}{1+i°} = \frac{1+i}{1+g}$$

where i is the interest rate and g is the growth rate. The growth adjusted interest rate is used in computing the geometric gradient to present worth conversion factor.

income statement: A financial statement which summarizes an enterprise's revenues and expenses over a specified accounting period.

independent projects: Two projects are independent if the expected costs and the expected benefits of each of the projects do not depend on whether or not the other one is chosen.

inefficient: An alternative that is not efficient.

inflation: The increase, over time, in average prices. It can also be described as the decrease in the purchasing power of money over time.

inflation rate: The rate of increase in average prices over a specified time period, usually a year; also, the rate of decrease in purchasing power of money over a specified time period, usually a year.

installation costs: Costs of acquiring capacity, excluding the purchase cost, which may include disruption of production, training of workers, and perhaps a reorganization of other production.

interest: The compensation for giving up the use of money.

interest period: The base unit of time over which an interest rate is quoted. The interest period is referred to as the compounding period when compound interest is used.

interest rate: If the right to P at the beginning of a time period exchanges for the right to F at the end of the period, where $F = P(1+i)$, i is the interest rate per time period. In this definition, P is called the *present worth* of F, and F is called the *future worth* of P.

internal rate of return (IRR): That interest rate, i^*, such that, when all cash flows associated with a project are discounted at i^*, the present worth of the cash inflows equals the present worth of the cash outflows.

inventory-turnover ratio: A financial ratio that captures the number of times that a firm's inventories are replaced (or turned over) per year. It provides a measure of whether the firm has more or less inventory than normal.

Laspeyres price index: A commonly used price index which measures weighted average changes in prices of a set of goods and services over time as compared with the prices in a base period. The weights are the expenditure shares in the base period. The weights are then converted to percentages by multiplying by 100.

leverage ratios: Financial ratios that capture the extent to which a firm relies on debt for its operations. These are also known as debt-management ratios. The equity ratio is an example of a leverage ratio.

liabilities: Claims, other than those of the owners, on a business's assets.

liquidity ratio: A financial ratio that evaluates the ability of a business to meet its current liability obligations. The current ratio and quick ratio are two examples of liquidity ratios.

long-term assets: Assets that are not expected to be converted to cash in the short term, usually taken to be one year.

long-term liabilities: Liabilities that are not expected to draw on the business's current assets.

management accounting: The process of analyzing and recording the costs and benefits of the various activities of an enterprise. The goal of management accounting is to provide managers with information to help in decision making.

market value: Usually taken as the actual value an asset can be sold for on an open market.

market equivalence: The ability to exchange one cash flow for another at zero cost.

market failure: Condition in which output or consumption decisions are made in which aggregate benefits to all persons who benefit from the decision are less than aggregate costs imposed on persons who incur costs which are due to the decision.

mathematical equivalence: An equivalence of cash flows due to the mathematical relationship between time and money.

minimum acceptable rate of return (MARR): An interest rate that must be earned for any project to be accepted.

modified benefit-cost ratio: The ratio of the present worth (or annual worth) of benefits minus the present worth (or annual worth) of operating costs to the present worth (or annual worth) of capital costs, that is,

$$BCRM = \frac{PW(\text{benefits}) - PW(\text{operating costs})}{PW(\text{capital costs})}$$

multi-attribute utility theory (MAUT): An MCDM approach in which criteria weights and preference measures are combined mathematically to determine a best alternative.

multi-criterion decision making (MCDM): Methods that explicitly take into account multiple criteria and guide a decision maker to superior or optimal choices.

mutually exclusive projects: Projects are mutually exclusive if, in the process of choosing one, all the other alternatives are excluded.

net cash flow: The difference between cash inflows and outflows for the period. The net cash flow, A_t, is given by $A_t = R_t - C_t$, where R_t is cash inflow in period t, and C_t is cash outflow in period t.

net-profit ratio: See **return on total assets**.

nominal dollars: See **actual dollars**.

nominal interest rate: The conventional method of stating the annual interest rate. It is calculated by multiplying the interest rate per compounding period by the number of compounding periods per year.

owners' equity: The interest of the owner or owners of a firm in its assets.

pairwise comparison: An evaluation of the importance or preference of criteria or alternatives respectively, using an AHP value scale.

pairwise comparison matrix (PCM): A device for storing pairwise comparison evaluations.

par value: The price per share set by a firm at the time the shares are originally issued.

payback period: The period of time it takes for an investment to be recouped when the interest rate is assumed to be zero.

payback period method: A method used for comparing alternatives by comparing the periods of time required for the investments to pay for themselves.

performance measures: Calculated values that allow conclusions to be drawn from data.

present worth: See the definition of **interest rate**.

present worth factor: Denoted by $(P/F,i,N)$, gives the present amount, P, that is equivalent to a future amount, F, when the interest rate is i and the number of periods is N.

present worth method: Comparing alternatives by taking all cash flows to present worth.

price index: A number, usually a percentage, that relates prices of a given set of goods and services in some period, t_1, to the prices of the same set of goods and service in another period, t_0.

principal eigenvector: The eigenvector associated with the largest eigenvalue, λ_{max}, of a PCM.

priority weights: Weights calculated for alternatives by normalizing the elements of a PCM and averaging the row entries.

profitability ratios: Financial ratios that give evidence of how productively assets have been employed in producing a profit. Return on total assets (or net-profit ratio) is an example of a profitability ratio.

project: A term used throughout this text to mean "investment opportunity."

project balance: If a project has a sequence of net cash flows $A_0, A_1, A_2, \ldots,$ A_T, and the interest rate is i°, there are $T + 1$ project balances, $B_0, B_1, \ldots B_T$, one at the end of each period t, t = 0,1, $\ldots$, T. A project balance, B_t, is the cumulated future value of all cash flows, up to the end of period t, compounded at the rate, i°.

quick ratio: See **acid-test ratio**.

real dollars: Monetary units of constant purchasing power.

real interest rate: The interest rate, i', is the interest rate that would yield the same number of real dollars in the absence of inflation as the actual interest rate yields in the presence of inflation at the rate f. It is given by

$$i' = \frac{(1+i)}{(1+f)} - 1$$

real internal rate of return: The internal rate of return on a project based on real dollar cash flows associated with the project.

real MARR: The minimum acceptable rate of return for *real dollar* cash flows.

recovery period: In U.S. tax law, the designated service life for depreciation calculation purposes.

related but not mutually exclusive projects: For pairs of projects in this category, the expected costs and benefits of one project depend on whether the other one is chosen.

repeated lives: Used for comparing alternatives with different service lives, based on the assumption that alternatives can be repeated in the future, with the same costs and benefits, as often as necessary. The life of each alternative is repeated until a common total time period is reached for all alternatives.

retained earnings: The cumulative sum of earnings from normal operations, in addition to gains (or losses) from transactions such as the sale of plant assets or investments that have been reinvested in the business, i.e., not paid out as dividends.

retire: To remove an asset from use without replacement.

return-on-total-assets ratio: A financial ratio that captures how productively assets have been employed in producing a profit. It is also known as the net-profit ratio

salvage value: Either the actual value of an asset at the end of its useful life (when it is sold), or an estimate of the salvage value calculated using a depreciation model.

scenario analysis: The process of examining the consequences of several possible sets of variables associated with a project.

scrap value: Either the actual value of an asset at the end of its physical life (when it is broken up for the material value of its parts), or an estimate of the scrap value calculated using a depreciation model.

sensitivity graph: A graph of the changes in a performance measure, holding all other variables fixed.

series present worth factor: Denoted by $(P/A,i,N)$, gives the present amount, P, that is equivalent to an annuity, A, when the interest rate is i and the number of periods is N.

simple interest: A method of computing interest where interest earned during an interest period is not added to the principal amount used to calculate interest in the next period. Simple interest is rarely used, except as a method of calculating approximate interest.

simple investment: A project that consists of one or more outflows at the beginning, followed only by one or more inflows.

sinking fund: Interest bearing account into which regular deposits are made in order to accumulate some amount.

sinking fund factor: Denoted by $(A/F,i,N)$, gives the size, A, of a repeated receipt or disbursement that is equivalent to a future amount, F, when the interest rate is i and the number of periods is N.

specialist company: A firm that concentrates on manufactuing a limited range of very specialized products.

statement of changes in financial position: An accounting report which shows how much cash was generated by a company's operation and by other sources of financing during an accounting period.

straight-line method of depreciation: A method of modelling depreciation which assumes that the rate in loss of value of an asset is constant over its useful life.

study period: A period of time used to compare alternatives.

sunk costs: Costs that were incurred in the past and are no longer relevant in replacement decisions.

term: The duration over which a loan agreement is valid.

trend analysis: A form of financial analysis which traces the financial ratios of a firm over several accounting periods.

undepreciated capital cost (UCC): The remaining book value of assets subject to depreciation for taxation purposes. For any given year, the UCC balance can be calculated as follows:

$$UCC_{opening} + \text{additions} - \text{disposals} - CCA = UCC_{ending}$$

uniform series compound amount factor: Denoted by $(F/A,i,N)$, gives the future value, F, that is equivalent to a series of equal-sized receipts or disbursements, A, when the interest rate is i and the number of periods is N.

weighted average cost of capital: A weighted average of the costs of borrowing and of selling shares. The weights are the fractions of total capital that come from the different sources.

working capital: The difference between total current assets and total current liabilities.

working capital ratio: See **current ratio**.

Index

acid test ratio 209, 211
actual dollars,
    defined 321-322
    converting from real dollars 322-324
actual interest rate,
    defined 325
    converting from real interest rate 325
actual MARR,
    defined 326
    converting from real MARR 326
AHP (see analytic hierarchy process) 434, 441-447
analytic hierarchy process (AHP),
    introduced 434
    consistency ratio for 447, 460-465
    pairwise comparison matrix for 442, 443-446
    steps in process 441-442
annual worth comparison method, 95
    comparison to IRR and PW methods 159, 165
annuity,
    defined 50
    annuity due 57
    non standard 69-71
answers to selected problems 528-529
arithmetic gradient series,
    defined 50
    cash flow pattern 50, 63-65
    treatment of non standard gradients 69-71
arithmetic gradient to annuity conversion factor 64-65
assets
    defined 199
    current 199
    long term 199
balance sheet 196, 197-200
BCR (see also benefit-cost ratios) 406
BCRM (see also benefit-cost ratios) 406
beginning and ending of periods, defined 31
benefit-cost ratios,
    conventional, defined 406
    modified, defined 406
    problems associated with use 406-408
    use of in comparing projects 409-413
bonds 62-63
book value,
    defined 188
    resulting from the straight line depreciation model 190

resulting from the declining balance depreciation model 192
breakeven analysis,
    defined 363
    for multiple projects 366-371
    for a single project 364-366
capacity, defined 241
capacity costs,
    defined 241
    capital costs as part of capacity costs 241, 242-243
    installation costs as part of capacity costs 241, 242-243
capital cost allowance (CCA) defined 286, 288
capital cost allowance (CCA) system,
    introduced 288
    CCA asset class 288,289
    CCA rate 288,289
capital cost tax factors (CCTF),
    introduced 293-295
    $CCTF_{NEW}$, (post 1981) 295
    $CCTF_{NEW}$, derived 315-316
    $CCTF_{OLD}$, (pre 1981) 294
    $CCTF_{OLD}$, derived 315-316
    in a complete after-tax evaluation 296-297
capital cost, as part of capacity cost 241
capital expense 285
capital recovery factor 55
capital recovery formula 55-56
capitalized value formula 71
cash flow diagrams,
    introduced 30-31
    summary form 31-32
cash flow models,
    as approximations 49-50
    continuous cash flows 50
    discrete cash flows 50
cash flow patterns,
    annuities 50, 54-63
    arithmetic gradient series 50, 63-65
    geometric gradient series 50, 66-68
    single disbursement or receipt 50, 51-54
CCA (see capital cost allowance)
CCTF (see capital cost tax factors)
challenger, in replacement analysis 242, 245
comparison of alternatives with unequal lives, the
    repeated service lives method 107, 109-110
    the study period method 107, 110-112
compound amount factor 51
compound interest, defined 24

compound interest factors,
    defined 49, 50
    arithmetic gradient to annuity conversion
      factor 64-65
    capital recovery factor 55
    compound amount factor 51
    geometric gradient to present worth
      conversion factor 66-68
    present worth factor 52
    series present worth factor 56
    sinking fund factor 54
    uniform series compound amount factor 55
    formulas for continuous cash flows,
    continuous compounding 87
    formulas for discrete cash flows, continuous
      compounding 86
    formulas for discrete cash flows, discrete
      compounding 76
    tables for continuous compounding, con-
      tinuous cash flows 510-526
    tables for continuous compounding, dis-
      crete cash flows 492-508
    tables for discrete compounding, discrete
      cash flows 468-490
compounding period, defined 24
consistency ratio, for the analytic hierarchy
    process 447, 460-465
consumer price index (CPI),
    defined 319
    as an inflation index 319-320
    base period for 319
contingent projects 98
continuous cash flow models 50
continuous cash flows 85
continuous compounding,
    defined 29
    and continuous cash flows, compound
      interest factors 87
    and continuous cash flows, tables 510-526
    and discrete cash flows, compound interest
      factors 86
    and discrete cash flows, tables 492-508
cost of capital,
    defined 100, 132
    how determined 132-134
cost principle of accounting 203
CPI (see also consumer price index) 319-320
current ratio 208, 211
debt management financial ratios 209, 211
debt, as a source of capital 132-133
decision making,
    ethical aspects of 10-12
    multiple objectives in 9
decision matrices 434, 438-441
decisional equivalence 33, 34

decisions, political and preference aspects 4-5
declining balance depreciation model 191-195
defender, in replacement analysis 242, 245
deflation 318
depreciation,
    defined 187
    alternative models for 189-195
    declining balance model 191-195
    reasons for 187
    straight line model 189-191
discounted payback period 114
discrete cash flow models 50
discrete cash flows,
    and discrete compounding, derivation of
      compound interest factors 89-92
    and discrete compounding, table of
      compound interest factors 468-490
do nothing alternative 97,98
dominated alternative (in multi-criteria decision
    making) 435
EAC (equivalent annual cost) 243
economic life 245-249
effective interest rate,
    defined 27
    obtaining from nominal rate 28
efficiency, in multi-criteria decision making
    434-437
efficient alternative, in multi-criteria decision
    making 435
ending and beginning of periods, defined 31
engineering economics,
    defined 4
    historical aspects 3-4
    importance 6
equity ratio 209, 211
equity, as a source of capital 132-133
equivalence, 33-35
    decisional 33,34
    market 33,35
    mathematical 33-34
equivalent annual cost 243
ethical aspects of decision making 10-12
expected value, as a method for dealing with
    uncertainty 388-389
explicit rate of return 150
external rate of return,
    defined 150
    approximate 152-153, 178
    exact 150-152
    when to use 153-154
extraordinary items, on income statement 210
financial accounting, defined 195
financial ratio analysis 204-212
financial ratios,
    defined 204

acid (or, quick) ratio 209, 211
current (or, working capital) ratio 208, 211
equity ratio 209, 211
inventory turnover ratio 209-210, 211
return on total assets (or, net-profit) ratio
    210, 211
as measures of profitability 210, 211
as measures of efficiency or asset-manage-
    ment 209, 211
as measures of leverage or debt management
    209, 211
as measures of liquidity 208-209
cautionary notes on use 212
industry standards 204
financial statements,
    balance sheet 196,197-200
    estimated values in 203-204
    income statement 196-197, 200-202
    statement of changes in financial position
        202-203
future amount 21-22
future worth comparison method 105
geometric gradient series,
    defined 50
    cash flow pattern 50,66-68
geometric gradient to present worth conversion
    factor 66-68
glossary 531-538
gradient,
    see geometric gradient and arithmetic
        gradient series treatment of non standard
        gradients 69-71
growth adjusted interest rate 67
historical aspects of engineering economics 13-
    4
income statement 196-197, 200-202
income taxes 285
incremental investment, IRR on 144, 156-157
independent projects,
    defined 96-97
    comparisons using annual worth 104-107
    comparisons using IRR 140-142
    comparisons using present worth 101-104
inefficient alternative (in multi-criteria decision
    making) 435
inflation rate,
    defined 319
    estimated by the consumer price index 319
    sources of estimates 331
inflation,
    defined 318
    treatment in doing economic evaluations
        329-330
installation cost, as part of capacity cost 241
interest period 22, 23

interest rate,
    defined 21-22
    actual, defined (in the context of inflation)
        325
    effective, defined 27
    nominal, defined 26
    real , defined (in the context of inflation)
        325
    real and actual compared for 1956-1993 327
interest,
    concept, defined 21-22
    compound, defined 24
    simple, defined 25
internal rate of return,
    defined 137
    actual (in context of inflation) 328
    after-tax, approximate 300-301
    after-tax, exact 299
    compared to PW and AW methods 159, 165
    comparison of independent projects
        140-142
    comparison of mutually exclusive projects
        142-147
    equivalence to PW and AW 154-156
    multiple 148-150
    on incremental investment 144
    real (in context of inflation) 328
    tests for multiple rates 174-182
inventory turnover financial ratio 209-210, 211
IRR, see internal rate of return
Laspeyres price index 353-356
liabilities,
    defined 199
    current 199
    long term 199
linear interpolation 60-61
liquidity financial ratios 208, 211
management accounting, defined 195
market equivalence 33, 35
market failure,
    defined 398
    reasons for 398
    remedies for 399
market value,
    defined 187-188
    use of depreciation models to estimate
        market value 188
MARR (see minimum acceptable rate of return)
mathematical equivalence 33-34
MAUT (multi-attribute utility theory) 434, 438
MCDM (multi-criteria decision making) 434
minimum acceptable rate of return,
    defined 100
    real (in context of inflation) 326
    actual (in context of inflation) 326

in the public sector 413
    use of in IRR comparisons 140, 143-146
modelling, as an abstraction of reality 7
Monte Carlo simulation 389-393
mortgages,
    amortization period 59
    term 59
multi-attribute utility theory (MAUT) 434, 438
multi-criteria decision making (MCDM) 434
multiple internal rates of return, tests for
    174-182
multiple IRRs 148-150
mutually exclusive projects,
    defined 96-97
    comparisons using annual worth 104-107
    comparisons using IRR 142-147
    comparisons using present worth 104
net cash flow 149
net-profit financial ratio 210,211
nominal interest rate defined 26
non standard annuities and gradients 69-71
normalization (in the use of decision matrices)
    439-440
owners' equity, defined 199
pairwise comparison matrix (PCM), 442,
    443-446
par value (shares) 199
payback period,
    defined 112
    comparison method 95, 112-116
present cost or annual cost comparisons 101
present worth comparisons,
    introduced 95
    compared to IRR and AW methods 159, 165
present worth factor 52
present, or principle amount, P 21-22
price index,
    base period 353
    defined 353
    Laspeyres 353-356
principle, or present amount, P 21-22
profitability financial ratios 210, 211
project balances 149, 175-178
public sector decision making,
    choice of the MARR in 413
    measuring costs and benefits 402-404
    see also benefit cost ratios
qualitative criteria in decisions, how to accom-
    modate 433-434
quick assets 209, 211
quick ratio 209, 211
real dollars,
    defined 321-322
    converting from actual dollars 322-324
real interest rate,
    defined 325

    converting from actual interest rate 325
real MARR,
    defined 326
    converting from actual MARR 325-326
related, but not mutually exclusive projects,
    defined 96-97
    converting into mutually exclusive projects
    98-99
repeated lives comparison method for alterna-
    tives with unequal lives 107, 109-110
replacement,
    reasons for 239, 240
    when challengers are identical 250-253
    when challengers are not identical 253-255
    when defender is the same as the challenger
    245-249
retained earnings 199-200
retirement (of assets), reasons for 239, 240
return on total assets financial ratio 210, 211
salvage value, defined 188
scenario analysis 359, 371-374
scrap value, defined 188
sensitivity analysis 13-14, 358-378
sensitivity graphs 359, 360-363
series present worth factor 56
significant digits used in text 14
simple interest, defined 25
simple investments 153, 174
sinking fund 54
sinking fund factor 54
specialist companies 240
statement of changes in financial position
    202-203
straight line depreciation model 189-191
study period comparison method
    for alternatives with unequal lives 107,
    110-112
subjective evaluation of alternatives (with deci-
    sion matrices) 440
sunk costs, irrelevancy in replacement decisions
    243-244
taxes,
    income 285
    inclusion in economic evaluations 296-297
    see also the capital cost allowance (CCA)
    system
trend analysis, as part of a financial ratio
    analysis 204
undepreciated capital cost (UCC) 290-293
unequal lives, comparison of assets with, the re-
    peated service lives method 107, 109-110
    the study period method 107, 110-112
uniform series compound amount factor 55
weighted average cost of capital 133
working capital 208
working capital ratio 208, 211